Study Guide and Selected Solutions Manual

Susan McMurry

Fundamentals of
General, Organic, and Biological

Chemistry

Third Edition

McMurry • Castellion

PRENTICE HALL, Upper Saddle River, NJ 07458

Senior Editor: John Challice
Associate Editor: Mary Hornby
Special Projects Manager: Barbara A. Murray
Production Editor: Barbara A. Till
Supplement Cover Manager: Paul Gourhan
Supplement Cover Designer: Liz Nemeth
Manufacturing Buyer: Ben Smith

Printed in the United States of America

10 9 8 7 6 5 4 3

ISBN 0-13-010898-7

Prentice-Hall International (UK) Limited, *London*
Prentice-Hall of Australia Pty. Limited, *Sydney*
Prentice-Hall Canada, Inc., *London*
Prentice-Hall Hispanoamericana, S.A., *Mexico*
Prentice-Hall of India Private Limited, *New Delhi*
Prentice-Hall of Japan, Inc., *Tokyo*
Simon & Schuster Asia Pte. Ltd., *Singapore*
Editora Prentice-Hall do Brazil, Ltda., *Rio de Janeiro*

Contents

Preface

How is food digested? What is DNA fingerprinting? How do anesthetics work?

For all of these questions, chemistry provides an answer. Chemistry, the study of matter, is essential for understanding the physical world, from acid rain to gene therapy to the ozone layer. Chemical laboratory tests are a routine part of medical care. The functioning of our bodies is a result of thousands of biochemical reactions. To study life, you must first study chemistry.

Both the textbook and this Study Guide and Partial Solutions Manual are designed to be as helpful as possible to you in your chemistry course. The textbook contains numerous solved problems that show you techniques for solving specific types of chemistry problems. In addition, the text includes applications of the material in each chapter to contemporary science problems. This Study Guide consists of several types of study aids: detailed solutions to many textbook problems, outlines of the chapters, and self-tests.

The following suggestions may help you:

(1) Attend all classes. Although it's possible to learn chemistry just by reading the textbook and study guide, a lecturer makes difficult topics much easier to understand and ties together seemingly unrelated topics.

(2) Read the textbook. The best way to study is to skim the chapter to be covered before class, and then to read it more thoroughly after the lecturer has discussed the material. Use the textbook to help you understand subjects you find especially difficult. It is also helpful to use the chapter outlines in the Study Guide after reading the textbook.

(3) Work the problems. Start by reading carefully the Solved Problems in the textbook. Next, try to work the Practice Problems, using the steps outlined in the Solved Problems. Finally, attempt the Additional Problems at the end of the chapter. Although this Study Guide and Partial Solutions Manual has detailed solutions to many text problems, it's better to use the solutions in this book as a last resort. You will learn more if you first struggle a bit with a problem before checking its answer, than if you look up the answer right away.

(4) Use the supplementary material in the Study Guide to help you review each chapter. The chapter outlines organize and restate both the major themes of each chapter and the detailed contents. Go over the list of key terms in the textbook to make sure that you know the meaning of each important term. Test yourself with the self-tests, which include multiple choice, sentence completions, matching, and true/false questions.

Acknowledgments

I would like to thank the following people for their assistance with this book: John McMurry (of course), Mary Castellion, John Challice, Larry Jackson, and Donna Young. I am grateful to my entire family for their patience and support.

Chapter Outline

I. Matter and its properties (Sections 1.1–1.2).
   A. Matter is anything that is physically real (Section 1.1).
   B. Properties are the characteristics of matter.
      1. Physical properties are those properties that can be measured without altering the identity of a substance. Examples include mass, melting point, boiling point, color.
      2. Chemical properties must be determined by changing the identity of the substance. Examples include rusting, combustion and chemical reactivity.
      3. A chemical reaction is a process in which one or more substances undergoes a change in identity.
   C. States of matter (Section 1.2).
      1. The states of matter are solid, liquid and gas.
         a. Solids have definite volume and definite shape.
         b. Liquids have definite volume and indefinite shape.
         c. Gases have indefinite volume and indefinite shape.
      2. Changes of state are: melting, boiling, condensing, freezing.
II. Classification of matter (Sections 1.3–1.6).
   A. Mixtures (Section 1.3).
      1. Mixtures vary in composition and properties.
      2. Mixtures can be separated by physical methods.
   B. Pure substances.
      1. Pure substances include chemical compounds and chemical elements.
      2. Pure substances don't vary in composition and properties.
      3. Chemical compounds can be broken down to elements by chemical change.
         a. A chemical reaction represents a chemical change between pure substances (Section 1.4).
         b. In a chemical reaction, the reactants are written on the left, the products are written on the right, and an arrow connects them
      4. Chemical elements can't be broken down.
   C. Elements (Sections 1.5–1.6).
      1. There are 112 elements; 90 of them occur naturally.
      2. Elements are represented by one or two-letter symbols.
      3. The symbols for elements can be combined to produce chemical formulas.
      4. Elements are presented in a table – the Periodic Table
      5. Elements can be classified as metals, nonmetals or metalloids.
         a. Metals are solids that are lustrous, brittle, malleable and good conductors of heat and electricity.
         b. Nonmetals may be solid, liquid or gas and are poor conductors.
         c. Metalloids have characteristics intermediate between metals and nonmetals.
III. Energy (Section 1.7).
   A. Energy is the capacity to do work or provide heat.
   B. Energy is classified as either kinetic energy or potential energy.
      1. Kinetic energy is the energy of motion.
      2. Potential energy is stored energy.
   C. Chemical energy is a type of potential energy that is stored in chemical compounds.
   D. The various forms of energy are interchangeable.
   E. Energy changes accompany all chemical reactions.
   F. A spontaneous chemical reaction yields products that are more stable than their reactants.

Solutions to Chapter 1 Problems

1.1   All of the listed items are made of chemicals.

1.2   *Change in physical properties*:   (a) grinding a metal surface   (d) a puddle evaporating
          Change in chemical properties: (b) fruit ripening   (c) wood burning

1.3   Formaldehyde is a gas at room temperature (25°C).

1.4   At 10°C, acetic acid is a solid.

1.5   *Mixtures*: (a) concrete; (d) wood
          Pure substances: (b) helium; (c) a lead weight

1.6   *Physical changes*: (a) separation by filtration; (c) mixing alcohol and water
          Chemical changes: (b) production of carbon dioxide by heating limestone

1.7   (a) U = uranium;   (b) Ti = titanium;   (c) W = tungsten

1.8   (a) Na = sodium;   (b) Ca = calcium;   (c) Pd = palladium;   (d) K = potassium
          (e) Sr = strontium;   (f) Sn = tin

1.9   (a) Ammonia (NH_3) contains one nitrogen atom and three hydrogen atoms.
          (b) Sodium bicarbonate ($NaHCO_3$) contains one sodium atom, one hydrogen atom, one
              carbon atom, and three oxygen atoms.
          (c) Octane (C_8H_{18}) contains eight carbon atoms and eighteen hydrogen atoms.
          (d) Vitamin C ($C_6H_8O_6$) contains six carbon atoms, eight hydrogen atoms, and six oxygen
              atoms.

1.10

Element	Name	Number in Periodic Table
(a) Cr	Chromium	24
(b) Na	Sodium	11
(c) Ag	Silver	47
(d) Pb	Lead	82

1.11

(a) Ne	Neon	10
(b) Cl	Chlorine	17
(c) P	Phosphorus	15
(d) Rn	Radon	86

1.12

(a) B	Boron	5
(b) Si	Silicon	14
(c) Ge	Germanium	32
(d) As	Arsenic	33
(e) Sb	Antimony	51
(f) Te	Tellurium	52
(g) At	Astatine	85

The metalloids occur at the boundary between metals and nonmetals.

1.13   *Potential energy* (a) a book on the edge of a desk;   (c) sandwich;   (d) flashlight battery
           Kinetic energy: (b) a just-pitched baseball

Understanding Key Concepts

1.14 From top to bottom: helium (He), neon (Ne), argon (Ar), krypton (Kr), xenon (Xe), radon (Rn).

1.15 From top to bottom: copper (Cu), silver (Ag), gold (Au)

Chemistry and the Properties of Matter

1.16 Chemistry is the study of matter – its nature, properties and transformations.

1.18 Physical properties: (a) boiling point of water;   (c) solubility of sugar in water; (e) brittleness of glass

1.20 Physical properties: (a) floating of oil on water; (b) condensation of steam; (c) softness of potassium metal
Chemical property: (d) ignition of matches

States and Classification of Matter

1.22 A *gas* is a substance that has no definite shape or volume.
A *liquid* has no definite shape but has a definite volume.
A *solid* has a definite volume and a definite shape.

1.24 Sulfur dioxide is a gas at 25°C.

1.26 Mixtures: (a) pea soup; (b) seawater; (d) urine; (f) multi-vitamin tablet
Pure substances: (c) C_3H_8; (e) lead

1.28 An *element* is a pure substance that can't be broken down chemically into simpler substances.

A *compound* is a pure substance that has a definite composition and that can be broken down chemically to yield elements.

1.30 Element: (a) aluminum foil
Compounds: (b) table salt;   (c) water
Mixtures: (d) air;   (e) banana;   (f) notebook paper

1.32   *Reactant*   *Products*

Hydrogen peroxide $\longrightarrow$ water   +   oxygen
chemical compound   *chemical compound   element*

Elements and Their Symbols

1.34 *Metals* are lustrous malleable elements that are good conductors of heat and electricity.

Nonmetals are elements that are gases or brittle solids (except for Br) and are poor conductors.

Metalloids are elements that have properties intermediate between those of metals and nonmetals.

1.36   (a) Zn; (b) Hg; (c) Ba; (d) Au; (e) Si; (f) C; (g) Na; (h) Pb

1.38   The first letter of a chemical symbol is always capitalized; the second letter, if any, is never capitalized. Thus, Co stands for cobalt, and CO stands for carbon monoxide, a compound composed of carbon (C) and oxygen (O).

1.40   (a) Water has the formula H_2O (the number 2 is a subscript).
(b) Water is composed of hydrogen and oxygen.

1.42   (a) $MgSO_4$: magnesium, sulfur, oxygen
(b) $FeBr_2$: iron, bromine
(c) CoP: cobalt, phosphorus
(d) AsH_3: arsenic, hydrogen
(e) $CaCr_2O_7$: calcium, chromium, oxygen

1.44   Carbon, hydrogen, nitrogen and oxygen are present in glycine. The formula $C_2H_5NO_2$ represents ten atoms.

1.46   Ibuprofen: $C_{13}H_{18}O_2$

1.48   (a) Osmium (Os) is a metal.
(b) Xenon (Xe) is a nonmetal.

Energy

1.50   *Kinetic energy* is the energy of an object in motion. *Potential energy* is stored energy.

1.52   Potential energy: (a) a tankful of gasoline, (c) an automobile battery
Potential and kinetic energy: (b) a downhill skier

General Questions and Problems

1.56   (a) See Problem 1.50.
(b) *Melting point* is the temperature at which a change of state from solid to liquid occurs.
Boiling point is the temperature at which a change of state from liquid to gas occurs.
(c) A *reactant* is a substance that undergoes change in a chemical reaction.
A *product* is a substance formed as a result of a chemical reaction.
(d) A *metal* is a lustrous malleable element that is a good conductor of heat and electricity; a *nonmetal* is an element that is a poor conductor.

1.58   (a) True; (b) False. Melting is a physical change.

1.60   Chemical compounds: (a) H_2O_2; (d) NO; (e) $NaHCO_3$
Elements: (b) Mo; (c) C

1.62   The liquid is a mixture.

1.64   (a) Fe; (b) Cu; (c) Co; (d) Mo; (e) Cr; (f) F; (g) S

Self-Test for Chapter 1

Multiple choice:

1. Which of the following is a chemical property?
   (a) melting point   (b) reaction with acid   (c) hardness   (d) transparency

2. The change of state that occurs when a gas is cooled to a liquid is called:
   (a) boiling   (b) melting   (c) evaporation   (d) condensation

3. Which of the following is not an element?
   (a) Fluorine   (b) Freon   (c) Neon   (d) Radon

4. The chemical formula for fructose is $C_6H_{12}O_6$. How many different elements does fructose contain?
   (a) 24   (b) 18   (c) 6   (d) 3

5. How many atoms does the formula for fructose represent?
   (a) 24   (b) 18   (c) 6   (d) 3

6. A solution of fructose in water is a:
   (a) mixture   (b) pure substance   (c) chemical compound   (d) element

7. Which of the following is not a characteristic of a metal?
   (a) electrical conductivity   (b) malleability   (c) brittleness   (d) luster

8. An example of kinetic energy is:
   (a) a rock at the top of a hill   (b) a rock rolling down a hill   (c) a rock at the bottom of a hill
   (d) a rock undergoing chemical analysis in a laboratory

Complete the following sentences:

1. A swinging pendulum has _____ energy.

2. Color is a _____ property.

3. _____ is the symbol for the element bismuth.

4. When a substance _____, it changes from gas to liquid.

5. Matter is anything that has _____ and _____.

6. A _____ has definite volume but indefinite shape.

7. A _____ _____ doesn't vary in its properties or composition.

8. Energy stored in chemical compounds is _____ energy.

9. A _____ substance can be beaten or rolled into different shapes.

10. ____, ____, ____, and ____ are four elements present in all living organisms.

Tell whether each of the following statements is true or false:

1. The forms of energy are interchangeable.

2. Rust formation is a chemical change.

3. A chemical compound is a pure substance.

4. The components of a solution are separable by chemical methods.

5. The formula C_2H_4O represents three atoms.

6. Spontaneous changes lead to lower potential energy.

7. The chemical symbol for silver is Si.

8. In the chemical reaction carbon + oxygen —> carbon dioxide, the reactants are elements.

9. Methyl bromide, a compound formerly used for fumigation, has a melting point of –93.7°C and a boiling point of 3.6°C and is a liquid at room temperature.

10. Nonmetals may be solids, liquids or gases.

Chapter 2 – Measurements in Chemistry

Chapter Outline

I. Measurements (Sections 2.1–2.3).
    A. Physical quantities (Section 2.1).
        1. All physical quantities consist of a number plus a unit.
            a. SI units, the standard units for scientists, are the kilogram, the meter, and the Kelvin.
            b. Metric units are the gram, the meter, the liter and the degree Celsius.
            c. Other units, such as those for speed and concentration, can be derived from SI and metric units.
        2. Prefixes are used with units to indicate multiples of ten.
    B. Measuring mass (Section 2.2).
        1. Mass is the amount of matter in a substance.
        2. The SI unit of mass is the kilogram, but in chemistry the gram and milligram are more often used.
    C. Measuring length (Section 2.3).
        The meter is the standard unit for length.
    D. Measuring volume.
        1. Volume is the amount of space that a substance occupies.
        2. Units for volume are the liter (L) and the cubic meter (m^3).
II. Numbers in measurement (Sections 2.4–2.6).
    A. Significant figures (Section 2.4).
        1. All measurements have a degree of uncertainty.
        2. For any measurement, the number of digits known with certainty, plus one digit considered uncertain, is known as the number of significant figures.
        3. Rules for significant figures:
            a. Zeroes in the middle of a number are always significant.
            b. Zeroes at the beginning of a number are never significant.
            c. Zeroes at the end of a number but after a decimal point are significant.
            d. Zeroes at the end of a number but before an implied decimal point may or may not be significant.
        4. Some numbers are exact and have an unlimited number of significant figures,
    B. Scientific notation (Section 2.5).
        1. In scientific notation, a number is written as the product of a number between 1 and 10 times 10 raised to a power.
            a. For numbers greater than 10, the power of 10 is positive.
            b. For numbers less than 10, the power of 10 is negative.
        2. Scientific notation is helpful in indicating the number of significant figures in a number.
    C. Rounding off numbers (Section 2.6).
        1. Numbers must be rounded off if they contain more digits than are significant.
        2. Rounding in calculations.
            a. In multiplication or division, the result can't have more significant figures than any of the original numbers.
            b. In addition or subtraction, the result can't have more digits to the right of the decimal point than any of the original numbers.
        3. Rules of rounding:
            a. If the digit to be removed is 4 or less, drop it and remove all following digits.
            b. If the digit to be removed is 5 or greater, add 1 to the digit to the left of the digit you drop.

III. Calculations (Sections 2.7–2.8).
    A. Converting a quantity from one unit to another (Section 2.7).
        1. In the <u>factor-label</u> method:
            (quantity in old units) x (conversion factor) = (quantity in new units)
            a. The conversion factor is a fraction that converts one unit to another.
            b. All conversion factors are equal to 1.
        2. In the factor-label method, units are treated as numbers.
        3. In the factor-label method, all unwanted units cancel.
    B. Problem solving (Section 2.8).
        1. Make a "ballpark" estimate of the answer.
        2. Use the factor-label method to calculate the exact answer and compare it to the estimate.
            a. Identify the information known.
            b. Identify the information needed in the answer.
            c. Use conversion factors to convert the given information to the answer.
IV. Heat (Sections 2.9–2.10).
    A. Measuring temperature (Section 2.9).
        1. Units of temperature are the degree Fahrenheit, the degree Celsius, and the Kelvin.
        2. Temperature in °C = Temperature in K + 273.15°.
        3. °F = (1.8 x °C) + 32°.
        4. $°C = \dfrac{(°F - 32°)}{1.8}$
    B. Heat and energy (Section 2.10).
        1. Heat is the energy transferred from a hotter object to a cooler object when the two are in contact.
        2. Units of energy are the joule and the calorie.
        3. $Specific\ heat = \dfrac{calories}{grams\ x\ °C}$.
V. Density and specific gravity (Sections 2.11–2.12).
    A. Density (Section 2.11).
        1. Density = mass (g) / volume (mL or cm^3).
        2. Density is temperature-dependent.
    B. Specific gravity (Section 2.12).
        1. $Specific\ gravity = \dfrac{density\ of\ substance\ (g/mL)}{density\ of\ water\ (1\ g/mL)}$.
        2. Specific gravity has no units.

Solutions to Chapter 2 Problems

2.1   cL = centiliter

2.2   (a) mL = milliliter   (b) kg = kilogram
          (c) cm = centimeter   (d) km = kilometer
          (e) µg = microgram

2.3   (a) liter = L   (b) microliter = µL
          (c) nanometer = nm   (d) megameter = Mm

2.4   (a) 1 nm = 0.000 000 001 m   (b) 1 dg = 0.1 g
          (c) 1 km = 1000 m   (d) 1 mL = 0.001 L
          (e) 1 ng = 0.000 000 001 g

2.5

Number	Significant Figures	Reason
(a) 3.45 m	3	
(b) 0.1400 kg	4	Rule 3
(c) 10.003 L	5	Rule 1
(d) 35 cents	Exact	

2.6 In scientific notation, a number is written as the product of a number between one and ten times ten raised to a power. In (a), 58 g = 5.8 x 10^1 g.

Value	Scientific Notation
(a) 58 g	5.8 x 10^1 g
(b) 46,792 m	4.6792 x 10^4 m
(c) 0.000 672 0 cm	6.720 x 10^{-4} cm
(d) 345.3 kg	3.453 x 10^2 kg

2.7

Value in Scientific Notation	Value in Normal Notation
(a) 4.885 x 10^4 mg	48,850 mg
(b) 8.3 x 10^{-6} m	0.000 008 3 m
(c) 4.00 x 10^{-2} m	0.0400 m

2.8 (a) 6.0 x 10^5 (b) 1.300 x 10^3 (c) 7.942 x 10^{11}

2.9 0.000 000 000 278 m = 2.78 x 10^{-10} m. (The decimal point must be moved ten places to the right.)

$$2.78 \text{ x } 10^{-10} \text{ m } \times \frac{1 \text{ pm}}{10^{-12} \text{ m}} = 2.78 \text{ x } 10^2 \text{ pm}$$

2.10 (a) 2.30 g   (b) 188.38 mL   (c) 0.009 L   (d) 1.000 kg

2.11 Remember:
(1) The sum or difference of two numbers can't have more digits to the right of the decimal point than either of the two numbers.
(2) The product or quotient of two numbers can't have more significant figures than either of the two numbers.

Calculation	Rounded to:
(a) 4.87 mL + 46.0 mL = 50.87 mL	50.9 mL
(b) 3.4 x 0.023 g = 0.0782 g	0.078 g
(c) 19.333 m – 7.4 m = 11.933 m	11.9 m
(d) 55 mg – 4.671 mg + 0.894 mg = 51.223 mg	51 mg
(e) 62,911 ÷ 611 = 102.96399	103

2.12

(a) $\dfrac{1 \text{ L}}{1000 \text{ mL}}$, $\dfrac{1000 \text{ mL}}{1 \text{ L}}$; $\dfrac{1 \text{ mL}}{0.001 \text{ L}}$, $\dfrac{0.001 \text{ L}}{1 \text{ mL}}$

(b) $\dfrac{1 \text{ g}}{0.03527 \text{ oz}}$, $\dfrac{0.03527 \text{ oz}}{1 \text{ g}}$; $\dfrac{1 \text{ oz}}{28.35 \text{ g}}$, $\dfrac{28.35 \text{ g}}{1 \text{ oz}}$

(c) $\dfrac{1\ L}{1.057\ qt}$, $\dfrac{1.057\ qt}{1\ L}$; $\dfrac{1\ qt}{0.9461\ L}$, $\dfrac{0.9461\ L}{1\ qt}$

2.13

(a) $16.0\ oz\ \times\ \dfrac{28.35\ g}{1\ oz} = 454\ g$

(b) $2500\ mL\ \times\ \dfrac{1\ L}{1000\ mL} = 2.5\ L$

(c) $99.0\ L\ \times\ \dfrac{1\ qt}{0.9461\ L} = 105\ qt$

2.14

$0.840\ quart\ \times\ \dfrac{1\ L}{1.057\ quart}\ \times\ \dfrac{1000\ mL}{1\ L} = 795\ mL$

2.15

(a) $7.5\ lb\ \times\ \dfrac{1\ kg}{2.205\ lb} = 3.4\ kg$

(b) $4.0\ oz\ \times\ \dfrac{29.57\ mL}{1\ oz} = 120\ mL$

Remember: The answers must have the correct number of significant figures.

2.16

$2 \times 0.324\ g\ \times\ \dfrac{1000\ mg}{1\ g}\ \times\ \dfrac{1}{135\ lb}\ \times\ \dfrac{2.205\ lb}{1\ kg} = 10.6\ \dfrac{mg}{kg}$

$2 \times 0.324\ g\ \times\ \dfrac{1000\ mg}{1\ g}\ \times\ \dfrac{1}{40\ lb}\ \times\ \dfrac{2.205\ lb}{1\ kg} = 36\ \dfrac{mg}{kg}$

2.17 From Section 2.9, we find the formula:

$(°F - 32°F)\ \times\ \dfrac{1°C}{1.8°F} = °C$

Substituting 136°F into the above formula:

$(136°F - 32°F)\ \times\ \dfrac{1°C}{1.8°F} = 57.8°C$

2.18

$°F = \left(\dfrac{1.8°F}{1.0°C}\ \times\ °C\right) + 32°F$; In this problem, $°C = -38.9°$

$= (1.8°F\ \times\ -38.9°) + 32°F = -38.0°F$

$= 273.15\ K - 38.9 = 234.3\ K$

2.19

$$\text{Heat (cal)} = \text{mass (g)} \times \text{temperature change (°C)} \times \text{specific heat} \left(\frac{\text{cal}}{\text{g} \cdot \text{°C}} \right)$$

$$= 350 \text{ g} \times (25°C - 3°C) \times \frac{1.0 \text{ cal}}{\text{g} \cdot \text{°C}}$$

$$= 7700 \text{ cal} = 7.7 \times 10^3 \text{ cal}$$

2.20

$$\text{Specific heat} = \frac{\text{calories}}{\text{grams} \times \text{°C}}$$

$$\text{Specific heat} = \frac{161 \text{ cal}}{75 \text{ g} \times 10°C} = 0.21 \frac{\text{cal}}{\text{g} \cdot \text{°C}}$$

2.21 Solids with densities greater than water will sink; solids with densities less than water will float.
Solids that float: ice, human fat, cork, balsa wood
Solids that sink: gold, table sugar, earth

2.22

$$12.37 \text{ g} \times \frac{1 \text{ mL}}{1.474 \text{ g}} = 8.392 \text{ mL}$$

2.23

$$\text{Density} = \frac{\text{Mass}}{\text{Volume}} = \frac{16.8 \text{ g}}{7.60 \text{ cm}^3} = 2.21 \frac{\text{g}}{\text{cm}^3}$$

Understanding Key Concepts

2.24 The graduated cylinder contains 34 mL; the paperclip is 2.7 cm long. Both answers have two significant figures.

2.25 Lead will float on mercury because it is less dense than mercury.

2.26

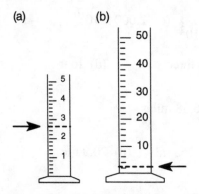

The smaller graduated cylinder is more accurate for two reasons. (1) The distance between two gradations represents a smaller volume, making it easier to measure volumes more accurately. (2) The percent error is greater when a small volume is measured in a large graduated cylinder.

2.27 If two identical hydrometers are placed in ethanol and in chloroform, the hydrometer in chloroform will float higher. Since a hydrometer bulb sinks until it displaces a volume of liquid equal to its mass, it displaces a smaller volume of chloroform, the denser liquid, and the bulb floats higher

Definitions and Units

2.28 A *physical quantity* is a physical property that can be measured; it consists of a number plus a unit.

2.30

Quantity	SI Unit
Mass	kilogram (kg)
Volume	cubic meter (m^3)
Length	meter (m)
Temperature	kelvin (K)

2.32 A cubic decimeter and a liter represent the same volume expressed in two different systems of units.

2.34 (a) centiliter   (b) decimeter   (c) millimeter   (d) nanoliter
(e) milligram   (f) cubic meter   (g) cubic centimeter

2.36

$$\frac{10^{-3}\ g}{1\ mg} \times \frac{10^{12}\ pg}{1\ g} = \frac{10^9\ pg}{1\ mg}$$

$$35\ ng \times \frac{10^{-9}\ g}{1\ ng} \times \frac{10^{12}\ pg}{1\ g} = 3.5 \times 10^4\ pg$$

Scientific Notation and Significant Figures

2.38 (a) 9.457×10^3 (b) 7×10^{-5} (c) 2.000×10^{10}
(d) 1.2345×10^{-2} (e) 6.5238×10^2

2.40 (a) six   (b) three   (c) three   (d) four
(e) 1–5   (f) 2–3

2.42 (a) 7,926 miles; 7,900 miles; 7,926.38 miles
(b) $7.926\ 381 \times 10^3$ miles

2.44 (a) 12.1 g   (b) 96.19 cm   (c) 263 mL   (d) 20.9 mg

Unit Conversions and Problem Solving

2.46 (a) 0.3614 cg   (b) 0.0120 ML   (c) 0.0144 mm   (d) 60.3 ng

2.48 (a) 97.8 kg   (b) 0.133 mL   (c) 0.46 ng

2.50

$$\frac{100 \text{ km}}{1 \text{ hr}} \text{ x } \frac{0.6214 \text{ mi}}{1 \text{ km}} = 62.1 \frac{\text{mi}}{\text{hr}}$$

$$\frac{62.1 \text{ mi}}{1 \text{ hr}} \text{ x } \frac{5280 \text{ ft}}{1 \text{ mi}} \text{ x } \frac{1 \text{ hr}}{60 \text{ min}} \text{ x } \frac{1 \text{ min}}{60 \text{ s}} = 91.1 \frac{\text{ft}}{\text{s}}$$

2.52

$$\frac{1 \text{ cell}}{6 \text{ x } 10^{-6} \text{ m}} \text{ x } \frac{1 \text{ m}}{39.37 \text{ in}} = 4 \text{ x } 10^3 \frac{\text{cells}}{\text{in}}$$

2.54

$$\frac{200 \text{ mg}}{1 \text{ dL}} \text{ x } \frac{10 \text{ dL}}{1 \text{ L}} \text{ x } 5 \text{ L} = 10^4 \text{ mg} = 10 \text{ g}$$

2.56

$$\frac{1.2 \text{ x } 10^4 \text{ cells}}{1 \text{ mm}^3} \text{ x } \frac{10^6 \text{ mm}^3}{1 \text{ L}} \text{ x } 5 \text{ L} = 6 \text{ x } 10^{10} \text{ cells}$$

Temperature and Heat

2.58

$$°\text{C} = \frac{(°\text{F} - 32°)}{1.8} = \frac{(98.6° - 32°)}{1.8} = \frac{66.6°}{1.8} = 37.0 \text{ °C, or } 310.2 \text{ K}$$

2.60

$$\text{Heat (cal)} = \text{mass (g) x temperature change (°C) x specific heat} \left(\frac{\text{cal}}{\text{g} \cdot °\text{C}} \right)$$

$$= 30.0 \text{ g x } 20.0 \text{ °C x } \frac{0.895 \text{ cal}}{\text{g} \cdot °\text{C}} = 537 \text{ cal}$$

$$= 0.537 \text{ kcal}$$

2.62

$$\text{Temperature change (°C)} = \frac{\text{heat (cal)}}{\text{mass(g) x specific heat} \left(\frac{\text{cal}}{\text{g} \cdot °\text{C}} \right)}$$

$$\text{Temperature change (°C)} = \frac{50 \text{ cal}}{15 \text{ g x } 0.175 \frac{\text{cal}}{\text{g} \cdot °\text{C}}} = 19°\text{C}$$

Since 19°C is the difference between the initial and final temperature, and since 20°C is the initial temperature, the final temperature is 20°C + 19°C = 39°C.

Density and Specific Gravity

2.64

$$250 \text{ mg x } \frac{1 \text{ g}}{10^3 \text{ mg}} \text{ x } \frac{1 \text{ cm}^3}{1.40 \text{ g}} = 0.179 \text{ cm}^3$$

2.66   To find the density of lead, divide the mass of lead by the volume of the bar in cm³.
0.500 cm x 1.55 cm x 25.00 cm = 19.375 cm³

$$\frac{220.9 \text{ g}}{19.375 \text{ cm}^3} = 11.4 \ \frac{\text{g}}{\text{cm}^3}$$

2.68

$$\frac{3.928 \text{ g}}{5.000 \text{ mL}} = 0.7856 \ \frac{\text{g}}{\text{mL}}; \ \ \text{specific gravity} = 0.7856$$

Applications

2.70

(a) $\dfrac{1 \text{ grain}}{64.8 \text{ mg}} = \dfrac{0.0154 \text{ grain}}{1 \text{ mg}}$ (b) $\dfrac{1 \text{ fluid oz}}{8 \text{ fluidram}} = \dfrac{0.125 \text{ fluid oz}}{1 \text{ fluidram}}$

(c) $\dfrac{1 \text{ fluidram}}{3.72 \text{ mL}} = \dfrac{0.269 \text{ fluidram}}{1 \text{ mL}}$ (d) $\dfrac{1 \text{ minim}}{0.062 \text{ mL}} = \dfrac{16 \text{ minim}}{1 \text{ mL}}$

(e) $\dfrac{1 \text{ fluid oz}}{480 \text{ minim}} = \dfrac{2.08 \times 10^{-3} \text{ fluid oz}}{1 \text{ minim}}$

2.72   BMI is defined as a person's weight in kilograms, divided by the square of height in meters. Alternatively, a person's weight in pounds, divided by the square of height in inches, and multiplied by 703, also gives the same value for BMI.

2.74   Body fat acts as a shock absorber, a thermal insulator, and as an energy storehouse.

General Questions and Problems

2.76   One carat = 200 mg = 0.200 g

$$\frac{0.200 \text{ g}}{1 \text{ carat}} \times 44.4 \text{ carat} = 8.88 \text{ g}$$

2.78

$$2 \times 250 \text{ mg} \times \frac{1 \text{ g}}{1000 \text{ mg}} \times \frac{1}{130 \text{ lb}} \times \frac{2.21 \text{lb}}{1 \text{ kg}} = 8.5 \times 10^{-3} \ \frac{\text{g}}{\text{kg}} \text{ for the woman}$$

$$\frac{8.5 \times 10^{-3} \text{g}}{1 \text{kg}} \times 40 \text{ lb} \times \frac{0.454 \text{ kg}}{1 \text{ lb}} = 0.154 \text{ g}$$

A 40-lb child would need 0.154 g, or 154 mg, of penicillin to receive the same dose as a 130-lb woman. The child would thus need about 1.2 of the 125 mg penicillin tablets.

2.80

$$1.3 \frac{g}{L} \times 4.0 \text{ m} \times 3.0 \text{ m} \times 2.5 \text{ m} \times 1000 \frac{L}{m^3} = 3.9 \times 10^4 \text{ g}$$

$$3.9 \times 10^4 \text{ g} \times \frac{1 \text{ lb}}{453 \text{ g}} = 86 \text{ lb}$$

2.82

$$15 \text{ g} \times \frac{1000.0 \text{ mL}}{50.00 \text{ g}} = 300 \text{ mL}$$

2.84

$$\frac{85 \text{ mg}}{100 \text{ mL}} \times \frac{10^3 \text{ mL}}{1 \text{ L}} \times \frac{0.9464 \text{ L}}{1 \text{ qt}} \times \frac{1 \text{ qt}}{2 \text{ pt}} \times 11 \text{ pt} = 4.4 \text{ g}$$

$$4.4 \text{ g} \times \frac{1 \text{ lb}}{454 \text{ g}} = 0.0097 \text{ lb}$$

2.86

$$\left(\frac{100 \text{ mL}}{1 \text{ kg}} \times 10 \text{ kg}\right) + \left(\frac{50 \text{ mL}}{1 \text{ kg}} \times 10 \text{ kg}\right) + \left(\frac{20 \text{ mL}}{1 \text{ kg}} \times 35 \text{ kg}\right) = 2200 \text{ mL}$$

2.88

$$\text{Heat (cal)} = \text{mass (g)} \times \text{temperature change (°C)} \times \text{specific heat}\left(\frac{\text{cal}}{\text{g} \cdot \text{°C}}\right)$$

for water: specific heat = 1.00 cal /(g·°C);

$$\text{mass} = 3.00 \text{ L} \times \frac{10^3 \text{ mL}}{1 \text{ L}} \times \frac{1.00 \text{ g}}{1 \text{ mL}} = 3.00 \times 10^3 \text{ g};$$
$$\text{temperature change} = 90.0\text{°C} - 18.0\text{°C} = 72.0\text{°C}$$

$$\text{calories needed} = 3.00 \times 10^3 \text{ g} \times 72.0\text{°C} \times \frac{1.00 \text{ cal}}{\text{g} \cdot \text{°C}} = 2.16 \times 10^5 \text{ cal} = 216 \text{ kcal}$$

$$216 \text{ kcal} \times \frac{1.0 \text{ tbsp}}{100 \text{ kcal}} = 2.2 \text{ tbsp butter}$$

2.90

$$9.40 \times 10^{10} \text{ lb} \times \frac{1 \text{ gal}}{15.28 \text{ lb}} \times \frac{3.7856 \text{ L}}{1 \text{ gal}} = 2.33 \times 10^{10} \text{ L}$$

2.92 (a)   (b)

$$\frac{200 \text{ mg}}{100 \text{ mL}} \times \frac{1000 \text{ mL}}{1 \text{ L}} = 2 \times 10^3 \frac{\text{mg}}{\text{L}} \qquad \frac{200 \text{ mg}}{100 \text{ mL}} \times \frac{10^3 \mu g}{\text{mg}} = 2 \times 10^3 \frac{\mu g}{\text{mL}}$$

(c)

$$\frac{200 \text{ mg}}{100 \text{ mL}} \times \frac{1 \text{ g}}{1000 \text{ mg}} \times \frac{1000 \text{ mL}}{1 \text{ L}} = 2 \frac{\text{g}}{\text{L}}$$

(d)

$$\frac{200 \text{ mg}}{100 \text{ mL}} \times \frac{10^6 \text{ng}}{1 \text{ mg}} \times \frac{1 \text{ mL}}{10^3 \mu L} = 2 \times 10^3 \frac{\text{ng}}{\mu L}$$

Self-Test for Chapter 2

1.   Write the full name of these units:
      (a) μm   (b) dL   (c) Mg   (d) L   (e) ng

2.   Write the abbreviation for each of the following units:
      (a) kiloliter   (b) picogram   (c) centimeter   (d) hectoliter

3. | Quantity | Significant Figures? |
      | --- | --- |

      (a) 1.0037 g
      (b) 0.0080 L
      (c) 0.008 L
      (d) 2 aspirin
      (e) 273,000 mi

4.   Express the following in scientific notation:
      (a) 0.000 070 3 g   (b) 137,100 m   (c) 0.011 L   (d) 18,371,008 mm
      How many significant figures do each of the above quantities have?

5.   Round the following to three significant figures:
      (a) 807.3 L   (b) 4,773,112 people   (c) 0.00127 g   (d) 10370 μm
      Express each of the above quantities in scientific notation.

6.   Convert the following quantities:
      (a) 256 g = _____ lb   (b) 417 mm = _____ m
      (c) 2.0 gallons = _____ L   (d) 2.17 m = _____ inches
      (e) 35°C = _____ °F   (f) 298 K = _____ °C
      (g) 175 mL = _____ fl oz   (h) 175 mg = _____ oz

7.   If the specific heat of gold is 0.031 cal/g °C, how many calories does it take to heat 10 g of gold from 0°C to 100°C?

8.   If the density of ethanol is 0.7893 g/mL, how many grams does 275 mL weigh?

Multiple choice:

1.   Which of the following is not an SI unit?
      (a) kg   (b) L   (c) m   (d) K

2.   How many significant figures does the number 4500 have?
      (a) 2   (b) 3   (c) 4   (d) any of the above

3.   Which of the following quantities is larger than a gram?
      (a) 1 nanogram   (b) 1 dekagram   (c) 1 centigram   (d) 1 microgram

4.   Which of the following conversion factors do you need for converting 3.2 lb/qt to kg/L?
      (a) $\dfrac{1\ kg}{2.2\ lb} \times \dfrac{1\ qt}{0.95\ L}$ (b) $\dfrac{2.2\ lb}{1\ kg} \times \dfrac{1\ qt}{0.95\ L}$ (c) $\dfrac{2.2\ lb}{1\ kg} \times \dfrac{0.95\ L}{1\ qt}$ (d) $\dfrac{1\ kg}{2.2\ lb} \times \dfrac{0.95\ L}{1\ qt}$

5.   When written in scientific notation, the exponent in the number 0.000 007 316 is:
      (a) 10^{-6} (b) 6   (c) –6   (d) 10^{6}

6.   Which of the following is more dense than water?
      (a) ice   (b) human fat   (c) ethyl alcohol   (d) urine

7.   How many zeros are significant in the number 0.007 006?
      (a) 1   (b) 2   (c) 3   (d) 4

8.   Which of the following temperatures doesn't equal the other two?
      (a) 100°F   (b) 37.8°C   (c) 297.8 K

9.   To measure the amount of heat needed to raise the temperature of a given substance, you
      need to know all of the following except:
      (a) the mass of the substance   (b) the specific heat of the substance   (c) the density of the
      substance   (d) the initial and final temperature

10.   For which of the following is specific gravity a useful measure?
      (a) to describe the amount of solids in urine   (b) to indicate the amount of heat necessary to
      raise the temperature of one gram of a substance by 1°   (c) to determine if an object will float
      on water

Complete the following sentences:

1.   The fundamental SI units are _____, _____, _____, and _____.

2.   Physical quantities are described by a _____ and a _____.

3.   The amount of heat necessary to raise the temperature of one gram of a substance by one
      degree is the substance's _____ _____.

4.   The prefix _____ indicates 10^{-9}.

5.   The number 0.003 06 has _____ significant figures.

6.   To convert from grams to pounds, use the conversion factor _____.

7.   Two units for measuring energy are _____ and _____.

8.   The method used for converting units is called the _____ _____ method.

9.   _____ _____ is the density of a substance divided by the density of water at the same
      temperature.

10.   The size of a degree is the same in both _____ and _____ units.

Tell whether the following statements are true or false:

1.   The units of specific gravity are g/mL.

2.   The number 0.07350 has four significant figures.

3.   The sum of 57.35 and 1.3 has four significant figures.

4.   The conversion factor 1.057 quarts/liter is used to convert quarts into liters.

5.   Some SI units are the same as metric units.

6.   The temperature in °C is always a larger number than the temperature in K.

7.   Raising the temperature of 10 g of water by 10°C takes less heat than raising the temperature of 10 g of gold by 10°C.

8.   Mass measures the amount of matter in an object.

9.   Ice is more dense than water.

10.   A nanogram is larger than a picogram.

Match each entry on the left with its partner on the right:

1.   5003   (a) Converts pounds to kilograms

2.   1 centimeter   (b) 0.1 grams

3. $\dfrac{2.205\ \text{lb}}{1\ \text{kg}}$ (c) Larger than one inch

4.   263 K   (d) −17.8°C

5.   1 dekagram   (e) Four significant figures

6.   0.0486   (f) SI unit of volume measure

7.   1 m^3 (g) Converts kilograms to pounds

8.   1 liter   (h) 10 grams

9.   1 decimeter   (i) −10°C

10. $\dfrac{1\ \text{kg}}{2.205\ \text{lb}}$ (j) Smaller than one inch

11.   0°F   (k) Metric unit of volume measure

12.   1 decigram   (l) Three significant figures

Chapter 3 – Atoms and the Periodic Table

Chapter Outline

I. Atomic Theory (Sections 3.1–3.3).
   A. Fundamental assumptions about atoms (Section 3.1).
      1. All matter is composed of atoms.
      2. The atoms of each element are different from the atoms of all other elements.
      3. Chemical compounds consist of elements combined in definite proportions.
      4. Chemical reactions only change the way that atoms are combined in compounds; the atoms themselves are unchanged.
   B. Nature of the atom (Sections 3.1–3.2).
      1. Atoms are very small ($\sim 10^{-11}$ m in diameter).
      2. Atoms consist of subatomic particles.
         a. A proton is positively charged and has a mass of 1.6726×10^{-24} g.
         b. A neutron has no charge and has a mass of 1.6749×10^{-24} g.
         c. An electron is negatively charged and has a mass of 9.1094×10^{-28} g.
      3. The masses of atoms are expressed in relative terms.
         a. Under this system, a carbon atom with 6 protons and 6 neutrons is given a mass of 12 atomic mass units (amu).
         b. Consequently, a proton and a neutron each have a mass of approximately 1 amu.
      4. Atoms are held together by the interplay of attractive and repulsive forces of positively charged protons and negatively charged electrons.
      5. Protons and neutrons are located in the nucleus of an atom, and electrons move around the nucleus.
   C. Composition of atoms (Section 3.2).
      1. Atoms of different elements differ from each other according to how many protons they contain.
      2. Z stands for the number of protons an atom has and is known as the atomic number.
      3. The number of electrons in an atom is the same as the number of protons.
      4. The mass number A stands for the number of protons plus the number of neutrons.
   D. Isotopes and atomic weight (Section 3.3).
      1. Isotopes are atoms of the same element that differ only in the number of neutrons.
      2. Isotopes are represented by showing the mass number as a superscript on the left side of the symbol for the chemical element; the atomic number is shown as a subscript on the left side.
      3. Most elements occur in nature as a mixture of isotopes.
      4. The atomic weight of an element can be calculated if the percent of contributing isotopes is known.
II. The Periodic Table (Sections 3.4–3.5).
   A. The periodic table is a classification of elements according to their properties (Section 3.4).
      1. Elements are arranged by increasing atomic number in 7 rows called periods.
      2. Elements are also arranged in 18 vertical columns called groups.
         a. Main group elements occur on the left and right of the periodic table.
         b. Transition-metal groups occur in the middle of the periodic table.
         c. Inner transition-metal groups are shown separately at the bottom.
      3. The elements in each group have similar chemical properties.
   B. Chemical characteristics of groups of elements (Section 3.5).
      1. Group 1A – Alkali metals (Li, Na, K, Rb, Cs).
         a. Shiny, soft, low-melting.
         b. React violently with water.

      2. Group 2A – Alkaline earth metals (Be, Mg, Ca, Sr, Ba, Rd).
         a. Lustrous, shiny metals.
         b. Less reactive than metals in group 1A.
      3. Group 7A – Halogens (F, Cl, Br, I).
         a. Corrosive, nonmetals.
         b. Found in nature only in combination with other elements.
      4. Group 8A – Noble gases (He, Ne, Ar, Kr, Xe, Ra). Extremely unreactive.
  C. Neighboring groups have similar behaviors.
      1. Metals.
         a. Found on the left side of the periodic table.
         b. Silvery, ductile, good conductors.
      2. Nonmetals.
         a. Found on the right side of the periodic table.
         b. Eleven of the 17 nonmetals are gases.
         c. Solid nonmetals are brittle and are poor conductors of electricity.
      3. Metalloids.
         a. Occur on the boundary between metals and nonmetals.
         b. Have intermediate chemical behavior.
III. Electrons (Sections 3.6–3.8).
  A. The properties of the elements are due to the distribution of electrons in their atoms (Section 3.6).
  B. Location of electrons .
      1. Electrons are located in specific regions about the nucleus.
      2. The energies of electrons are quantized.
      3. The locations of electrons are described by shells, subshells and orbitals.
         a. Shells.
            i. Shells describe the energy level of an electron.
           ii. Shells are related to an electron's distance from the nucleus.
         b. Subshells.
            i. Subshells describe the energy levels of electrons within each shell.
           ii. The four types of subshell are *s, p, d* and *f*.
         c. Orbitals.
            i. Orbitals are the regions of subshells in which electrons of a specific energy can be found.
           ii. An *s* subshell contains one orbital, a *p* subshell contains three orbitals, a *d* subshell contains five orbitals and an *f* subshell contains seven orbitals.
           iii. Each orbital can hold two electrons, and they must be of opposite spin.
      4. Since the exact position of electrons can't be specified, orbitals are often referred to as electron clouds.
  C. Electron configurations (Section 3.7)
      1. The specific arrangement of electrons in an atom's shells and subshells is known as its electron configuration.
      2. This arrangement can be predicted by using three rules.
         a. Electrons occupy the lowest orbitals available within each subshell
            Within each shell, the subshell energy levels increase in the order *s,p,d,f.*
         b. If two or more orbitals have the same energy, each orbital is half filled before any orbital is completely filled.
         c. Each orbital can hold only two electrons, and they must be of opposite spin.
      3. The number of electrons in each subshell is given by a superscript.
  D. Electron configuration and the periodic table (Section 3.8).
      1. Properties of elements are determined by their location in the periodic table.
      2. The periodic table is divided into four regions.
         a. Elements in groups 1A and 2A are *s*-block elements because they result from filling *s* orbitals.

b. Groups 3A–8A are *p*-block elements.
c. Transition metals are *d*-block elements.
d. Inner transition metals are *f*-block elements.
3. The periodic table can be used as a reminder of the order of orbital filling.
4. Elements within a group of the periodic table have similar electronic configurations of their valence electronic shells and thus similar chemical behavior.

Solutions to Chapter 3 Problems

3.1

$$2.33 \times 10^{-23} \text{ g } \times \frac{1 \text{ amu}}{1.6606 \times 10^{-24} \text{ g}} = 14.0 \text{ amu}$$

3.2

$$10^5 \text{ atoms } \times \frac{197 \text{ amu}}{1 \text{ atom}} \times \frac{1.6606 \times 10^{-24} \text{ g}}{1 \text{ amu}} = 3.27 \times 10^{-17} \text{ g}$$

3.3

(a) $1.0 \text{ g } \times \dfrac{1 \text{ amu}}{1.6606 \times 10^{-24} \text{ g}} \times \dfrac{1 \text{ atom}}{1.0 \text{ amu}} = 6.0 \times 10^{23} \text{ atoms}$

(b) $12.0 \text{ g } \times \dfrac{1 \text{ amu}}{1.6606 \times 10^{-24} \text{ g}} \times \dfrac{1 \text{ atom}}{12.0 \text{ amu}} = 6.02 \times 10^{23} \text{ atoms}$

(c) $230 \text{ g } \times \dfrac{1 \text{ amu}}{1.6606 \times 10^{-24} \text{ g}} \times \dfrac{1 \text{ atom}}{230 \text{ amu}} = 6.02 \times 10^{23} \text{ atoms}$

3.4   In each of the above examples, the mass in grams equals the mass in amu, and the number of atoms in all three samples is identical.

3.5   (a) Re   (b) Li   (c) Te

3.6   Recall that the *atomic number* (Z) shows how many protons an atom contains. Uranium, with an atomic number of 92 thus contains 92 protons.
Uranium also contains 92 electrons, since the number of protons equals the number of electrons.
The *mass number* (A) shows the number of protons plus the number of neutrons. To find the number of neutrons in an atom, subtract the atomic number from the mass number.
For uranium: Mass number – atomic number = 235 – 92 = 143
The uranium atom has 143 neutrons.

3.7   From Problem 3.6, we know that $A - Z$ = number of neutrons
In this problem, $A = 52$, and the number of neutrons = 28. Thus $Z = 24$. The table of elements in the front of the book shows that chromium is the element with $Z = 24$.

3.8   Both chlorine isotopes have 17 protons. The chlorine isotope with mass number 35 has 18 neutrons, and the isotope with mass number 37 has 20 neutrons.
The atomic number is written at the lower left of the element symbol, and the mass number is written at the upper left.

$$^{35}_{17}\text{Cl} \quad \text{and} \quad ^{37}_{17}\text{Cl}$$

3.9

(a) $^{11}_{5}B$ (b) $^{56}_{26}Fe$

3.10 Aluminum is in group 3A (or 13) and period 3.

3.11

Group 5A Element	Period
Nitrogen	1
Phosphorus	2
Arsenic	3
Antimony	4
Bismuth	5

3.12 Metals: Titanium (Ti), Scandium (Sc)
Nonmetals: Selenium (Se), Argon (Ar)
Metalloids: Tellurium (Te), Astatine (At)

3.13 (a) Krypton – nonmetal, main group element, noble gas
(b) Strontium – metal, main group element
(c) Nitrogen – nonmetal, main group element
(d) Cobalt – metal, transition element

3.14 (a) A maximum of six electrons can occupy a $3p$ subshell.
(b) A maximum of two electrons can occupy a $2s$ subshell.
(c) A maximum of six electrons can occupy a $2p$ subshell.

3.15 Ten electrons are present in this atom, which is neon.

3.16 Twelve electrons are present in this atom, which is magnesium.

3.17 To find the electron configuration of an atom, first find its atomic number. For C (carbon), the atomic number is 6; thus carbon has 6 protons and 6 electrons. Then, assign electrons to the proper orbitals. For carbon, the electron configuration is $1s^2 2s^2 2p^2$.

Element	Atomic Number	Electron Configuration
(a) C (carbon)	6	$1s^2 2s^2 2p^2$
(b) Na (sodium)	11	$1s^2 2s^2 2p^6 3s^1$
(c) Cl (chlorine)	17	$1s^2 2s^2 2p^6 3s^2 3p^5$
(d) Ca (calcium)	20	$1s^2 2s^2 2p^6 3s^2 3p^6 4s^2$

3.18 Element 14 (Si): $1s^2 2s^2 2p^6 3s^2 3p^2$
Element 36 (Kr): $1s^2 2s^2 2p^6 3s^2 3p^6 4s^2 3d^{10} 4p^6$

3.19 Element 33 (As): $1s^2 2s^2 2p^6 3s^2 3p^6 4s^2 3d^{10} 4p^3$. The $4p$ shell is incompletely filled. Notice that only one electron occupies each orbital of the $4p$ subshell.

$\uparrow \ \uparrow \ \uparrow$ $4p^3$

3.20 Arsenic: $1s^2 2s^2 2p^6 3s^2 3p^6 4s^2 3d^{10} 4p^3$

3.21 In group 2A, all elements have the outer-shell configuration ns^2.

3.22 Chlorine, in group 7A (17), has seventeen electrons. Its electron configuration is $1s^2\,2s^2$ $2p^6\,3s^2\,3p^5$. Two electrons are in shell 1, eight electrons are in shell 2, and seven electrons are in shell 3. The outer shell configuration is $3s^2\,3p^5$.

Understanding Key Concepts

3.23

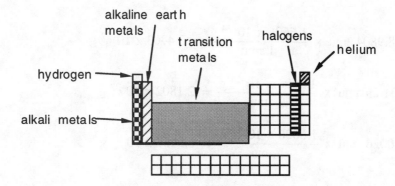

3.24

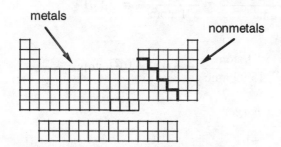

3.25 The element marked in red is a gas (argon – a group 8A noble gas)
The element marked in blue has atomic number 42 (molybdenum).
All elements in group 1A have chemical behavior similar to the element marked in green (cesium). These include lithium, sodium, potassium and rubidium.

3.26

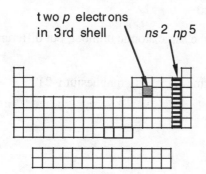

3.27 Tellurium has a greater atomic weight because its nuclei contain, on the average, more neutrons than an iodine nucleus.

Atomic Theory and the Composition of Atoms

3.28 (1) All matter is composed of atoms.
(2) The atoms of a given element differ from the atoms of all other elements.
(3) Chemical compounds consist of atoms combined in specific proportions.
(4) Chemical reactions change only the way that atoms are combined in compounds; the atoms themselves are unchanged.

3.30

(a) Bi: $208.9804 \text{ amu} \times \dfrac{1.6606 \times 10^{-24} \text{ g}}{1 \text{ amu}} = 3.4703 \times 10^{-22} \text{ g}$

(b) Xe: $131.29 \text{ amu} \times \dfrac{1.6606 \times 10^{-24} \text{ g}}{1 \text{ amu}} = 2.1802 \times 10^{-22} \text{ g}$

(c) He: $4.0026 \text{ amu} \times \dfrac{1.6606 \times 10^{-24} \text{ g}}{1 \text{ amu}} = 6.6467 \times 10^{-24} \text{ g}$

3.32

$6.022 \times 10^{23} \text{ atoms} \times \dfrac{1.6606 \times 10^{-24} \text{ g}}{1 \text{ amu}} \times \dfrac{14.01 \text{ amu}}{1 \text{ atom}} = 14.01 \text{ g}$

3.34

$15.99 \text{ g} \times \dfrac{1 \text{ amu}}{1.6606 \times 10^{-24} \text{ g}} \times \dfrac{1 \text{ atom}}{15.99 \text{ amu}} = 6.022 \times 10^{23} \text{ atoms}$

3.36

Particle	Mass in amu	Charge
Proton	1.0073	+1
Neutron	1.0087	0
Electron	5.486×10^{-4}	−1

3.38 (a) potassium   (b) tin   (c) zinc

3.40

Isotope	Argon-36	Argon-38	Argon-40
Number of neutrons	18	20	22

3.42 (a) and (c) are isotopes because they have the same atomic number, but different mass numbers.

3.44 (a) fluorine–19   (b) neon–19   (c) fluorine–21   (d) magnesium–21

3.46

(a) $^{14}_{6}\text{C}$ (b) $^{39}_{19}\text{K}$ (c) $^{20}_{10}\text{Ne}$

3.48

$^{12}_{6}\text{C}$ – six neutrons $^{13}_{6}\text{C}$ – seven neutrons

3.50 Contribution from ^{63}Cu: 69.09% of 62.93 amu = 43.48 amu
Contribution from ^{65}Cu: 30.91% of 64.93 amu = 20.07 amu

Atomic weight = 63.55 amu

The Periodic Table

3.52 The third period in the periodic table contains eight elements because eight electrons are needed to fill the *s* and *p* subshells of the third shell.

3.54 Americium (Am; atomic number 95) is a metal.

3.56 (a) They are metals.
(b) They are transition metals.
(c) The 3*d* subshell is being filled.

3.58 Selenium is chemically most similar to sulfur.

3.60 The alkali metal family is composed of lithium, sodium, potassium, rubidium, cesium and francium.

Electron Configuration

3.62 A maximum of two electrons can go into an orbital.

3.64 First shell – 2 electrons
Second shell – 8 electrons
Third shell – 18 electrons

3.66 Ten electrons are present; the element is neon.

3.68 (a) sulfur   (b) bromine   (c) silicon

$$\underset{3p^4}{\uparrow\downarrow\ \uparrow\ \uparrow}\qquad\qquad \underset{4p^5}{\uparrow\downarrow\ \uparrow\downarrow\ \uparrow}\qquad\qquad \underset{3p^2}{\uparrow\ \uparrow}$$

3.70 The element with atomic number 20 (Ca) has two electrons in its outer shell.

3.72 beryllium: 2*s*   arsenic: 4*p*

3.74

Element	(a) Kr	(b) C	(c) Ca	(d) K	(e) B	(f) Cl
# of valence-shell electrons	8	4	2	1	3	7

Applications

3.76 A normal light microscope can't reach the degree of precision of a scanning tunneling microscope.

3.78 Hydrogen and helium are the first two elements made in stars.

3.80

	Higher energy	Lower energy
(a)	ultraviolet	infrared
(b)	gamma waves	microwaves
(c)	X rays	visible light

General Questions and Problems

3.82 Helium, neon, argon, krypton, xenon, and radon make up the noble gas family.

3.84 Pb: $1s^2\, 2s^2\, 2p^6\, 3s^2\, 3p^6\, 4s^2\, 3d^{10}\, 4p^6\, 5s^2\, 4d^{10}\, 5p^6\, 6s^2\, 4f^{14}\, 5d^{10}\, 6p^2$
Shell 1: 2 electrons   Shell 2: 8 electrons   Shell 3: 18 electrons
Shell 4: 32 electrons   Shell 5: 18 electrons   Shell 6: 4 electrons

3.86 Contribution from ^{79}Br: 50.54% of 78.92 amu = 39.89 amu
Contribution from ^{81}Br: 49.46% of 80.91 amu = 40.02 amu

Atomic weight = 79.91 amu

3.88 One atom of carbon weighs more than one atom of hydrogen because the mass of carbon (12 amu) is greater than the mass of hydrogen (1 amu).

3.90 If 10^{23} hydrogen atoms weigh about 1 g, then 10^{23} carbon atoms will weigh about 12 g.

3.92 The unidentified element is strontium, which occurs directly below calcium in group 2A and thus has similar chemical behavior. Strontium is a metal, has 38 protons, and is in the fifth period.

3.94 Zirconium, a metal, has an electron configuration by shell of 2 8 18 10 2.

3.96 (a) Electrons must fill the $4s$ subshell before entering the $3d$ subshell. The correct configuration:

$$1s^2\, 2s^2\, 2p^6\, 3s^2\, 3p^6\, 4s^2\, 3d^8$$

(b) Electrons must fill the $2s$ subshell before entering the $2p$ subshell. The correct configuration:

$$1s^2\, 2s^2\, 2p^3$$

(c) Silicon has fourteen electrons. The correct configuration:

$$1s^2\, 2s^2\, 2p^6\, 3s^2\, \uparrow\ \uparrow\ \_$$
$$3p$$

(d) The $3s$ electrons must have opposite spins. The correct configuration:

$$1s^2\, 2s^2\, 2p^6\, \uparrow\downarrow$$
$$3s$$

Self-Test for Chapter 3

Multiple choice:

1. Which of the following is a metalloid?
    (a) Carbon   (b) Aluminum   (c) Silicon   (d) Phosphorus

2. Which of the following has a partially filled d subshell?
    (a) Calcium   (b) Vanadium   (c) Zinc   (d) Arsenic

3. Which of the following is not a part of atomic theory?
    (a) All metal is composed of atoms.   (b) The atoms of each element are different from the atoms of other elements.   (c) In chemical compounds, atoms are combined in specific proportions.   (d) Chemical reactions only change the way that atoms are combined.

4. How many isotopes of hydrogen are there?
    (a) one   (b) two   (c) three   (d) can't be determined

5. What holds protons and neutrons together in the nucleus?
    (a) attraction   (b) repulsion   (c) electrons   (d) internuclear forces

6. Which of the following has a mass number of 33?
    (a) $^{74}_{33}$As   (b) $^{35}_{17}$Cl   (c) $^{32}_{16}$S   (d) $^{33}_{16}$S

7. In which order are subshells usually filled?
    (a) s, p, d, f (b) d, f, p, s (c) s, p, f, d (d) s, d, p, f

8. An element with atomic number 38 is likely to be:
    (a) an alkali metal   (b) an alkaline earth metal   (c) a transition metal   (d) a metalloid

9. The element that has atomic weight = 91 and has 40 electrons is:
    (a) Protactinium   (b) Niobium   (c) Antimony   (d) Zirconium

10. The element that has electron configuration $1s^2\ 2s^2\ 2p^6\ 3s^2\ 3p^6\ 4s^2\ 3d^7$ is:
    (a) Copper   (b) Rhodium   (c) Arsenic   (d) Cobalt

11. An element that has electrons in its f subshell is:
    (a) Europium   (b) Technetium   (c) Antimony   (d) Xenon

12. $^{195}_{78}$X is the symbol for:
    (a) Gold   (b) Platinum   (c) Iridium   (d) Iron

Complete the following statements:

1. A _____ orbital is dumbbell-shaped.

2. An atomic mass unit is also known as a _____.

3. The nucleus of an atom is made up of _____ and _____.

4. The _____ _____ indicates the number of protons in an atom.

5. The electrons in an atom are grouped by energy into _____.

6. Elements belonging to the same _____ have similar chemical properties.

7. The atomic number of aluminum is _____.

8. Protons, neutrons, and electrons are known as _____ _____.

9. Atoms having the same number of protons but different numbers of neutrons are called _____.

10. The third shell contains _____ electrons.

11. The word _____ means that electrons can have certain energy values and no others.

Tell whether the following statements are true or false:

1. Bismuth is a metal.

2. The mass of an electron is approximately 1 amu.

3. A 4s electron is higher in energy than a 3d electron.

4. Isotopes have the same number of protons but different numbers of neutrons.

5. An atom's atomic number indicates the number of protons and neutrons the atom has.

6. Elements in group 2A are more reactive than elements in group 1A.

7. Elements in the same period have similar chemical properties.

8. More elements are metals than are nonmetals.

9. All compounds consist of atoms combined in specific proportions.

10. A subshell contains only two electrons.

11. An element can have the same number of protons, neutrons and electrons.

12. Atomic weight always increases with atomic number.

Match the items on the left with those on the right.

1. $1s^2\,2s^2$ (a) Mendeleev

2. Group   (b) Number of protons in an element

3. Atomic mass unit   (c) Reactive metals

4. Formulated the periodic   (d) Average mass of a large number of an
   table   element's atoms

5. Neutron   (e) Column in the periodic table

6. $^{28}_{14}\text{Si}$ (f) Row in the periodic table

7. Group 1A   (g) Element with atomic mass of 14 amu

8. Atomic number   (h) Electron configuration of beryllium

9. $^{29}_{14}\text{Si}$ (i) Element having 15 neutrons

10. Atomic weight   (j) Subatomic particle with zero charge

11. $^{14}_{7}\text{N}$ (k) Dalton

12. Period   (l) Element with atomic number 14

Chapter 4 – Ionic Compounds

Chapter Outline

I. Ions (Sections 4.1–4.2).
   A. Ions are formed when a neutral atom either gains an electron (to form an anion) or loses an electron (to form a cation).
      1. Ionization energy measures the ease with which an atom gives up an electron.
         a. Energy must be supplied in order to remove an electron.
         b. Elements on the far left of the periodic table have smaller ionization energies and lose electrons more easily.
         c. Elements on the far right of the periodic table have larger ionization energies and lose electrons with difficulty.
      2. Electron affinity measures the ease with which an atom gains an electron.
         a. Energy is released when an atom gains an electron.
         b. Elements on the far right of the periodic table have larger electron affinities and gain electrons easily.
         c. Elements on the far left of the periodic table have smaller electron affinities and gain electrons less easily.
   B. Main group elements in the middle of the periodic table neither lose or gain electrons easily.
II. Formation of ionic compounds (Sections 4.3–4.6).
   A. Compounds formed between an element on the far left side of the periodic table and an element on the far right of the periodic table are electronically neutral (Section 4.3).
      1. These compounds consist of a large number of cations and anions packed together in a crystal.
      2. The bonds between ions in the crystal are known as ionic bonds.
      3. The crystal is known as an ionic solid.
   B. Properties of ionic compounds (Section 4.4)
      1. Ionic compounds are crystalline.
      2. Ionic compounds conduct electricity.
      3. Ionic compounds are high-melting.
      4. Many, but not all, ionic compounds are water-soluble.
   C. The Octet Rule (Sections 4.5–4.6).
      1. Main group elements undergo reactions that leave them with eight valence electrons – an octet (Section 4.5).
      2. The valence electrons in an ionic compound can be represented by electron dots (Section 4.6).
III. Ions of some common elements (Sections 4.7–4.9).
   A. Cations (Section 4.7)

      1. Group 1A $\quad M\cdot \longrightarrow M^+ + e^-$

      2. Group 2A $\quad \cdot M\cdot \longrightarrow M^{2+} + 2e^-$
      3. Group 3A $\quad Al^{3+}$ is the only common cation.
      4. Transition metals often form more than one cation.
   B. Anions.

      1. Group 6A $\quad :\overset{\cdot}{X}: + 2e^- \longrightarrow :\overset{\cdot\cdot}{\underset{\cdot\cdot}{X}}:^{2-}$

2. Group 7A $\quad :\overset{\displaystyle ..}{\underset{\displaystyle ..}{X}}: \ + \ e^- \ \longrightarrow \ :\overset{\displaystyle ..}{\underset{\displaystyle ..}{X}}:^-$

    C. Group 4A, Group 5A and Group 8A elements don't form cations or anions.
    D. Naming ions (Section 4.8).
        1. Main group cations are named by identifying the metal and then adding the word "ion".
        2. Transition metal cations are named by identifying the metal, specifying the charge and adding the word "ion".
        3. Anions are named by replacing the end of the name of the element with "-ide" and adding the word "ion".
        4. Polyatomic ions (Section 4.9).
            a. Polyatomic ions are composed of more than one atom.
            b. Subscripts in polyatomic ions indicate how many of each atom are present in the formula unit (no subscripts are necessary if only one atom is present).
            c. The names of polyatomic ions should be memorized.
IV. Ionic compounds (Sections 4.10–4.12).
    A. Formulas of ionic compounds (Section 4.10).
        1. Formulas are written so that the number of positive charges equals the number of negative charges.
            a. Cations are listed first, anions second.
            b. It is not necessary to write the charges of the ions.
            c. Use parentheses around a polyatomic ion if it has a subscript.
        2. A formula unit shows the simplest neutral unit of an ionic compound.
    B. Naming ionic compounds (Section 4.11).
    Ionic compounds are named by citing the cation and then the anion, with a space between the two words.
    C. Acids and bases (Section 4.12).
        1. Acids are compounds that provide H^+ ions in solution.
        2. Bases are compounds that provide OH^- ions in solution.
        3. Acids and bases can each provide more than one H^+ or OH^- ion in solution.

Solutions to Chapter 4 Problems

4.1   The Mg^{2+} ion is a cation.

4.2   The O^{2-} ion is an anion.

4.3   Figure 4.1 shows approximate ionization energies for argon and krypton. In line with this trend, it is predicted that the ionization energy of xenon should be somewhat less than that of krypton but greater than the ionization energy of most other elements.

4.4   (a) According to Figure 4.1a, B ($Z = 5$) loses an electron more easily than Be ($Z = 4$).
        (b) Ca ($Z = 20$) loses an electron more easily than Co ($Z = 27$).
        (c) Sc ($Z = 21$) loses an electron more easily than Se($Z = 34$).

4.5   (a) According to Figure 4.1, H gains an electron more easily than He. Because the electron affinity for He is zero, it does not accept an electron.
        (b) S gains an electron more easily than Si.
        (c) Na gains an electron slightly more easily than Mg. Because both electron affinities are close to zero, neither element accepts an electron readily.

4.6   Electron configuration for F⁻: $1s^2\,2s^2\,2p^6$
Electron configuration for Cl⁻: $1s^2\,2s^2\,2p^6\,3s^2\,3p^6$
Electron configuration for Br⁻: $1s^2\,2s^2\,2p^6\,3s^2\,3p^6\,4s^2\,3d^{10}\,4p^6$
The electron configurations of the ions of the group 7A elements are the same as those of the neighboring noble gases.

4.7   Potassium (atomic number 19): $1s^2\,2s^2\,2p^6\,3s^2\,3p^6\,4s^1$
Argon (atomic number 18): $1s^2\,2s^2\,2p^6\,3s^2\,3p^6$
Potassium can attain the noble-gas configuration of argon by losing an electron from its $4s$ subshell, forming the K⁺ cation.

4.8   Aluminum (atomic number 13): $1s^2\,2s^2\,2p^6\,3s^2\,3p^1$
Neon (atomic number 10): $1s^2\,2s^2\,2p^6$
Aluminum can attain the noble-gas configuration of neon by losing three electrons, two from its $3s$ subshell and one from its $3p$ subshell, resulting in the formation of the Al³⁺ ion.

4.9   Oxygen atom (atomic number 8): $1s^2\,2s^2\,2p^4$
Neon atom (atomic number 10): $1s^2\,2s^2\,2p^6$
Oxygen can attain the noble-gas configuration of neon by gaining two electrons in its $2p$ subshell.

4.10

$\cdot\dot{\text{X}}\cdot$

4.11

$:\ddot{\text{Rn}}:$ $\cdot\dot{\text{Pb}}\cdot$ $:\ddot{\text{Xe}}:$ $\cdot\text{Ra}\cdot$

4.12

(a) $:\dot{\ddot{\text{Se}}}\cdot\; +\; 2\,e^-\; \longrightarrow\; :\ddot{\ddot{\text{Se}}}:^{2-}$; $\text{Se}\; +\; 2\,e^-\; \longrightarrow\; \text{Se}^{2-}$

(b) $\cdot\text{Ba}\cdot\; \longrightarrow\; \text{Ba}^{2+}\; +\; 2\,e^-$; $\text{Ba}\; \longrightarrow\; \text{Ba}^{2+}\; +\; 2\,e^-$

(c) $:\dot{\ddot{\text{Br}}}\cdot\; +\; e^-\; \longrightarrow\; :\ddot{\ddot{\text{Br}}}:^-$; $\text{Br}\; +\; e^-\; \longrightarrow\; \text{Br}^-$

4.13   Molybdenum, a transition metal, is more likely to form a cation than an anion.

4.14   Strontium loses two electrons to form the Sr²⁺ cation, and bromine gains an electron to form the Br⁻ anion. Only chromium, a transition metal, can form more than one cation.

4.15   (a) Al⁺² is not likely to form because loss of two electrons doesn't give a cation with a noble-gas configuration. Al⁺³ is the cation that forms from the loss of three electrons from the outermost subshells of aluminum.
(b) O⁻ doesn't form because it is one electron short of having a noble-gas configuration. O²⁻ is the ion that is formed from oxygen.
(c) Se²⁻ has a noble-gas configuration and is produced by the gain of two electrons by selenium.

4.16   (a) Cu^{2+} – copper(II) ion (cupric ion)   (b) F^- – fluoride ion
       (c) Mg^{2+} – magnesium ion   (d) S^{2-} – sulfide ion

4.17   (a) Ag^+ (b) Fe^{2+} (c) Cu^+ (d) Te^{2-}

4.18 Na^+ – sodium ion K^+ – potassium ion
       Ca^{2+} – calcium ion Cl^- – chloride ion

4.19   (a) NO_3^- – nitrate ion   (b) CN^- – cyanide ion
       (c) OH^- – hydroxide ion   (d) HPO_4^{2-} – hydrogen phosphate ion

4.20   (a) HCO_3^- – bicarbonate ion   (b) OH^- – hydroxide ion
       (c) PO_4^{3-} – phosphate ion   (d) MnO_4^- – permanganate ion

4.21   (a) The two ions are Ag^+ and I^-. Since they have the same charge, only one of each ion is
         needed. The formula is AgI.
       (b) Ions: Ag^+, O^{2-}. Two Ag^+ ions will balance the O^{2-} ion. The formula is Ag_2O.
       (c) The ions are Ag^+ and PO_4^{3-}. Three Ag^+ ions are needed to balance the PO_4^{3-} anion.
         The formula is Ag_3PO_4.

4.22   (a) Na_2SO_4 (b) $FeSO_4$ (c) $Cr_2(SO_4)_3$

4.23 $(NH_4)_2CO_3$

4.24 $Al_2(SO_4)_3$, $Al(CH_3CO_2)_3$

4.25 $BaSO_4$. One barium ion is present for each sulfate ion.

4.26 Ag_2S – silver(I) sulfide. The charge on silver is +1.

4.27   (a) CuO – copper(II) oxide   (b) $Ca(CN)_2$ – calcium cyanide
       (c) $NaNO_3$ – sodium nitrate   (d) Cu_2SO_4 – copper(I) sulfate
       (e) Li_3PO_4 – lithium phosphate   (f) NH_4Cl – ammonium chloride

4.28   (a) $Ba(OH)_2$ (b) $CuCO_3$ (c) $Mg(HCO_3)_2$ (d) CuF (e) $Fe_2(SO_4)_3$
       (f) $Fe(NO_3)_2$

4.29   Acids provide H^+ ions when dissolved in water.
       Bases provide OH^- ions when dissolved in water.

Acids: HF $\xrightarrow{\text{dissolve in water}}$ H^+ + F^-

         HCN $\xrightarrow{\text{dissolve in water}}$ H^+ + CN^-

Bases: $Ca(OH)_2$ $\xrightarrow{\text{dissolve in water}}$ Ca^{2+} + $2\,OH^-$

         LiOH $\xrightarrow{\text{dissolve in water}}$ Li^+ + OH^-

Understanding Key Concepts

4.30

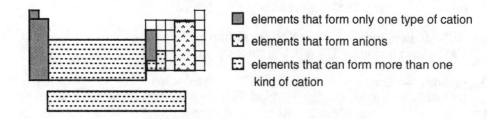

☐ elements that form only one type of cation

☐ elements that form anions

☐ elements that can form more than one kind of cation

4.31

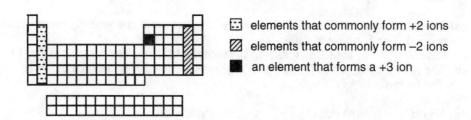

☐ elements that commonly form +2 ions

▨ elements that commonly form −2 ions

■ an element that forms a +3 ion

4.32 Drawing (a) shows an ion that has one more electron than proton and thus represents an F⁻ ion.
Drawing (b) represents sodium, a neutral atom.
Drawing (c) represents Ca^{2+}, an ion with two more protons than electrons.

4.33

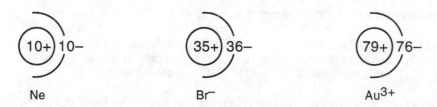

4.34 Drawing (a) represents a sodium atom, and drawing (b) represents an Na^+ ion. The Na atom is larger because its $3s$ electron lies in an orbital that is farther from the nucleus.

4.35 Drawing (a) represents a chlorine atom, and drawing (b) represents a Cl^- anion. The anion is larger because its extra electron is not as tightly held by the positively charged nucleus as are the electrons of the atom.

Ions and Ionic Bonding

4.36 (a) H·   (b) He: (c) Li·

4.38 (a) $Ca \rightarrow Ca^{2+} + 2\,e^-$ (b) $Au \rightarrow Au^+ + e^-$

(c) $F + e^- \rightarrow F^-$ (d) $Cr \rightarrow Cr^{3+} + 3\,e^-$

4.40 (a) False. A cation is formed by *loss* of one or more electrons from an atom. (b), (c) False. Group 4A elements don't form ions. (d) True.

Ions and the Octet Rule

4.42 The *octet rule* states that main-group atoms undergo reactions in order to achieve a noble-gas electron configuration with eight outer-shell electrons.

4.44 An ion with 34 protons and 36 electrons has a –2 charge.

4.46 (a) $X^{2+} = Sr^{2+}$; $X = Sr$
(b) $X^- = Br^-$; $X = Br$

4.48 (a) Rb^+ $1s^2\,2s^2\,2p^6\,3s^2\,3p^6\,4s^2\,3d^{10}\,4p^6$
(b) Br^- $1s^2\,2s^2\,2p^6\,3s^2\,3p^6\,4s^2\,3d^{10}\,4p^6$
(c) S^{2-} $1s^2\,2s^2\,2p^6\,3s^2\,3p^6$
(d) Ba^{2+} $1s^2\,2s^2\,2p^6\,3s^2\,3p^6\,4s^2\,3d^{10}\,4p^6\,5s^2\,4d^{10}\,5p^6$
(e) Al^{3+} $1s^2\,2s^2\,2p^6$

Periodic Properties and Ion Formation

4.50 (a) O   (b) Li   (c) Zn   (d) N

4.52 None of the ions are stable because all lack eight outer-shell electrons.

4.54 Cr^{2+}: $1s^2\,2s^2\,2p^6\,3s^2\,3p^6\,3d^4$
Cr^{3+}: $1s^2\,2s^2\,2p^6\,3s^2\,3p^6\,3d^3$

4.56 The ionization energy of Li^+ is much greater than that of Li. Li readily loses an electron to form an ion with eight outer-shell electrons, but Li^+ would need to lose one electron from a stable octet in order to form the Li^{2+} cation.

Symbols, Formulas, and Names for Ions

4.58 (a) S^{2-} – sulfide ion   (b) Sn^{2+} – tin(II) ion   (c) Sr^{2+} – strontium ion
(d) Mg^{2+} – magnesium ion   (e) Au^+ – gold(I) ion

4.60 (a) Se^{2-} (b) O^{2-} (c) Ag^+

4.62 (a) OH^- (b) $SO_4{}^{2-}$ (c) $CH_3CO_2{}^-$ (d) $MnO_4{}^-$ (e) OCl^- (f) $NO_3{}^-$
(g) $HCO_3{}^-$

Names and Formulas For Ionic Compounds

4.64 (a) $Al(NO_3)_3$ (b) $AgNO_3$ (c) $Zn(NO_3)_2$ (d) $Ba(NO_3)_2$

4.66 (a) $NaHCO_3$ (b) KNO_3 (c) $CaCO_3$

4.68

	S^{2-}	Cl^-	$PO_4{}^{3-}$	$CO_3{}^{2-}$
copper(II)	CuS	$CuCl_2$	$Cu_3(PO_4)_2$	$CuCO_3$
Ca^{2+}	CaS	$CaCl_2$	$Ca_3(PO_4)_2$	$CaCO_3$
$NH_4{}^+$	$(NH_4)_2S$	NH_4Cl	$(NH_4)_3PO_4$	$(NH_4)_2CO_3$
ferric ion	Fe_2S_3	$FeCl_3$	$FePO_4$	$Fe_2(CO_3)_3$

4.70 (a) $MgCO_3$ magnesium carbonate   (b) $Ca(CH_3CO_2)_2$ calcium acetate
(c) AgCN   silver(I) cyanide   (d) $Na_2Cr_2O_7$ sodium dichromate

4.72 $Ca_3(PO_4)_2$ is the correct formula because the six positive charges from the three Ca^{2+} ions are balanced by the six negative charges of the two PO_4^{3-} ions.

Acids and Bases

4.74 An acid provides H^+ ions when dissolved in water. A base provides OH^- ions when dissolved in water.

4.76

(a) HNO_2 $\xrightarrow{\text{dissolve in water}}$ H^+ + NO_2^-

(b)   HCN $\xrightarrow{\text{dissolve in water}}$ H^+ + CN^-

(c) $Ca(OH)_2$ $\xrightarrow{\text{dissolve in water}}$ Ca^{2+} + $2\ OH^-$

(d) CH_3CO_2H $\xrightarrow{\text{dissolve in water}}$ H^+ + CH_3COO^-

Applications

4.78 To a geologist, a mineral is a naturally occurring crystalline compound. To a nutritionist, a mineral is a metal ion essential for human health.

4.80 For most people, the effect of salt consumption on blood pressure elevation is slight, but a small proportion of people may suffer high blood pressure as a result of excessive salt consumption.

4.82 Sodium protects against fluid loss and is necessary for muscle contraction and transmission of nerve impulses.

4.84 The prefix "hypo-" means "too low", or below normal. The prefix "hyper-" means "too high", or above normal.

General Questions and Problems

4.86

Ion	Name	Charge	Total charge
Ca^{2+}	calcium ion	2+	5 x (2+) = 10+
PO_4^{3-}	phosphate ion	3–	3 x (3–) = 9–
OH^-	hydroxide ion	1–	1–

The formula correctly represents a neutral compound because the number of positive charges equals the number of negative charges.

4.88 (a) CrO_3 (b) VCl_5 (c) MnO_2 (d) MoS_2

4.90 (a) A gluconate ion has one negative charge.
     (b) Three gluconate ions are in one formula unit of iron(III) gluconate, and the formula is
        Fe(gluconate)$_3$.

4.92 (a) Co(CN)$_2$ (b) UO$_3$ (c) SnSO$_4$ (d) K$_3$PO$_4$ (e) Ca$_3$P$_2$ (f) LiHSO$_4$

Self-Test for Chapter 4

Multiple choice:

1. How many atoms does a formula unit of Li$_2$CO$_3$ contain?
    (a) 3   (b) 4   (c) 5   (d) 6

2. How many ions are produced when a formula unit of Li$_2$CO$_3$ is dissolved in water?
    (a) 3   (b) 4   (c) 5   (d) 6

3. Which of the following is not a property of ionic compounds?
    (a) crystalline   (b) conductor of electricity   (c) high melting   (d) 1:1 ratio of cations to anions

4. Which of the following is the correct name for Fe(NO$_3$)$_3$?
    (a) Ferrous nitrate   (b) Iron nitrate   (c) Iron(III) nitrate   (d) Iron(II) nitrate

5. Bromine has a:
    (a) large ionization energy and large electron affinity   (b) large ionization energy and small
    electron affinity   (c) small ionization energy and large electron affinity   (d) small ionization
    energy and small electron affinity

6. H$_2$CrO$_4$ is an acid that :
    (a) provides one H$^+$ ion when dissolved   (b) provides two H$^+$ ions when dissolved
    (c) provides one OH$^-$ when dissolved   (d) H$_2$CrO$_4$ is not an acid

7. An element that loses three electrons to attain the electron configuration of argon is:
    (a) Titanium   (b) Scandium   (c) Calcium   (d) Potassium

8. The formula for gold(III) chloride is:
    (a) Au$_3$Cl   (b) AuCl   (c) AuCl$_2$ (d) AuCl$_3$

9. Which of the following anions is not biologically important?
    (a) Cl$^-$ (b) Br$^-$ (c) HCO$_3^-$ (d) HPO$_4^-$

10. The redness of rubies is due to which ion?
    (a) Iron   (b) Titanium   (c) Aluminum   (d) Chromium

Complete the following sentences:

1. _____ _____ measures the ease with which an atom gives up an electron.

2. The name of K_3PO_4 is _____ _____.

3. Radium (atomic number 88) loses _____ electrons to achieve a noble-gas configuration.

4. NO_3^- is an example of a _____ ion.

5. The formulas of ionic compounds are _____ formulas.

6. Atoms of main-group elements tend to combine in chemical compounds so that they attain _____ outer-shell electrons.

7. A _____ provides OH^- ions in water.

8. _____ is a low concentration of potassium in the bloodstream.

9. Ionic compounds are usually _____ solids.

10. The first three elements in group _____ form neither cations nor anions.

Tell whether the following statements are true or false:

1. Zinc can form ions with different charges.

2. Na^+ and F^- have the same electron configuration.

3. Ionization energy measures the amount of energy released when an ion is formed from a neutral atom.

4. $Co(CO_3)_2$ is a possible compound.

5. A solution of H_3PO_4 contains only H^+ and $H_2PO_4^-$ ions.

6. Ionic crystals conduct electricity.

7. Cuprous ion is the same as copper(II) ion.

8. Many ionic compounds are not water-soluble.

9. Group 5A consists of metals and nonmetals.

10. Elements in group 7A have the largest ionization energies.

11. The octet rule is limited to main-group elements.

12. Hyponatremia means too much sodium in the bloodstream.

Match each item on the left with its partner on the right:

1. $FeBr_2$

2. S^{2-}

3. NH_4^+

4. SO_3^{2-}

5. Ca

6. $FeBr_3$

7. Ar

8. ·Be·

9. Co

10. SO_4^{2-}

11. Ne

12. K

(a) sulfite anion

(b) electron-dot symbol

(c) alkali metal

(d) has the same electron configuration as Na^+

(e) iron(II) bromide

(f) transition metal

(g) sulfate anion

(h) alkaline earth metal

(i) has the same electron configuration as Cl^-

(j) iron(III) bromide

(k) polyatomic cation

(l) sulfide anion

Chapter 5 – Molecular Compounds

Chapter Outline

I. Covalent bonds (Sections 5.1–5.4).
  A Formation of covalent bonds (Section 5.1).
    1. Covalent bonds occur when two atoms share electrons.
    2. Electron sharing results from the overlap of orbitals of two atoms.
    3. The optimum distance between nuclei of two atoms is the bond length.
    4. Seven elements exist as diatomic molecules: H_2, N_2, O_2, F_2, Cl_2, Br_2, I_2.
  B. Covalent bonds and the periodic table (Section 5.2).
    1. Molecular compounds result when atoms form covalent bonds to another atom or to more than one atom.
    2 The octet rule states that each atom in a molecular compound shares the number of electrons necessary to achieve a noble-gas configuration.
    3 Most main-group elements form from one to four covalent bonds and obey the octet rule.
      a. Boron forms only three bonds because it has only 3 valence electrons.
      b. Sulfur and phosphorus may form 5 or 6 bonds if they use *d* orbitals.
  C. Multiple covalent bonds (Section 5.3).
    1. Some atoms can share more than one electron pair to form multiple bonds.
      a. A double bond is formed when two pairs are shared.
      b. A triple bond is formed when three pairs are shared.
    2. Even when multiple bonds occur, the atoms still obey the octet rule.
  D. Coordinate bonds occur when one atom donates both of the shared electrons (Section 5.4).
II. Formulas, structures and shapes (Sections 5.5–5.7).
  A. Formulas (Section 5.5).
    1. Molecular formulas show the numbers and kinds of atoms in one molecule of a compound.
    2. Structural formulas show how atoms are connected.
  B. Lewis structures are structural formulas that show electron lone pairs (Section 5.6).
    1. One approach to drawing Lewis structures involves knowing common bonding patterns.
    2. The other approach is a general method.
      a. Find the number of valence electrons for all atoms.
      b. Draw a line between each pair of connected atoms to represent an electron pair.
      c. Place lone pairs around all peripheral atoms to give them octets.
      d. Place remaining electrons around the central atom.
      e. If the central atom doesn't have an octet, use an electron pair from a neighboring atom to form a multiple bond to the central atom.
  C. Molecular shapes can be predicted by using the VSEPR model (Section 5.7).
    1. Draw a Lewis structure of the molecule, and identify the atom whose geometry you want to know.
    2. Count the number of charge clouds around the atom.
    3. Predict shape by assuming that the charge clouds orient in space so that they are as far apart as possible.
      a. If there are two charge clouds, the geometry is linear.
      b. If there are three charge clouds, the geometry is linear or bent.
      c. If there are four charge clouds, the geometry is tetrahedral, trigonal pyramidal or bent.

III. Polar covalent bonds (Sections 5.8–5.9).
   A. Polar covalent bonds occur when the electrons in a covalent bond are attracted more to one atom than another (Section 5.8).
     1. The ability of an atom to attract electrons is called electronegativity.
     2. Atoms with electronegativity differences < 1.9 form polar covalent bonds.
     3. Atoms with electronegativity differences > 1.9 form ionic bonds.
   B. Molecules containing polar covalent bonds can be polar (Section 5.9).
     1. Molecular polarity depends on both the presence of polar covalent bonds and on molecular shape.
     2. Polarity has a dramatic effect on molecular properties.
IV. Molecular compounds (Sections 5.10–5.11).
   A. Naming binary molecular compounds (Section 5.10).
     1. Name the first element in the compound, using a prefix if necessary.
     2. Name the second element, using an -ide ending and using a prefix if necessary.
   B. Properties of molecular compounds (Section 5.11).
     1. Molecular compounds are electrically neutral.
     2. Molecular compounds have low melting and boiling points.
     3. Molecular compounds may be solids, liquids or gases.

Solutions to Chapter 5 Problems

5.1   The two bromine atoms achieve the electron configuration of krypton:

$$1s^2\ 2s^2\ 2p^6\ 3s^2\ 3p^6\ 4s^2\ 3d^{10}\ 4p^6$$

5.2

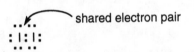

shared electron pair

Each iodine atom achieves the noble-gas configuration of xenon.

5.3   (a) PH_3 hydrogen – one covalent bond;   phosphorus – three covalent bonds
        (b) H_2Se hydrogen – one covalent bond;   selenium – two covalent bonds
        (c) HCl   hydrogen – one covalent bond;   chlorine – one covalent bond
        (d) SiF_4 fluorine – one covalent bond;   silicon – four covalent bonds

5.4   Lead is a member of group 4A and should form four covalent bonds, as do carbon and silicon. $PbCl_4$ is thus a more likely formula for a compound containing lead and chlorine than is $PbCl_5$.

5.5   (a) CH_2Cl_2. Carbon forms four covalent bonds. Two bonds form between carbon and hydrogen, and the other two form between carbon and chlorine.
        (b) BH_3. Boron forms three covalent bonds.
        (c) NI_3
        (d) $SiCl_4$

5.6   In acetic acid, all hydrogen atoms have two outer-shell electrons and all carbon and oxygen atoms have eight outer-shell electrons.

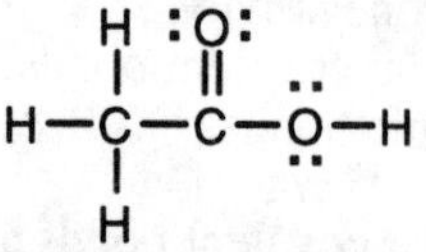

$$
\begin{array}{ccc}
 & H & :\overset{\cdot\cdot}{O}: \\
 & | & \| \\
H- & C-C-\overset{\cdot\cdot}{\underset{\cdot\cdot}{O}}- & H \\
 & | & \\
 & H &
\end{array}
\qquad \text{Acetic acid}
$$

5.7   C and N must be bonded to each other. After drawing the C–N bond and all bonds to hydrogens, two electrons remain; they are a lone pair on nitrogen. All atoms now have a noble-gas configuration.

CH$_5$N : 14 valence electrons

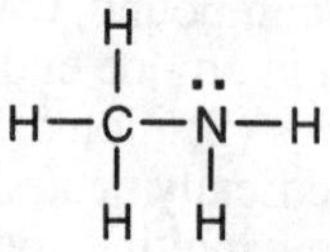

$$
\begin{array}{c}
H \\
| \\
H-C-\overset{\cdot\cdot}{N}-H \\
| \quad | \\
H \quad H
\end{array}
$$

5.8

C$_3$H$_8$: 20 valence electrons

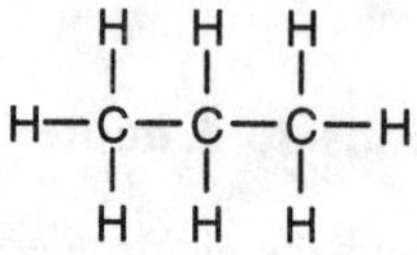

$$
\begin{array}{ccc}
H & H & H \\
| & | & | \\
H-C- & C- & C-H \\
| & | & | \\
H & H & H
\end{array}
$$

5.9

CH$_2$O: 12 valence electrons

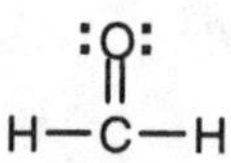

$$
\begin{array}{c}
:\overset{\cdot\cdot}{O}: \\
\| \\
H-C-H
\end{array}
$$

5.10

(a)

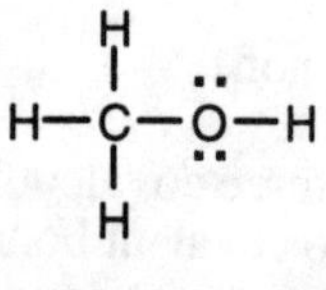

$$
\begin{array}{c}
H \\
| \\
H-C-\overset{\cdot\cdot}{\underset{\cdot\cdot}{O}}-H \\
| \\
H
\end{array}
$$

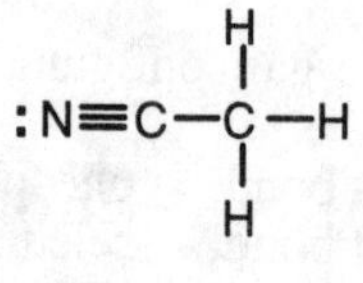

(b)

$$
\begin{array}{c}
H \\
| \\
:N\equiv C-C-H \\
| \\
H
\end{array}
$$

(c)

$$
\begin{array}{c}
\overset{\cdot\cdot}{\underset{\cdot\cdot}{:Cl:}} \\
| \\
:\overset{\cdot\cdot}{N}-\overset{\cdot\cdot}{\underset{\cdot\cdot}{Cl}}: \\
| \\
:\overset{\cdot\cdot}{\underset{\cdot\cdot}{Cl}}:
\end{array}
$$

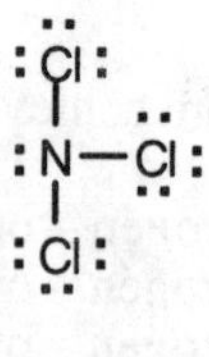

5.11   (a) For phosgene, COCl$_2$:

Step 1:   Total valence electrons –
4 e$^-$ (from C) + 6 e$^-$ (from O) + 2 x 7 e$^-$ (from Cl) = 24 e$^-$

Step 2:   Six electrons are involved in the covalent bonds.

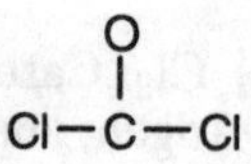

$$
\begin{array}{c}
O \\
| \\
Cl-C-Cl
\end{array}
$$

Step 3:   The other 18 electrons are placed in nine lone pairs.

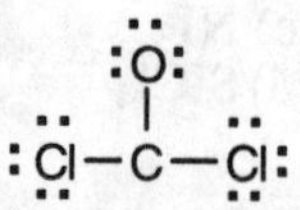

$$
\begin{array}{c}
:\overset{\cdot\cdot}{\underset{\cdot\cdot}{O}}: \\
| \\
:\overset{\cdot\cdot}{\underset{\cdot\cdot}{Cl}}-C-\overset{\cdot\cdot}{\underset{\cdot\cdot}{Cl}}:
\end{array}
$$

Step 4:   All electrons are used up in the above structure, but carbon doesn't have an electron octet, so one electron pair must be moved from oxygen to form a carbon-oxygen double bond.

Step 5:   The 24 electrons have been used up, and all atoms have a complete octet.

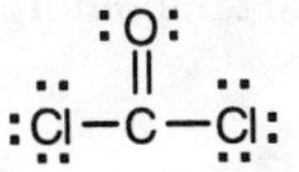

$$:\overset{\displaystyle :O:}{\underset{\displaystyle}{\overset{\displaystyle \|}{:Cl-C-Cl:}}}$$

(b) For OCl⁻:

Step 1:   Total valence electrons –
6 e⁻ (from O) + 7 e⁻ (from Cl) + 1 e⁻ (negative charge) = 14 e⁻

Step 2:   Two electrons used. O—Cl

Step 3:   Twelve additional electrons used. $:\overset{..}{\underset{..}{O}}-\overset{..}{\underset{..}{Cl}}:^-$

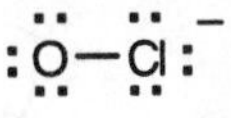

Step 4:   The above structure uses fourteen valence electrons, and all atoms have complete octets.

5.12   (a) For H₂O₂:

Step 1:   2 e⁻ (from 2 H) + 2 x 6 e⁻ (from O) = 14 electrons
Step 2:   Six electrons are involved in covalent bonds.   H—O—O—H

Step 3:   The other 8 electrons are placed in four lone pairs. $H-\overset{..}{\underset{..}{O}}-\overset{..}{\underset{..}{O}}-H$

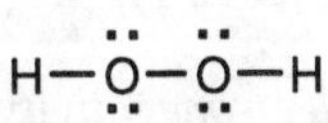

Step 4:   The 14 electrons have been used up, and all atoms have complete octets.

(b) SCl₂ : 20 electrons

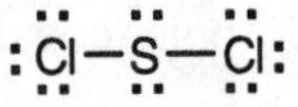

$$:\overset{..}{\underset{..}{Cl}}-\overset{..}{\underset{..}{S}}-\overset{..}{\underset{..}{Cl}}:$$

5.13

HNO₃ :   24 electrons

$$:\overset{\displaystyle :O:}{\underset{\displaystyle}{\overset{\displaystyle \|}{:\overset{..}{\underset{..}{O}}-N-\overset{..}{\underset{..}{O}}-H}}}$$

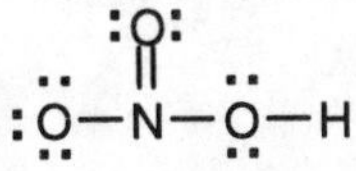

5.14   Carbon, the central atom, is surrounded by four bonds. Referring to Table 5.1, we see that chloroform has tetrahedral geometry.

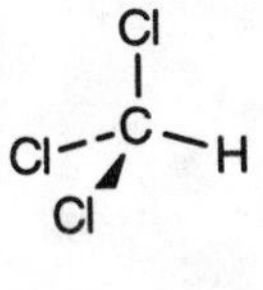

$$\underset{\displaystyle Cl}{\overset{\displaystyle Cl}{Cl-\overset{|}{C}-H}}$$ Chloroform

Each carbon of dichloroethylene is surrounded by three charge clouds. Dichloroethylene is planar, with 120° bond angles.

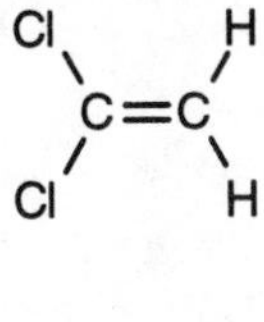

$$\underset{Cl}{\overset{Cl}{}}\diagup C=C \diagdown \underset{H}{\overset{H}{}}$$ Dichloroethylene

5.15   Both ammonium ion and sulfate ion are tetrahedral.

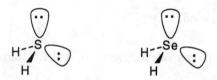

5.16   Both molecules are bent and have bond angles of approximately 105°.

5.17   Use Figure 5.7 to predict electronegativity:

Least electronegative ——————————> *Most electronegative*

H (2.1),   P (2.1) < S (2.5) < N (3.0) < O (3.5)

5.18 | *Electronegativity* | | *Difference* | *Type of Bond* |
|---|---|---|---|
| (a) I (2.5), | Cl (3.0) | 0.5 | polar covalent |
| (b) Li (1.0), | O (3.5) | 2.5 | ionic |
| (c) Br (2.8), | Br (2.8) | 0 | covalent |
| (d) P (2.1), | Br (2.8) | 0.7 | polar covalent |

5.19   *Electronegativity*   *Bond polarity*

(a)   F (4.0) , S (2.5) $\overset{\delta-\quad\delta+}{\text{F—S}}$

(b)   P (2.1) , O (3.5) $\overset{\delta+\quad\delta-}{\text{P—O}}$

(c)   As (2.0) , Cl (3.0) $\overset{\delta+\quad\delta-}{\text{As—Cl}}$

5.20

(a)   (b)

The bonds of PH$_3$ are nonpolar covalent, but the molecule is polar because of the lone electron pair on phosphorus. Formaldehyde is also polar.

5.21 The –CH$_3$ portions of diethyl ether are tetrahedral. The C–O–C portion is bent, and has a bond angle of 112°. The molecule has the indicated polarity because of the polar C–O bonds and because of the two lone pairs of electrons.

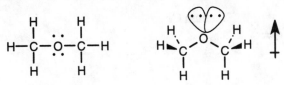

5.22 (a) S$_2$Cl$_2$ disulfur dichloride   (b) ICl   iodine chloride
(c) ICl$_3$ iodine trichloride

5.23 (a) SeF$_4$ (b) P$_2$O$_5$ (c) BrF$_3$

Understanding Key Concepts

5.24 Drawing (a) represents an ionic compound because ions are held together by strong attractive forces in all directions. Drawing (b) represents a covalent compound because the covalent bonds that hold atoms together in a molecule are much stronger than the forces between molecules.

5.25 Drawing (a), which shows molecules composed of one sulfur atom and two oxygen atoms, depicts SO$_2$.

5.26 (a) tetrahedral geometry   (b) pyramidal geometry   (c) planar triangular geometry

5.27 All models except (c) represent a molecule with a tetrahedral central atom.

5.28

(a) (b)   Acetaminophen   C$_8$H$_9$NO$_2$

(c) All carbons except for the starred carbon have planar triangular geometry.
The starred carbon has tetrahedral geometry.
Nitrogen has pyramidal geometry.

5.29

(a)   Glycine

(b) H–C–H bond angle: 109.5°
O–C–O bond angle: 120°
H–N–H bond angle: 107°

5.30

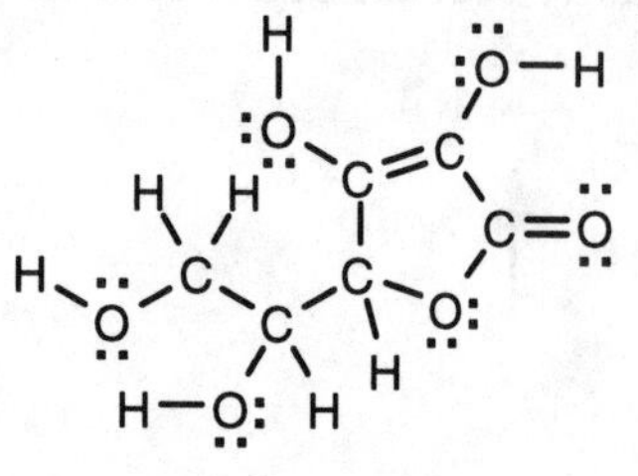

Vitamin C

5.31

(a) (b)

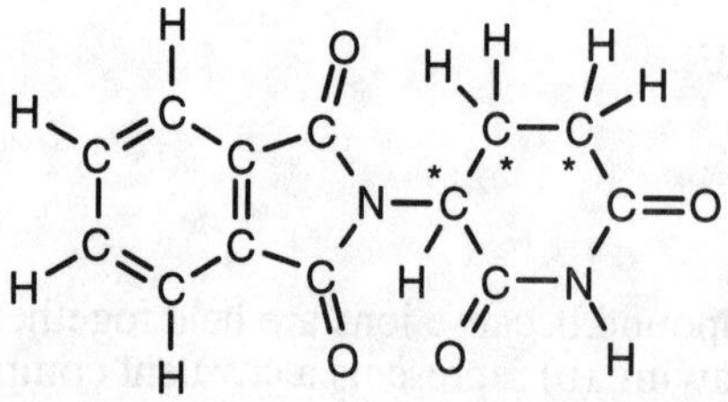

Thalidomide $C_{13}H_{10}N_2O_4$

(c) All carbons except for the starred carbons have planar triangular geometry.
The starred carbons have tetrahedral geometry.
The nitrogens have pyramidal geometry.

Covalent Bonds

5.32 A covalent bond is a chemical bond in which two electrons are shared between two atoms. An ionic bond is formed by the attraction of a positively charged ion to a negatively charged ion. In an ionic bond, both electrons of the electron pair "belong" to the negatively charged ion.

5.34 (a) oxygen (i) (iv)   (b) potassium (iii)
(c) phosphorus (ii)   (d) iodine (i) (iv)
(e) hydrogen (i) (ii)   (f) cesium (iii)

5.36 Tellurium, a group 6A element, forms two covalent bonds, as do oxygen, sulfur, and other members of group 6A.

5.38 Coordinate covalent bonds: (b) $Cu(NH_3)_4^{2+}$ (c) NH_4^+

5.40 Since tin is a member of group 4A, it forms four covalent bonds. $SnCl_4$ is the most likely formula for a molecular compound of tin and chlorine.

Structural Formulas

5.42 (a) A *molecular formula* shows the numbers and kinds of atoms in a molecule; a *structural formula* shows how the atoms in a molecule are bonded to one another.

(b) A *structural formula* shows the bonds between atoms; a *condensed structure* shows central atoms and the atoms connected to them written as groups but does not show bonds.

(c) A *lone pair* of valence electrons is a pair that is not shared; a *shared pair* of electrons is shared between two atoms.

5.44 (a) N_2 – 10 valence electrons   (b) CO – 10 valence electrons
(c) CH_3CH_2CHO – 24 valence electrons   (d) OF_2 – 20 valence electrons

5.46 A compound with the formula C_2H_8 can't exist because any structure drawn would violate the rules of valence.

5.48

(a)

$$H-\overset{\cdot\cdot}{\underset{\cdot\cdot}{O}}-\overset{\cdot\cdot}{N}=\overset{\cdot\cdot}{\underset{\cdot\cdot}{O}}$$

(b)

$$H-\overset{\overset{\displaystyle H}{|}}{\underset{\underset{\displaystyle H}{|}}{C}}-C\equiv N:$$

(c)

$$H-\overset{\cdot\cdot}{\underset{\cdot\cdot}{F}}:$$

5.50 (a) $CH_3CH_2CH_3$ (b) $H_2C=CHCH_3$ (c) CH_3CH_2Cl

Drawing Lewis Structures

5.52

(a)

$$:\overset{\cdot\cdot}{F}:\\ \overset{\displaystyle|}{}\\ :\overset{\cdot\cdot}{F}-\underset{\underset{\displaystyle:\overset{\cdot\cdot}{F}:}{|}}{Si}-\overset{\cdot\cdot}{F}:$$

(b)

$$:\overset{\cdot\cdot}{Cl}:\\ \overset{\displaystyle|}{}\\ :\overset{\cdot\cdot}{Cl}-Al-\overset{\cdot\cdot}{Cl}:$$

(c)

$$:\overset{\cdot\cdot}{Cl}:\\ \overset{\displaystyle|}{}\\ :\overset{\cdot\cdot}{F}-\underset{\underset{\displaystyle:\overset{\cdot\cdot}{F}:}{|}}{C}-\overset{\cdot\cdot}{Cl}:$$

(d)

$$:\overset{\cdot\cdot}{O}:\\ \overset{\displaystyle||}{}\\ :\overset{\cdot\cdot}{O}-S-\overset{\cdot\cdot}{O}:$$

(e)

$$:\overset{\cdot\cdot}{Br}:\\ \overset{\displaystyle|}{}\\ :\overset{\cdot\cdot}{Br}-B-\overset{\cdot\cdot}{Br}:$$

(f)

$$:\overset{\cdot\cdot}{F}:\\ \overset{\displaystyle|}{}\\ :\overset{\cdot\cdot}{F}-N-\overset{\cdot\cdot}{F}:$$

5.54

Ethanol

5.56

$$H-\underset{\cdot\cdot}{\overset{\overset{\displaystyle H}{|}}{N}}-\underset{\cdot\cdot}{\overset{\overset{\displaystyle H}{|}}{N}}-H$$

Hydrazine

5.58

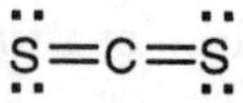

$$\ddot{S}=C=\ddot{S}$$

Carbon disulfide contains two carbon–sulfur double bonds.

5.60 Cyanide ion has 4 inner-shell electrons, plus the 10 electrons pictured, for a total of 14 electrons. Together, carbon and nitrogen have 13 protons. Since there is one more electron than proton, cyanide ion has a charge of -1.

$$:C\equiv N:{}^-$$

Molecular Geometry

5.62 Use Table 5.1 to predict the molecular geometry. **B** equals the number of bonds, and **E** equals the number of lone pairs:

Molecule	# of bonds	# of lone pairs	Shape	Bond angle
(a) AB_3	3	0	planar triangular	120°
(b) AB_2E	2	1	bent	120°

5.64

(a)

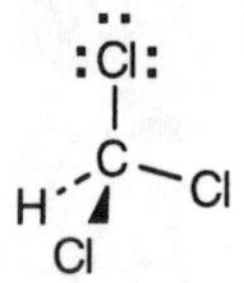

bond angle – 109°

(b)

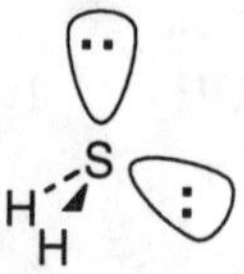

bond angle – 105°

(c)

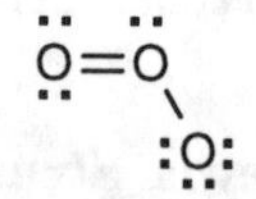

bond angle – 120°

(d)

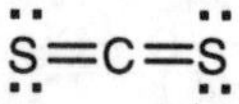

$$\ddot{S}=C=\ddot{S}$$

bond angle – 180°

(e)

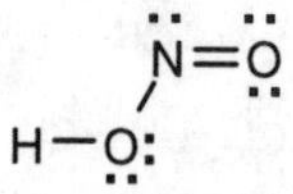

bond angle – 120°

5.66

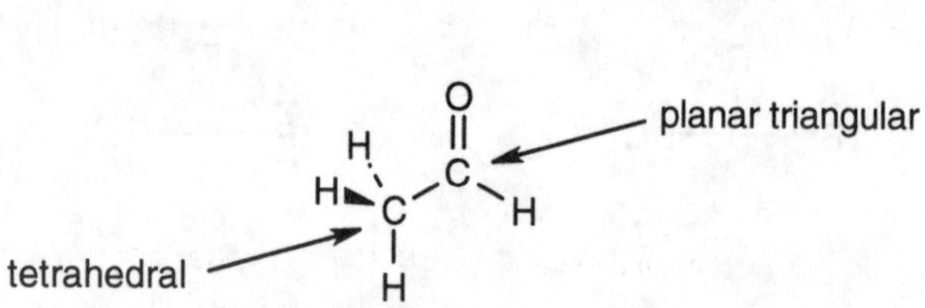

planar triangular

tetrahedral

Polarity of Bonds and Molecules

5.68 The most electronegative elements are found on the upper right side of the periodic table. The least electronegative elements are found on the left side of the periodic table.

5.70 *Less electronegative* ———> *More electronegative*

$$K < Li < C < Br < Cl$$

5.72

$$\overset{\delta+}{\text{I}}\overset{\delta-}{\text{—Br}} \qquad \overset{\delta-}{\text{O}}\overset{\delta+}{\text{—H}} \qquad \overset{\delta+}{\text{C}}\overset{\delta-}{\text{—F}} \qquad \overset{\delta-}{\text{N}}\overset{\delta+}{\text{—C}}$$

(a) I—Br   (b) O—H   (c) C—F   (d) N—C   (e) nonpolar

5.74

Electronegativity		Difference	Type of bond
(a) Na (0.9) ,	F (4.0)	3.1	ionic
(b) C (2.5) ,	Cl (3.0)	0.5	polar covalent
(c) N (3.0) ,	H (2.1)	0.9	polar covalent
(d) Be (1.5) ,	Br (2.8)	1.3	polar covalent

5.76 The individual bonds in BCl_3 are polar, but BCl_3 is nonpolar overall because all bond polarities cancel.

Names and Formulas of Molecular Compounds

5.78   (a) PI_3 phosphorus triiodide   (b) $AsCl_3$ arsenic trichloride
(c) P_4S_3 tetraphosphorus trisulfide   (d) Al_2F_6 dialuminum hexafluoride
(e) NI_3 nitrogen triiodide   (f) IF_7 iodine heptafluoride

5.80   (a) NO_2 (b) SF_6 (c) BrI_5 (d) N_2O_3 (e) N_2O_4 (f) $AsCl_5$

Applications

5.82 Carbon monoxide serves as a stimulus to production of cyclic GMP, which regulates many cellular functions. It is also involved with long-term memory.

5.84 A polymer is formed of many repeating units contained in a long chain.

5.86 Chemical names are complicated because the name of each of the 15 million known chemicals must be unique and must contain enough information for chemists to identify the composition and structure of each chemical.

5.88 Homeostasis is the maintenance of a constant internal environment in the body.

General Questions and Problems

5.90   (a) It was thought that noble gases couldn't form bonds because they already had eight valence electrons.

(b)

```
        ..
       :F:
        |
  ..    |    ..
 :F —— Xe —— F:
  ..    |    ..
        |
       :F:
        ..
```
Xenon tetrafluoride

5.92   Consult Figure 5.3 for help.

(a) Carbon forms four bonds. The correct formula is CCl_4.
(b) Nitrogen forms three bonds. The correct formula is N_2H_4.
(c) Sulfur forms two bonds. The correct formula is H_2S.
(d) C_2OS *could* actually be correct (S=C=C=O), but compounds with such adjacent double bonds are rare. More likely is the formula COS, a structural relative of carbon dioxide (S=C=O).

5.94

(a)

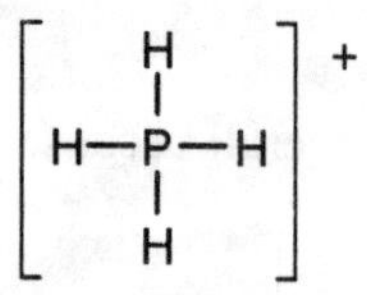

(b) Phosphonium ion is tetrahedral.

(c) Phosphorus donates its lone pair of electrons to H^+ to form a coordinate covalent bond.
(d) # of electrons: 15 (from P) + 3 (from 3 H) = 18
    # of protons: 15 (from P) + 4 (from 4 H) = 19
PH_4^+ is positive because the number of protons exceeds the number of electrons by one.

5.96

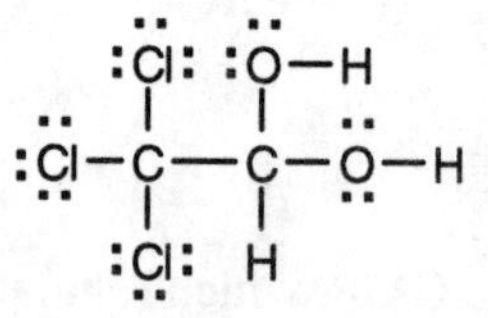

Chloral hydrate

5.98

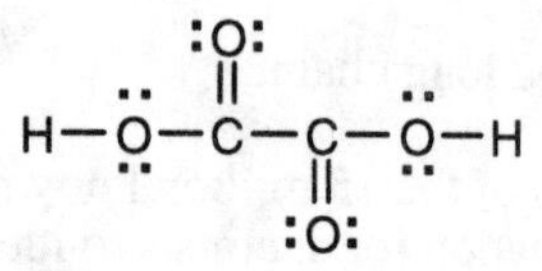

Oxalic acid

5.100

(a)

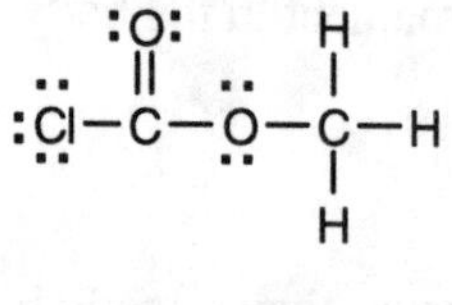

(b)

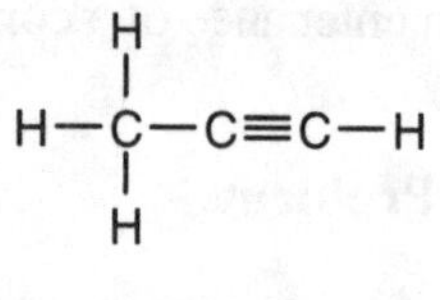

Self-Test for Chapter 5

Multiple choice:

1. Which of these diatomic molecules contains a double bond?
   (a) H_2 (b) I_2 (c) O_2 (d) N_2

2. Which of these molecules is pyramidal?
   (a) CBr_4 (b) $AlCl_3$ (c) SF_6 (d) PH_3

3. Choose the element that forms three covalent bonds and has one lone pair of electrons.
   (a) C   (b) N   (c) O   (d) F

4. How many charge clouds does the molecule H_2S have?
   (a) 2   (b) 3   (c) 4   (d) can't tell

5. Which of the following double bonds is not likely to be found in organic molecules?
   (a) O=O   (b) C=C   (c) C=O   (d) C=N

6. All of the following are true about the polyatomic ion BF_4^- except:
   (a) All atoms don't have electron octets.   (b) It has polar covalent bonds.   (c) It contains a coordinate covalent bond.   (d) It has a tetrahedral shape.

7. One of these molecules doesn't contain a polar covalent bond. Which is it?
   (a) $BeBr_2$ (b) PCl_3 (c) CO_2 (d) CS_2

8. Which of the following compounds is polar?
   (a) $BeBr_2$ (b) PCl_3 (c) CO_2 (d) CS_2

9. A name for S_2F_2 is:
   (a) Sulfur fluoride   (b) Sulfur difluoride   (c) Disulfur fluoride   (d) Disulfur difluoride

10. Which of the following is not true for molecular compounds?
    (a) They are water-soluble.   (b) They can be solids, liquids or gases.   (c) They are composed of nonmetals.   (d) They have low melting points.

Complete the following sentences:

1. An _____ element strongly attracts electrons.

2. A molecular compound that occurs in living organisms is called a _____ .

3. In Lewis structures, a line represents a _____ bond.

4. _____ and _____ are the most common triple bonds in chemical compounds.

5. The formula X_2 represents a _____ molecule.

6. A molecule whose central atom forms three bonds and has no lone pairs has a _____ _____ shape.

7. _____ orbitals in sulfur and phosphorus can be used for covalent bonds.

8. N_2 contains a _____ bond.

9. _____ molecular compounds are formed from only two elements.

10. Many molecular compounds are soluble in _____ liquids.

11. _____ is the maintenance of a constant internal environment in the body.

Tell whether the following statements are true or false:

1. Br_2 is a molecular compound.

2. Six electrons are used to form a triple bond.

3. Coordinate covalent bonds occur only in cations or anions, not in neutral compounds.

4. The first step in drawing a Lewis structure is to find the total number of electrons in the combined atoms.

5. $AlCl_3$ is a pyramidal molecule.

6. The shape of ionic compounds can be predicted by the VSEPR model.

7. Electronegativity decreases in going down the periodic table.

8. CI_4 contains polar covalent bonds.

9. Both planar and bent molecules have bond angles of 120°.

10. Group 7A elements can form more than one covalent bond.

11. Bent compounds may have either 1 or 2 lone pairs.

Match each item on the left with its partner on the right:

1. BCl_3 (a) contains a pure covalent bond

2. planar molecule   (b) $BeCl_2$

3. bent molecule   (c) exception to the octet rule

4. Cl_2 (d) NH_3

5. BCl_4^- (e) contains a triple bond

6. NaI   (f) H_2O

7. $C\equiv O$ (g) contains a double bond

8. SF_6 (h) central atom doesn't have an electron octet

9. linear molecule   (i) contains an ionic bond

10. $O=C=O$ (j) $AlCl_3$

11. pyramidal molecule   (k) contains a coordinate covalent bond

12. CH_3Cl (l) contains a polar covalent bond

Chapter 6 – Chemical Reactions: Classification and Mass Relationships

Chapter Outline

I. Chemical equations (Sections 6.1–6.2).
   A. Writing chemical equations (Section 6.1).
      1. A chemical equation describes a chemical reaction.
         a. The reactants are written on the left.
         b. The products are written on the right.
         c. An arrow goes between them.
      2. The number and kinds of atoms must be the same on both sides of the equation. This is known as the Law of Conservation of Mass.
      3. Numbers that are placed in front of formulas are called coefficients.
      4. States of matter (s), (g), (l) are often placed after chemical formulas.
   B. Balancing chemical equations (Section 6.2).
      1. Write an unbalanced equation using the correct formulas for all substances.
      2. Add appropriate coefficients to balance the atoms of each type, one at a time.
      3. Check to make sure that the numbers and kinds of atoms are balanced.
      4. Make sure all coefficients are reduced to their lowest whole-number values.
II. Molar relationships (Sections 6.3–6.7).
   A. The mole (Section 6.3).
      1. Avogadro's number (6.02×10^{23}) is known as the mole.
      2. Molecular weight is the sum of the atomic weights of atoms in a molecule.
      3. Formula weight is the sum of the atomic weights of atoms in a formula unit.
      4. One mole of any pure substance has a mass equal to its molecular or formula weight in grams.
   B. Mole–mass relationships (Section 6.4–6.6).
      1. Gram–mole conversions (Section 6.4).
         a. Molar mass is the mass in grams of one mole of any substance.
         b. Molar mass is a conversion factor that allows calculation of moles from grams and *vice versa*.
      2. Molar relationships from chemical equations (Section 6.5).
         a. The coefficients in an equation tell how many moles of reactant or product are involved in the reaction.
         b. The coefficients can be put in a mole ratio, which can be used as a conversion factor.
      3. Mass relationships (Section 6.6).
         a. Mole–mole conversions are made by using mole ratios.
         b. Mole–mass conversions are made by using molar mass as a conversion factor.
         c. Mass–mass conversions can be made by a mass–mole conversion of one substance, using mole ratios, and making a mole–mass conversion of the other substance.
      4. A summary of calculations using mole–mass relationships:
         a. Write the balanced equation.
         b. Choose mole–mass relationships and mole ratios to calculate the desired quantity.
         c. Set up the factor-label method to calculate the answer.
         d. Check the answer with a ballpark solution.
   C. Percent yield (Section 6.7).
      1. Percent yield = actual yield / theoretical yield x 100%
      2. Theoretical yield is found by using a mass–mass calculation.

III. Chemical reactions (Sections 6.8–6.14).
   A. Classes of chemical reactions (Section 6.8).
      1. Precipitation reactions occur when an insoluble solid is formed.
      2. Acid–base reactions occur when an acid and a base react to yield water and a salt.
      3. Redox reactions occur when electrons are transferred between reaction partners.
   B. Precipitation reactions (Section 6.9)
      1. To predict whether a precipitation reaction occurs, you must know the solubilities of the products.
      2. Table 6.1 gives general solubility rules to predict if a precipitation reaction will occur.
   C. Acid–base reactions (Section 6.10).
      1. Acid–base reactions are known as neutralization reactions because when reaction is complete the solution is neither acidic nor basic.
      2. An example: $HA(aq) + MOH(aq) \longrightarrow H_2O(l) + MA(aq)$
      3. When a carbonate or bicarbonate is one of the reactants, CO_2 is also produced.
   D. Net ionic equations (Section 6.11).
      1. A molecular equation shows reactants and products as molecules and doesn't indicate if they are ions.
      2. An ionic equation is written if ions are involved and shows all ionic reactants and products.
      3. A net ionic equation includes only the ions that undergo change and deletes spectator ions.
   E. Redox reactions (Sections 6.12–6.14).
      1. Definition of redox reactions (Section 6.12).
         a. A redox reaction occurs when electrons are transferred from one atom to another.
         b. The substance that loses electrons is oxidized and is known as the reducing agent.
         c. The substance that gains electrons is reduced and is known as the oxidizing agent.
         d. Redox reactions occur during corrosion, combustion, respiration, and photography.
      2. Recognizing redox reactions (Section 6.13).
         a. With some substances, it isn't obvious if a redox reaction has occurred.
         b. In a neutral compound, oxidation numbers are assigned to each element to indicate electron ownership.
         c. To assign oxidation numbers:
            i. An element has an oxidation number of 0.
            ii. A monoatomic ion has an oxidation number equal to its charge.
            iii. In a molecular compound, an atom usually has the same oxidation number that it would have if it were a monoatomic ion.
            iv. The sum of the oxidation numbers in a neutral compound is zero.
      3. Organic redox reactions (Section 6.14).
         a. An organic redox reaction refers to the degree of electron ownership by carbon.
         b. An organic oxidation decreases electron ownership by carbon by formation of a bond between carbon and a more electronegative atom.
         c. An organic reduction increases electron ownership by carbon by formation of a bond between carbon and a less electronegative atom.

Solutions to Chapter 6 Problems

6.1 An equation is balanced if the number and types of atoms on the left side equals the number and types of atoms on the right side.

(a) On the left: 2 H + Cl + K + O
On the right: 2 H + Cl + K + O The equation is balanced.

(b) On the left: 1 C + 4 H + 2 Cl
On the right: 1 C + 3 H + 3 Cl The equation is not balanced.

(c) Balanced

(d) Not balanced in H, O.

6.2 (a) Solid cobalt(II) chloride plus gaseous hydrogen fluoride yield solid cobalt(II) fluoride plus gaseous hydrogen chloride.

(b) Aqueous lead(II) nitrate plus aqueous potassium iodide yield solid lead(II) iodide plus aqueous potassium nitrate.

6.3 *Step 1.* Write the unbalanced equation

$$Na + Cl_2 \longrightarrow NaCl$$

Step 2. Balance the atoms of each type, one by one. Here, the equation is balanced for sodium. To balance for chlorine, add a coefficient of 2 to NaCl:

$$Na + Cl_2 \longrightarrow 2\,NaCl$$

Unfortunately, the equation is no longer balanced for sodium. To balance for sodium, add a coefficient of 2 to Na:

$$2\,Na + Cl_2 \longrightarrow 2\,NaCl$$

The equation is now balanced.

6.4 *Step 1:* $O_2 \longrightarrow O_3$
Step 2: $3\,O_2 \longrightarrow 2\,O_3$ The equation is balanced.

6.5 (a) $Ca(OH)_2 + 2\,HCl \longrightarrow CaCl_2 + 2\,H_2O$

(b) $4\,Al + 3\,O_2 \longrightarrow 2\,Al_2O_3$

(c) $2\,CH_3CH_3 + 7\,O_2 \longrightarrow 4\,CO_2 + 6\,H_2O$

(d) $2\,AgNO_3 + MgCl_2 \longrightarrow 2\,AgCl + Mg(NO_3)_2$

6.6 (a) For ibuprofen, $C_{13}H_{18}O_2$:

at. wt of 13 C = 13 x 12.0 amu = 156.0 amu
at. wt of 18 H = 18 x 1.0 amu =   18.0 amu
at. wt of 2 O = 2 x 16.0 amu =   32.0 amu

MW of $C_{13}H_{18}O_2$ = 206.0 amu

(b) For phenobarbital, $C_{12}H_{12}N_2O_3$:

at. wt of 12 C = 12 x 12.0 amu = 144.0 amu
at. wt of 12 H = 12 x 1.0 amu = 12.0 amu
at. wt of 2 N = 2 x 14.0 amu = 28.0 amu
at. wt of 3 O = 3 x 16.0 amu = 48.0 amu

MW of $C_{12}H_{12}N_2O_3$ = 232.0 amu

6.7   at. wt of 6 C = 6 x 12.0 amu = 72.0 amu
at. wt of 8 H = 8 x 1.0 amu =   8.0 amu
at. wt of 6 O = 6 x 16.0 amu =   96.0 amu

MW of $C_6H_8O_6$ = 176.0 amu

Since the molecular weight of ascorbic acid is 176 amu, 6.02×10^{23} molecules have a mass of 176 g.

$$500 \text{ mg ascorbic acid } \times \frac{1 \text{ g}}{10^3 \text{ mg}} \times \frac{6.02 \times 10^{23} \text{ molecules}}{176 \text{ g}} = 1.71 \times 10^{21} \text{ molecules}$$

A 500 mg tablet contains 1.71×10^{21} molecules of ascorbic acid.

6.8

at. wt of 9 C = 9 x 12.0 amu = 108.0 amu
at. wt of 8 H = 8 x 1.0 amu =   8.0 amu
at. wt of 4 O = 4 x 16.0 amu =   64.0 amu

MW of $C_9H_8O_4$ = 180.0 amu

$$5.0 \times 10^{20} \text{ molecules } \times \frac{180 \text{ g}}{6.02 \times 10^{23} \text{ molecules}} = 0.15 \text{ g}$$

5.0×10^{23} molecules of aspirin weigh 0.15 g

6.9   Molar mass of C_2H_6O = 46.0 g/mol

$$10.0 \text{ g } \times \frac{1 \text{ mol}}{46.0 \text{ g}} = 0.217 \text{ mol in a 10.0 g sample}$$

$$0.10 \text{ mol } \times \frac{46.0 \text{ g}}{1 \text{ mol}} = 4.6 \text{ g in a 0.10 mol sample}$$

6.10   Molar mass of acetaminophen = 151 g

$$0.0225 \text{ mol } \times \frac{151 \text{ g}}{1 \text{ mol}} = 3.40 \text{ g}$$

5.00 g acetaminophen weigh more than 0.0225 mol.

6.11   Molar mass of NaOH = 40.0 g

$$1.0 \text{ L } \times \frac{1.5 \text{ mol}}{1 \text{ L}} \times \frac{40.0 \text{ g}}{1 \text{ mol}} = 60 \text{ g NaOH}$$

6.12 (a) $Ni(s) + 2 HCl(aq) \longrightarrow NiCl_2(aq) + H_2(g)$

$$9.81 \text{ mol HCl} \times \frac{1 \text{ mol Ni}}{2 \text{ mol HCl}} = 4.90 \text{ mol Ni}$$

(b) $6.00 \text{ mol Ni} \times \dfrac{1 \text{ mol NiCl}_2}{1 \text{ mol Ni}} = 6.00 \text{ mol NiCl}_2$ from 6.00 mol Ni

$6.00 \text{ mol HCl} \times \dfrac{1 \text{ mol NiCl}_2}{2 \text{ mol HCl}} = 3.00 \text{ mol NiCl}_2$ from 6.00 mol HCl

3.00 mol $NiCl_2$ can be formed from 6.00 mol Ni and 6.00 mol HCl.

(c) $6.00 \text{ mol Ni} \times \dfrac{1 \text{ mol NiCl}_2}{1 \text{ mol Ni}} = 6.00 \text{ mol NiCl}_2$ from 6.00 mol Ni

$12.00 \text{ mol HCl} \times \dfrac{1 \text{ mol NiCl}_2}{2 \text{ mol HCl}} = 6.00 \text{ mol NiCl}_2$ from 12.00 mol HCl

6.00 mol $NiCl_2$ can be formed from 6.00 mol Ni and 12.00 mol HCl.

6.13 $6 CO_2 + 6 H_2O \longrightarrow C_6H_{12}O_6 + 6 O_2$

$$15.0 \text{ mol glucose} \times \frac{6 \text{ mol CO}_2}{1 \text{ mol glucose}} = 90.0 \text{ mol CO}_2$$

6.14 (a) This is a mole-to-mole problem.

$$9.90 \text{ mol SiO}_2 \times \frac{4 \text{ mol HF}}{1 \text{ mol SiO}_2} = 39.6 \text{ mol HF}$$

(b) This is a mass-to-mass problem.

$$23.0 \text{ g SiO}_2 \times \frac{1 \text{ mol SiO}_2}{60.1 \text{ g SiO}_2} \times \frac{2 \text{ mol H}_2O}{1 \text{ mol SiO}_2} \times \frac{18.0 \text{ g H}_2O}{1 \text{ mol H}_2O} = 13.8 \text{ g H}_2O$$

6.15 For WO_3:

$$5.00 \text{ g W} \times \frac{1 \text{ mol W}}{183.8 \text{ g W}} \times \frac{1 \text{ mol WO}_3}{1 \text{ mol W}} \times \frac{231.8 \text{ g WO}_3}{1 \text{ mol WO}_3} = 6.31 \text{ g WO}_3$$

For H_2:

$$5.00 \text{ g W} \times \frac{1 \text{ mol W}}{183.8 \text{ g W}} \times \frac{3 \text{ mol H}_2}{1 \text{ mol W}} \times \frac{2.02 \text{ g H}_2}{1 \text{ mol H}_2} = 0.165 \text{ g H}_2$$

6.31 g WO_3 and 0.165 g H_2 are needed to produce 5.00 g W.

6.16   The molar mass of ethylene is 28.0 g/mol; the molar mass of ethyl chloride is 64.5 g/mol.

$$19.4 \text{ g ethylene} \times \frac{1 \text{ mol ethylene}}{28.0 \text{ g ethylene}} \times \frac{1 \text{ mol ethyl chloride}}{1 \text{ mol ethylene}} \times \frac{64.5 \text{ g ethyl chloride}}{1 \text{ mol ethyl chloride}}$$

$$= 44.7 \text{ g ethyl chloride}$$

$$\frac{25.5 \text{ g ethyl chloride actually formed}}{44.7 \text{ g theoretical yield of ethyl chloride}} \times 100 \% = 57.0 \%$$

6.17   (a) $AgNO_3(aq) + KCl(aq) \longrightarrow AgCl(s) + KNO_3(aq)$
           Precipitation: Solid AgCl is formed.

   (b) $2 \text{ Al}(s) + 3 \text{ Br}_2(l) \longrightarrow 2 \text{ AlBr}_3(s)$
       Redox reaction: Al^{+3} is formed from Al, and Br^- is formed from Br_2.

   (c) $Ca(OH)_2(aq) + 2 \text{ HNO}_3(aq) \longrightarrow 2 \text{ H}_2O(l) + Ca(NO_3)_2(aq)$
       Acid–base neutralization

6.18   *Insoluble*   *Soluble*

   (a) $CdCO_3$ (b) Na_2S
   (c) $PbSO_4$ (d) $(NH_4)_3PO_4$
   (e) Hg_2Cl_2

6.19   As in Solved Problem 6.11, identify the products, and use Table 6.1 to predict their solubility. If the products are insoluble, a precipitation reaction will occur.

   (a) $NiCl_2(aq) + (NH_4)_2S(aq) \longrightarrow 2 \text{ NH}_4Cl(aq) + NiS(s)$
       A precipitation reaction will occur.

   (b) $2 \text{ AgNO}_3(aq) + CaBr_2(aq) \longrightarrow Ca(NO_3)_2(aq) + 2 \text{ AgBr}(s)$
       A precipitation reaction will occur.

6.20   (a) $2 \text{ CsOH}(aq) + H_2SO_4(aq) \longrightarrow Cs_2SO_4(aq) + 2 \text{ H}_2O(l)$

   (b) $Ca(OH)_2(aq) + 2 \text{ CH}_3COOH(aq) \longrightarrow Ca(CH_3COO)_2(aq) + 2 \text{ H}_2O(l)$

   (c) $NaHCO_3(aq) + HBr(aq) \longrightarrow NaBr(aq) + CO_2(g) + H_2O(l)$

6.21   (a) Write the equation, including all ions.

   $$2 \text{ Li}(s) + Pb^{2+} + 2 \text{ NO}_3^- \longrightarrow 2 \text{ Li}^+ + 2 \text{ NO}_3^- + Pb(s)$$

   The nitrate ions on each side cancel.

   $$2 \text{ Li}(s) + Pb^{2+}(aq) \longrightarrow 2 \text{ Li}^+(aq) + Pb(s)$$

(b) $OH^-(aq) + H^+(aq) \longrightarrow H_2O(l)$

K^+ and SO_4^{2-} cancel, and coefficients are reduced.

(c) $CuS(s) + 2 H^+(aq) \longrightarrow Cu^{2+}(aq) + H_2S(g)$

6.22

	Oxidized reactant/ Reducing agent	Reduced reactant/ Oxidizing agent
(a)	Fe	Cu^{2+}
(b)	Mg	Cl_2
(c)	Al	Cr_2O_3

The oxidizing agent is the reduced reactant, and the reducing agent is the oxidized reactant.

6.23 $\underset{\text{Reducing agent}}{2 \text{ K}(s)} + \underset{\text{Oxidizing agent}}{\text{Br}_2(l)} \longrightarrow 2 \text{ KBr}(s)$

6.24

Compound	Oxidation number of metal	Name
(a) VCl_3	+3	vanadium(III) chloride
(b) $SnCl_4$	+4	tin(IV) chloride
(c) CrO_3	+6	chromium(VI) oxide
(d) $Cu(NO_3)_2$	+2	copper(II) nitrate
(e) $NiSO_4$	+2	nickel(II) sulfate

6.25

Compound	Atom	Oxidation number
(a) N_2O_4	N	+4
	O	−2
(b) $HClO_4$	H	+1
	Cl	+7
	O	−2
(c) MnO_4^-	Mn	+7
	O	−2
(d) H_2SO_4	H	+1
	S	+6
	O	−2

6.26 Oxidation numbers are written above the atoms.

(a) $\overset{+1-2}{Na_2S}(aq) + \overset{+2-1}{NiCl_2}(aq) \longrightarrow \overset{+1-1}{2 NaCl}(aq) + \overset{+2-2}{NiS}(s)$
This reaction is not a redox reaction because no atoms change oxidation numbers.

(b) $\overset{0}{2 Na}(s) + \overset{+1-2}{2 H_2O}(l) \longrightarrow \overset{+1-2+1}{2 NaOH}(aq) + \overset{0}{H_2}(g)$
Sodium is oxidized and hydrogen is reduced in this reaction.

(c) $\overset{0}{C}(s) + \overset{0}{O_2}(g) \longrightarrow \overset{+4-2}{CO_2}(g)$
Carbon is oxidized and oxygen is reduced in this redox reaction.

$$\overset{+2-2}{\text{(d) CuO}}(s) + \overset{+1-1}{2\text{HCl}}(aq) \longrightarrow \overset{+2-1}{\text{CuCl}_2}(aq) + \overset{+1-2}{\text{H}_2\text{O}}(l)$$

This is not a redox reaction because no atoms change oxidation number.

$$\overset{+7-2}{\text{(e) 2 MnO}_4^-}(aq) + \overset{+4-2}{5\text{SO}_2}(g) + \overset{+1-2}{2\text{H}_2\text{O}}(l) \longrightarrow \overset{+2}{2\text{Mn}^{2+}}(aq) + \overset{+6-2}{\text{SO}_4^{2-}}(aq) + \overset{+1}{4\text{H}^+}(aq)$$

In this redox reaction, the oxidation number of Mn changes from +7 to +2 and the oxidation number of S changes from +4 to +6.

6.27

(a) $H_2C=CH_2 \longrightarrow$ HO OH | H_2C-CH_2

This reaction is an oxidation because two C—O bonds are formed.

(b) $CH_3CH=CH_2 \longrightarrow CH_3CH_2CH_3$

This is a reduction because two C—H bonds are formed.

(c) $CH_3CH=CH_2 \longrightarrow$ Cl | CH_3CHCH_2Cl

This reaction is an oxidation.

6.28 The addition of water to propylene oxide is neither an oxidation nor a reduction because the types of atoms bonded to the carbons are the same in both the reactants and the products.

Understanding Key Concepts

6.29 Product mixture (d) is the only mixture that contains the same number of atoms as (a).

6.30 (c) $2A + B_2 \longrightarrow A_2B_2$

6.31 (d) $\longrightarrow$ (c)
reactants   products

6.32 Methionine: $C_5H_{11}NO_2S$
at. wt of 5 C =   5 x 12.0 amu =   60.0 amu
at. wt of 11 H = 11 x 1.0 amu =   11.0 amu
at. wt of   N =   =   14.0 amu
at. wt of 2 O =   2 x 16.0 amu =   32.0 amu
at. wt of   S =   =   32.1 amu

MW of $C_5H_{11}NO_2S$ = 149.1 amu

6.33 (a) $A_2 + 3 B_2 \longrightarrow 2 AB_3$

(b) $1.0 \text{ mol } A_2 \times \dfrac{2 \text{ mol } AB_3}{1 \text{ mol } A_2} = 2.0 \text{ mol } AB_3$

$1.0 \text{ mol } B_2 \times \dfrac{2 \text{ mol } AB_3}{3 \text{ mol } B_2} = 0.67 \text{ mol } AB_3$

6.34 (a) Mixing of sodium and carbonate ions produces outcome (1). No insoluble product is formed, and sodium and carbonate ions remain in solution.
(b) Mixing barium and chromate ions produces outcome (2). $BaCrO_4$ precipitate forms (one barium ion for each chromate ion), and the excess barium ions remain in solution.
(c) Mixing silver and sulfate ions yields outcome (3). Ag_2SO_4 precipitate forms (two silver ions for each sulfate ion), and no Ag^+ or SO_4^{2-} ions remain in solution.

6.35 The observed product is a precipitate that contains two cations per anion. From the list of cations, Ag^+ is the only one that forms precipitates and has a 2:1 cation:anion ratio with the anions listed. The anion can be either CO_3^{2-} or CrO_4^{2-}, since both form precipitates with Ag^+. Thus, the possible products are Ag_2CO_3 and Ag_2CrO_4.

Balancing Chemical Equations

6.36 A balanced equation is an equation in which the number of atoms of each kind is the same on both sides of the reaction arrow.

6.38 (a) $SO_2(g) + H_2O(g) \longrightarrow H_2SO_3(l)$

(b) $2 K(s) + Br_2(l) \longrightarrow 2 KBr(s)$

(c) $C_3H_8(g) + 5 O_2(g) \longrightarrow 3 CO_2(g) + 4 H_2O(l)$

6.40 (a) $2 C_2H_6(g) + 7 O_2(g) \longrightarrow 4 CO_2(g) + 6 H_2O(l)$

(b) balanced

(c) $2 Mg(s) + O_2(g) \longrightarrow 2 MgO(s)$

(d) $2 K(s) + 2 H_2O(l) \longrightarrow 2 KOH(aq) + H_2(g)$

6.42 $2 NaHCO_3(aq) + H_2SO_4(aq) \longrightarrow 2 CO_2(g) + Na_2SO_4(aq) + 2 H_2O(l)$

6.44 $C_6H_{12}O_6(s) + 6 O_2(g) \longrightarrow 6 CO_2(g) + 6 H_2O(l)$
Glucose metabolism is the reverse of photosynthesis

Molar Masses and Moles

6.46 One mole of a substance is an amount equal to its formula weight in grams. One mole of a molecular compound contains 6.02×10^{23} molecules.

6.48

$$\frac{6.02 \times 10^{23} \text{ units CaCl}_2}{1 \text{ mol CaCl}_2} \times \frac{1 \text{ Ca}^{2+} \text{ ion}}{1 \text{ unit CaCl}_2} = \frac{6.02 \times 10^{23} \text{ Ca}^{2+} \text{ ions}}{1 \text{ mol CaCl}_2}$$

$$\frac{6.02 \times 10^{23} \text{ units CaCl}_2}{1 \text{ mol CaCl}_2} \times \frac{2 \text{ Cl}^- \text{ ions}}{1 \text{ unit CaCl}_2} = \frac{1.20 \times 10^{24} \text{ Cl}^- \text{ ions}}{1 \text{ mol CaCl}_2}$$

6.50

$$16.2 \text{ g Ca} \times \frac{1 \text{ mol}}{40.1 \text{ g Ca}} \times \frac{6.02 \times 10^{23} \text{ atoms}}{1 \text{ mol}} = 2.43 \times 10^{23} \text{ atoms}$$

6.52 Molar mass of caffeine = 194 g

$$125 \text{ mg} \times \frac{1 \text{ g}}{10^3 \text{ mg}} \times \frac{1 \text{ mol}}{194 \text{ g}} = 6.44 \times 10^{-4} \text{ mol caffeine}$$

6.54 Molar mass of $C_{16}H_{13}ClN_2O$:
$(16 \times 12.0 \text{ g}) + (13 \times 1.0 \text{ g}) + (35.5 \text{ g}) + (2 \times 14.0 \text{ g}) + 16.0 \text{ g} = 284.5 \text{ g/mol}$

6.55, 6.56

Compound	Molar Mass	Number of Moles in 5.00 g
(a) C_6H_6	78.0 g	0.0641 mol
(b) $NaHCO_3$	84.0 g	0.0595 mol
(c) $CHCl_3$	119.5 g	0.0418 mol
(d) $C_{16}H_{18}N_2O_5S$	350.1 g	0.0143 mol

6.58 Molar mass of aspirin = 180 g

$$0.0015 \text{ mol} \times \frac{180 \text{ g}}{1 \text{ mol}} = 0.27 \text{ g aspirin}$$

Mole and Mass Relationships from Chemical Equations

6.60 (a) $N_2(g) + O_2(g) \longrightarrow 2 NO(g)$

(b) 7.50 mol of N_2 are needed to react with 7.50 mol of O_2.

(c) $3.81 \text{ mol N}_2 \times \frac{2 \text{ mol NO}}{1 \text{ mol N}_2} = 7.62 \text{ mol NO}$

(d) $0.250 \text{ mol NO} \times \frac{1 \text{ mol O}_2}{2 \text{ mol NO}} = 0.125 \text{ mol O}_2$

6.62 (a) $N_2(g) + 3 H_2(g) \longrightarrow 2 NH_3(g)$

(b) $16.0 \text{ g NH}_3 \times \dfrac{1 \text{ mol NH}_3}{17.0 \text{ g NH}_3} \times \dfrac{1 \text{ mol N}_2}{2 \text{ mol NH}_3} = 0.471 \text{ mol N}_2$

(c) $75.0 \text{ g N}_2 \times \dfrac{1 \text{ mol N}_2}{28.0 \text{ g N}_2} \times \dfrac{3 \text{ mol H}_2}{1 \text{ mol N}_2} \times \dfrac{2.0 \text{ g H}_2}{1 \text{ mol H}_2} = 16.1 \text{ g H}_2$

6.64 (a) $Fe_2O_3(s) + 3 CO(g) \longrightarrow 2 Fe(s) + 3 CO_2(g)$

(b) $3.02 \text{ g Fe}_2O_3 \times \dfrac{1 \text{ mol Fe}_2O_3}{159.6 \text{ g Fe}_2O_3} \times \dfrac{3 \text{ mol CO}}{1 \text{ mol Fe}_2O_3} \times \dfrac{28.0 \text{ g CO}}{1 \text{ mol CO}} = 1.59 \text{ g CO}$

(c) $1.68 \text{ mol Fe}_2O_3 \times \dfrac{3 \text{ mol CO}}{1 \text{ mol Fe}_2O_3} \times \dfrac{28.0 \text{ g CO}}{1 \text{ mol CO}} = 141 \text{ g CO}$

6.66 $TiO_2(s) \longrightarrow Ti(s) + O_2(g)$

$95 \text{ kg Ti} \times \dfrac{1 \text{ mol Ti}}{47.9 \text{ g Ti}} \times \dfrac{1 \text{ mol TiO}_2}{1 \text{ mol Ti}} \times \dfrac{79.9 \text{ g TiO}_2}{1 \text{ mol TiO}_2} = 158 \text{ kg TiO}_2$

Percent Yield

6.68

(a) $10.0 \text{ g CO} \times \dfrac{1 \text{ mol CO}}{28.0 \text{ g CO}} \times \dfrac{1 \text{ mol CH}_3OH}{1 \text{ mol CO}} \times \dfrac{32.0 \text{ g CH}_3OH}{1 \text{ mol CH}_3OH} = 11.4 \text{ g CH}_3OH$

(b) $\dfrac{9.55 \text{ g}}{11.4 \text{ g}} \times 100 \% = 83.8\% \text{ yield}$

6.70 (a) $CH_4(g) + 2 Cl_2(g) \longrightarrow CH_2Cl_2(l) + 2 HCl(g)$

(b) $50.0 \text{ g CH}_4 \times \dfrac{1 \text{ mol CH}_4}{16.0 \text{ g CH}_4} \times \dfrac{2 \text{ mol Cl}_2}{1 \text{ mol CH}_4} \times \dfrac{71.0 \text{ g Cl}_2}{1 \text{ mol Cl}_2} = 444 \text{ g Cl}_2$

(c) If the reaction occurred in 100% yield:

$50.0 \text{ g CH}_4 \times \dfrac{1 \text{ mol CH}_4}{16.0 \text{ g CH}_4} \times \dfrac{1 \text{ mol CH}_2Cl_2}{1 \text{ mol CH}_4} \times \dfrac{85.0 \text{ g CH}_2Cl_2}{1 \text{ mol CH}_2Cl_2} = 266 \text{ g CH}_2Cl_2$

Since the reaction occurs in 76% yield:

$266 \text{ g} \times 0.76 = 202 \text{ g CH}_2Cl_2$ are actually formed

Types of Chemical Reactions

6.72

(a) $2 H^+(aq) + 2 F^-(aq) + Ca^{2+}(aq) + 2 OH^-(aq) \rightarrow Ca^{2+}(aq) + 2 F^-(aq) + 2 H_2O(l)$

$$H^+(aq) + OH^-(aq) \rightarrow H_2O(l)$$

(b) $2 H^+(aq) + 2 NO_3^-(aq) + Mg^{2+}(aq) + 2 OH^-(aq) \rightarrow 2 NO_3^-(aq) + Mg^{2+}(aq) + 2 H_2O(l)$

$$H^+(aq) + OH^-(aq) \rightarrow H_2O(l)$$

6.74 Use Section 6.9 as a guide.
All of the listed compounds are insoluble in water ($PbCl_2$ is soluble in hot water).

6.76 A precipitation reaction occurs only in (b). A neutralization occurs with the reagents in (a).

(b) $FeCl_2(aq) + 2 KOH(aq) \longrightarrow Fe(OH)_2(s) + 2 KCl(aq)$

6.78 In net ionic reactions, no spectator ions appear. Otherwise, the equations are balanced for number of atoms and charge, and coefficients are reduced to their lowest common denominators.

(a) $Mg(s) + Cu^{2+}(aq) \longrightarrow Mg^{2+}(aq) + Cu(s)$

(b) $2 Cl^-(aq) + Pb^{2+}(aq) \longrightarrow PbCl_2(s)$

(c) $2 Cr^{3+}(aq) + 3 S^{2-}(aq) \longrightarrow Cr_2S_3(s)$

Redox Reactions and Oxidation Numbers

6.80 In general, the best reducing agents are metals. The most reactive reducing agents are in groups 1A and 2A. The most reactive oxidizing agents are in groups 6A and 7A.

6.82 Gains electrons: (a) oxidizing agent, (d) substance undergoing reduction
Loses electrons: (b) reducing agent, (c) substance undergoing oxidation

6.84

+4 -2	+6 -2	+4 -2 -1	0 +1 -1
(a) NO_2	(b) SO_3	(c) $COCl_2$	(d) CH_2Cl_2

6.86 The reduced element gains electrons, and the oxidized element loses electrons.

	(a)	(b)	(c)
Reduced	Cl_2	Cl_2	Cl_2
Oxidized	Si	Br_2	Bi^{3+}

6.88 (a) This is a reduction because a C—O bond is broken and a C—H bond is formed.
(b) This is also a reduction because a C—N bond is broken and a C—H bond is formed.
(c) This is neither an oxidation nor a reduction because both a C—O bond and a C—H bond are formed.

Applications

6.90 The most serious error in calculating Avogadro's number by spreading oil on water is the estimate of the size of the area the oil covered. Some approximations that Franklin made, but that can be determined with reasonable precision, are the volume of oil, the mass of the oil, its density and its molar mass. Other assumptions, involving the thickness of the oil layer and the arrangement of oil molecules on the surface of the water, are also sources of error.

6.92 Zinc is the reducing agent in a dry-cell battery.

General Questions and Problems

6.94

(a) $15.0 \text{ g Zn} \times \dfrac{1 \text{ mol Zn}}{65.4 \text{ g Zn}} \times \dfrac{1 \text{ mol H}_2}{1 \text{ mol Zn}} \times \dfrac{2.0 \text{ g H}_2}{1 \text{ mol H}_2} = 0.459 \text{ g H}_2$

(b) In this redox reaction, H^+ is reduced (oxidizing agent) and Zn is oxidized (reducing agent).

6.96 (a) $2 \text{ Al}(s) + \text{Fe}_2\text{O}_3(s) \longrightarrow \text{Al}_2\text{O}_3(l) + 2 \text{ Fe}(l)$

(b) $2 \text{ NH}_4\text{NO}_3(s) \longrightarrow 2 \text{ N}_2(g) + \text{O}_2(g) + 4 \text{ H}_2\text{O}(g)$

6.98 $3 \text{ CuCl}_2(aq) + 2 \text{ Na}_3\text{PO}_4(aq) \longrightarrow \text{Cu}_3(\text{PO}_4)_2(s) + 6 \text{ NaCl}(aq)$
A precipitate of $\text{Cu}_3(\text{PO}_4)_2$ forms

$3 \text{ Cu}^{2+}(aq) + 2 \text{ PO}_4^{3-}(aq) \longrightarrow \text{Cu}_3(\text{PO}_4)_2(s)$

6.100 (a) $\text{Cu}(s) + 4 \text{ H}^+(aq) + 2 \text{ NO}_3^-(aq) \longrightarrow \text{Cu}^{2+}(aq) + 2 \text{ NO}_2(g) + 2 \text{ H}_2\text{O}(l)$

(b) $35.0 \text{ g HNO}_3 \times \dfrac{1 \text{ mol HNO}_3}{63.0 \text{ g HNO}_3} \times \dfrac{1 \text{ mol Cu}}{4 \text{ mol HNO}_3} \times \dfrac{63.5 \text{ g Cu}}{1 \text{ mol Cu}} = 8.82 \text{ g Cu}$

35.0 g HNO_3 is more than enough to dissolve 5.00 g Cu.

6.102

$100.0 \text{ lb C}_6\text{H}_{12}\text{O}_6 \times \dfrac{454 \text{ g}}{1 \text{ lb}} \times \dfrac{1 \text{ mol C}_6\text{H}_{12}\text{O}_6}{180.0 \text{ g C}_6\text{H}_{12}\text{O}_6} \times \dfrac{2 \text{ mol C}_2\text{H}_6\text{O}}{1 \text{ mol C}_6\text{H}_{12}\text{O}_6} \times \dfrac{46.0 \text{ g C}_2\text{H}_6\text{O}}{1 \text{ mol C}_2\text{H}_6\text{O}}$

$= 2.32 \times 10^4 \text{ g C}_2\text{H}_6\text{O}$

$2.32 \times 10^4 \text{ g C}_2\text{H}_6\text{O} \times \dfrac{1 \text{ mL}}{0.789 \text{ g}} \times \dfrac{1 \text{ qt}}{946.4 \text{ mL}} = 31.1 \text{ qts ethanol}$

Self-Test for Chapter 6

Multiple choice:

1. Which of the following salts is soluble in water?
   (a) $FeSO_4$ (b) $BaSO_4$ (c) $CaSO_4$ (d) $PbSO_4$

2. Which of the following compounds has sulfur in a +1 oxidation state?
   (a) S_2F_2 (b) H_2SO_4 (c) SO_2 (d) Na_2S

3. What mass of $CaCO_3$ has the same number of atoms as 21 g of NaF?
   (a) 10 g (b) 20 g (c) 50 g (d) 100 g

4. In the equation $P_2O_5 + 3 H_2O \longrightarrow 2 H_3PO_4$ the mole ratio of product to H_2O is:
   (a) 2:1 (b) 2:3 (c) 3:2 (d) 1:2

5. When the equation $SiCl_4 + H_2O \longrightarrow SiO_2 + HCl$ is balanced, the coefficients are:
   (a) 1,1,1,1 (b) 1,1,1,2 (c) 1,2,1,2 (d) 1,2,1,4

6. Which of these bonds is not formed in an organic oxidation?
   (a) C—O (b) C—N (c) C—H (d) C—Hal

7. If you wanted to remove Ba^{2+} from solution, which reagent would you add?
   (a) CH_3COOH (b) NaOH (c) H_2SO_4 (d) HCl

8. In the reaction $2 Ca + O_2 \longrightarrow 2 CaO$, how many grams of CaO can be produced from 20 g of Ca? (a) 20 g (b) 28 g (c) 40 g (d) 56 g

9. When HCl is added to a solution, bubbles of gas appear. Which compound is probably present in the solution?
   (a) $SrCO_3$ (b) $Ca(OH)_2$ (c) AgBr (d) K_2SO_4

10. $3 NO_2 + H_2O \longrightarrow 2 HNO_3 + NO$

   All the following statements about the above reaction are true except:
   (a) The starting material is both oxidized and reduced.
   (b) NO_2 in the atmosphere might contribute to acid rain.
   (c) At least 6 g of H_2O are needed to react completely with 46 g of NO_2.
   (d) 92 g of NO_2 produces 28 g of NO.

Complete the following sentences:

1. The numbers placed in front of formulas to balance equations are called _____.

2. A _____ is a solid that forms during a reaction.

3. Ions that appear on both sides of the reaction arrow are _____ ions.

4. The substances in a reaction can be solids, liquids, or gases, or they can be in _____

   solution.

5. Grams and moles can be converted by using _____ _____ as a conversion factor.

6. The amount of a substance produced in a reaction, divided by the amount that could theoretically be produced, is the _____ _____.

7. In a chemical equation, _____ are shown on the left of the reaction arrow.

8. The oxidation state of gold in $AuCl_3$ is _____.

9. In the reaction $2\,Mg + O_2 \longrightarrow 2\,MgO$, Mg is the _____ agent.

10. A reaction between an acid and a base is a _____ reaction.

Tell whether the following statements are true or false:

1. A mole of oxygen atoms has the same mass as a mole of nitrogen atoms.

2. The coefficients in chemical reactions show the relative numbers of moles of reactants and products.

3. The reaction of an organic molecule with Cl_2 is an oxidation.

4. In a redox equation, the oxidizing agent is oxidized and the reducing agent is reduced.

5. If all coefficients in a chemical equation are even numbers, the equation is not completely balanced.

6. Mole ratios are used to convert between moles and grams of a compound.

7. In the reaction between K and Cl_2, K is the oxidizing agent.

8. In the reaction $4\,Al + 3\,O_2 \longrightarrow 2\,Al_2O_3$, the mole ratio of product to Al is 2.

9. Most sodium salts are soluble in water.

10. The same compound can be both oxidized and reduced in a reaction.

Match each item on the left with its partner on the right:

1. $H_2C=CH_2 + H_2 \longrightarrow CH_3CH_3$ (a) converts moles Na to grams Na

2. $C_3H_8O + O_2 \longrightarrow C_3H_6O + H_2O$ (b) molar mass of NaF

3. 42.0 amu   (c) redox reaction

4. 23.0 g sodium / 1 mol   (d) precipitation reaction

5. $CoCO_3$ (e) salt soluble in water

6. $S + O_2 \longrightarrow SO_2$ (f) unbalanced equation

7. $HCl + NaOH \longrightarrow NaCl + H_2O$ (g) converts grams Na to moles Na

8. 42.0 g   (h) organic reduction

9. 1 mol / 23.0 g sodium   (i) salt insoluble in water

10. $H_2C=CH_2 + Cl_2 \longrightarrow CH_2ClCH_2Cl$ (j) neutralization reaction

11. $AgNO_3 + NaCl \longrightarrow AgCl + NaNO_3$ (k) formula weight of NaF

12. $CoCl_2$ (l) organic oxidation

Chapter 7 – Chemical Reactions: Energy, Rates, and Equilibrium

Chapter Outline

I. Energy (Sections 7.1–7.3).
  A. Heat changes during chemical reactions (Section 7.1).
    1. Bond dissociation energies measure the strength of covalent bonds.
      a. Bond breaking requires heat and is endothermic.
      b. Bond formation releases heat and is exothermic.
    2. The reverse of an endothermic process is exothermic, and the reverse of an exothermic process is endothermic.
    3. The Law of Conservation of Energy states that energy can neither be created nor destroyed during any physical or chemical change.
    4. The difference between the energy needed for breaking bonds and the energy released in forming bonds is the heat of reaction, also known as enthalpy (ΔH).
  B. Exothermic and endothermic reactions: ΔH (Section 7.2).
    1. In exothermic reactions, the bond dissociation energies of the products are greater than the bond dissociation energies of the reactants, and ΔH is negative.
    2. In endothermic reactions, the bond dissociation energies of the products are smaller than the bond dissociation energies of the reactants, and ΔH is positive.
    3. The amount of heat absorbed or released in the reverse of a reaction is equal to that absorbed in the forward reaction, but ΔH has the opposite sign.
  C. Free energy: ΔG (Section 7.3).
    1. Spontaneous processes.
      a. A spontaneous process proceeds without any external influence.
      b. A nonspontaneous process needs a constant external source of energy.
    2. Entropy (ΔS) measures the amount of disorder in a system.
      a. If disorder increases, ΔS is positive.
      b. If disorder decreases, ΔS is negative.
    3. The absorption of heat and the increase or decrease in disorder determine if a reaction will be spontaneous.
      a. $\Delta G = \Delta H - T\Delta S$.
      b. If ΔG is negative, the process is spontaneous, and the reaction is exergonic.
      c. If ΔG is positive, the process isn't spontaneous, and the reaction is endergonic.
    4. ΔG for the reverse of a reaction is equal in value to ΔG for the forward reaction, but the sign is changed.
    5. Some nonspontaneous processes become spontaneous when temperature increases.
II. Reaction rates (Sections 7.4–7.5).
  A. How reactions occur (Section 7.4).
    1. In addition to the value of ΔG, other factors determine if a reaction will occur.
      a. Reactants must collide in the correct orientation.
      b. The energy of collision must be great enough to cause bond breaking.
      c. Many reactions with a favorable free energy don't occur at room temperature, and heat must be added to get them started
    2. The energy changes during a reaction can be graphed on a reaction energy diagram.
    3. The amount of energy needed to produce favorable collisions is the activation energy E_{act}.
      a. E_{act} determines the reaction rate.
      b. The size of E_{act} is unrelated to the size of ΔH.

   B. Factors that affect reaction rate (Section 7.5).
      1. Increasing temperature increases reaction rate.
      2. Increasing the concentration of reactants increases reaction rate.
      3. Catalysts increase the reaction rate by lowering E_{act}.
III. Chemical equilibrium (Sections 7.6–7.8).
   A. Reversible reactions (Section 7.6).
      1. Some reactions proceed to virtual completion.
      2. Other reactions go to partial completion, at which point products begin to reform starting material.
         a. These reactions are reversible.
         b. The reaction from left to right is the forward reaction.
         c. The reaction from right to left is the reverse reaction.
      3. At some point the rate of the forward reaction equals the rate of the reverse reaction, and equilibrium is established.
      4. It is not necessary for the concentrations of products and reactants to be equal at equilibrium.
   B. Equilibrium (Section 7.7).
      1. Equilibrium equations.
         a. For the reaction a A + b B —> c C + d D,

$$K = \frac{[C]^c[D]^d}{[A]^a[B]^b}$$

         b. K = equilibrium constant.
         c. Expression on the right = equilibrium constant expression.
      2. The value of K determines the position of equilibrium.
         a. When $K \gg 1$, reaction goes to completion.
         b. When $K > 1$, the forward reaction is favored.
         c. When K is of intermediate value, significant amounts of reactants and products are present at equilibrium.
         d. When $K < 1$, the reverse reaction is favored.
         e. When $K \ll 1$, there is essentially no reaction.
   C. Effect of changing reaction conditions (Section 7.8).
      1. LeChâtelier's principle: When a stress is applied to a system, the equilibrium shifts to remove the stress.
      2. Effect of changing concentration.
         a. Increasing the concentration of reactants favors the forward reaction.
         b. Increasing the concentration of products favors the reverse reaction.
      3. Effect of changing temperature.
         a. Decreasing temperature favors an exothermic reaction.
         b. Increasing temperature favors an endothermic reaction.
      4. Effect of changing pressure.
         a. No effect unless one of the reactants or products is a gas.
         b. Increasing pressure shifts the equilibrium in the direction that produces fewer gas molecules.

Solutions to Chapter 7 Problems

7.1 (a) The reaction is endothermic because heat appears on the left side of the equation and is absorbed in the reaction.

(b) $\Delta H = +678$ kcal

(c) $C_6H_{12}O_6(aq) + 6\ O_2(g) \longrightarrow 6\ CO_2(g) + 6\ H_2O(l) + 678$ kcal

7.2 (a) The reaction is endothermic because ΔH is positive.

(b) $\dfrac{801\ \text{kcal}}{4\ \text{mol Al}} \times 1.00\ \text{mol Al} = 200$ kcal required.

(c) $10.0\ \text{g Al} \times \dfrac{1\ \text{mol Al}}{27.0\ \text{g Al}} \times \dfrac{200\ \text{kcal}}{1\ \text{mol Al}} = 74.1$ kcal required

7.3

$145\ \text{g NO} \times \dfrac{1\ \text{mol}}{30.0\ \text{g NO}} \times \dfrac{43\ \text{kcal}}{2\ \text{mol NO}} = 104$ kcal absorbed

7.4 (a) Entropy increases.
(b) Entropy increases because disorder increases when fuel vaporizes.
(c) Entropy decreases because one mole of product is formed for each two moles of reactant and because a gaseous reactant is converted into a solid product.

7.5 Formation of lime from limestone doesn't occur at 25°C because ΔG is positive. Entropy increases because a gas is formed from a solid. The reaction is spontaneous at higher temperatures. In the expression $\Delta G = \Delta H - T\Delta S$, the term $T\Delta S$ becomes larger at high temperature and causes ΔG to become negative.

7.6

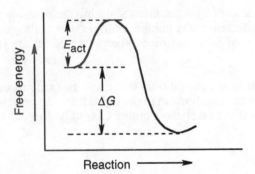

In this reaction, E_{act} is large, the reaction is slow, and the free energy change is large and negative.

7.7

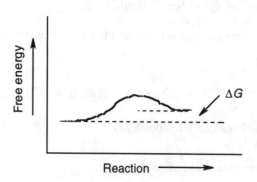

In this reaction, ΔG is small and positive. E_{act} can be small or large, but it is always larger than ΔG.

7.8

$$K = \frac{[\text{products}]}{[\text{reactants}]}$$

(a) $K = \dfrac{[NO_2]^2}{[N_2O_4]}$ (b) $K = \dfrac{[CH_3Cl][HCl]}{[CH_4][Cl_2]}$ (c) $K = \dfrac{[Br_2][F_2]^5}{[BrF_5]^2}$

7.9   If K is greater than 1, the reaction favors products. If K is less than 1, the reaction favors reactants.
(a) Products are strongly favored.
(b) Reactants are strongly favored.
(c) Products are somewhat favored.

7.10 High pressure favors the production of SO_3 because increasing the pressure shifts the equilibrium in the direction that decreases the number of molecules in the gas phase. Low temperature favors the production of SO_3 because exothermic reactions are favored by lower temperatures.

7.11 (a) Increasing the temperature shifts the equilibrium to the left, favoring reactants.
(b) Increasing the pressure shifts the equilibrium to the right, favoring product.
(b) Removing CH_4 from the reaction vessel causes more CH_4 to be formed and shifts the equilibrium toward the right.

Understanding Key Concepts

7.12 ΔH is positive because energy must be supplied in order to break the attractive forces between molecules of the crystal. ΔS is also positive because the molecules of gas are more disordered than the molecules of solid. ΔG is negative because it is stated in the problem that the reaction is spontaneous.

7.13 ΔH is negative because energy is released when a liquid condenses. ΔS is negative because disorder decreases when a gas condenses. ΔG is negative because it is stated in the problem that the reaction is spontaneous.

7.14   (a) $2\,A_2 + B_2 \longrightarrow 2\,A_2B$

       (b) ΔG is negative because the reaction is spontaneous. ΔS is negative because the product mixture has fewer gas molecules and less disorder than the reactant mixture. ΔH must be negative in order for ΔG to be negative since $(-T\,\Delta S)$ is positive.

7.15   (a) The higher curve represents the slower reaction, since more energy is needed to surmount the energy barrier.
       (b) The reaction that has a lower value for the energy of products relative to starting material is spontaneous, since its ΔG is negative.

7.16   The reaction with the lower energy maximum represents the catalyzed reaction, since a catalyst lowers the energy barrier of a reaction.

7.17

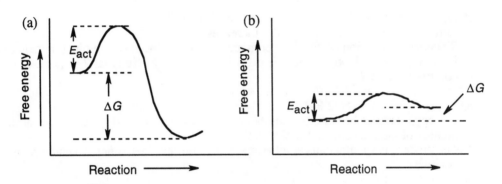

Enthalpy and Heat of Reaction

7.18   In an endothermic reaction, the total enthalpy of the reactants is greater than the total enthalpy of the products. In other words, the reactants have stronger bonds and are more stable, while the products have weaker bonds and are less stable. Energy must therefore be supplied for the reaction to take place.

7.20   (a) ΔH is positive.

       (b) $6.5 \text{ mol } Br_2 \ \times \ \dfrac{7.4 \text{ kcal}}{1 \text{ mol } Br_2} = 48 \text{ kcal needed}$

       (c) $75 \text{ g } Br_2 \ \times \ \dfrac{1 \text{ mol } Br_2}{159.8 \text{ g } Br_2} \ \times \ \dfrac{7.4 \text{ kcal}}{1 \text{ mol } Br_2} = 3.5 \text{ kcal needed}$

7.22   (a) $C_6H_{12}O_6 + 6\,O_2 \longrightarrow 6\,CO_2 + 6\,H_2O$

       (b) $\dfrac{-3.8 \text{ kcal}}{1 \text{ g glucose}} \ \times \ \dfrac{180 \text{ g glucose}}{1 \text{ mol glucose}} \ \times \ 1.50 \text{ mol glucose} = -1.0 \times 10^3 \text{ kcal}$

       (c) The production of glucose from CO_2 and H_2O is an endothermic process.

         $\dfrac{3.8 \text{ kcal}}{1 \text{ g glucose}} \ \times \ 15.0 \text{ g glucose} = 57 \text{ kcal needed to produce 15 g glucose}$

Entropy and Free Energy

7.24 Increased disorder: (a)
Decreased disorder: (b) (c)

7.26 A spontaneous process is one that, once started, proceeds without any external influence.

7.28 The two factors that influence the spontaneity of a reaction are (1) the release or absorption of heat, and (2) the increase or decrease in entropy.

7.30 The free energy change (ΔG) of a chemical reaction shows whether or not a reaction is spontaneous. If the sign of ΔG is negative, the reaction is spontaneous. Of the two factors that contribute to ΔG (ΔH and ΔS), ΔH is usually larger at low temperatures. Thus if a reaction is spontaneous (negative ΔG) it is usually exothermic (negative ΔH).

7.32 (a) Dissolution of NaCl is endothermic since ΔH is positive.
(b Entropy increases because disorder increases.
(c) Since the dissolution of NaCl is spontaneous, ΔG for the reaction must be negative. Because we already know that ΔH is positive, it must be true that $T\Delta S$ is the major contributor to ΔG.

7.34 (a) $H_2(g) + Br_2(l) \longrightarrow 2\ HBr(g)$
(b) Entropy increases because the number of gaseous product molecules is greater than the number of gaseous reactant molecules.
(c) The process is spontaneous at all temperatures because ΔH is negative and ΔS is positive.

Rates of Chemical Reactions

7.36 The *activation energy* of a reaction is the amount of energy needed for reactants to surmount the energy barrier to reaction.

7.38

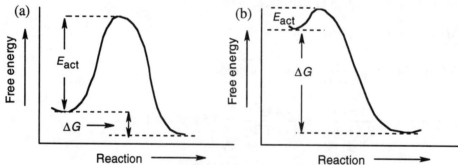

7.40 Increasing temperature increases reaction rate for two reasons:
1. Particles move faster and are more likely to collide.
2. Collisions occur with more energy.

7.42 A catalyst is a substance that increases reaction rate by lowering the activation energy barrier, yet remains unchanged when the reaction is completed.

7.44 (a) The negative value of ΔG indicates that diamonds spontaneously turn into graphite at 25°C.
(b) Because this behavior is not observed, the activation energy of the above reaction must be extremely high and the reaction rate must be extremely slow.

Chemical Equilibria

7.46 In a reversible reaction, chemical equilibrium is a state in which the rates of the forward reaction and the reverse reaction are equal. The amounts of reactants and products need not be equal at equilibrium.

7.48

(a) $K = \dfrac{[CO_2]^2}{[CO]^2[O_2]}$ (b) $K = \dfrac{[C_2H_4Cl_2][HCl]^2}{[C_2H_6][Cl_2]^2}$

(c) $K = \dfrac{[H_3O^+][F^-]}{[HF][H_2O]}$ (d) $K = \dfrac{[O_3]^2}{[O_2]^3}$

7.50

$$K = \frac{[N_2O_4]}{[NO_2]^2} = \frac{(0.0869 \text{ mol/L})}{(0.025 \text{ mol/L})^2} = 140$$

7.52

(a) $140 = \dfrac{[N_2O_4]}{(0.12 \text{ mol/L})^2}$; $[N_2O_4] = 140 \times (0.12 \text{ mol/L})^2 = 2.0 \text{ mol/L}$

(b) $140 = \dfrac{0.12 \text{ mol/L}}{[NO_2]^2}$; $[NO_2]^2 = \dfrac{0.12 \text{ mol/L}}{140} = 0.000\ 86$

$[NO_2] = 0.029 \text{ mol/L}$

7.54 If the pressure is raised, relatively more products than reactants are found at equilibrium, because high pressure favors the reaction that produces fewer gas molecules.

Le Châtelier's Principle

7.56 (a) The reaction is endothermic.
(b) Reactants are favored at equilibrium.
(c) (1) Increasing pressure favors formation of ozone, since increased pressure shifts the equilibrium in the direction of the reaction that produces fewer gas molecules.
(2) Increasing the O_2 concentration increases the amount of O_3 formed.
(3) Increasing the concentration of O_3 shifts the equilibrium to the left.
(4) A catalyst has no effect on the equilibrium.
(5) Increasing the temperature shifts the equilibrium to the right.

7.58 According to LeChâtelier's principle, an increase in pressure shifts the equilibrium in the direction that decreases the number of molecules in the gas phase.
(a) The concentration of products decreases.
(b) The concentration of products remains the same.
(c) The concentration of products increases.

7.60 $CO(g) + H_2O(g) \rightleftharpoons CO_2(g) + H_2(g)$ $\Delta H = -9.8$ kcal/mol

Because it has a negative value of ΔH, the reaction is exothermic, and the equilibrium favors products. Increasing the temperature shifts the equilibrium to favor reactants and decreases the amount of H_2.

7.62 $H_2(g) + I_2(g) \rightleftharpoons 2\,HI(g)$ $\Delta H = -2.2$ kcal/mol

(a) Adding I_2 to the reaction mix increases the equilibrium concentration of HI.
(b) Removing H_2 causes the equilibrium concentration of HI to decrease.
(c) Addition of a catalyst does not change the equilibrium concentration of HI.
(d) Increasing the temperature decreases the concentration of HI.

Applications

7.64   A gram of fat contains more energy (9 kcal/g) than a gram of carbohydrate (4 kcal/g).

7.66   Dilation of the blood vessels cools the body by allowing more blood to flow close to the surface of the body.

General Questions and Problems

7.68 $N_2(g) + 3\,H_2(g) \longrightarrow 2\,NH_3(g)$ $\Delta H = -22$ kcal/mol

(a) The production of ammonia from its elements is an exothermic process.

(b) $\dfrac{-22 \text{ kcal}}{2 \text{ mol NH}_3}$ x 0.500 mol NH_3 $= -5.5$ kcal

7.70   (a) CO removes Hb from the bloodstream because the reaction of CO with Hb is more favored than the reaction of O_2 with Hb. Less Hb is available to react with O_2, and less HbO_2 is available to the tissues.

(b) Administering high doses of O_2 to a victim of CO poisoning shifts the equilibrium in the following reaction to the right.

  $Hb(CO)(aq) + O_2(aq) \rightleftharpoons HbO_2(aq) + CO(aq)$

This shift results in displacement of CO from Hb(CO) and in formation of HbO_2 to replenish body tissues with O_2.

7.72

(a) 10.0 g H_2O x $\dfrac{1 \text{ mol H}_2\text{O}}{18.0 \text{ g H}_2\text{O}}$ x $\dfrac{9.72 \text{ kcal}}{1 \text{ mol H}_2\text{O}}$ = 5.40 kcal needed

(b) 5.40 kcal are released.

7.74   (a) $2\,CH_3OH(l) + 3\,O_2(g) \longrightarrow 2\,CO_2(g) + 4\,H_2O(g)$

(b) 50.0 g CH_3OH x $\dfrac{1 \text{ mol CH}_3\text{OH}}{32.0 \text{ g CH}_3\text{OH}}$ x $\dfrac{-174 \text{ kcal}}{1 \text{ mol CH}_3\text{OH}}$ $= -272$ kcal

7.76

$$5.00 \text{ g} \times \frac{1 \text{ mol Al}}{27.0 \text{ g Al}} \times \frac{-337 \text{ kcal}}{2 \text{ mol Al}} = -31.2 \text{ kcal}$$

Self-Test for Chapter 7

Multiple choice:

1. In which of the following processes does entropy decrease?
   (a) $C_6H_{12}O_6(s) + 6\ O_2(g) \longrightarrow 6\ CO_2(g) + 6\ H_2O(l)$
   (b) $2\ Na(s) + 2\ H_2O(l) \longrightarrow 2\ NaOH(aq) + H_2(g)$
   (c) $2\ Mg(s) + O_2(g) \longrightarrow 2\ MgO(s)$
   (d) $Zn(s) + CuSO_4(aq) \longrightarrow Cu(s) + ZnSO_4(aq)$

2. The reaction that is most likely to proceed has:
   (a) negative ΔH, negative ΔS (b) negative ΔH, positive ΔS (c) positive ΔH, positive ΔS
   (d) positive ΔH, negative ΔS

3. Which of the conditions in Problem 2 indicates the reaction with the largest positive value of ΔG?

4. In the reaction $CH_3COOH + CH_3OH \rightleftharpoons CH_3COOCH_3 + H_2O$, the yield of CH_3COOCH_3 can be improved by :
   (a) distilling off the CH_3COOCH_3 (b) removing the water (c) using more CH_3COOH and CH_3OH (d) all of the above

5. The equilibrium expression for the reaction $C_6H_6 + 3\ H_2 \longrightarrow C_6H_{12}$ is:

   (a) $\dfrac{[C_6H_{12}]}{[C_6H_6]\,[H_2]}$ (b) $\dfrac{[C_6H_{12}]}{[C_6H_6]\,[H_2]^3}$ (c) $\dfrac{[C_6H_{12}]}{[C_6H_6]\,[3\ H_2]}$ (d) $\dfrac{[C_6H_6]\,[H_2]^3}{[C_6H_{12}]}$

6. A reaction with which of the following K values is most likely to go to completion at room temperature?
   (a) $K = 10^5$ (b) $K = 10^2$ (c) $K = 10^{-1}$ (d) $K = 10^{-4}$

7. In which of the following reactions will increasing the pressure decrease the yield of product?
   (a) $2\ Mg(s) + O_2(g) \longrightarrow 2\ MgO(s)$
   (b) $H_2C=CH_2(g) + H_2(g) \longrightarrow CH_3CH_3(g)$
   (c) $C(s) + H_2O(g) \longrightarrow CO(g) + H_2(g)$
   (d) $3\ O_2(g) \longrightarrow 2\ O_3(g)$

8. According to LeChâtelier's principle, which of the following changes also changes the value of K?
   (a) changing temperature (b) changing concentration (c) changing pressure (d) all of the above

9. All of the following statements are true about the reaction $3\ O_2(g) \longrightarrow 2\ O_3(g)$ (heat of formation = +34 kcal/mol at 25°C) except :
   (a) The reaction is endothermic. (b) ΔS is negative. (c) ΔG is positive. (d) The rate of the reverse reaction increases with temperature.

10. In the reaction $Si + O_2 \longrightarrow SiO_2$ ($\Delta H = -218$ kcal/mol at 25°C), what is ΔH in kcal when 80 g of O_2 reacts with 70 g of Si?
(a) 218 kcal   (b) –218 kcal   (c) –436 kcal   (d) –545 kcal

Complete the following sentences:

1.   A reaction that has equal amounts of reactants and products at equilibrium has $K =$ ___.

2.   The Law of _____ ___ _____ states that energy can be neither created nor destroyed.

3.   Addition of a _____ increases the rate of a reaction.

4.   A reaction that easily proceeds in either direction is _____.

5.   A reaction that absorbs heat from the surroundings is an _____ reaction.

6.   An _____ _____ ____ gives the relationship between the concentrations of products and reactants at equilibrium.

7.   The rate of a reaction can be increased by increasing _____ or ____ or by adding a _____.

8.   The reactions that continually take place in the body are known as _____.

9.   _____ ___ is unrelated to reaction spontaneity.

10.   For a chemical reaction to occur, reactant molecules must _____.

Match the entries on the left with their partners on the right:

1.   Enzyme   (a) Shows energy relationships in a reaction

2.   Exergonic reaction   (b) A reaction that gives off heat

3. K (c) Reduces the size of E_{act}

4.   Enthalpy   (d) Energy needed for a reaction to occur

5.   Reaction energy diagram   (e) Measure of the amount of disorder in a reaction.

6.   Free energy   (f) Reaction that is not spontaneous

7.   Exothermic reaction   (g) Reaction that can go in either direction

8.   Endergonic reaction   (h) Reaction that absorbs heat

9. E_{act} (i) Difference in energy of products and reactants

10.   Entropy   (j) Reaction that is spontaneous

11.   Reversible reaction   (k) Determines if a reaction is spontaneous

12.   Endothermic reaction   (l) Measures the ratio of products to reactants

Tell whether the following statements are true or false:

1. The caloric value of food tells how much energy is absorbed when food is burned in oxygen.

2. In a chemical equilibrium, both product and reactant concentrations remain constant.

3. According to LeChâtelier's Principle, changing pressure only affects equilibrium if gaseous reactants or products are involved.

4. In an exothermic reaction, the bond dissociation energies of the products are greater than the bond dissociation energies of the reactants.

5. A reaction with a large E_{act} will probably have a large heat of reaction.

6. Raising the temperature of a reaction always increases the rate of reaction.

7. A very unfavorable reaction can take place if the temperature is high enough.

8. Catalysts increase the rate of a reaction by increasing the number of collisions between reactants.

9. At chemical equilibrium, all chemical reaction stops.

10. At low temperatures, the spontaneity of a reaction is determined by ΔH.

Chapter 8 – Gases, Liquids, and Solids

Chapter Outline

I. Introduction to gases, liquids and solids (Section 8.1).
   A. Phases of matter are determined by the attractive forces between molecules.
      1. In gases, attractive forces are very weak.
      2. In liquids, attractive forces are strong.
      3. In solids, forces are so strong that atoms are held in place.
   B. During changes of phase, heat is either absorbed or released.
      1. At the temperature where a change of phase occurs, two states are in equilibrium.
      2. At the change from solid to liquid, two phases are at equilibrium at the melting point.
      3. At the change from liquid to gas, two phases are at equilibrium at the boiling point.
II. Gases (Sections 8.2–8.10).
   A. The kinetic-molecular theory explains the behavior of gases (Section 8.2).
      1. A gas consists of a great many molecules moving about with no attractive forces.
      2. The amount of space that molecules occupy is much smaller than the space between molecules.
      3. The energy of the molecules is related to Kelvin temperature.
      4. When molecules collide, their total kinetic energy is conserved.
      5. A gas that obeys all these behaviors is an ideal gas.
   B. Pressure (Sections 8.3).
      1. Pressure is defined as force per unit area.
      2. Units of pressure are mm Hg, Pascal (in the SI system), atmosphere and pounds per square inch.
      3. Gas pressure can be measured by using a barometer or a manometer.
   C. Gas laws (Sections 8.4–8.10).
      1. Boyle's law (for a fixed amount of gas at constant T) (Section 8.4):
         a. The pressure of a gas is inversely proportional to its volume.
         b. $P_1V_1 = P_2V_2$.
      2. Charles' law (for a fixed amount of gas at constant P) (Section 8.5):
         a. The volume of a gas is directly proportional to its temperature in K.
         b. $V_1/T_1 = V_2/T_2$.
      3. Gay-Lussac's law (for a fixed amount of gas at constant V) (Section 8.6):
         a. Pressure is directly proportional to temperature in K.
         b. $P_1/T_1 = P_2/T_2$.
      4. Combined gas law (Section 8.7).
         $P_1V_1/T_1 = P_2V_2/T_2$ for a fixed amount of gas.
      5. Avogadro's law (at constant T and P) (Section 8.8):
         a. The volume of a gas is directly proportional to its molar amount at constant T and P.
         b. $V_1/n_1 = V_2/n_2$.
         c. Standard temperature and pressure = 273.16 K and 1 atm.
         d. Standard molar volume of a gas = 22.4 L.
      6. Ideal gas law (Section 8.9).
         $PV = nRT$, where R is a gas constant.
      7. Dalton's Law of Partial Pressure (Section 8.10).
         a. Mixtures of gases behave the same as a pure gas.
         b. The partial pressure of a gas in a mixture is the same as the gas would have if it were alone.

III. Intermolecular forces (Sections 8.11–8.12).
   A. Intermolecular forces are the forces that act between molecules (Section 8.11).
   B. In an ideal gas, intermolecular forces are unimportant.
   C. Three types of intermolecular forces are important.
      1. Dipole–dipole forces occur when the positive end of a polar molecule is attracted to the negative end of a second molecule.
      2. London forces.
         a. Short-lived polarity in molecules causes a temporary attraction between molecules.
         b. London forces increase with increasing molecular weight and vary with molecular shape.
      3. Hydrogen bonding (Section 8.12).
         a. Hydrogen bonds occur between a hydrogen atom bonded to an electronegative atom and a nearby electronegative atom.
         b. In hydrogen bonds, the hydrogen atom is partially bonded to two different electronegative atoms.
         c. Hydrogen bonds can be quite strong, and hydrogen bonding is responsible for elevated boiling points.
IV. Liquids and solids (Sections 8.13–8.16).
   A. Liquids (Section 8.13–8.14).
      1. Evaporation occurs when molecules near the surface of a liquid escape into the gaseous state.
      2. When molecules are in the gaseous state, they obey gas laws.
      3. The contribution of the partial pressure of the escaped gas to the total pressure is known as vapor pressure.
      4. Vapor pressure rises with increasing temperature.
      5. The normal boiling point of a liquid is at 760 mm Hg.
         The boiling point rises or falls with atmospheric pressure.
      6. Viscosity and surface tension are properties of liquids.
         a. Viscosity is a liquid's resistance to flow.
         b. Surface tension is the resistance of a liquid to spread out.
      7. Water is a unique liquid (Section 8.14).
         a. Water has very high specific heat, heat of vaporization and strong hydrogen bonding.
         b. Solid water is less dense than liquid water.
   B. Solids (Section 8.15).
      1. A crystalline solid has atoms, molecules or ions rigidly held in an orderly arrangement. Categories of crystalline solids include ionic solids, molecular solids, covalent network solids and metallic solids.
      2. Particles in an amorphous solid do not have an orderly arrangement.
   C. Changes of phase (Section 8.16).
      1. The heat needed to completely melt a solid is the heat of fusion.
      2. The heat needed to completely vaporize a liquid is the heat of vaporization.

Solutions to Chapter 8 Problems

8.1   Use the appropriate conversion factor from Section 8.3

$$220 \text{ mm Hg} \times \frac{1 \text{ atm}}{760 \text{ mm Hg}} = 0.29 \text{ atm}$$

$$0.29 \text{ atm} \times 14.7 \frac{\text{psi}}{\text{atm}} = 4.3 \text{ psi}$$

$$0.29 \text{ atm} \times 101{,}325 \frac{\text{Pa}}{\text{atm}} = 29{,}000 \text{ Pa}$$

8.2   *Ballpark Solution:* Since the pressure is reduced by almost 100 times, the volume must increase by almost 100 times, from 5 L to 500 L.

Solution: $P_1 \times V_1 = P_2 \times V_2$

$$V_2 = \frac{P_1 \times V_1}{P_2} = \frac{(90 \text{ atm})(5.0 \text{ L})}{(1.0 \text{ atm})} = 450 \text{ L}$$

The ballpark solution and the detailed solution agree.

8.3   *Ballpark Solution:* Since the volume increases by four times, the pressure must decrease by four times, from 5.0 atm to 1.25 atm.

Solution: $P_1 \times V_1 = P_2 \times V_2$

$$P_2 = \frac{P_1 \times V_1}{V_2} = \frac{(5.0 \text{ atm})(2.5 \text{ L})}{(10.0 \text{ L})} = 1.2 \text{ atm}$$

At a volume of 0.20 L: $P_2 = \dfrac{P_1 \times V_1}{V_2} = \dfrac{(5.0 \text{ atm})(2.5 \text{ L})}{(0.20 \text{ L})} = 62 \text{ atm}$

8.4   *Ballpark Solution:* Since the temperature increases by about 25%, the volume must also increase by about 25%, from 0.30 L to around 0.38 L.

Solution:

$$\frac{V_1}{T_1} = \frac{V_2}{T_2}$$

$$V_2 = \frac{V_1 \times T_2}{T_1} = \frac{(0.30 \text{ L})(350 \text{ K})}{273 \text{ K}} = 0.38 \text{ L}$$

At 500°C (773 K): $V_2 = \dfrac{V_1 \times T_2}{T_1} = \dfrac{(0.30 \text{ L})(773 \text{ K})}{273 \text{ K}} = 0.85 \text{ L}$

8.5 *Ballpark Solution:* Since the pressure increases by 50%, the temperature must also increase by 50%, from 273 K to around 400 K.

Solution:

$$\frac{P_1}{T_1} = \frac{P_2}{T_2}$$

$$T_2 = \frac{P_2 \times T_1}{P_1} = 45 \text{ psi} \times \frac{273 \text{ K}}{30.0 \text{ psi}} = 410 \text{ K} \quad (137°\text{C})$$

8.6 In this problem, P, V, and T vary.

$$\frac{P_1V_1}{T_1} = \frac{P_2V_2}{T_2}; \qquad P_1 = 745 \text{ mm Hg}; \; V_1 = 250 \text{ L}; \; T_1 = 295 \text{ K}$$

$$P_2 = 570 \text{ mm Hg}; \; V_2 = 232 \text{ L}; \; T_2 = ?$$

$$T_2 = \frac{P_2V_2T_1}{P_1V_1} = \frac{(570 \text{ mm Hg}) \, (232 \text{ L}) \, (295 \text{ K})}{(745 \text{ mm Hg}) \, (250 \text{ L})} = 209 \text{ K, or } -64°\text{ C}$$

8.7 *Ballpark Solution:* Since one mole of a gas occupies 22.4 L at STP, a 100,000 L container holds 100,000/22.4 moles, or about 4500 moles.

Solution:

$$\frac{V_1}{n_1} = \frac{V_2}{n_2}$$

$$n_2 = \frac{V_2 \times n_1}{V_1} = 100,000 \text{ L CH}_4 \times \frac{1.0 \text{ mol}}{22.4 \text{ L}} = 4460 \text{ mol CH}_4 = 4.46 \times 10^3 \text{mol}$$

The same container could also hold 4460 moles of CO_2. Thus, the ballpark solution and the exact solution agree.

$$4.46 \times 10^3 \text{ mol CH}_4 \times \frac{16.0 \text{ g CH}_4}{1 \text{ mol CH}_4} = 7.14 \times 10^4 \text{ g CH}_4$$

$$4.46 \times 10^3 \text{ mol CO}_2 \times \frac{44.0 \text{ g CO}_2}{1 \text{ mol CO}_2} = 1.96 \times 10^5 \text{ g CO}_2$$

8.8 $PV = nRT$; $\quad P = nRT/V$

$$n = 3.2 \text{ g} \times \frac{1 \text{ mol}}{44.0 \text{ g}} = 0.073 \text{ mol}; \quad R = 0.0821 \frac{\text{L·atm}}{\text{mol·K}}$$

$$T = 20°\text{C} = 293 \text{ K}; \quad V = 350 \text{ mL} = 0.35 \text{ L}$$

$$P = \frac{0.073 \text{ mol} \times \dfrac{0.0821 \text{ L·atm}}{\text{mol·K}} \times 293 \text{ K}}{0.35 \text{ L}} = 5.0 \text{ atm}$$

8.9 $PV = nRT$; $n = PV/RT$

$P = 150\ \text{atm};\ V = 180\ \text{L He};\ R = 0.0821\ \dfrac{\text{L·atm}}{\text{mol·K}}\ ;\ T = 25°\text{C} = 298\ \text{K}$

$n = \dfrac{150\ \text{atm}\ \text{x}\ 180\ \text{L He}}{0.0821\ \dfrac{\text{L·atm}}{\text{mol·K}}\ \text{x}\ 298\ \text{K}} = 1.1\ \text{x}\ 10^3\ \text{mol He}$

$1.1\ \text{x}\ 10^3\ \text{mol He}\ \ \text{x}\ \dfrac{4.0\ \text{g}}{1\ \text{mol He}} = 4.4\ \text{x}\ 10^3\ \text{g He}$

8.10   0.98 x 9.5 atm = 9.3 atm He
0.020 x 9.5 atm = 0.19 atm O_2

8.11   The partial pressure of oxygen in diving gas (0.19 atm) is approximately equal to the partial pressure of oxygen in air (0.21 atm).

8.12

$\dfrac{573\ \text{mm Hg}}{760\ \text{mm Hg}}\ \text{x}\ 100\% = 75.4\%\ N_2;$ $\dfrac{100\ \text{mm Hg}}{760\ \text{mm Hg}}\ \text{x}\ 100\% = 13.2\%\ O_2$

$\dfrac{40\ \text{mm Hg}}{760\ \text{mm Hg}}\ \text{x}\ 100\% = 5.3\%\ CO_2;$ $\dfrac{47\ \text{mm Hg}}{760\ \text{mm Hg}}\ \text{x}\ 100\% = 6.2\%\ H_2O$

8.13   We know from the previous problem that the partial pressure of O_2 at atmospheric pressure is 13.2%. Thus, at 685 mm Hg:

685 mm x 0.132 = 90.4 mm Hg

8.14   Boiling points generally increase with increasing molecular (or atomic) weight.

(a) Kr, Ar, Ne. This series is arranged in order of decreasing boiling point.
(b) Cl_2, Br_2, I_2. This series is arranged in order of increasing boiling point.

8.15   Methyl alcohol (a) and methylamine (c) are capable of hydrogen bonding because each contains a hydrogen atom bonded to an electronegative atom. Ethylene (b) does not form hydrogen bonds.

8.16   (a) *London forces* are the only intermolecular forces between nonpolar ethane molecules, and thus ethane has a low boiling point.
(b) The major intermolecular force between ethyl alcohol molecules is *hydrogen bonding*, which causes ethyl alcohol to be high boiling. Dipole–dipole interactions and London forces are also present but are weaker than hydrogen bonding.
(c) *Dipole–dipole* interactions are the principal forces between ethyl chloride molecules and cause the boiling point of ethyl chloride to be higher than that of ethane. London forces are also present.

8.17   To melt isopropyl alcohol:

$$1.50 \text{ mol } \times \frac{60.0 \text{ g}}{1 \text{ mol}} \times \frac{21.4 \text{ cal}}{1 \text{ g}} = 1.93 \times 10^3 \text{ cal required}$$

To boil isopropyl alcohol:

$$1.50 \text{ mol } \times \frac{60.0 \text{ g}}{1 \text{ mol}} \times \frac{159 \text{ cal}}{1 \text{ g}} = 1.43 \times 10^4 \text{ cal required}$$

Understanding Key Concepts

8.18

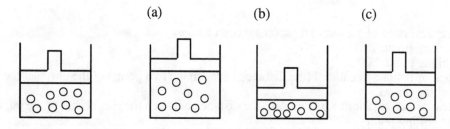

(a)   (b)   (c)

(a) According to Charles' Law, the volume of a gas at fixed pressure is directly proportional to its temperature. Since the temperature increases by 50% (from 300 K to 450 K), volume also increases by 50%.
(b) Boyle's Law states that the volume of a gas is inversely proportional to its pressure. Doubling the pressure halves the volume.
(c) For changes in both pressure and temperature, the Combined Gas Law states that *PV/T* is constant. Thus, reducing both the pressure and the temperature by one-third leaves the volume unchanged.

8.19   Drawing (c) represents the gas in a sealed container after the temperature has been lowered from 350 K to 150 K. The gas remains a gas and its volume is unchanged; only pressure is reduced.

8.20   Drawing (c) represents the mixture of He and Xe because each gas in a mixture of gases acts independently of the other gases, according to kinetic-molecular theory.

8.21

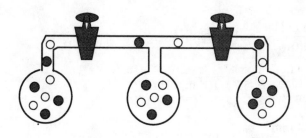

8.22

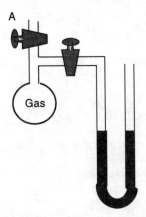

8.23   The vertical parts of the curve represent phase changes.
(a) Melting point: 10°C.
(b) Boiling point: 80°C.
(c) Heat of fusion: 1 kcal/mol (the distance between the two points of the curve at the melting point).
(d) Heat of vaporization: 7.5 kcal/mol (the distance between the two points of the curve at the boiling point).

Gases and Pressure

8.24   One atmosphere is the amount of pressure needed to hold a column of mercury 760 mm high.

8.26   (1) A gas consists of many tiny particles moving about at random with no attractive forces between particles.
(2) The amount of space occupied by gas molecules is much smaller than the amount of space between molecules.
(3) The average kinetic energy of gas particles is proportional to Kelvin temperature.
(4) When molecules collide, they spring apart elastically, and their total energy is constant.

8.28

(a) $1 \text{ atm} \times \dfrac{760 \text{ mm Hg}}{1 \text{ atm}} = 760 \text{ mm Hg}$

(b) $0.25 \text{ atm} \times \dfrac{760 \text{ mm Hg}}{1 \text{ atm}} = 190 \text{ mm Hg}$

(c) $7.5 \text{ atm} \times \dfrac{760 \text{ mm Hg}}{1 \text{ atm}} = 5.7 \times 10^3 \text{ mm Hg}$

(d) $28.0 \text{ in. Hg} \times \dfrac{25.4 \text{ mm}}{1 \text{ in.}} = 711 \text{ mm Hg}$

(e) $41.8 \text{ Pa} \times \dfrac{760 \text{ mm Hg}}{101,325 \text{ Pa}} = 0.314 \text{ mm Hg}$

8.30 When the level in the arm connected to the container is 176 mm (17.6 cm) lower than the level open to the atmosphere, the pressure in the gas container is greater than atmospheric pressure.

754.3 mm Hg + 176 mm Hg = 930 mm Hg

Boyle's Law

8.32 Boyle's law: Volume varies inversely with pressure at constant temperature and number of moles; that is, $P_1V_1 = P_2V_2$.

8.34 $P_1V_1 = P_2V_2$; $P_1 = 65.0$ mm Hg; $P_2 = 385$ mm Hg; $V_1 = 600.0$ mL $= 0.600$ L; $V_2 = ?$

$$V_2 = \frac{P_1V_1}{P_2} = \frac{65.0 \text{ mm Hg} \times 0.600 \text{ L}}{385 \text{ mm Hg}} = 0.101 \text{ L} = 101 \text{ mL}$$

8.36 $P_1V_1 = P_2V_2$; $P_1 = 150$ atm; $P_2 = 1.00$ atm; $V_1 = 50.0$ L; $V_2 = ?$

$$V_2 = \frac{P_1V_1}{P_2} = \frac{150 \text{ atm} \times 50.0 \text{ L}}{1.00 \text{ atm}} = 7500 \text{ L}$$

Charles's Law

8.38 Charles's law: Volume varies directly with temperature at constant pressure and number of moles; that is, $V_1/T_1 = V_2/T_2$.

8.40

$$\frac{V_1}{T_1} = \frac{V_2}{T_2}; \qquad V_1 = 960 \text{ L}; \ V_2 = 1200 \text{ L}; \ T_1 = 18°C = 291 \text{ K}; \ T_2 = ?$$

$$T_2 = \frac{V_2T_1}{V_1} = \frac{1200 \text{ L} \times 291 \text{ K}}{960 \text{ L}} = 364 \text{ K} = 91° \text{ C}$$

8.42

$$\frac{V_1}{T_1} = \frac{V_2}{T_2}; \qquad V_1 = 125 \text{ mL}; \ V_2 = ?; \ T_1 = 25° \text{ C} = 298 \text{ K}; \ T_2 = 37° \text{ C} = 310 \text{ K}$$

$$V_2 = \frac{V_1T_2}{T_1} = \frac{125 \text{ mL} \times 310 \text{ K}}{298 \text{ K}} = 130 \text{ mL}$$

Gay-Lussac's Law

8.44 Gay-Lussac's law: Pressure varies directly with temperature at constant volume and number of moles; that is, $P_1/T_1 = P_2/T_2$.

8.46

$$\frac{P_1}{T_1} = \frac{P_2}{T_2}; \qquad P_1 = 0.95 \text{ atm}; \ P_2 = ?; \ T_1 = 25°C = 298 \text{ K}; \ T_2 = 125°C = 398 \text{ K}$$

$$P_2 = \frac{P_1 T_2}{T_1} = \frac{0.95 \text{ atm} \ \times \ 398 \text{ K}}{298 \text{ K}} = 1.3 \text{ atm}$$

Combined Gas Law

8.48

$$\frac{P_1 V_1}{T_1} = \frac{P_2 V_2}{T_2}; \qquad P_1 = 760 \text{ mm Hg}; \ V_1 = 2.84. \text{ L}; \ T_1 = 273 \text{ K}$$
$$P_2 = 520 \text{ mm Hg}; \ V_2 = 7.50 \text{ L}; \ T_2 = ?$$

$$T_2 = \frac{P_2 V_2 T_1}{P_1 V_1} = \frac{520 \text{ mm Hg} \ \times \ 7.50 \text{ L} \ \times \ 273 \text{ K}}{760 \text{ mm Hg} \ \times 2.84 \text{ L}} = 493 \text{ K} = 220° \text{ C}$$

8.50

$$\frac{P_1 V_1}{T_1} = \frac{P_2 V_2}{T_2}; \qquad P_1 = 749 \text{ mm Hg}; \ V_1 = 55.0 \text{ mL}; \ T_1 = 26° \text{ C} = 299 \text{ K}$$
$$P_2 = 760 \text{ mm Hg}; \ V_2 = ?; \ T_2 = 0°C = 273 \text{ K}$$

$$V_2 = \frac{P_1 V_1 T_2}{T_1 P_2} = \frac{749 \text{ mm Hg} \ \times \ 55.0 \text{ mL} \ \times \ 273 \text{ K}}{299 \text{ K} \ \times \ 760 \text{ mm Hg}} = 49.5 \text{ mL}$$

8.52   (a) For one mole of gas, the combined gas law states that P is proportional to T/V, or $P \propto$ T/V. Thus, if the temperature doubles and the volume is halved, the new pressure is four times greater than the original pressure:

$$\frac{P_1 V_1}{T_1} = \frac{P_2 V_2}{T_2}; \qquad V_2 = 0.5 V_1; \ T_2 = 2T_1; \ P_2 = ?$$

$$P_2 = \frac{P_1 V_1 T_2}{T_1 V_2} = \frac{P_1 V_1 \ \times \ 2T_1}{T_1 \ \times \ 0.5 V_1} = 4 P_1$$

(b) If the temperature is halved and the volume is doubled, the new pressure is one fourth the original pressure:

$$\frac{P_1 V_1}{T_1} = \frac{P_2 V_2}{T_2}; \qquad V_2 = 2V_1; \ T_2 = 0.5 T_1; \ P_2 = ?$$

$$P_2 = \frac{P_1 V_1 T_2}{T_1 V_2} = \frac{P_1 V_1 \ \times \ 0.5 T_1}{T_1 \ \times \ 2V_1} = 0.25 P_1$$

8.54

$$\frac{P_1V_1}{T_1} = \frac{P_2V_2}{T_2}; \qquad P_1 = 775 \text{ mm Hg}; \ V_1 = 590 \text{ mL}; \ T_1 = 352 \text{ K}$$

$$P_2 = 800.0 \text{ mm Hg}; \ V_2 = ?; \ T_2 = 298 \text{ K}$$

$$V_2 = \frac{P_1V_1T_2}{P_2T_1} = \frac{775 \text{ mm Hg} \ \text{x} \ 590 \text{ mL} \ \text{x} \ 298 \text{ K}}{800.0 \text{ mm Hg} \ \text{x} \ 352 \text{ K}} = 484 \text{ mL}$$

Avogadro's Law and Standard Molar Volume

8.56 Avogadro's Law states that equal volumes of gases at the same temperature and pressure contain equal numbers of molecules. Since the volume of space taken up by gas molecules is so much smaller than the amount of space between molecules, Avogadro's Law is true regardless of the chemical identity of the gas.

8.58 A mole of gas at STP occupies 22.4 L.

8.60

$$0.20 \text{ g Cl}_2 \ \text{x} \ \frac{1 \text{ mol Cl}_2}{71 \text{ g Cl}_2} \ \text{x} \ \frac{22.4 \text{ L}}{1 \text{ mol Cl}_2} = 0.063 \text{ L} = 63 \text{ mL}$$

8.62

$$V = 4.0 \text{ m} \ \text{x} \ 5.0 \text{ m} \ \text{x} \ 2.5 \text{ m} = 50 \text{ m}^3; \ 50 \text{ m}^3 \ \text{x} \ \frac{1000 \text{ L}}{1 \text{ m}^3} = 5.0 \ \text{x} \ 10^4 \text{ L}$$

$$\frac{1 \text{ mol}}{22.4 \text{ L}} \ \text{x} \ 5.0 \ \text{x} \ 10^4 \text{ L} = 2230 \text{ mol gas}$$

$$0.21 \ \text{x} \ 2230 \text{ mol O}_2 = 470 \text{ mol O}_2$$

$$470 \text{ mol O}_2 \ \text{x} \ \frac{32.0 \text{ g O}_2}{1 \text{ mol O}_2} = 15000\text{g O}_2 = 15 \text{ kg O}_2$$

The Ideal Gas Law

8.64 The ideal gas law : $PV = nRT$

8.66 $PV = nRT$; $n = PV/RT$;

For Cl_2: $P = 1.0$ atm; $V = 2.0$ L; $R = 0.082 \ \dfrac{\text{L atm}}{\text{mol K}}$; $T = 273$ K

$$n = \frac{1.0 \text{ atm} \ \text{x} \ 2.0 \text{ L}}{0.082 \ \dfrac{\text{L·atm}}{\text{mol·K}} \ \text{x} \ 273 \text{ K}} = 0.089 \text{ mol Cl}_2$$

$$0.089 \text{ mol Cl}_2 \ \text{x} \ \frac{71 \text{ g}}{1 \text{ mol Cl}_2} = 6.3 \text{ g Cl}_2$$

For CH$_4$: $P = 1.5$ atm; $V = 3.0$ L; $R = 0.082 \dfrac{\text{L·atm}}{\text{mol·K}}$; $T = 300$ K

$$n = \frac{1.5 \text{ atm } \times 3.0 \text{ L}}{0.082 \dfrac{\text{L·atm}}{\text{mol·K}} \times 300 \text{ K}} = 0.18 \text{ mol CH}_4$$

$$0.18 \text{ mol CH}_4 \times \frac{16.0 \text{ g}}{1 \text{ mol CH}_4} = 2.9 \text{ g CH}_4$$

There are more molecules in the CH$_4$ sample than in the Cl$_2$ sample. The Cl$_2$ sample, however, weighs more.

8.68

$$n = 15.0 \text{ g CO}_2 \times \frac{1 \text{ mol}}{44 \text{ g}} = 0.34 \text{ mol CO}_2 ;   T = 310 \text{ K} ;   V = 0.30 \text{ L}$$

$$P = \frac{nRT}{V} = \frac{0.34 \text{ mol CO}_2 \times 62.4 \dfrac{\text{mm Hg·L}}{\text{mol·K}} \times 310 \text{ K}}{0.30 \text{ L}} = 2.2 \times 10^4 \text{ mm Hg}$$

8.70

$$n = 18.0 \text{ g O}_2 \times \frac{1 \text{ mol}}{32.0 \text{ g}} = 0.56 \text{ mol O}_2 ;   T = 350 \text{ K} ;   P = 550 \text{ mm Hg}$$

$$V = \frac{nRT}{P} = \frac{0.56 \text{ mol O}_2 \times 62.4 \dfrac{\text{mm Hg·L}}{\text{mol·K}} \times 350 \text{ K}}{550 \text{ mm Hg}} = 22 \text{ L O}_2$$

Dalton's Law and Partial Pressure

8.72   Partial pressure is the pressure contribution of one component of a mixture of gases to the total pressure.

8.74

$$440 \text{ mm Hg} \times \frac{1 \text{ atm}}{760 \text{ mm Hg}} \times \frac{160 \text{ mm Hg}}{1 \text{ atm}} = 93 \text{ mm Hg}$$

Liquids and Intermolecular Forces

8.76   The vapor pressure of a liquid is the partial pressure of the vapor above the liquid.

8.78   Increased pressure raises a liquid's boiling point; decreased pressure lowers a liquid's boiling point.

8.80   (a) All molecules exhibit London forces, which increase in strength with increasing molecular weight.
(b) Dipole-dipole interactions are important for molecules that have polar covalent bonds.
(c) Hydrogen bonding occurs between a molecule that contains an electronegative atom (O, N, or F) and a molecule that has a hydrogen bonded to an electronegative atom (–OH or –NH).

8.82 Ethanol is higher boiling than dimethyl ether because of hydrogen bonding. Since molecules of ethanol are strongly attracted to each other, the boiling point of ethanol is higher than that of dimethyl ether, whose molecules are held together by weaker dipole-dipole interactions.

8.84

(a) $\dfrac{9.72 \text{ kcal}}{1 \text{ mol } H_2O}$ x $3.00 \text{ mol } H_2O$ = $29.2 \text{ kcal of heat required}$

(b) $\dfrac{9.72 \text{ kcal}}{1 \text{ mol } H_2O}$ x $\dfrac{1 \text{ mol } H_2O}{18.0 \text{ g}}$ x 255 g = $138 \text{ kcal of heat is released}$

Solids

8.86 The atoms in a crystalline solid are arranged in a regular, orderly network. The atoms in an amorphous solid have no regular arrangement.

8.88

$\dfrac{45.9 \text{ cal}}{1 \text{ g}}$ x $\dfrac{1 \text{ kcal}}{1000 \text{ cal}}$ x $\dfrac{60.0 \text{ g}}{1 \text{ mol}}$ x 1.66 mol = 4.57 kcal

Applications

8.90 *Systolic pressure* is the maximum blood pressure developed in the artery just after contraction. *Diastolic pressure* is the minimum pressure that occurs at the end of the heartbeat cycle.

8.92 The three most important greenhouse gases are carbon dioxide, water vapor and methane.

8.94 A *composite* is a mixture of two or more solids united so that the properties of the composite depend on the properties of all of the combined materials.

8.96 The supercritical state of matter is a situation intermediate between solid and gas, in which there is some space between molecules yet they are too close together to be truly a gas.

General Questions and Problems

8.98 As the temperature increases, the kinetic energy of gas molecules increases, and the force per unit area which they exert in colliding against the walls of a container increases, thus increasing pressure.

8.100 3.0 L of H_2 and 1.5 L of O_2 react completely. At STP, one mole of H_2 occupies 22.4 L. Thus, 3.0 L of hydrogen = 3.0/22.4 or 0.13 mol. This is also the number of moles of H_2O formed.

$$n = 0.13 \text{ mol } H_2O \; ; \quad T = 373 \text{ K} \; ; \quad P = 1.0 \text{ atm}$$

$$V = \dfrac{nRT}{P} = \dfrac{0.13 \text{ mol } H_2O \text{ x } 0.0821 \dfrac{\text{L·atm}}{\text{mol·K}} \text{ x } 373 \text{ K}}{1.0 \text{ atm}} = 4.0 \text{ L } H_2O$$

8.102

$$0.0094 \text{ mol } CO_2 \quad \text{x} \quad \frac{44.0 \text{ g } CO_2}{1 \text{ mol } CO_2} = 0.41 \text{ g } CO_2$$

$$\frac{0.41 \text{ g } CO_2}{1 \text{ min}} \quad \text{x} \quad \frac{60 \text{ min}}{1 \text{ hr}} \quad \text{x} \quad \frac{24 \text{ hr}}{1 \text{ day}} = \frac{590 \text{ g } CO_2}{\text{day}}$$

8.104

Gas	Molecular Weight	Density (g/L) at STP
(a) CH_4	16.0 amu	0.714
(b) CO_2	44.0 amu	1.96
(c) O_2	32.0 amu	1.43

8.106

(a)   (b)

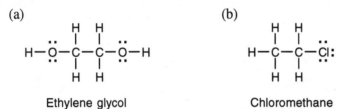

Ethylene glycol   Chloromethane

(c) Ethylene glycol is higher boiling than chloroethane because it forms hydrogen bonds.

Self-Test for Chapter 8

Multiple choice:

1. Which of the following units would you be least likely to use in a laboratory?
   (a) Pascal   (b) pounds per square inch   (c) mm Hg   (d) atmosphere

2. A fixed amount of a gas has its temperature and volume doubled. What happens to its pressure?
   (a) increases fourfold   (b) doubles   (c) stays the same   (d) is halved

3. In which of the gas laws is the amount of gas not fixed?
   (a) Boyle's law   (b) Charles' law   (c) Gay-Lussac's law   (d) Avogadro's law

4. Which of the following compounds does not exhibit hydrogen bonding?
   (a) CH_3OCH_3 (b) CH_3OH (c) HF   (d) CH_3NH_2

5. Which of the following compounds is the lowest melting?
   (a) NaI   (b) Au   (c) SiO_2 (d) sugar

6. Which term describes the change of state that occurs when a gas changes to a solid?
   (a) fusion   (b) condensation   (c) deposition   (d) sublimation

7. When does a gas obey ideal behavior?
   (a) at low density   (b) at high pressure   (c) at low temperature   (d) in a large container

8. If 22.0 g of CO_2 has a pressure of 1.00 atm at 300 K, what is its volume?
   (a) 22.4 L   (b) 12.3 L   (c) 11.2 L   (d) 9.5 L

9. What volume does the amount of gas in the previous problem occupy at STP?
   (a) 22.4 L   (b) 12.3 L   (c) 11.2 L   (d) 9.5 L

10. What is the density of CO_2 gas in g/L at STP if one mole of gas has a volume of 22.4 L?
    (a) 44.0 g/L   (b) 11.0 g/L   (c) 6.4 g/L   (d) 1.96 g/L

Complete the following sentences:

1. In Boyle's law, the _____ of a gas is inversely proportional to its _____.

2. A liquid has _____ volume and _____ shape.

3. _____ law states that the total pressure of a gas mixture is the sum of the individual pressure of the components in the mixture.

4. A pressure of 760 mm Hg and a temperature of 273 K are known as _____.

5. _____ law says that equal volumes of gases at the same temperature contain equal numbers of molecules.

6. In a closed container, liquid and vapor are at _____.

7. Units for measuring pressure include _____, _____, _____, and _____.

8. The _____ _____ _____ is the heat necessary to melt one gram of a solid at its melting point.

9. In Charles' law, _____ and _____ are kept constant.

10. Gas particles move in straight lines, with energy proportional to _____.

11. The transformation of a substance from one state to another is known as a _____ _____ _____.

12. A liquid that evaporates readily is said to be _____.

Tell whether the following statements are true or false:

1. Molecules of ethyl alcohol exhibit hydrogen bonding.

2. All gases are similar in their physical behavior.

3. Molecules of CH_3Cl experience both dipole–dipole interactions and London forces.

4. Doubling the pressure of a gas at constant temperature doubles the volume.

5. $R = 0.082$ L atm/(mol·K) is a value for the gas constant.

6. Atoms in solids have an orderly arrangement.

7.   Standard temperature and pressure are 760 mm Hg and 273°C.

8.   All substances become solids if the temperature is low enough.

9.   The atmospheric pressure in Death Valley (282 ft below sea level) is lower than the atmospheric pressure at sea level.

10.   The more liquid there is in a closed container, the higher the vapor pressure.

11.   Surface tension is a liquid's resistance to flow.

Match the entries on the left with their partners on the right

1.	$P_1V_1 = P_2V_2$	(a) Avogadro's law
2.	Dipole–dipole attraction	(b) Gas constant
3.	$P_{total} = P_{gas\ 1} + P_{gas\ 2} + ...$	(c) Force per unit area
4.	760 mm Hg at 273 K	(d) Charles' law
5.	Hydrogen bonding	(e) Occurs between molecules of CH_3Br
6.	$V_1/n_1 = V_2/n_2$	(f) STP
7.	0.007500 mm Hg	(g) Boyle's law
8.	London forces	(h) Occurs between molecules of CH_3OH
9.	62.3 mm Hg L / mol K	(i) Universal gas law
10.	$V_1/T_1 = V_2/T_2$	(j) Pascal
11.	Pressure	(k) Dalton's law of partial pressure
12.	$PV = nRT$	(l) Occurs between molecules of N_2

Chapter 9 – Solutions

Chapter Outline

I. Characteristics of solutions (Sections 9.1–9.6).
  A. Mixtures and solutions (Section 9.1).
    1. Mixtures are either heterogeneous or homogeneous.
      a. Heterogeneous mixtures have non-uniform mixing.
      b. Homogeneous mixtures have uniform mixing.
    2. Homogeneous mixtures can be classified by particle size.
      a. In solutions, particles range in size from 0.1–2 nm.
      b. In colloids, particles range in size from 2–1000 nm.
    3. When a solid is dissolved in a liquid, the liquid is the solvent and the solid is the solute.
  B. The solution process (Sections 9.2–9.3).
    1. Solubility depends on the strength of attraction between solute particles and solvent relative to the attractions in the pure substances.
    2. In predicting solubility, polar solvents dissolve polar substances, and nonpolar solvents dissolve nonpolar substances.
    3. Solution can be either an exothermic or an endothermic process.
    4. Some ionic compounds attract water to form solid hydrates (Section 9.3).
  C. Solubility (Sections 9.4–9.6).
    1. Solubility is a dynamic process (Section 9.4).
      a. When no more of an added solute will dissolve, the solution is said to be saturated.
      b. In a saturated solution, an equilibrium is established between dissolving and crystallizing.
      c. Two liquids are miscible if they are mutually soluble in all proportions.
    2. The solubility of a substance is the maximum amount of the substance that will dissolve in a solvent.
    3. Effect of temperature on solubility (Section 9.5).
      a. The effect of temperature on the solubility of a solid solute is unpredictable.
      b. A gas is always less soluble as temperature increases.
      c. A solid that is more soluble at high temperature than at low may form a supersaturated solution.
    4. Effect of pressure on solubility (Section 9.6).
      a. Increased pressure makes gas molecules more soluble in a liquid.
      b. Henry's law: $P_{gas} = kC$.
        The solubility of a gas in a liquid is proportional to its partial pressure over the liquid at constant T.
      c. When the partial pressure of a gas changes:

$$\frac{C_1}{P_1} = \frac{C_2}{P_2} = k \text{ (at constant T)}$$

II. Quantitative relationships in solutions (Sections 9.7–9.10).
  A. Concentration (Section 9.7).

    1. Molarity $= \dfrac{\text{moles of solute}}{\text{volume of solution (L)}}$.
    Molarity can be used as a conversion factor.

    2. weight/volume % concentration $= \dfrac{\text{grams of solute}}{\text{mL of solution}} \times 100\%$.

3. volume/volume % concentration $= \dfrac{\text{volume of solute (mL)}}{\text{volume of solution (mL)}} \times 100\%$.

4. parts per million (ppm) $= \dfrac{\text{mass of solute (g)}}{\text{mass of solution (g)}} \times 10^6$.

$\phantom{4. \text{parts per million (ppm)}} = \dfrac{\text{volume of solute (mL)}}{\text{volume of solution (mL)}} \times 10^6$.

B. Dilution (Section 9.8).
  1. During dilution, the number of moles of solute remains constant, while volume changes.
  2. $M_1 \times V_1 = M_2 \times V_2$.
  3. V_1 / V_2 is known as a dilution factor.
C. Equivalents and milliequivalents (Sections 9.9–9.10).
  1. Electrolytes (Section 9.9).
    a. Substances that ionize completely are strong electrolytes.
    b. Substances that ionize partially are weak electrolytes.
  2. The concentration of electrolytes is expressed in equivalents (Section 9.10).
    a. 1 equivalent of an ion $= \dfrac{\text{molar mass of the ion}}{\text{number of charges on the ion}}$
    b. Milliequivalents are useful when measuring ion concentrations in body fluids.
III. Properties of solutions (Sections 9.11–9.14).
  A. Effects of particles in solution (Section 9.11).
    1. Lowering of vapor pressure.
    2. Boiling point elevation.
    3. Freezing point depression.
    4. These effects don't depend on the identity of the particles.
  B. Osmosis (Section 9.12–9.13).
    1. When two solutions of different concentrations are separated by a semipermeable membrane, water passes through to the more concentrated side. This is known as osmosis.
    2. Osmotic pressure can be applied to establish an equilibrium between the rates of forward and reverse passage of water across the membrane.
    3. The osmotic pressure of a solution depends only on the number of particles in solution.
    4. Osmolarity = molarity x number of particles per formula unit.
    5. Two solutions that are isotonic have the same osmolarity.
      a. In cells, a hypotonic solution causes hemolysis.
      b. A hypertonic solution causes crenation.
    6. Dialysis is a process similar to osmosis except that the pores in the membrane allow small solute molecules to pass (Section 9.13).
         Hemodialysis is used to cleanse the blood of people whose kidneys malfunction.
  C. Colloids (Section 9.14).
    1. Solute particles in colloids are larger than those in solutions.
    2. Sols and gels.
      a. Sols have colloidal particles dispersed throughout the solution.
      b. In gels, large molecules tangle to make the mixture semisolid.
    3. An emulsion is a colloidal dispersion of a liquid in a liquid.
    4. Colloidal particles are too large to pass through semipermeable membranes.

Solutions to Chapter 9 Problems

9.1   Orange juice is heterogeneous, and all of the other mixtures are homogeneous, although hand lotion might be heterogeneous in some cases. Apple juice and tea are solutions because they are nonfilterable and transparent to light. Hand lotion is a colloid.

9.2   Remember the rule "like dissolves like".
(a) CCl_4 and H_2O don't form solutions because CCl_4 is nonpolar and H_2O is polar.
(b) Gasoline and $MgSO_4$ don't form solutions because $MgSO_4$ is polar and gasoline is nonpolar.
(c)(d) These two pairs of substances form solutions because they are chemically similar.

9.3   Glauber's salt: $Na_2SO_4 \cdot 10H_2O$

9.4   Molar mass of Glauber's salt: 322 g/mol. 322 g of Glauber's salt provides 1.00 mol of sodium sulfate.

9.5   The solubility of KBr at 50°C is approximately 80 g/100 mL.

9.6

$$\frac{C_1}{P_1} = \frac{C_2}{P_2}; P_1 = 760 \text{ mm Hg}; C_1 = 0.169 \text{ g/100 mL}; P_2 = 2.5 \times 10^4 \text{ mm Hg}; C_2 = ?$$

$$C_2 = \frac{C_1 P_2}{P_1} = \frac{\left(\frac{0.169 \text{ g}}{100 \text{ mL}}\right) \times 2.5 \times 10^4 \text{ mm Hg}}{760 \text{ mm Hg}} = 5.6 \text{ g } CO_2/100 \text{ mL}$$

9.7

$$50.0 \text{ g} \times \frac{1 \text{ mol}}{337 \text{ g}} = 0.148 \text{ mol}; \quad \frac{0.148 \text{ mol}}{0.160 \text{ L}} = 0.925 \text{ M}$$

9.8

$$\# \text{moles} = \text{molarity(M)} \times \text{volume} = \frac{\text{mol}}{\text{L}} \times \text{L}$$

(a) $M = \dfrac{0.25 \text{ mol } NaNO_3}{1 \text{ L}}; \quad V = 125 \text{ ml} = 0.125 \text{ L}$

$$\# \text{moles} = \frac{0.25 \text{ mol}}{1 \text{ L}} \times 0.125 \text{ L} = 0.031 \text{ mol } NaNO_3$$

(b) $M = \dfrac{1.5 \text{ mol } HNO_3}{1 \text{ L}}; V = 450 \text{ ml} = 0.45 \text{ L}$

$$\# \text{moles} = \frac{1.5 \text{ mol}}{1 \text{ L}} \times 0.45 \text{ L} = 0.68 \text{ mol } HNO_3$$

9.9   First, find the number of moles of cholesterol in 250 mL of blood:

$$250 \text{ mL} \ \times \ \frac{0.0050 \text{ mol cholesterol}}{1000 \text{ mL}} \ = \ 0.001\ 25 \text{ mol cholesterol}$$

Next, find the molar mass of cholesterol:

$$(27 \times 12.0 \text{ g/mol C}) + (46 \times 1.0 \text{ g/mol H}) + (16.0 \text{ g/mol O}) \ = \ 386.0 \text{ g/mol}$$

Now, convert moles into grams:

$$0.001\ 25 \text{ mol cholesterol} \ \times \ \frac{386.0 \text{ g}}{1 \text{ mol}} \ = \ 0.48 \text{ g cholesterol}$$

9.10   Molar mass of $CaCO_3$ = 100.0 g

$$0.075 \text{ L} \ \times \ \frac{0.10 \text{ mol HCl}}{1 \text{ L}} \ \times \ \frac{1 \text{ mol CaCO}_3}{2 \text{ mol HCl}} \ \times \ \frac{100.0 \text{ g CaCO}_3}{1 \text{ mol CaCO}_3} \ = \ 0.38 \text{ g CaCO}_3$$

9.11   1 dL = 100 mL

$$\frac{8.6 \text{ mg}}{100 \text{ mL}} \ \times \ \frac{1 \text{ g}}{1000 \text{ mg}} \ \times \ 100\% \ = \ 0.0086\% \text{ (w/v) Ca}^{2+}$$

9.12

$$\frac{23 \text{ g KI}}{350 \text{ mL}} \ \times \ 100\% \ = \ 6.6\% \text{ (w/v) KI}$$

9.13   (a) A 12% solution contains 12 g of solute per 100 mL of solution. Thus, 12 g of glucose are needed.

(b) A 2% solution contains 2 g of solute per 100 mL of solution.

$$75 \text{ mL} \ \times \ \frac{2.0 \text{ g KCl}}{100 \text{ mL}} \ = \ 1.5 \text{ g KCl}$$

9.14   A 7.5% (v/v) solution contains 7.5 mL of solute per 100 mL of solution.

$$500 \text{ mL solution} \ \times \ \frac{7.5 \text{ mL acetic acid}}{100 \text{ mL solution}} \ = \ 38 \text{ mL acetic acid}$$

To prepare the desired solution, measure 38 mL of acetic acid into a 500.0 mL volumetric flask and add water to the 500.0 mL mark.

9.15   (a) 22 mL of ethyl alcohol are needed.

(b) $150 \text{ mL solution} \ \times \ \dfrac{12 \text{ mL acetic acid}}{100 \text{ mL solution}} \ = \ 18 \text{ mL acetic acid}$

9.16

$$\frac{32 \text{ mg NaF}}{20 \text{ kg}} \ \times \ \frac{1 \text{ kg}}{10^6 \text{ mg}} \ \times \ 10^6 \ = \ 1.6 \text{ ppm}$$

9.17 $M_1 = 12.0\ M$; $V_1 = 100.0\ mL$; $V_2 = 500.0\ mL$

$$M_2 = M_1 \times \frac{V_1}{V_2}$$

$$= 12.0\ M \times \frac{100.0\ mL}{500.0\ mL} = 2.40\ M$$

9.18 $V_2 = 500.0\ mL$; $M_2 = 1.25\ M$; $M_1 = 16.0\ M$

$$V_1 = V_2 \times \frac{M_2}{M_1}$$

$$= 500.0\ mL \times \frac{1.25\ M}{16.0\ M} = 39.1\ mL$$

9.19 – 9.20

Ion	Molar Mass	Charge	Equivalent Weight	Milliequivalent Weight
(a) K^+	39.1 g	+1	39.1 g	39.1 mg, or 3.91×10^{-2} g
(b) Br^-	79.9 g	−1	79.9 g	79.9 mg, or 7.99×10^{-2} g
(c) Mg^{2+}	24.3 g	+2	12.2 g	12.2 mg, or 1.22×10^{-2} g
(d) SO_4^{2-}	96.0 g	−2	48.0 g	48.0 mg, or 4.80×10^{-2} g

9.21 One equivalent of Mg^{2+} = 12.2 g [Problem 9.19 (c)].

$$\frac{g\ Mg^{2+}}{1\ L} = \frac{12\ g\ Mg^{2+}}{1\ Eq} \times \frac{1\ Eq}{1000\ mEq} \times \frac{3.0\ mEq}{1\ L} = \frac{0.036\ g\ Mg^{2+}}{1\ L}$$

$$\frac{0.036\ g\ Mg^{2+}}{L} \times \frac{1000\ mg}{1\ g} \times \frac{1\ L}{1000\ mL} \times 250\ mL = 9.0\ mg\ Mg^{2+}$$

9.22 Glucose is not an electrolyte. Thus 1.0 mol glucose lowers the freezing point of 1.0 kg H_2O by 1.9°C.

Freezing point $= 0°C - 1.9°C = -1.9°C$

9.23 0.75 mol of KBr yields 1.5 mol solute particles, which raise the boiling point of 1.0 kg H_2O by 1.5 x 0.51°C = 0.76°C.

Boiling point $= 100\ °C + 0.76°C = 100.76°C$

9.24 Osmolarity = molarity x number of particles

(a) For 0.35 M KBr, osmolarity = 0.35 M x 2 = 0.70 Osmol, since KBr yields two particles (K^+ and Br^-) in solution.

(b) For 0.15 M glucose, osmolarity = 0.15 M x 1 = 0.15 Osmol, since glucose yields only one particle in solution. For K_2SO_4, osmolarity = 0.05 M x 3 = 0.15 Osmol, since K_2SO_4 provides 3 particles per mole in solution. Total osmolarity = 0.30 Osmol.

9.25 For the oral rehydration solution, osmolarity is equal to the sum of the osmolarities of the individual components. For each of the ionic components, the number of millimoles = the number of mEq, since each ion has one charge. Thus,

$$90 \text{ mM Na}^+ + 20 \text{ mM K}^+ + 110 \text{ mM Cl}^- = 220 \text{ mM ions} = 0.22 \text{ M ions}$$

For glucose:

$$\frac{2.0 \text{ g glucose}}{100 \text{ mL}} \times \frac{1000 \text{ mL}}{1 \text{ L}} \times \frac{1 \text{ mol}}{180 \text{ g glucose}} = 0.11 \text{ M glucose}$$

Osmolarity = molarity x number of particles. In this problem, all components yield 1 particle in solution.
Osmolarity = 0.22 M + 0.11 M = 0.33 Osmol

Understanding Key Concepts

9.26

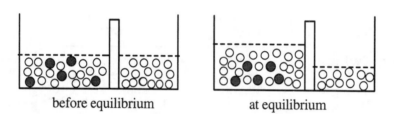

before equilibrium   at equilibrium

The membrane is permeable to the unshaded spheres but impermeable to the shaded spheres. Solvent (unshaded spheres) passes through the membrane until equilibrium is reached.

9.27 The boiling point of water is elevated by 0.5°C for every mole of dissolved particles. 1 mol of HCl dissolves to form 2 mol particles, which elevate the boiling point of water by 1°C. Acetic acid exists in solution almost completely as CH_3COOH, and 1 mol acetic acid dissolves to form 1 mol particles, which elevate the boiling point of water by only 0.5°.

9.28 The same reasoning used in the previous problem applies here. The freezing point of water is depressed by 1.9°C for every mole of dissolved particles. 1 mol HBr dissociates to form 2 mol ions, which lower the freezing point of water by 3.7°C, but 1 mol HF is undissociated and lowers the freezing point by 1.9°C.

9.29 The lower line on the graph represents the solubility of a gas as a function of temperature. The solubility of a solid may increase or decrease with increasing temperature, but the solubility of a gas *always* decreases when temperature is raised.

9.30

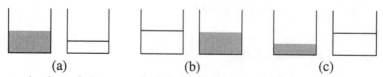

(a)   (b)   (c)

When a beaker of glucose solution (shaded) and a beaker of pure water (unshaded) stand for several days, the liquid levels appear as those pictured in (a). The dissolved glucose particles lower the vapor pressure of water and slow evaporation.

9.31 Drawing (d) represents the solution that results when 50.0 mL of (a) is withdrawn and diluted by a factor of 4.

Solutions and Solubility

9.32 In a homogeneous mixture (such as tea), mixing is uniform throughout because the particle size is small. In a heterogeneous mixture (such as chicken soup), mixing is nonuniform because particle size is larger.

9.34 The polarity of water enables it to dissolve many ionic solids.

9.36 Because the surface area of powdered salt is greater than that of a salt block, powdered salt dissolves more rapidly.

9.38 Rubbing alcohol (b) and black coffee (d) are true solutions.

9.40

$$C_2 = \frac{C_1 P_2}{P_1}; \quad C_1 = 51.8 \text{ g/100 mL}; \quad P_1 = 760.0 \text{ mm Hg}; \quad P_2 = 250.0 \text{ mm Hg}$$

$$= \frac{(51.8 \text{ g/100 mL}) \times 250.0 \text{ mm Hg}}{760.0 \text{ mm Hg}} = 17.0 \text{ g/100 mL}$$

Concentration and Dilution of Solutions

9.42 Depending on the solubility of the solute in the solvent, a saturated solution may be either dilute or concentrated. If a solute is only slightly soluble in a solvent, a saturated solution will be dilute. If the solute is very soluble in the solvent, a saturated solution will be concentrated. For a highly soluble solute, even a highly concentrated solution may be unsaturated.

9.44 Molarity (M) is defined as the number of moles of solute per liter of solution.

9.46

$$\frac{5.0 \text{ mL ethyl alcohol}}{100.0 \text{ mL solution}} \times 500.0 \text{ mL solution} = 25.0 \text{ mL ethyl alcohol}$$

Add water to 25.0 mL of ethyl alcohol to make a final volume of 500.0 mL.

9.48

$$250 \text{ mL solution} \times \frac{0.10 \text{ mol NaCl}}{1000 \text{ mL solution}} = 0.025 \text{ mol NaCl}$$

$$0.025 \text{ mol NaCl} \times \frac{58.5 \text{ g}}{1 \text{ mol}} = 1.5 \text{ g NaCl}$$

Dissolve 1.5 g NaCl in water to a final volume of 250 mL.

9.50

(a) $\dfrac{5.0 \text{ g KCl}}{75 \text{ mL}}$ x 100 mL = 6.7 g KCl ; $\dfrac{6.7 \text{ g KCl}}{100 \text{ mL}}$ x 100% = 6.7% (w/v) KCl

(b) $\dfrac{15 \text{ g sucrose}}{350 \text{ mL}}$ x 100 mL = 4.3 g sucrose ; $\dfrac{4.3 \text{ g}}{100 \text{ mL}}$ x 100% = 4.3% (w/v) sucrose

9.52

(a) 50.0 mL x $\dfrac{8.0 \text{ g KCl}}{100 \text{ mL}}$ = 4.0 g KCl

(b) 200.0 mL x $\dfrac{7.5 \text{ g acetic acid}}{100 \text{ mL}}$ = 15 g acetic acid

9.54

23 g KOH x $\dfrac{100 \text{ mL}}{10.0 \text{ g KOH}}$ = 230 mL of a 10.0% (w/v) solution

23 g KOH x $\dfrac{1 \text{ mol}}{56.1 \text{ g KOH}}$ = 0.41 mol KOH

0.41 mol KOH x $\dfrac{1000 \text{ mL}}{0.25 \text{ mol KOH}}$ = 1600 mL of 0.25 M solution

9.56

1 kg = 10^6 mg; $\dfrac{10 \text{ mg}}{10^6 \text{ mg}}$ x 10^6 = 10 ppm

9.58

(a) 12.5 g NaHCO$_3$ x $\dfrac{1 \text{ mol}}{84.0 \text{ g}}$ = 0.149 mol NaHCO$_3$; $\dfrac{0.149 \text{ mol}}{0.350 \text{ L}}$ = 0.425 M

(b) 45.0 g H$_2$SO$_4$ x $\dfrac{1 \text{ mol}}{98.0 \text{ g}}$ = 0.459 mol H$_2$SO$_4$; $\dfrac{0.459 \text{ mol}}{0.300 \text{ L}}$ = 1.53 M

(c) 30.0 g NaCl x $\dfrac{1 \text{ mol}}{58.5 \text{ g}}$ = 0.512 mol NaCl; $\dfrac{0.512 \text{ mol}}{0.500 \text{ L}}$ = 1.02 M

9.60

0.0040 mol HCl x $\dfrac{1000 \text{ mL}}{0.75 \text{ mol}}$ = 5.3 mL HCl

9.62   First, calculate the number of moles of H_2SO_4 spilled:

$$0.450 \text{ L} \times \frac{0.50 \text{ mol } H_2SO_4}{1 \text{ L}} = 0.22 \text{ mol } H_2SO_4$$

According to the equation given in the problem, each mole of H_2SO_4 reacts with two moles of $NaHCO_3$. Thus, the 0.22 mol of H_2SO_4 spilled needs to be neutralized with 0.44 mol of $NaHCO_3$.

$$0.44 \text{ mol } NaHCO_3 \times \frac{84 \text{ g}}{1 \text{ mol}} = 37 \text{ g } NaHCO_3$$

9.64

$$20.0\% \, (\text{v/v}) \ \text{means}: \quad \frac{20.0 \text{ mL concentrate}}{100.0 \text{ mL juice}}$$

$$\text{Thus,} \quad 100.0 \text{ mL concentrate} \times \frac{100.0 \text{ mL juice}}{20.0 \text{ mL concentrate}} = 500.0 \text{ mL juice}$$

Since the final volume of the diluted juice is 500.0 mL, you would have to add 400.0 mL water to the original 100.0 mL of concentrate.

9.66

$$V_2 = V_1 \times \frac{M_1}{M_2}; \ V_1 = 25.0 \text{ mL}; \ M_1 = 12.0 \text{ M}; \ M_2 = 0.500 \text{ M}$$

$$= 25.0 \text{ mL} \times \frac{12.0 \text{ M}}{0.500 \text{ M}} = 6.00 \times 10^2 \text{ mL of 0.500 M HCl solution}$$

Electrolytes

9.68   An electrolyte is a substance that conducts electricity when dissolved in water.

9.70   If the concentration of Ca^{2+} is 3.0 mEq/L, there are 3.0 mmol of charges due to calcium per liter of blood. Since calcium has a charge of +2, there are 1.5 mmol of calcium per liter of blood.

9.72

$$10\% \, (\text{w/v}) = \frac{10 \text{ g KCl}}{100 \text{ mL}} \ ; \quad 30 \text{ mL} \times \frac{10 \text{ g KCl}}{100 \text{ mL}} = 3.0 \text{ g KCl}$$

The molar mass of KCl is 74.6 g/mol. Thus:

$$3.0 \text{ g KCl} \times \frac{1 \text{ mol}}{74.6 \text{ g}} = 0.040 \text{ mol KCl}$$

Since one equivalent equals one mole when an ion has only one charge, there are 0.040 Eq, or 40 mEq, of K^+ in a 30 mL dose.

9.74   Use the value 100 mEq/L for the concentration of Cl^- in blood:
For Cl^- ion, 100 mEq = 100 mmol = 0.100 mol

$$\frac{0.100 \text{ mol } Cl^-}{1 \text{ L}} \times 0.100 \text{ L} = 0.0100 \text{ mol } Cl^- \text{ in } 100.0 \text{ mL blood}$$

$$0.0100 \text{ mol } Cl^- \times \frac{35.5 \text{ g}}{1 \text{ mol}} = 0.355 \text{ g } Cl^- \text{ in } 100.0 \text{ mL blood}$$

Properties of Solutions

9.76   0.20 mol NaOH contains 0.40 mol solute particles, and 0.20 mol $Ba(OH)_2$ contains 0.60 mol solute particles. Since $Ba(OH)_2$ produces more solute particles, it produces greater freezing point lowering of 2.0 kg of water.

9.78   Methanol has a molar mass of 32.0 g and provides one mole of solute particles per mole of methanol.

$$10.0° \text{ C } \times \frac{1 \text{ mol}}{1.86° \text{ C} \times 1 \text{ kg}} \times 5.00 \text{ kg} = 26.9 \text{ mol methanol}$$

$$26.9 \text{ mol } \times \frac{32.0 \text{ g}}{1 \text{ mol}} = 861 \text{ g of methanol needed}$$

Osmosis

9.80   The inside of a red blood cell contains dissolved substances and therefore has a higher osmolarity than pure water. Water thus passes through the cell membrane to dilute the cell contents until pressure builds up and the cell eventually bursts.

9.82

Solution	Molarity	# of Particles	Osmolarity
(a) 0.25 M KBr	0.25 M	2	0.50 Osmol
0.20 M Na_2SO_4	0.20 M	3	0.60 Osmol (greater)
(b) 0.30 M NaOH	0.30 M	2	0.60 Osmol
3% (w/v) NaOH	0.75 M	2	1.5 Osmol (greater)

Applications

9.84   At high altitude, P_{O2} is low, and not enough oxygen is available to cause 100% saturation of hemoglobin. In order to deliver enough oxygen to body tissues, the body compensates by manufacturing more hemoglobin, which drives the hemoglobin equilibrium to the right.

9.86   In addition to fluid replacement, sports drinks provide electrolytes to replenish those lost during exercise, they furnish soluble complex carbohydrates for slow-release energy, and they may contain vitamins to protect cells from damage.

General Questions and Problems

9.88   Molar mass of uric acid ($C_5H_4N_4O_3$) = 168 g.

(a) (w/v)%: $\dfrac{0.067 \text{ g}}{1 \text{ L}} = \dfrac{0.0067 \text{ g}}{100 \text{ mL}}$; $\dfrac{0.0067 \text{ g}}{100 \text{ mL}} \times 100\% = 0.0067\%$ (w/v)

(b) ppm: One L of water weighs 1 kg. Thus:

$$\dfrac{0.067 \text{ g}}{1 \text{ L}} = \dfrac{0.067 \text{ g}}{1 \text{ kg}} \times \dfrac{1 \text{ kg}}{1000 \text{ g}};\ \dfrac{0.067 \text{ g}}{1000 \text{ g}} \times 10^6 = 67 \text{ ppm}$$

(c) $\dfrac{0.067 \text{ g}}{1 \text{ L}} \times \dfrac{1 \text{ mol}}{168 \text{ g}} = 0.000\ 40 \text{ M} = 4.0 \times 10^{-4} \text{ M}$

9.90 $M_1 = 16 \text{ M}$, $M_2 = 0.20 \text{ M}$, $V_2 = 750 \text{ mL}$

$$V_1 = V_2 \times \dfrac{M_2}{M_1} = 750 \text{ mL} \times \dfrac{0.20 \text{ M}}{16 \text{ M}} = 9.4 \text{ mL HNO}_3$$

9.92 $M_1 = 12.0 \text{ M}$, $V_1 = 25 \text{ mL}$, $V_2 = 525 \text{ mL}$

$$M_2 = M_1 \times \dfrac{V_1}{V_2} = 12.0 \text{ M} \times \dfrac{25 \text{ mL}}{525 \text{ mL}} = 0.57 \text{ M}$$

9.94

Component	Weight	Molar Mass	Molarity
(a) NaCl	8.6 g	58.5 g	0.147 M
(b) KCl	0.30 g	74.6 g	0.0040 M
(c) CaCl$_2$	0.33 g	111 g	0.0030 M

9.96

$$0.080\% \text{ (v/v)} = \dfrac{0.080 \text{ mL}}{100 \text{ mL}} = \dfrac{0.80 \text{ mL}}{1 \text{ L}}$$

$$\dfrac{0.80 \text{ mL}}{1 \text{ L}} \times 5.0 \text{ L} = 4.0 \text{ mL alcohol}$$

9.98   (a) $CoCl_2 + 6 H_2O \rightleftharpoons CoCl_2 \cdot 6H_2O$

(b) Molar mass of $CoCl_2 \cdot 6H_2O$ = 238 g

$$2.50 \text{ g CoCl}_2 \times \dfrac{1 \text{ mol CoCl}_2 \cdot 6 \text{ H}_2\text{O}}{238 \text{ g}} \times \dfrac{6 \text{ mol H}_2\text{O}}{1 \text{ mol CoCl}_2 \cdot 6 \text{ H}_2\text{O}} \times \dfrac{18.0 \text{ g H}_2\text{O}}{1 \text{ mol H}_2\text{O}} = 1.13 \text{ g H}_2\text{O}$$

Self-Test for Chapter 9

Multiple choice:

1. 50 mL of a 1.0 M NaOH solution is diluted to 1.0 L. What is the dilution factor?
   (a) 1/50   (b) 1/20   (c) 1/10   (d) 1/2

2. Which of the following will not speed up the rate of solution of a solid?
   (a) stirring   (b) heating   (c) grinding the solid into powder   (d) increasing pressure on the solution

3. To make up 500 mL of a 5% (v/v) solution of methanol (CH_3OH ; molar mass = 32 g) in water:
   (a) dilute 25 mL of CH_3OH with water to a volume of 500 mL
   (b) dilute 5 mL of CH_3OH with water to a volume of 500 mL
   (c) add 32 g of CH_3OH to 500 g of water
   (d) add 25 mL of CH_3OH to 500 mL of water

4. Which solution has the greatest osmolarity?
   (a) 0.2 M $CaCl_2$ (b) 0.3 M Na_3PO_4 (c) 0.5 M Na Cl   (d) 0.8 M glucose

5. Which of the following is a colloid?
   (a) wine   (b) maple syrup   (c) milkshake   (d) salad oil

6. How many mL of a 12.0 M HCl solution are needed to make 1.0 L of 0.10 M HCl?
   (a) 120 mL   (b) 83 mL   (c) 50 mL   (d) 8.3 mL

7. Which of the following properties do not depend on the number of particles in solution?
   (a) boiling point elevation   (b) osmotic pressure   (c) heat of solution   (d) freezing point depression

8. How many grams of NaOH are needed to make 300 mL of a 0.3 M solution?
   (a) 40 g   (b) 12 g   (c) 3.6 g   (d) 1.0 g

9. How many moles of glucose are present in 250 mL of a 0.25 M solution?
   (a) 0.0625 mol   (b) 0.1 mol   (c) 0.25 mol   (d) 1.0 mol

10. How many mL of a 0.20 M solution of NaF contain 2.1 g of NaF?
    (a) 500 mL   (b) 250 mL   (c) 100 mL   (d) 50 mL

Complete the following sentences:

1. Two liquids soluble in each other are said to be _____.

2. An _____ is the amount of an ion in grams that contains Avogadro's number of charges.

3. A weight/volume solution can be made up in a piece of glassware called a _____ _____.

4. According to Henry's law, the _____ of a gas varies with its _____ _____.

5. Two solutions that have the same osmolarity are _____.

6. Compounds that attract water from the atmosphere are called _____.

7. The formula used for calculating dilutions is _____.

8. Milk is an example of a _____.

9. _____ and _____ _____ _____ can pass through a dialysis membrane.

10. A solution that has reached its solubility limit is said to be _____.

11. An example of a nonelectrolyte is _____.

12. A solution that is hypotonic with respect to blood has a _____ osmolarity than blood plasma.

Tell whether the following statements are true or false:

1. A solute is the liquid used to dissolve a substance.

2. It is possible to have a solution of a solid in a solid.

3. In making a volume/volume percent solution, one liquid is added to 100 mL of the other liquid.

4. All ionic compounds are soluble in water.

5. A solution of 0.10 M Na_3PO_4 has a greater osmolarity than a solution of 0.15 M NaCl.

6. Weight/weight percent is a useful way to express concentration.

7. In carrying out a dilution, the number of moles of solute remains constant.

8. The solubility of most substances increases with temperature.

9. A colloid differs from a solution in its ability to transmit light.

10. A blood cell undergoes crenation when placed in distilled water.

11. Particles dissolved in water lower the boiling point of water.

12. The amount of gas dissolved in a liquid increases with increasing pressure.

Match the entries on the left with their partners on the right.

1. Osmotic membrane

(a) Muddy water

2. V_1/V_2

(b) Molarity x number of particles

3. Solution

(c) Conducts electricity in water

4. Equivalent

(d) Vinegar

5. Suspension

(e) Crystalline compound that holds water

6. Dialysis membrane

(f) Dilution factor

7. Osmolarity

(g) Butter

8. Hypotonic

(h) Permeable only to water

9. Colloid

(i) A solution of lower osmolarity than another

10. Crenation

(j) Formula weight / number of charges

11. Hydrate

(k) Permeable to water and small molecules

12. Electrolyte

(l) Happens to cell in hypertonic solution

Chapter 10 – Acids and Bases

Chapter Outline

I. Introduction to acids and bases (Sections 10.1–10.4).
  A. Definition of acids and bases (Sections 10.1, 10.3).
    1. Arrhenius definition (Section 10.1).
      a. Acids donate H^+ ions in solution.
      b. Bases donate OH^- ions in solution.
      c. Acid + base —> salt + H_2O.
    2. Brønsted–Lowry definition (Section 10.3).
      a. A Brønsted–Lowry acid is a proton donor (an H_3O^+ donor).
        Some acids can donate more than one proton.
      b. A Brønsted–Lowry base is a proton acceptor.
        The base may be negatively charged or neutral.
      c. An acid–base reaction is one in which a proton is transferred.
      d. Products of acid–base reactions are also acids and bases.
        In the reaction $HA + B: \longrightarrow A^- + BH^+$
        i. HA and A^- are an acid–conjugate base pair.
        ii. B: and BH^+ are a base–conjugate acid pair.
  B. Many common substances are acids or bases (Section 10.2).
  C. Water as acid and a base (Section 10.4).
    1. Water can act both as an acid and a base.
    2. Substances that can act as both acids and bases are amphoteric.
II. Common acid–base reactions (Section 10.5).
  A. Acid + hydroxide ion —> water + salt
  B. Acid + carbonate or bicarbonate —> water + salt + CO_2
  C. Acid + ammonia —> ammonium salt
III. Acid / base strength (Sections 10.6–10.11).
  A. Strong / weak acids and bases (Section 10.6).
    1. Strong acids and bases are 100% dissociated in water.
    2. Weak acids and bases are less than 100% dissociated in solution.
    3. The stronger the acid, the weaker the conjugate base.
      The weaker the acid, the stronger the conjugate base.
    4. An acid–base proton transfer always favors formation of the weaker acid.
  B. Acid dissociation constants (Section 10.7).
    1. K_a is a measure of the degree to which an acid HA dissociates to H_3O^+ and A^-.
    2. K_a values for weak acids are much less than 1.
    3. Donation of each successive H^+ ion from a polyprotic acid becomes successively more difficult.
    4. Most organic acids have K_a near 10^{-5}.
  C Dissociation of H_2O (Section 10.8).
    1. $K_w = [H_3O^+][OH^-] = 1.00 \times 10^{-14}$ at 25°C.
    2. This relationship is true for any aqueous solution.
    3. Thus, we can calculate $[H_3O^+]$ or $[OH^-]$ for any aqueous solution.
  D. Measuring acidity (Sections 10.9–10.11).
    1. pH (Sections 10.9–10.10).
      a. A pH of < 7 indicates acidity; a pH of > 7 indicates basicity.
      b. pH is the negative logarithm of $[H_3O^+]$.
      c. The pH scale is logarithmic.
      d. pH can be computed with a calculator.

2. In the laboratory, pH can be measured with indicators or a pH meter (Section 10.11).
IV. Buffers (Sections 10.12–10.13).
    A. Characteristics of buffers (Section 10.12).
        1. A buffer is the solution of a weak acid and its salt (or a weak base and its salt) at similar concentration.
        2. When a small amount of acid or base is added to a buffered solution, pH changes very little.
        3. The effective pH range of a buffer solution is determined by the K_a of the acid or base.
            a. A buffer solution works best when [HA] is close in value to [A$^-$].
            b. A buffer solution works best when [HA] and [A$^-$] are approximately ten times greater than the amount of acid or base added.
    B. Buffers in the body (Section 10.13).
        1. The carbonate / bicarbonate buffer system is the major regulator of the pH of body fluids.
            a. An increase of [CO_2] makes blood more acidic.
            b. A decrease in [CO_2] makes blood less acidic.
            c. The acidity of blood is regulated by:
                i. A reservoir of excess HCO_3^- that keeps pH fluctuations small.
                ii Change of breathing rate.
                iii. The kidneys.
            d. This regulation prevents alkalosis (pH greater than 7.45) and acidosis (pH lower than 7.35).
        2. The phosphate system and proteins are two other buffer systems in the body.
V. Equivalents of acids and bases (Sections 10.14–10.15).
    A. Normality (Section 10.14).
        1. An equivalent of acid or base $= \dfrac{\text{molar mass}}{\text{\# of } H^+ \text{ or } OH^- \text{ produced}}$.
        2. One equivalent of acid neutralizes one equivalent of base.
        3. Normality $= \dfrac{\text{equivalents of acid or base}}{\text{liters of solution}}$.
        4. Normality = (molarity of acid or base) x (# of H^+ or OH^- produced).
    B. Titration (Section 10.15).
        1. Titration is used to determine the acid or base concentration of a solution.
        2. In titration, a known volume of a solution of unknown acid or base concentration completely reacts with a solution of known concentration.
        3. The volume of solution of known concentration is measured, and the concentration of the unknown is calculated.
VI. Acidity and basicity of salt solutions (Section 10.16).
    A. The salt of a strong base and a strong acid is neutral in solution.
    B. The salt of a strong base and a weak acid is basic in solution.
    C. The salt of a weak base and a strong acid is acidic in solution.
    D. The pH of the salt of a weak base and a weak acid can be predicted only if K_a values are known.

Solutions to Chapter 10 Problems

10.1   HCOOH (a) and H_2S (b) are Brønsted–Lowry acids because they have protons to donate.

10.2 SO_3^{2-} (a) and F^- (c) are Brønsted–Lowry bases because they can be proton acceptors.

10.3   (a) The conjugate acid of HS^- is H_2S.
    (b) The conjugate acid of PO_4^{3-} is HPO_4^{2-}.
    (c) The conjugate base of H_2CO_3 is HCO_3^-.
    (d) The conjugate base of NH_4^+ is NH_3.

10.4   Water acts as an acid when it reacts to form OH^-; water acts as a base when it reacts to form H_3O^+.

Water as an acid: (b) $F^-(aq) + H_2O(l) \rightleftharpoons HF(aq) + OH^-(aq)$

Water as a base: (a) $H_3PO_4(aq) + H_2O(l) \rightleftharpoons H_2PO_4^-(aq) + H_3O^+(aq)$

(c) $NH_4^+(aq) + H_2O(l) \rightleftharpoons H_3O^+(aq) + NH_3(aq)$

10.5 $3\,HCl(aq) + Al(OH)_3(aq) \longrightarrow 3\,H_2O(l) + AlCl_3(aq)$

$2\,HCl(aq) + Mg(OH)_2(aq) \longrightarrow 2\,H_2O(l) + MgCl_2(aq)$

10.6   (a) $2\,KHCO_3(aq) + H_2SO_4(aq) \longrightarrow 2\,H_2O(l) + 2\,CO_2(g) + K_2SO_4(aq)$

(b) $MgCO_3(aq) + 2\,HNO_3(aq) \longrightarrow H_2O(l) + CO_2(g) + Mg(NO_3)_2(aq)$

10.7 $H_2SO_4(aq) + 2\,NH_3(aq) \longrightarrow (NH_4)_2SO_4(aq)$

10.8

10.9   In Table 10.1, the stronger acid is listed *higher* in the table than the weaker acid.

Stronger acids: (a) NH_4^+ (b) H_2SO_4 (c) H_2CO_3

10.10 In Table 10.1, the stronger base is listed *lower* in the table than the weaker base.

Stronger bases: (a) F^- (b) OH^-

10.11 $HPO_4^{2-}(aq) + OH^-(aq) \rightleftharpoons PO_4^{3-}(aq) + H_2O(l)$
    acid   base   conjugate base   conjugate acid

From Table 10.1, we see that OH^- is a stronger base than PO_4^{3-} and that HPO_4^{2-} is a stronger acid than H_2O. Thus, the forward direction of the equilibrium is favored.

$HPO_4^{2-}(aq) + OH^-(aq) \rightleftharpoons PO_4^{3-}(aq) + H_2O(l)$
stronger acid   stronger base   weaker base   weaker acid

10.12 (a) Beer is slightly acidic. Since $10^{-14} = [H_3O^+][OH^-]$,

$$[OH^-] = \frac{K_w}{[H_3O^+]} = \frac{1.0 \times 10^{-14}}{3.2 \times 10^{-5}} = 3.1 \times 10^{-10} \text{ M}$$

(b) Ammonia is basic.

$$[OH^-] = \frac{K_w}{[H_3O^+]} = \frac{1.0 \times 10^{-14}}{3.1 \times 10^{-12}} = 3.2 \times 10^{-3} \text{ M}$$

10.13 (a) If $[H_3O^+] = 1 \times 10^{-5}$ M, then pH = 5.

(b) If $[OH^-] = 1 \times 10^{-9}$ M, then

$$[H_3O^+] = \frac{1 \times 10^{-14}}{1 \times 10^{-9}} = 1 \times 10^{-5} \text{ M ; pH} = 5$$

10.14 (a) For pH = 13, $[H_3O^+] = 1 \times 10^{-13}$ M
(b) For pH = 3, $[H_3O^+] = 1 \times 10^{-3}$ M
(c) For pH = 8, $[H_3O^+] = 1 \times 10^{-8}$ M

The solution of pH = 3 is most acidic, and the solution of pH = 13 is most basic.

10.15–10.16

Solution	pH	Acidic/Basic	$[H_3O^+]$
(a) Saliva	6.5	acidic	3×10^{-7} M
(b) Pancreatic juice	7.9	basic	1×10^{-8} M
(c) Orange juice	3.7	acidic	2×10^{-4} M
(d) Wine	3.5	acidic	3×10^{-4} M

| Pancreatic juice | Saliva | Orange juice | Wine |

Least acidic ────────────────────────────▶ Most acidic

10.17 Use a calculator to determine pH.

(a) $[H_3O^+] = 5.3 \times 10^{-9}$ mol/L: pH = 8.28
(b) $[H_3O^+] = 8.9 \times 10^{-6}$ mol/L: pH = 5.05

10.18 Refer to Solved Problems 10.9 and 10.10 in the text.
When 0.020 mol of HNO_3 is added, the HF concentration increases from 0.100 M to 0.120 M, and the F^- decreases from 0.100 M to 0.080 M because of the reaction:

$$F^-(aq) + HNO_3(aq) \longrightarrow HF(aq) + NO_3^-(aq)$$

$$[H_3O^+] = K_a \frac{[HA]}{[A^-]} = (3.5 \times 10^{-4})\frac{[0.120]}{[0.080]} = 5.2 \times 10^{-4} \text{ M}$$

$$pH = -\log(5.2 \times 10^{-4}) = 3.28$$

10.19

$$\left[H_3O^+\right] = K_a\frac{[HA]}{\left[A^-\right]} = \left(1.8 \times 10^{-4}\right)\frac{[0.050]}{[0.060]} = 1.5 \times 10^{-4}\ M$$

$$pH = -\log(1.5 \times 10^{-4}) = 3.82$$

10.20 If a small amount of extra base is added to a mixture of HCl and NaCl, the base is neutralized to form H_2O, and the pH of the solution changes slightly. If extra acid is added, however, it can't be neutralized because Cl^- is too weak a base. Thus, the HCl – NaCl system is a poor buffer. As we have seen in Problem 10.18 and Solved Problem 10.10, however, a small amount of added acid or added base changes the pH of the HF / NaF buffer system only slightly. Thus, the system of the weak acid HF and its conjugate base F^- is an effective buffer.

10.21–10.22

Sample	Mass	Molar Mass	# of Ions	Equivalent Mass	# of Eq	Normality of 300.0 mL
(a) HNO_3	5.0 g	63.0 g	1	63.0 g	0.079	0.26 N
(b) $Ca(OH)_2$	12.5 g	74.1 g	2	37.0 g	0.338	1.13 N
(c) H_3PO_4	4.5 g	98.0 g	3	32.7 g	0.14	0.47 N

The "number of ions" refers to the number of H^+ or OH^- ions produced for each mole of acid or base in solution

10.23 (a)

$$37\ \text{mL HCl} \times \frac{1\ L}{1000\ \text{mL}} \times \frac{0.50\ \text{mol HCl}}{1\ \text{L HCl}} = 0.019\ \text{mol HCl}$$

Since HCl produces only one H^+ ion, there are also 0.019 Eq (or 19 mEq) of HCl in 37 mL of 0.50 N solution.

(b) One Eq of OH^- ion neutralizes one Eq of H^+, and thus 19 mEq of NaOH will neutralize the 19 mEq of HCl from part (a).

10.24 First, write the balanced equation for the neutralization reaction:

$$HCl(aq) + NaOH(aq) \longrightarrow H_2O(l) + NaCl(aq)$$

We see from this equation that one mole of base is needed to neutralize each mole of acid.

$$\text{Moles HCl} = 58.4\ \text{mL} \times \frac{0.250\ \text{mol NaOH}}{1\ L} \times \frac{1\ L}{1000\ \text{mL}} \times \frac{1\ \text{mol HCl}}{1\ \text{mol NaOH}}$$

$$= 0.0146\ \text{mol HCl}$$

$$\frac{0.0146\ \text{mol HCl}}{20.0\ \text{mL}} \times \frac{1000\ \text{mL}}{1\ L} = 0.730\ M\ HCl$$

10.25 $2 \, NaOH(aq) \; + \; H_2SO_4(aq) \; \longrightarrow \; 2 \, H_2O(l) \; + \; Na_2SO_4(aq)$

Notice that two moles of base are needed to neutralize one mole of acid.

$$\text{Moles NaOH} \; = \; 50.0 \, mL \; \times \; \frac{0.200 \, mol \, H_2SO_4}{1 \, L} \; \times \; \frac{1 \, L}{1000 \, mL} \; \times \; \frac{2 \, mol \, NaOH}{1 \, mol \, H_2SO_4}$$

$$= \; 0.0200 \, mol \, NaOH$$

$$0.0200 \, mol \, NaOH \; \times \; \frac{1 \, L}{0.150 \, mol} \; = \; 0.133 \, L \, NaOH \; = \; 133 \, mL \, NaOH$$

10.26 $2 \, KOH(aq) \; + \; H_2SO_4(aq) \; \longrightarrow \; 2 \, H_2O(l) \; + \; Na_2SO_4(aq)$

$$16.1 \, mL \; \times \; \frac{1 \, L}{1000 \, mL} \; \times \; \frac{0.150 \, mol}{1 \, L} \; = \; 0.002 \, 42 \, mol \, H_2SO_4$$

From the equation, we see that one mol of H_2SO_4 neutralizes two mol of NaOH. Thus, 0.002 42 mol of H_2SO_4 neutralizes 0.004 84 mol of KOH.

$$\frac{0.004 \, 84 \, mol}{0.0215 \, L} \; = \; 0.225 \, M \, KOH$$

10.27 The salt of a weak acid and a strong base produces a basic solution; the salt of a strong acid and a weak base produces an acidic solution. Of the salts listed, only Na_2HPO_4 (b) and MgF_2 (c) produce a basic solution.

10.28 Only NH_4Br (d) produces an acidic solution.

Understanding Key Concepts

10.29

(a)

$$HCO_3^- \; + \; H_2O \; \longrightarrow \; CO_3^{2-} \; + \; H_3O^+$$

$\quad$ acid $\qquad$ base $\qquad\qquad$ base $\qquad$ acid

(b)

$$HCO_3^- \; + \; HF \; \longrightarrow \; H_2CO_3 \; + \; F^-$$

$\quad$ base $\qquad$ acid $\qquad\qquad$ acid $\qquad$ base

10.30 (a) The reaction of HF with OH^- is represented by outcome (2). One OH^- reacts with each HF to produce 3 F^- anions, and 9 OH^- anions are left over.
(b) The reaction of H_2SO_3 with OH^- is represented by outcome (3). Two OH^- ions react with each H_2SO_3 molecule to produce 3 SO_3^{2-} anions, and 6 OH^- anions are left over.
(c) The reaction of H_3PO_4 with OH^- is represented by outcome (1). Three OH^- anions react with each H_3PO_4 molecule to produce 3 PO_4^{3-} anions, and 3 OH^- anions are left over.

10.31 (a) The acid in the first picture is the weakest because it is the least dissociated.
(b) The acid in the second picture is the strongest acid because all molecules of the acid are dissociated
(c) The acid in the first picture has the smallest value of K_a because it is the weakest acid.

10.32 (a) Picture (c) represents a weak diprotic acid, which has dissociated slightly to form the HA^- anion.
(b) Picture (a) represents an impossible situation. H_2A dissociates stepwise to form HA^-. Only when virtually all H_2A has dissociated to form HA^- is A^{2-} formed by dissociation of HA^-.

10.33 The titration reaction uses up 2/3 of the 1.0 M solution in the buret. Since the solution in the buret is 1.0 M, the solution in the flask must be 0.67 M.

Acids and Bases

10.34 In water, HBr dissociates almost completely. Water acts as a base to accept a proton, and a solution of H_3O^+ and Br^- results.

10.36 In water, KOH dissociates completely to yield K^+ and OH^- ions.

10.38 A monoprotic acid, such as HCl, has only one proton to donate, whereas a diprotic acid, such as H_2SO_4, has two protons to donate.

10.40 Strong acids: (a) $HClO_4$ (e) HI

Brønsted–Lowry Acids and Bases

10.42 Brønsted–Lowry acids: (a) HCN (d) H_2CO_3 (f) $CH_3NH_3^+$
Brønsted–Lowry bases: (b) $CH_3CO_2^-$
Neither: (c) $AlCl_3$ (e) Mg^{2+}

10.44

| Base | (a) CH_2ClCOO^- | (b) C_5H_5N | (c) SeO_4^{2-} | (d) $(CH_3)_3N$ |
| Conjugate acid | $CH_2ClCOOH$ | $C_5H_5NH^+$ | $HSeO_4^-$ | $(CH_3)_3NH^+$ |

10.46 $HCO_3^-(aq) + HCl(aq) \longrightarrow H_2O(l) + CO_2(g) + Cl^-(aq)$

$HCO_3^-(aq) + NaOH(aq) \longrightarrow H_2O(l) + Na^+(aq) + CO_3^{2-}(aq)$

$H_2PO_4^-(aq) + HCl(aq) \longrightarrow H_3PO_4(aq) + Cl^-(aq)$

$H_2PO_4^-(aq) + NaOH(aq) \longrightarrow HPO_4^{2-}(aq) + H_2O(l) + Na^+(aq)$

10.48 $2 HCl(aq) + CaCO_3(s) \longrightarrow H_2O(l) + CO_2(g) + CaCl_2(aq)$

Acid and Base Strength: K_a and pH

10.50 For the reaction: $HA(aq) + H_2O(l) \rightleftharpoons H_3O^+(l) + A^-(aq)$

$$K = \frac{[H_3O^+][A^-]}{[HA][H_2O]}$$

Since $[H_2O]$ is constant, we define a new constant:

$$K_a = K[H_2O] = \frac{[H_3O^+][A^-]}{[HA]}$$

10.52 K_w is the product of the molar concentrations of H_3O^+ and OH^- in any aqueous solution and is numerically equal to 1.0×10^{-14} at 25°C.

$$K_a = \frac{[H_3O^+][OH^-]}{[H_2O]}; \quad K_a[H_2O] = K_w = [H_3O^+][OH^-]$$

10.54 $NH_4^+(aq) + H_2O(l) \rightleftharpoons NH_3(g) + H_3O^+(aq)$

$$K_a = \frac{[H_3O^+][NH_3]}{[NH_4^+]}$$

10.56 (a) HF is slightly stronger.   (b) HSO_4^- is a stronger acid.
(c) $H_2PO_4^-$ is a stronger acid.   (d) CH_3COOH is slightly stronger.

10.58 Urine (pH = 7.9) is weakly basic, since a solution with a pH greater than 7.0 is basic.

10.60 The concentration of HCl in gastric juice is 1×10^{-2} M.

10.62 $[H_3O^+] = 10^{-pH}$. Since in this problem, $[H_3O^+] = 0.10$ M $= 1.0 \times 10^{-1}$ M, the pH = 1.00.

10.64

	$[H_3O^+]$	pH
(a) Egg white	2.5×10^{-8} M	7.60
(b) Apple cider	5.0×10^{-4} M	3.30
(c) Ammonia	2.3×10^{-12} M	11.64

Ammonia is least acidic and apple cider is most acidic.

10.66 (a) $[OH^-] = 1 \times 10^{-10}$ M   (b) $[OH^-] = 1 \times 10^{-3}$ M
(c) $[OH^-] = 1 \times 10^{-14}$ M   (d) $[OH^-] = 2.4 \times 10^{-13}$ M
(e) $[OH^-] = 9.1 \times 10^{-7}$ M

Buffers

10.68 A buffer is composed of a weak acid and its conjugate base. Any added H_3O^+ can react with the conjugate base and be neutralized, and any added OH^- can react with the acid. In either case, the ratio of acid to conjugate base changes only slightly, and the pH of a buffered solution remains nearly constant.

10.70 $CH_3COO^- Na^+(aq) + HNO_3(aq) \longrightarrow CH_3COOH(aq) + NaNO_3(aq)$.
The added acid is neutralized by sodium acetate.

$CH_3COOH(aq) + OH^-(aq) \longrightarrow CH_3COO^-(aq) + H_2O(l)$
The added base is neutralized by acetic acid.

10.72

$$[H_3O^+] = \frac{K_a[HA]}{[A^-]} \; ; \; K_a = 4.9 \times 10^{-10}, [HCN] = 0.200 \text{ M}, [CN^-] = 0.150 \text{ M}$$

$$[H_3O^+] = \frac{4.9 \times 10^{-10}[0.200 \text{ M}]}{[0.150 \text{ M}]} = 6.5 \times 10^{-10} \text{ M}; \; pH = 9.19$$

Concentrations of Acid and Base Solutions

10.74 An equivalent of an acid or base is its formula weight in grams divided by the number of H_3O^+ or OH^- ions it produces.

10.76 The number of equivalents is equal to the number of moles times the number of H^+ or OH^- ions produced. In this problem, we first find the number of moles of each acid and then multiply by the number of H^+ ions produced.

For HNO_3 : $0.500 \text{ L} \times \dfrac{0.50 \text{ mol H}^+}{1 \text{ L}} \times \dfrac{1 \text{ Eq}}{1 \text{ mol}} = 0.25 \text{ Eq H}^+$

For H_3PO_4 : $0.500 \text{ L} \times \dfrac{0.50 \text{ mol H}^+}{1 \text{ L}} \times \dfrac{3 \text{ Eq}}{1 \text{ mol}} = 0.75 \text{ Eq H}^+$

10.78 Since a 0.0050 N solution of any acid has 0.0050 equivalents per liter, 25 mL of a 0.0050 N KOH solution is needed to neutralize 25 mL of either 0.0050 N H_2SO_4 or 0.0050 N HCl.

10.80 The molarity of an acid solution is equal to normality divided by the number of H^+ ions produced. Thus:

$\dfrac{0.10 \text{ N H}_3PO_4}{3} = 0.033 \text{ M H}_3PO_4$

10.82 (a) $0.25 \text{ mol Mg(OH)}_2 \times 2 \text{ Eq/mol} = 0.50 \text{ Eq Mg(OH)}_2$

(b) Molar mass of $Mg(OH)_2 = 58.3 \text{ g}$; $1 \text{ Eq Mg(OH)}_2 = 29.6 \text{ g}$

$2.5 \text{ g Mg(OH)}_2 \times \dfrac{1 \text{ Eq}}{29.6 \text{ g}} = 0.084 \text{ Eq Mg(OH)}_2$

(c) Molar mass of $CH_3COOH = 60.0 \text{ g}$; $1 \text{ Eq CH}_3COOH = 60.0 \text{ g}$

$15 \text{ g CH}_3COOH \times \dfrac{1 \text{ Eq}}{60 \text{ g}} = 0.25 \text{ Eq CH}_3COOH$

10.84 Molar mass of $Ca(OH)_2 = 74.1$ g; 1 Eq $Ca(OH)_2 = 37.0$ g

$$\frac{5.0 \text{ g}}{0.400 \text{ L}} \times \frac{1 \text{ mol}}{74.1 \text{ g}} = 0.17 \text{ M}; \quad \frac{0.17 \text{ mol}}{1 \text{ L}} \times \frac{2 \text{ Eq}}{1 \text{ mol}} = \frac{0.34 \text{ Eq}}{1 \text{ L}} = 0.34 \text{ N}$$

10.86 $2 \text{ KOH}(aq) + H_2SO_4(aq) \longrightarrow 2 \text{ H}_2O(l) + K_2SO_4(aq)$

$[H_2SO_4] = 0.0250 \text{ M} = 0.0500 \text{ N}$

$V_1 \times N_1 = V_2 \times N_2$; $V_1 = 15.0 \text{ mL}$; $N_1 = 0.0500 \text{ N}$; $V_2 = 10.0 \text{ mL}$

$$N_2 = \frac{V_1 \times N_1}{V_2} = \frac{15.0 \text{ mL} \times 0.0500 \text{ N}}{10.0 \text{ mL}} = 0.075 \text{ N} = 0.075 \text{ M KOH}$$

Applications

10.88 (a) $\text{NaAl(OH)}_2CO_3(aq) + 4 \text{ HCl}(aq) \longrightarrow$
$CO_2(g) + 3 \text{ H}_2O(l) + \text{NaCl}(aq) + \text{AlCl}_3(aq)$

(b) Molar mass of $\text{NaAl(OH)}_2CO_3(aq) = 144$ g/mol

$$\frac{0.0955 \text{ mol HCl}}{1 \text{ L}} \times 0.0150 \text{ L} = 0.001\,43 \text{ mol HCl}$$

$$0.001\,43 \text{ mol HCl} \times \frac{1 \text{ mol antacid}}{4 \text{ mol HCl}} \times \frac{144 \text{ g}}{1 \text{ mol antacid}} = 0.0515 \text{ g} = 51.5 \text{ mg}$$

10.90 pH of acid rain = 5.6; $[H_3O^+] = 2 \times 10^{-6}$ M

General Questions and Problems

10.92 Citric acid reacts with sodium bicarbonate to release CO_2 bubbles:
$C_6H_5O_7H_3(aq) + 3 \text{ NaHCO}_3(aq) \longrightarrow C_6H_5O_7Na_3(aq) + 3 \text{ H}_2O(l) + 3 \text{ CO}_2(g)$

Sodium bicarbonate is the antacid.

10.94 The concentrations of H_3O^+ and OH^- ions are too low for pure water to conduct electricity.

10.96 If aspirin were a strong acid, the H_3O^+ concentration of a 0.010 M solution would be nearly 0.010 M, or 10^{-2} M, and the pH of the solution would be around 2. Since the observed pH is 3.3, aspirin must be a weak acid.

10.98 $2 \text{ HCl}(aq) + Ca(OH)_2(aq) \longrightarrow 2 \text{ H}_2O(l) + CaCl_2(aq)$

$V_1 \times N_1 = V_2 \times N_2$; $V_1 = 140 \text{ mL}$; $N_1 = 0.15 \text{ N}$; $V_2 = 30.0 \text{ mL}$

$$N_2 = \frac{V_1 \times N_1}{V_2} = \frac{140 \text{ mL} \times 0.15 \text{ N}}{30.0 \text{ mL}} = 0.70 \text{ N Ca(OH)}_2$$

$$= 0.35 \text{ M Ca(OH)}_2$$

10.100   (a) $NH_4^+(aq)$ + $OH^-(aq)$ $\longrightarrow$ $NH_3(g)$ + $H_2O(l)$
          acid   base   conjugate base   conjugate acid

(b) $PV = nRT$; $P = 755$ mm Hg; $V = 2.86$ L; $T = 333$ K; $R = \dfrac{62.3 \text{ mm Hg·L}}{\text{mol·K}}$

$$n = \frac{PV}{RT} = \frac{755 \text{ mm} \times 2.86 \text{ L}}{\dfrac{62.3 \text{ mm Hg·L}}{\text{mol·K}} \times 333 \text{ K}} = 0.104 \text{ mol } NH_3$$

0.104 mol $\times \dfrac{53.5 \text{ g}}{1 \text{ mol}} = 5.56$ g NH_4Cl

Self-Test for Chapter 10

Multiple choice:

1. What volume of 0.10 M H_2SO_4 will neutralize 30 mL of 0.05 M $Ca(OH)_2$?
    (a) 30 mL   (b) 15 mL   (c) 10 mL   (d) 6.0 mL

2. Which of the following salts is acidic in solution?
    (a) NH_4Br (b) $NaBr$ (c) NH_4CN (d) $NaCN$

3. KCN is the salt of a:
    (a) strong acid and strong base   (b) strong acid and weak base   (c) weak acid and strong base
    (d) weak acid and weak base

4. A solution has a pH of 9. What is the value of $[OH^-]$?
    (a) 5   (b) 10^{-9} (c) 9   (d) 10^{-5}

5. Which of the following is a diprotic acid?
    (a) CH_3COOH (b) $Ba(OH)_2$ (c) H_2SO_3 (d) H_3PO_4

6. Look at Table 10.2 and decide which base is a weaker base than F^-:
    (a) $H_2PO_4^-$ (b) HCO_3^- (c) CN^- (d) NH_3

7. Which of the following substances turns phenolphthalein red?
    (a) urine   (b) milk of magnesia   (c) blood   (d) coffee

8. Which of the following bases is an Arrhenius base?
    (a) NaOH   (b) $Ca_3(PO_4)_2$ (c) NH_3 (d) LiF

9. In the reaction $Mg(OH)_2(aq)$ + 2 $HBr(aq) \longrightarrow 2$ $H_2O(l)$ + $MgBr_2(aq)$ what is the conjugate acid of $Mg(OH)_2$?
    (a) HBr   (b) H_2O (c) $MgBr_2$ (d) can't tell

10. How many water molecules are produced in the neutralization reaction of
    H_3PO_4 + $Mg(OH)_2$?
    (a) 2   (b) 3   (c) 4   (d) 6

Complete the following sentences:

1. One _____ of an acid reacts with one _____ of a base.

2. Phenolphthalein turns _____ in basic solution.

3. H_2CO_3 is a _____ acid.

4. The anion of a weak acid is a _____ base.

5. _____ is the splitting apart of an acid into a proton and an anion.

6. An Arrhenius base yields _____ when dissolved in water.

7. _____ is the reaction of an acid with a base.

8. _____ is the measure of a solution's acidity.

9. To completely neutralize 10.0 mL of 1.0 M H_3PO_4, you need _____ mL of 1.0 M NaOH.

10. CH_3COOH and CH_3COO^- are known as a _____ acid–base pair.

11. The buffer system of blood is the _____ / _____ system.

12. Substances that can act as either acids or bases are _____.

Tell whether the following statements are true or false:

1. 30.0 mL of 0.10 M H_2SO_4 is neutralized by 30.0 mL of 0.10 M NaOH.

2. A change of one pH unit is a tenfold change in $[H_3O^+]$.

3. H_2SO_4 / HSO_4^- is a good buffer system.

4. All bases are negatively charged.

5. Bicarbonate ion neutralizes more acid than carbonate ion.

6. If the pH of a solution is 7.0, $[OH^-] = 10^{-7}$.

7. Water can act as both an acid and a base.

8. According to the Brønsted definition, an acid is a substance that dissolves in water to give H_3O^+ ions.

9. Ammonia reacts with an acid to yield ammonium hydroxide.

10. Whether an acid or a base is strong or weak depends on its percent dissociation in water.

11. The reaction $H_2O + H_2PO_4^- \longrightarrow H_3O^+ + HPO_4^{2-}$ proceeds in the direction written.

12. One equivalent of $Ca(OH)_2$ equals 37 g.

Match the entries on the left with their partners on the right:

1. Strong acid
2. 1 M HCl
3. $[H_3O^+] = 10^{-8}$
4. Alkalosis
5. K_w
6. Weak base
7. Strong base
8. Salt
9. $[H_3O^+] = 10^{-6}$
10. Weak acid
11. 1 M H_3PO_4
12. Acidosis

(a) $[H_3O^+] [OH^-]$
(b) Cl^-
(c) pH = 6
(d) HCl
(e) 1 N acid
(f) CH_3COOH
(g) $[OH^-] = 10^{-6}$
(h) Blood pH lower than 7.35
(i) CH_3COO^-
(j) Na_2SO_4
(k) 3 N acid
(l) Blood pH higher than 7.35

Chapter 11 – Nuclear Chemistry

Chapter Outline

I. Introduction to radioactivity (Sections 11.1–11.3)
   A Nuclear reactions (Section 11.1).
      1. A nuclear reaction occurs when a nuclide spontaneously changes to a different nuclide.
      2. Nuclear reactions differ from chemical reactions in several ways.
         a. Nuclear reactions produce different elements.
         b. Different isotopes have the same behavior in chemical reactions but different behavior in nuclear reactions.
         c. The rate of a nuclear reaction is unaffected by a change in temperature.
         d. A nuclear reaction is the same whether an atom is in a compound or is elemental.
         e. The energy change in a nuclear reaction is immense.
   B. The discovery and nature of radioactivity (Section 11.2).
      1. Radioactivity was discovered by Becquerel and the Curies.
      2. Three types of radiation may be emitted:
         a. α radiation: He^{2+} nuclei with low penetrating power.
         b. β radiation: electrons (e^-) with medium penetrating power.
         c γ radiation: high energy light waves with very high penetrating power.
   C. Stable and unstable isotopes (Section 11.3).
      1. All elements have radioactive isotopes.
      2. Other radioisotopes are made in particle accelerators: these are known as artificial radioisotopes.
      3. Radioisotopes have the same chemical properties as their nonradioactive isotopes.
II. Nuclear decay (Sections 11.4–11.7).
   A. Nuclear emissions (Section 11.4)
      1. Alpha emission.
         After α emission, the atomic number of the resulting isotope decreases by 2, and the mass number decreases by 4.
      2. Beta emission.
         a. In β emission, a neutron decomposes to a proton and an electron.
         b. The electron is emitted, and the proton is retained.
         c. The atomic number of the resulting isotope increases by 1, and the mass number is unchanged.
      3. Gamma (γ) emission.
         Gamma (γ) emission usually accompanies α or β emission and doesn't affect either mass number or atomic number.
      4. Positron emission.
         a. Positron emission occurs when a proton is converted to a neutron and an ejected positron (positive electron).
         b. Positron emission changes the atomic number of a nucleus but does not change the mass number.
   B. Half-life (Section 11.5).
      1. Half-life is the amount of time it takes for half of a sample of a radioisotope to decay.
      2. Half-life doesn't depend on the amount of sample or on temperature.
      3. Each half-life sees the decay of half of what remains of the sample.
   C. Radioactive decay series (Section 11.6).
      Some heavy radioisotopes undergo a series of disintegrations until a nonradioactive product is reached.

D. Ionizing radiation (Section 11.7).
   1. Ionizing radiation is any high-energy radiation that can create reactive ions when it collides with a chemical compound.
   2. Ionizing radiation can injure the body.
      a. Gamma and X radiation are more harmful when radiation comes from outside the body.
      b. Alpha and β radiation are more dangerous when emitted from within the body.
   3. The intensity of radiation decreases with the square of the distance from the source.
III. Detecting radiation (Sections 11.8–11.9).
   A. Devices for detecting radiation (Section 11.8).
      1. Photographic film badges.
      2. Geiger counter.
      3. Scintillation counter.
   B. Units of radiation (Section 11.9).
      1. The *curie* measures the number of disintegrations per second.
      2. The *roentgen* measures the intensity of radiation.
      3. The *rad* measures the energy absorbed per gram tissue.
      4. The *rem* and the *sievert* measure tissue damage.
IV. Artificial transmutation (Section 11.10).
   A. Artificial transmutation occurs when nuclei are bombarded with high energy particles.
   B. After bombardment, a new nucleus is produced.
   C. The transuranium elements were all produced via artificial transmutation.
V. Nuclear fission and nuclear fusion (Section 11.11).
   A. Nuclear fission.
      1. Nuclear fission occurs when a heavy nucleus fragments after bombardment by a small particle, such as a neutron.
      2. Many different fission products can result from one bombardment.
      3. In some cases, bombardment with one neutron can cause production of more than one neutron, in addition to fragmentation.
         a. This is called a chain reaction.
         b. If the bombarded sample weighs more than a critical mass, a nuclear explosion can result.
         c. A controlled fission reaction can be used to produce energy.
   B. Nuclear fusion.
      1. If two light nuclei are made to collide, a nuclear fusion reaction occurs that produces a combined nucleus plus energy.
      2. Nuclear fusion reactions occur in stars.

Solutions to Chapter 11 Problems

11.1 For α emission, subtract 2 from the atomic number of radon and 4 from the mass number:

$$^{222}_{86}Rn \rightarrow {}^{4}_{2}He + {}^{218}_{84}?$$

Then, look in the periodic table for the element with atomic number 84:

$$^{222}_{86}Rn \rightarrow {}^{4}_{2}He + {}^{218}_{84}Po$$

11.2 Add 4 to the mass number of radon (222) to calculate the isotope of radium:

$$^{226}_{88}Ra \rightarrow {}^{4}_{2}He + {}^{222}_{86}Rn$$

11.3

$$^{14}_{6}C \rightarrow {}^{0}_{-1}e + ?$$

The mass number of the product element stays the same, but the atomic number increases by 1, to 7. Looking in the periodic table, we find that ^{14}N is the element formed:

$$^{14}_{6}C \rightarrow {}^{0}_{-1}e + {}^{14}_{7}N$$

11.4

(a) $^{3}_{1}H \rightarrow {}^{0}_{-1}e + {}^{3}_{2}He$ (b) $^{210}_{82}Pb \rightarrow {}^{0}_{-1}e + {}^{210}_{83}Bi$

11.5 $17,000 \div 5715 = 2.97$, or approximately 3 half-lives.

The percentage of $^{14}_{6}C$ is $(1/2) \times (1/2) \times (1/2) \times 100\% = 12.5\%$ of the original sample.

11.6

$$\frac{I_1}{I_2} = \frac{d_2^2}{d_1^2} : I_1 = 250 \text{ units}; I_2 = 25 \text{ units}; d_1^2 = (4.0 \text{ m})^2 = 16 \text{ m}^2$$

$$d_2^2 = \frac{d_1^2 \times I_1}{I_2} = \frac{16 \text{ m}^2 \times 250 \text{ units}}{25 \text{ units}} = 160 \text{ m}^2$$

$$d_2 = 13 \text{ m}$$

11.7

$$\frac{5 \text{ mrem}}{270 \text{ mrem}} \times 100\% = 1.9\%$$

The annual dose of radiation for most people will increase by approximately 2%.

11.8

$$\frac{175 \text{ } \mu Ci}{\text{dose}} \times \frac{1 \text{ mL}}{44 \text{ } \mu Ci} = \frac{4.0 \text{ mL}}{\text{dose}}$$

11.9

$$^{241}_{95}Am \rightarrow {}^{4}_{2}He + {}^{237}_{93}Np$$

11.10

$$^{241}_{95}\text{Am} + ^{4}_{2}\text{He} \rightarrow 2\,^{1}_{0}\text{n} + ^{243}_{97}\text{Bk}$$

11.11

$$^{40}_{18}\text{Ar} + ^{1}_{1}\text{H} \rightarrow ^{1}_{0}\text{n} + ^{40}_{19}\text{K}$$

11.12

$$^{235}_{92}\text{U} + ^{1}_{0}\text{n} \rightarrow 2\,^{1}_{0}\text{n} + ^{137}_{52}\text{Te} + ^{97}_{40}\text{Zr}$$

Understanding Key Concepts

11.13 After one half-life, the sample would consist of eight $^{28}_{13}\text{Al}$ atoms and eight $^{28}_{12}\text{Mg}$ atoms.
After two half-lives, the remaining eight $^{28}_{13}\text{Al}$ atoms would have decayed to four $^{28}_{12}\text{Mg}$ atoms, producing the outcome shown in the picture.

11.14

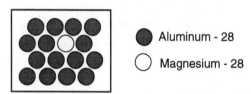

Aluminum - 28

Magnesium - 28

11.15 The illustrated isotope, with six protons and eight neutrons, is $^{14}_{6}\text{C}$.

11.16 The shorter arrows represent β emission because they show the decomposition of a neutron with an accompanying 1 unit increase in atomic number.
The longer arrows represent α emission because they indicate a decay that results in the loss of two protons and two neutrons (α particle).

11.17

$$^{241}_{94}\text{Pu} \rightarrow ^{241}_{95}\text{Am} \rightarrow ^{237}_{93}\text{Np} \rightarrow ^{233}_{91}\text{Pa} \rightarrow ^{233}_{92}\text{U}$$

Radioactivity

11.18 A substance is said to be radioactive if it emits radiation by decay of an unstable nucleus.

11.20

Nuclear Reaction	_Chemical Reaction_
involves change in an atom's nucleus	involves change in an atom's outer shell electrons
usually produces a different element	never produces a different element
different isotopes have different behavior in a nuclear reaction	different isotopes have the same behavior in a chemical reaction
rate is unaffected by a change in temperature or by a catalyst	rate changes with a change in temperature or by using a catalyst
rate is the same, whether the atom is in a compound or uncombined	
energy change is millions of times larger for a nuclear reaction	

11.22 The symbol for an α particle is $_2^4\text{He}$.

11.24 Gamma radiation has the highest penetrating power, and α radiation has the lowest penetrating power.

11.26 Ionizing radiation causes cell damage by breaking bonds in DNA. The resulting damage may lead to mutation, cancer, or cell death.

11.28 A neutron in the nucleus decomposes to a proton and an electron, which is emitted as a β particle.

11.30 If strontium-90 has a half-life of 28.8 years, half of a given quantity of strontium-90 will have decayed after 28.8 years.

Nuclear Decay and Transmutation

11.32 A nuclear equation is balanced if the number of nucleons is the same on both sides and if the sums of the charges on the nuclei and any elementary particles is the same on both sides.

11.34 For an atom emitting an α particle, the atomic number decreases by two, and the mass number decreases by four.
For an atom emitting a β particle, the atomic number increases by one, and the mass number is unchanged.

11.36 In nuclear fission, bombardment of a nucleus causes fragmentation in many different ways to yield a large number of smaller fragments. Normal radioactive decay of a nucleus produces an atom with a similar mass and yields a predictable product.

11.38

(a) $_{16}^{35}\text{S} \rightarrow _{-1}^{0}\text{e} + _{17}^{35}\text{Cl}$ (b) $_{10}^{24}\text{Ne} \rightarrow _{-1}^{0}\text{e} + _{11}^{24}\text{Na}$

(c) $_{38}^{90}\text{Sr} \rightarrow _{-1}^{0}\text{e} + _{39}^{90}\text{Y}$

11.40

(a) $_{55}^{140}\text{Cs} \rightarrow _{-1}^{0}\text{e} + _{56}^{140}\text{Ba}$ (b) $_{96}^{246}\text{Cm} \rightarrow _{2}^{4}\text{He} + _{94}^{242}\text{Pu}$

11.42

(a) $_{92}^{235}\text{U} + _{0}^{1}\text{n} \rightarrow _{62}^{160}\text{Sm} + _{30}^{72}\text{Zn} + 4\,_{0}^{1}\text{n}$

(b) $_{92}^{235}\text{U} + _{0}^{1}\text{n} \rightarrow _{35}^{87}\text{Br} + _{57}^{146}\text{La} + 3\,_{0}^{1}\text{n}$

11.44

$_{80}^{198}\text{Hg} + _{0}^{1}\text{n} \rightarrow _{79}^{198}\text{Au} + _{1}^{1}\text{H}$

A proton is produced in addition to gold-198.

Half-Life

11.46 $365 \div 120 = 3.04$, or approximately 3 half-lives.

$$0.050 \text{ g} \times \frac{1}{2} \times \frac{1}{2} \times \frac{1}{2} = 0.0062 \text{ g}$$

Approximately 0.006 grams of $^{75}_{34}\text{Se}$ will remain after a year.

11.48 If the half-life of mercury–97 is 65 hrs.,
6 days = 144 hrs = approx. 2 half-lives
27 days = 648 hrs = approx. 10 half-lives
5.0 ng x 1/2 x 1/2 = approx. 1 ng of mercury-197 remains after 6 days.
5.0 ng x $(1/2)^{10}$ = approx. 5×10^{-3} ng of mercury-197 remains after 27 days.

Measuring Radioactivity

11.50 The inside walls of a Geiger counter tube are negatively charged, and a wire in the center is positively charged. Radiation ionizes argon gas inside the tube, which creates a conducting path for current between the wall and the wire. The current is detected, and the Geiger counter makes a clicking sound.

11.52 Rems indicate the amount of tissue damage from any type of radiation, and allow comparisons between equivalent doses of different types of radiation to be made.

11.54 (1) curie (c) Number of disintegrations per second
(2) rem (b) Amount of tissue damage
(3) rad (d) Amount of radiation per gram of tissue
(4) roentgen (a) Ionizing intensity of radiation

11.56

$$\frac{I_1}{I_2} = \frac{d_2^2}{d_1^2}; \quad I_1 = 300.0 \text{ rem}; \quad I_2 = 25 \text{ rem}; \quad d_1^2 = (2.0 \text{ m})^2 = 4.0 \text{ m}^2$$

$$d_2^2 = \frac{d_1^2 \times I_1}{I_2} = \frac{4.0 \text{ m}^2 \times 300.0 \text{ rem}}{25 \text{ rem}} = 48 \text{ m}^2$$

$$d_2 = 6.9 \text{ m}$$

Applications

11.58 Radiation therapy is used in cancer treatment because ionizing radiation selectively destroys rapidly dividing cells, such as cancer cells.

11.60 The purpose of food irradiation is to kill harmful microorganisms by exposing food to ionizing radiation, which destroys the genetic material of the microorganisms.

11.62 The body-imaging techniques, CT and PET, are noninvasive and yield a large array of images that can be processed by computer to produce a three-dimensional image of an organ.

11.64 The leather is too new. The age of the leather sample is so much smaller than the half-life of $^{14}CO_2$ that the ratio of ^{14}C to ^{12}C is almost the same as the atmospheric ratio.

General Questions and Problems

11.66 Nuclear reactions occur spontaneously, and no substance can "react with" radioactive emissions to neutralize them.

11.68

(a) $^{99}_{42}Mo \rightarrow ^{0}_{-1}e + ^{99}_{43}Tc$ ^{99}Mo decays to Tc-99m by β emission.

(b) $^{98}_{42}Mo + ^{1}_{0}n \rightarrow ^{99}_{42}Mo$

11.70

(a) $^{238}_{94}Pu \rightarrow ^{4}_{2}He + ^{234}_{92}U$

(b) The metal case serves as a shield to protect the wearer from α radiation.

11.72 Embryos and fetuses are particularly susceptible to the effects of radiation because their cells divide frequently.

11.74

(a) $^{162}_{75}Re \rightarrow ^{4}_{2}He + ^{158}_{73}Ta$ (b) $^{188}_{74}W \rightarrow ^{0}_{-1}e + ^{188}_{75}Re$

11.76

$^{238}_{92}U + ^{1}_{0}n \rightarrow 2^{0}_{-1}e + ^{239}_{94}Pu$

11.78

$^{232}_{90}Th \rightarrow ^{208}_{82}Pb + 6^{4}_{2}He + 4^{0}_{-1}e$

The 24 amu loss in mass in going from $^{232}_{90}Th$ to $^{208}_{82}Pb$ is due to the emission of 6 α particles, which also account for the reduction in atomic number from 90 to 78. The emission of 4 β particles increases the atomic number from 78 to 82 and yields $^{208}_{82}Pb$.

Self-Test For Chapter 11

Multiple choice:

1. Bombardment of a uranium-235 atom with a neutron produces three neutrons, which can go on to bombard 3 more U-235 atoms. How many neutrons are produced after the fourth cycle?
   (a) 12   (b) 36   (c) 81   (d) 108

2. The product of the α emission of $^{146}_{62}Sm$ is:
   (a) $^{146}_{63}Eu$ (b) $^{144}_{61}Pm$ (c) $^{144}_{60}Nd$ (d) $^{142}_{60}Nd$

3. A half-inch thick piece of plastic blocks 50% of radiation. How much radiation passes through a one inch thick piece of plastic?
   (a) 50%   (b) 25%   (c) 12%   (d) 0%

4. The *curie* measures:
   (a) amount of radioactivity   (b) ionizing intensity of radiation   (c) amount of radiation absorbed   (d) tissue damage

5. A sample of a radionuclide has a half-life of 40 days. How much radioactivity remains after 160 days?
   (a) 25%   (b) 12.5%   (c) 6.25%   (d) 0%

6. How many disintegrations per second does one microcurie of a sample emit?
   (a) 3.7×10^{10} (b) 3.7×10^{7} (c) 3.7×10^{6} (d) 3.7×10^{4}

7. If a person standing 100 cm from a radiation source approaches to within 10 cm of the source, how much does the intensity of the radiation change?
   (a) increases by a hundredfold   (b) increases tenfold   (c) stays the same   (d) decreases tenfold

8. Artificial transmutation was probably used to produce which one of the following radionuclides?
   (a) $^{238}_{92}U$ (b) $^{210}_{82}Pb$ (c) $^{60}_{27}Co$ (d) $^{239}_{94}Pu$

9. Which of the following radioisotopes is not medically useful?
   (a) $^{131}_{53}I$ (b) $^{14}_{6}C$ (c) $^{11}_{24}Na$ (d) $^{60}_{27}Co$

10. In an experiment by the Curies, aluminum-27 was bombarded with α particles. If each aluminum-27 atom captured one α particle and emitted one neutron, what other atom was produced?
    (a) $^{29}_{13}Al$ (b) $^{28}_{14}Si$ (c) $^{30}_{15}P$ (d) $^{31}_{15}P$

Complete the following sentences:

1. The change of one element to another is called _____.

2. _____ _____ causes the most tissue damage.

3. A chemical compound tagged with a radioactive atom can be used as a _____.

4. All people are exposed to _____ radiation.

5. A nuclear equation is balanced when the number of _____ is the same on both sides of the equation.

6. The age of a sample can be determined by measuring the amount of _____ it contains.

7. The _____ is a unit for measuring the number of radioactive disintegrations per second.

8. In _____ _____, an atom is split apart by neutron bombardment to give small fragments.

9. People who work around radiation sources wear _____ _____ for detection of radiation.

10. PET and CT are techniques for _____ _____.

11. Very light elements release large amounts of energy when they undergo _____ _____.

12. The _____ _____ is the size of a radioactive sample that is needed for a nuclear reaction to be self-sustaining

Tell whether the following statements are true or false:

1. If a sample has a half-life of 12 days, it will have decayed completely in 24 days.

2. X-rays are considered to be ionizing radiation.

3. The ratio of carbon-14 to carbon-12 in the atmosphere is constant.

4. Pierre and Marie Curie discovered radioactivity.

5. A β particle travels at nearly the speed of light.

6. An α particle travels at nearly the speed of light.

7. The product of β emission has an atomic number one amu smaller than the starting material.

8. A nuclear power plant can undergo a nuclear explosion in an accident.

9. The rad is the unit most commonly used in medicine to measure radiation dosage.

10. Radiation causes injury by ionizing molecules.

11. Most of the known radioisotopes are naturally occurring.

12. Many isotopes undergo nuclear fission.

Match the entries on the left with their partners on the right:

1. Rutherford (a) Alpha particle

2. $^{245}_{96}Cm$ (b) Used in cancer therapy

3. $t_{1/2}$ (c) Discovered radioactivity

4. $^{0}_{-1}e$ (d) Neutron

5. Becquerel (e) Used for archeological dating

6. $^{90}_{38}Sr$ (f) Discovered α,β particles

7. $^{1}_{0}n$ (g) Natural radioactive element that undergoes fission

8. P. and M. Curie (h) Discovered radium

9. $^{60}_{27}Co$ (i) Transuranium element

10. $^{4}_{2}He$ (j) Component of radioactive waste

11. $^{14}_{6}C$ (k) Beta particle

12. $^{235}_{92}U$ (l) Half-life

Chapter 12 – Introduction to Organic Chemistry: Alkanes

Chapter Outline

I. Introduction to Organic Chemistry (Sections 12.1–12.5).
   A. The nature of organic molecules (Section 12.1).
      1. Carbon always forms four bonds.
      2. Almost all of the bonds in organic molecules are covalent.
         a. These bonds are polar covalent bonds when carbon forms a bond to an element on the far left of the periodic table.
         b. Carbon can form multiple bonds by sharing more than two electrons.
      3. Organic molecules have specific three-dimensional shapes.
      4. In addition to hydrogen, oxygen and nitrogen are often present in organic molecules.
      5. Organic molecules are low-melting and boiling.
      6. Organic molecules are usually insoluble in water and don't conduct electricity.
   B. Functional groups (Section 12.2).
      1. A functional group is an atom or group of atoms that has a characteristic reactivity.
      2. The chemistry of organic molecules is determined by functional groups.
      3. Functional groups fall into three categories.
         a. Hydrocarbons.
         b. Compounds with C–X single bonds, where X is electronegative.
         c. Compounds with C=O double bonds.
   C. Structures of organic molecules: alkane isomers (Sections 12.3–12.4).
      1. When hydrocarbons contain more than three carbons, there is more than one way to arrange the carbon atoms.
         a. Some alkanes are straight-chain.
         b. Other alkanes are branched.
      2. Compounds with the same formula but different orders of connecting the carbon atoms are called constitutional isomers.
         Constitutional isomers have different structures and different properties.
      3. Drawing structures (Section 12.4).
         a. Condensed structures are simpler to draw than structural formulas.
         b. In condensed structures, C–H and C–C single bonds are implied, rather than drawn.
         c. Vertical bonds are often shown for clarity.
         d. Occasionally, parentheses are used to show a row of $-CH_2-$ groups.
   D. The shapes of organic molecules (Section 12.5).
      1. The groups around a C–C bond are free to assume an infinite number of conformations.
      2. Molecules adopt the least crowded conformation.
      3. Two structures with identical connections between atoms are identical, no matter how they are drawn.
II. Alkanes (Sections 12.6–12.8).
   A. Naming alkanes (Section 12.6).
      1. Straight-chain alkanes.
         a. Count the carbons.
         b. Find the root name.
         c. Add -ane to the root name.

2. Alkyl groups.
   a. Remove a hydrogen from an alkane and replace -ane with -yl.
   b. More than one alkyl group can be formed from some alkanes.
      i. Isopropyl and *n*-propyl are the two groups that can be formed from propane.
      ii. Four groups can be formed from butane.
      iii. Alkyl groups can be substituents on a straight chain.
3. Substitution patterns.
   a. Primary carbon: $R–CH_3$.
   b. Secondary carbon: $R–CH_2–R'$.
   c. Tertiary carbon:
$$R–\overset{\overset{\displaystyle R'}{|}}{C}H–R$$
   d. Quaternary carbon:
$$R–\overset{\overset{\displaystyle R'}{|}}{\underset{\underset{\displaystyle R''}{|}}{C}}–R'$$
4. Naming branched-chain alkanes.
   a. Name the main chain by finding the longest continuous chain of carbons and naming it.
   b. Number the carbons in the main chain, starting from the end nearer the first branch point.
   c. Identify and number each branching substituent according to its point of attachment to the main chain.
   d. Write the name as a single word.
B. Properties of alkanes (Section 12.7).
   1. The boiling points and melting points of alkanes increase with the number of carbons.
   2. Alkanes are insoluble in water but are soluble in nonpolar organic solvents.
   3. Alkanes are colorless and odorless.
   4. Alkanes are flammable.
   5. Alkanes with four or fewer carbons are gases, those from C5 to C15 are liquids, and those with more than 15 carbons are solids.
C. Reactivity of alkanes (Section 12.8).
   1. Alkanes are very unreactive.
   2. Reactions that alkanes undergo:
      a. Combustion: alkane + O_2 —> CO_2 + H_2O
      b. Halogenation: alkane + X_2 —> halogenated alkane + HCl
III. Cycloalkanes (Sections 12.9–12.10).
   A. Properties of cycloalkanes (Section 12.9).
      1. Cycloalkanes contain rings of carbon atoms.
      2. Cyclopropane and cyclobutane are more reactive than other cycloalkanes.
      3. Cyclohexane exists in a chair-like conformation.
      4. Cycloalkanes have properties similar to those of acyclic alkanes.
      5. Free rotation is not possible around the carbon–carbon bonds of a cycloalkane ring.
   B. Drawing and naming cycloalkanes (Section 12.10).
      1. Drawing cycloalkanes.
            The cycloalkane ring is represented as a polygon.
      2. Naming cycloalkanes.
         a. Use the cycloalkane as the parent.
         b. Number the substituents.
            i. Start numbering at the group that has alphabetical priority.
            ii. Proceed around the ring to give to the second group the lowest possible number.

Solutions to Chapter 12 Problems

12.1

(a)

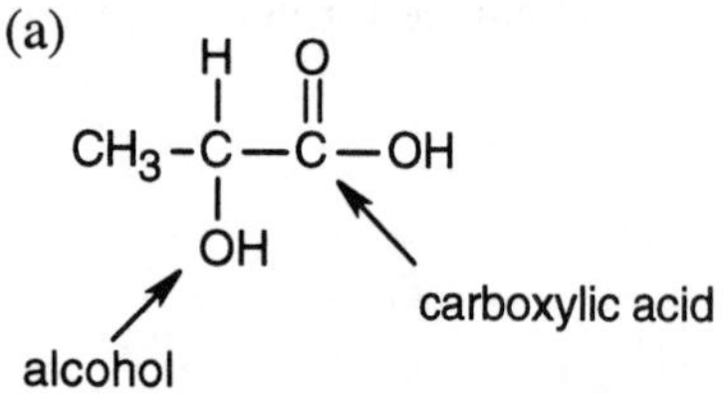

Lactic acid

(b)

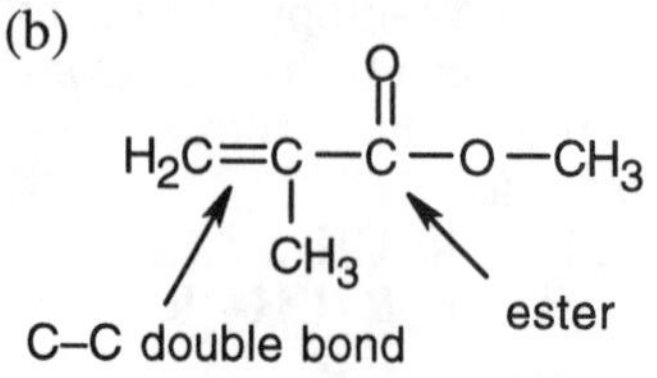

Methyl methacrylate

(c)

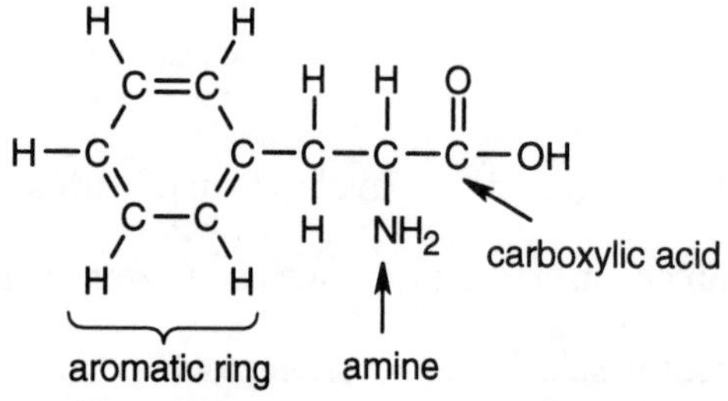

Phenylalanine

12.2

(a)

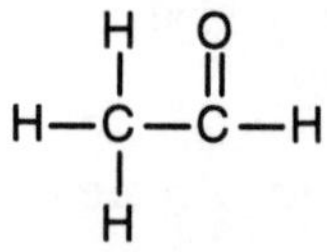

an aldehyde

(b)

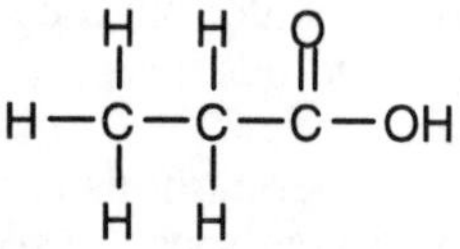

a carboxylic acid

12.3

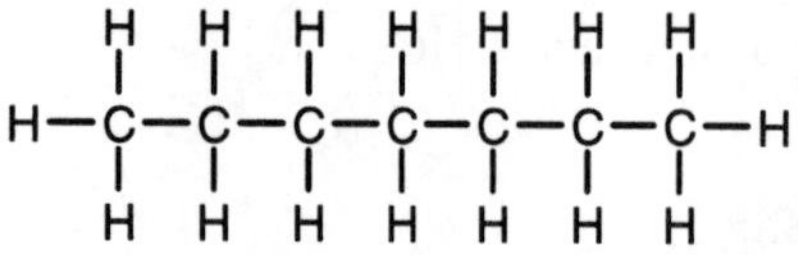

C_7H_{16} Heptane

12.4   There are eight branched-chain heptanes:

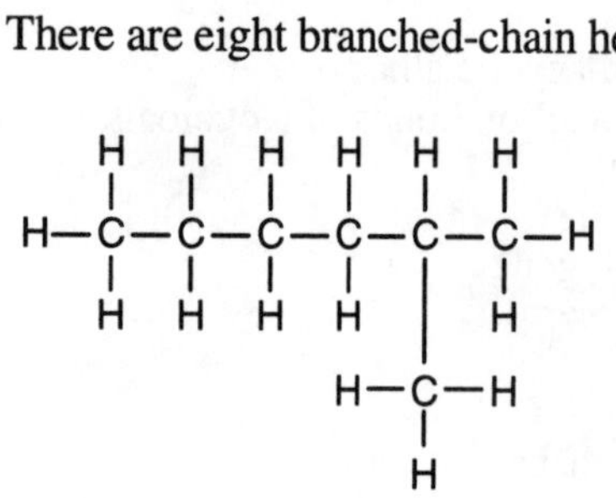

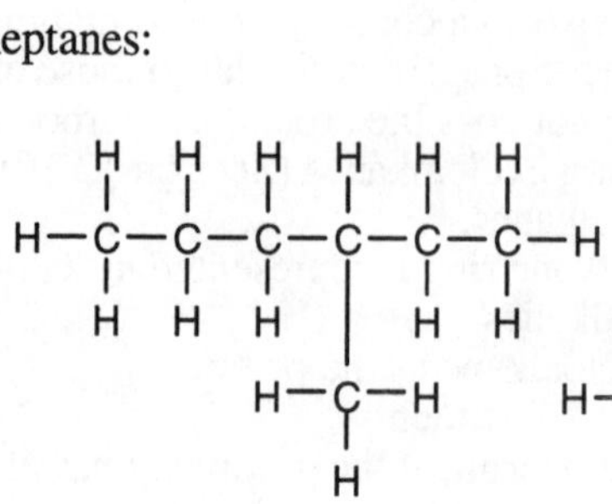

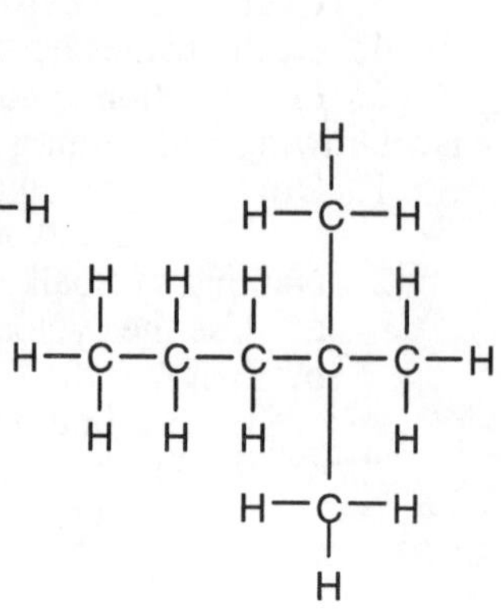

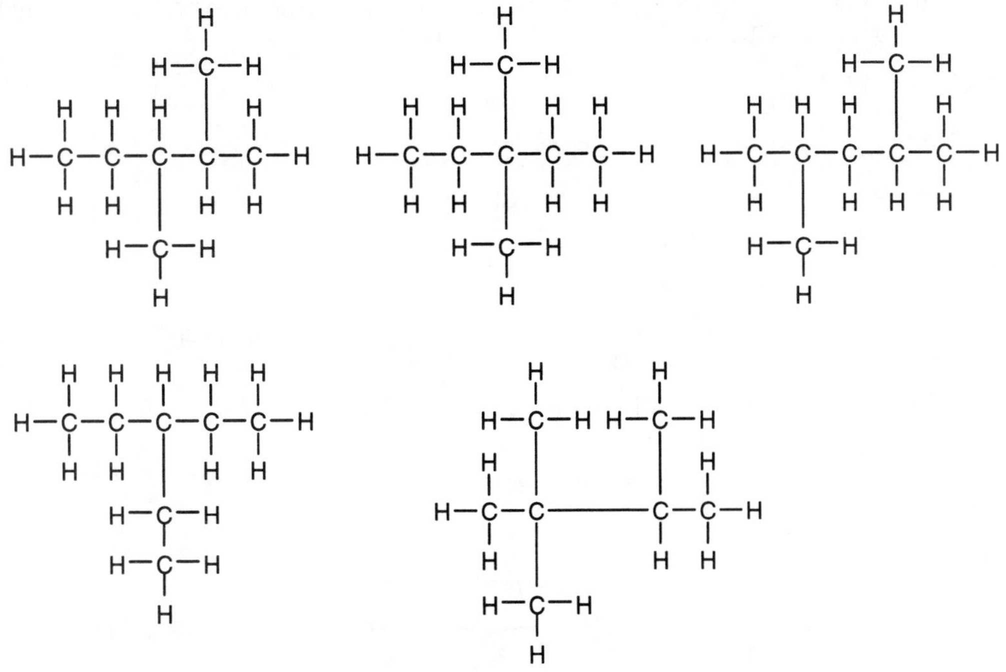

12.5

(a)

CH₃CH₂CH₂CH₂CH₃

Pentane

(b)

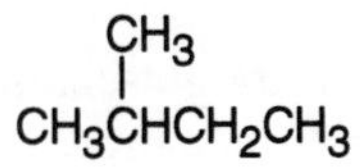

CH₃
|
CH₃CHCH₂CH₃

2–Methylbutane

(c)

CH₃
|
CH₃CCH₃
|
CH₃

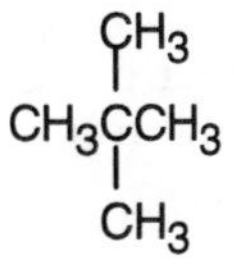

2,2–Dimethylpropane

12.6 All three structures have the same molecular formula (C_7H_{16}). Structures (a) and (c) are identical.

12.7 To solve this problem in a systematic way, use the following method:

(a) Draw the isomer of C_6H_{14} having no branches:

CH₃CH₂CH₂CH₂CH₂CH₃

(b) Draw the C_5H_{12} isomer having no branches, and replace one of the –CH₂– hydrogens with a –CH₃. There are two different isomers:

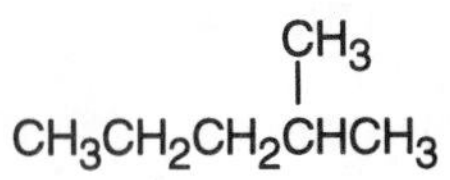

CH₃
|
CH₃CH₂CH₂CHCH₃

and

CH₃
|
CH₃CH₂CHCH₂CH₃

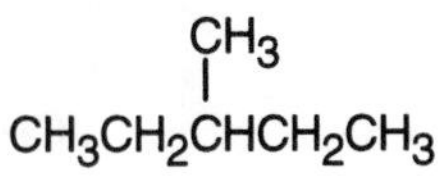

(c) Draw the C_4H_{10} isomer having no branches, and replace two of the $-CH_2-$ hydrogens with $-CH_3$ groups. There are two different isomers:

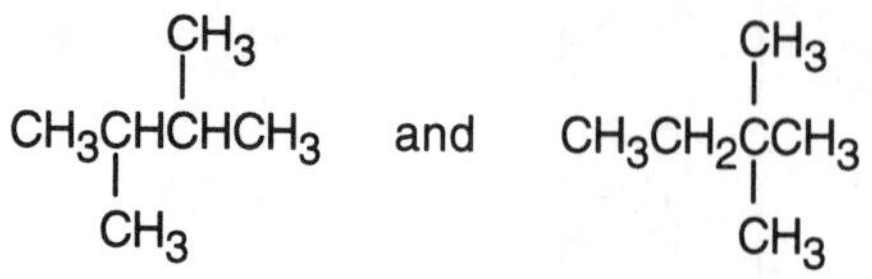

$$\underset{\underset{CH_3}{|}}{\overset{\overset{CH_3}{|}}{CH_3CHCHCH_3}} \quad \text{and} \quad \underset{\underset{CH_3}{|}}{\overset{\overset{CH_3}{|}}{CH_3CH_2CCH_3}}$$

12.9

(a)

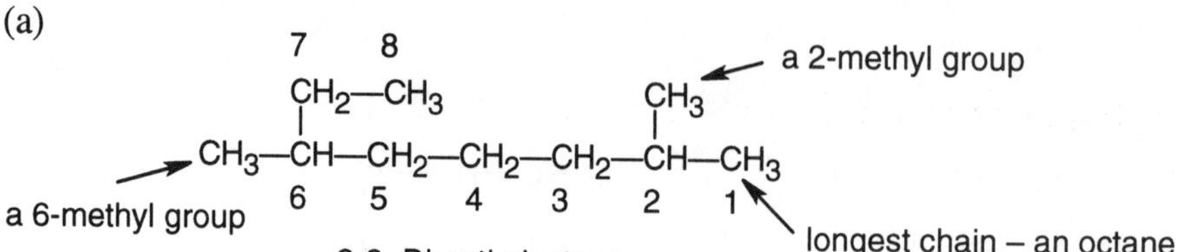

a 2-methyl group

a 6-methyl group

longest chain – an octane

2,6–Dimethyloctane

(b)

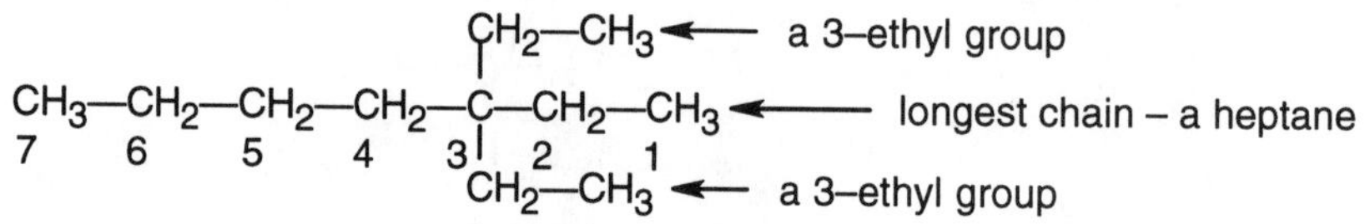

a 3–ethyl group

longest chain – a heptane

a 3–ethyl group

3,3–Diethylheptane

12.10 To answer this problem, draw the straight-chain hydrocarbon corresponding to the parent name, and replace $-H$'s with the groups indicated.

(a)

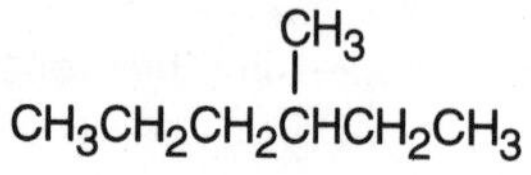

$$\overset{\overset{CH_3}{|}}{CH_3CH_2CH_2CHCH_2CH_3}$$

3–Methylhexane

(b)

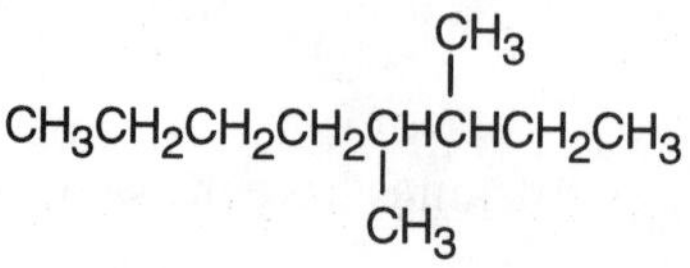

$$\underset{\underset{CH_3}{|}}{\overset{\overset{CH_3}{|}}{CH_3CH_2CH_2CH_2CHCHCH_2CH_3}}$$

3,4–Dimethyloctane

(c)

$$\underset{\underset{CH_3}{|}}{\overset{\overset{CH_3 \quad CH_3}{| \quad\;\; |}}{CH_3CHCH_2CCH_3}}$$

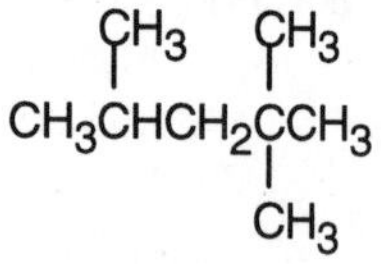

2,2,4–Trimethylpentane

12.11

(a)

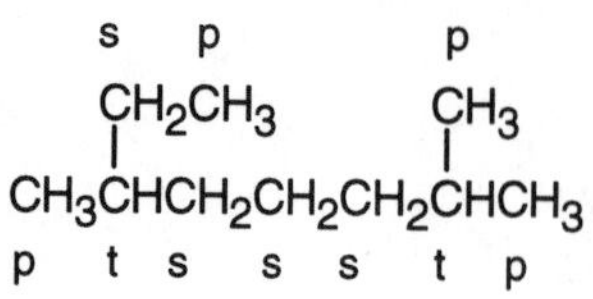

(b)

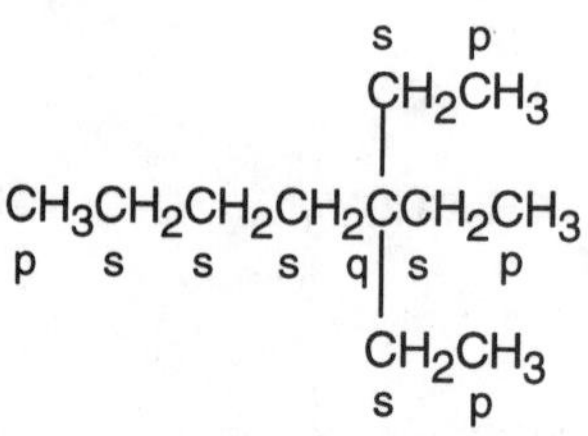

Where p = primary, s = secondary, t = tertiary, and q = quaternary

12.12 There are many answers to this question. For example:

(a)

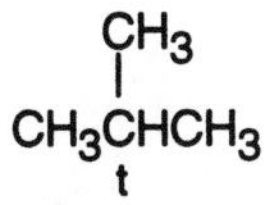

$$CH_3CHCH_3$$
$$|$$
$$CH_3$$
t

2–Methylpropane

(b)

$$CH_3CHCH_2CH_2CCH_3$$
with CH_3 groups and q

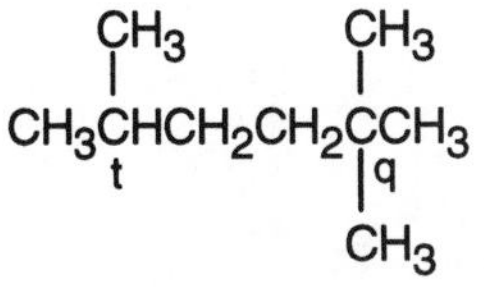

2,2,5–Trimethylhexane

12.13

$$2\ CH_3CH_3 + 7\ O_2 \longrightarrow 4\ CO_2 + 6\ H_2O$$

12.14

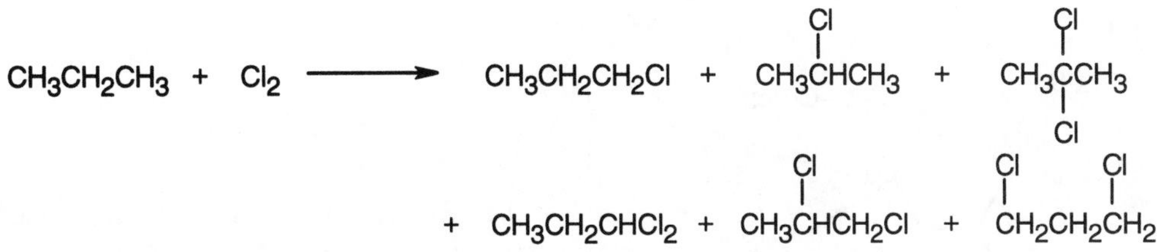

$$CH_3CH_2CH_3 + Cl_2 \longrightarrow CH_3CH_2CH_2Cl + CH_3CHCH_3 + CH_3CCH_3$$
$$| \qquad\qquad | $$
$$Cl \qquad\qquad Cl, Cl$$

$$+ CH_3CH_2CHCl_2 + CH_3CHCH_2Cl + CH_2CH_2CH_2$$
with Cl substituents

Six different mono- and disubstitution products can be formed from the reaction of propane with chlorine.

12.15

(a)

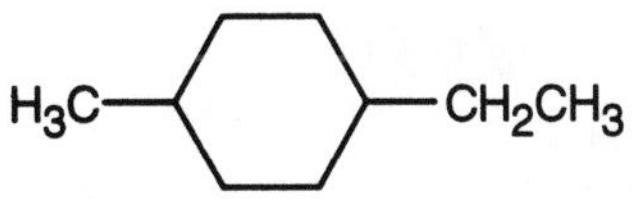

$$H_3C—\text{(cyclohexane)}—CH_2CH_3$$

1–Ethyl–4–methylcyclohexane

The parent ring is a cyclohexane The two substituents are an ethyl group and a methyl group. The ethyl group receives the smaller number because it has alphabetical priority

(b)

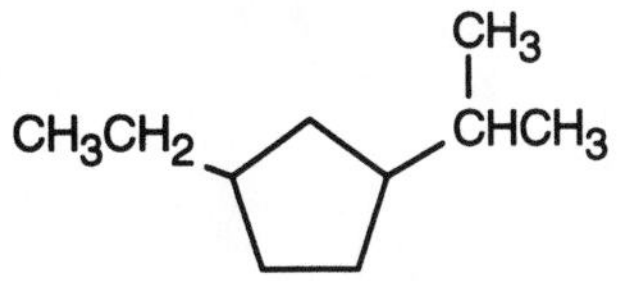

$$CH_3CH_2—\text{(cyclopentane)}—CHCH_3$$
with CH_3

1–Ethyl–3–isopropylcyclopentane

The parent ring is a cyclopentane. The two substituents are an ethyl group and an isopropyl group The ethyl group receives the smaller number because it has alphabetical priority.

12.16

(a)

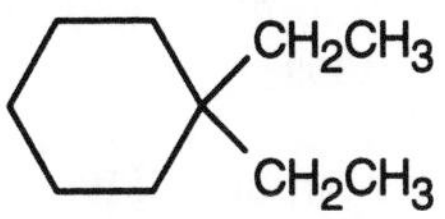

CH_2CH_3
CH_2CH_3 on cyclohexane

1,1–Diethylcyclohexane

(b)

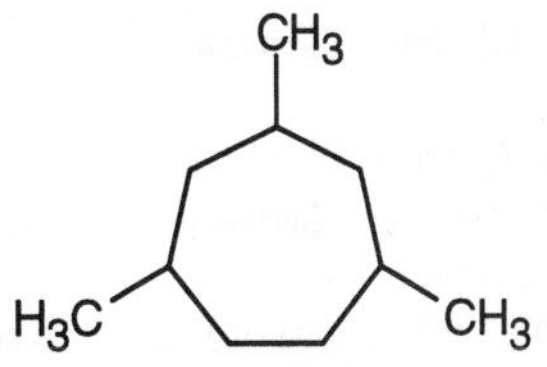

CH_3, H_3C, CH_3 on cycloheptane

1,3,5–Trimethylcycloheptane

Understanding Key Concepts

12.17

(a)

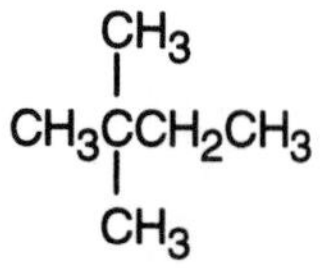

$$CH_3CCH_2CH_3$$
with CH_3 above and CH_3 below

(b)

$$CH_3CHCHCH_3$$
with CH_3 above and OH below

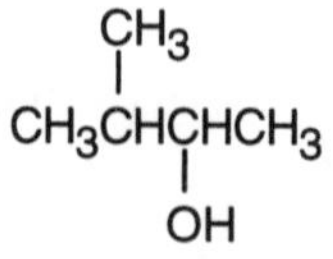

12.18

(a)

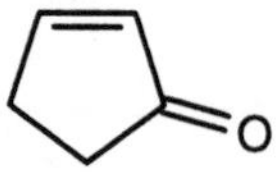

(b)

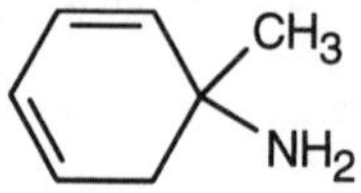

12.19

(a)

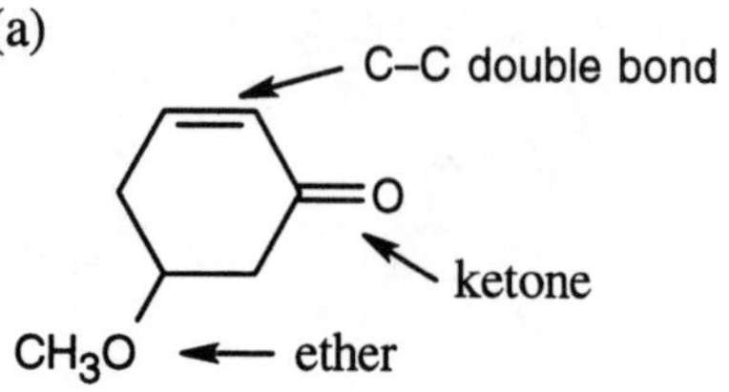

C–C double bond

ketone

CH₃O — ether

(b)

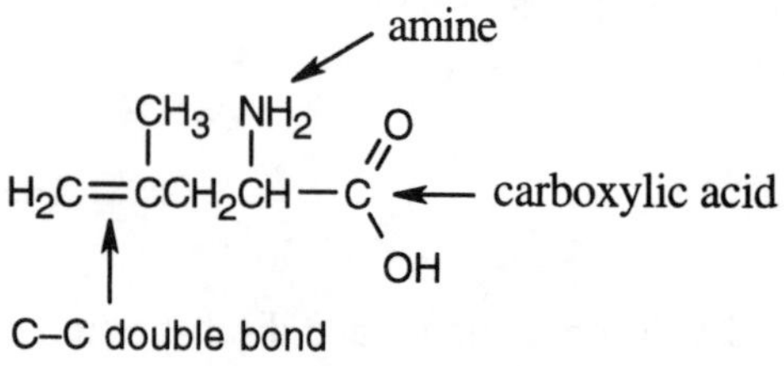

amine

$$H_2C=CCH_2CH-C$$
with CH_3 and NH_2 above, O and OH — carboxylic acid

C–C double bond

12.20

(a)

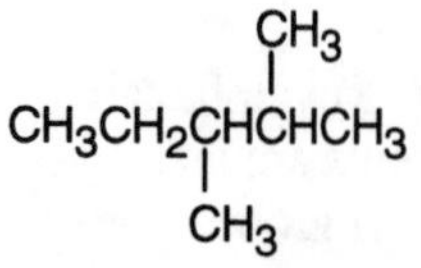

$$CH_3CH_2CHCHCH_3$$
with CH_3 above and CH_3 below

2,3–Dimethylpentane

(b)

$$CH_3CHCH_2CH_2CHCH_3$$
with CH_3 above and CH_3 below

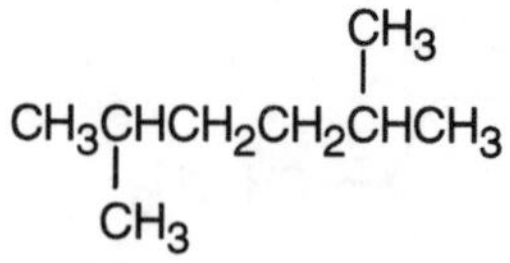

2,5–Dimethylhexane

12.21

(a)

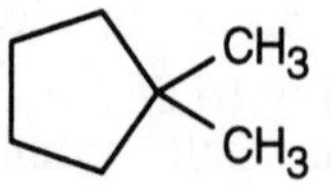

1,1–Dimethylcyclopentane

(b)

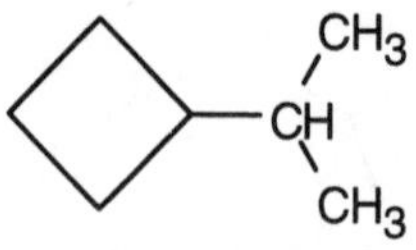

Isopropylcyclobutane

Organic Molecules and Functional Groups

12.22 Carbon is unique in that it can form four strong bonds to other elements and to other carbon atoms, making possible a great many different compounds.

12.24 Organic compounds don't dissolve in water because they are nonpolar. They don't conduct electricity because they are covalent, not ionic.

12.26 A polar covalent bond is a covalent bond in which electrons are shared unequally, being more attracted to one atom than the other. For example, the electrons in the C–Br bond of bromomethane are attracted more strongly to the electronegative bromine than to carbon.

12.28

(a)

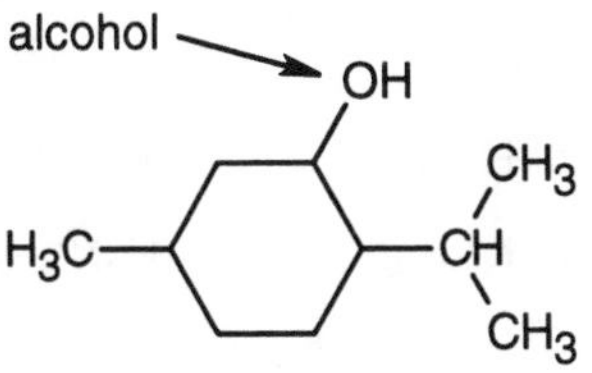

alcohol → OH

H₃C— —CH⟨CH₃⟩⟨CH₃⟩

Menthol

(b)

O
‖
C—OH ← carboxylic acid

aromatic ring

O—C(=O)—CH₃ — ester

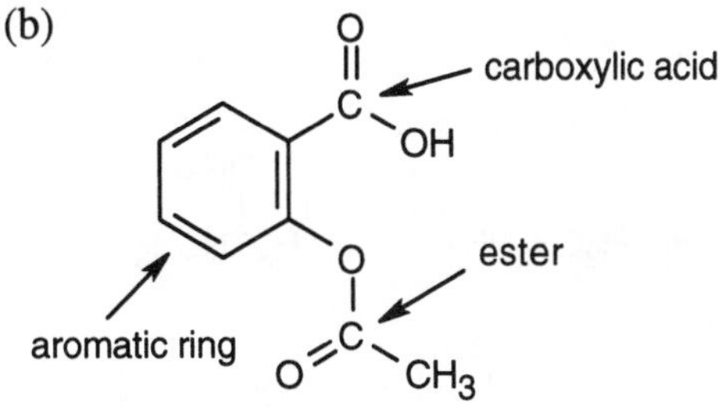

Aspirin

12.30 There are several possible answers to these questions. For example:

(a)

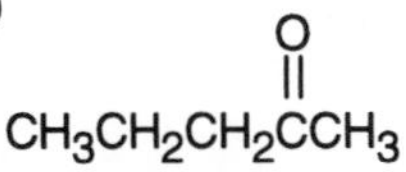

O
‖
CH₃CH₂CH₂CCH₃

ketone

(b)

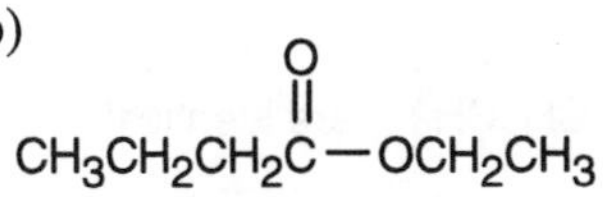

O
‖
CH₃CH₂CH₂C—OCH₂CH₃

ester

(c)

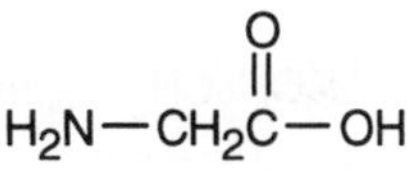

O
‖
H₂N—CH₂C—OH

amine
carboxylic acid

Alkanes and Isomers

12.32 For two compounds to be isomers, they must have the same molecular formula but different structures.

12.34 A primary carbon is bonded to one other carbon; a secondary carbon is bonded to two other carbons; a tertiary carbon is bonded to three other carbons; and a quaternary carbon is bonded to four other carbons.

12.36 There are many possible answers to this question. For example:

(a)

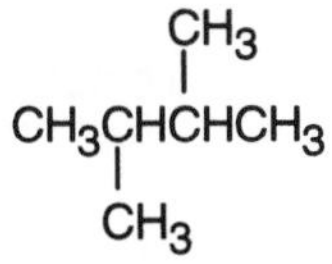

CH₃
|
CH₃CHCHCH₃
|
CH₃

2,3–Dimethylbutane

(b)

Cyclohexane

12.38

CH₃CH₂CH₂OH

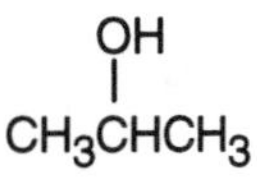

OH
|
CH₃CHCH₃

CH₃CH₂—O—CH₃

12.40

(a)

CH₃CH₂CH₂CH₂OH$\qquad$CH₃CH₂CHCH₃$\qquad$CH₃CHCH₂OH$\qquad$CH₃CCH₃

with OH on the second carbon of CH₃CH₂CHCH₃, CH₃ on CH₃CHCH₂OH, and OH above with CH₃ below on CH₃CCH₃

(b)

CH₃CH₂CH₂NH₂$\qquad$CH₃CHCH₃$\qquad$CH₃CH₂NCH₃$\qquad$CH₃NCH₃

with NH₂ on the middle carbon, H above the N, and CH₃ above the N

(c)

CH₃CH₂CH₂CCH₃$\qquad$CH₃CH₂CCH₂CH₃$\qquad$CH₃CHCCH₃

each with C=O (double-bonded O above the carbonyl carbon), and CH₃ below on the last structure

12.42

(a)

CH₃CH₂CH₃$\quad$and$\quad$CH₃CH₂$\quad$are identical
$\qquad\qquad\qquad\qquad\qquad$CH₃

(b)

CH₃—N—CH₃$\quad$and$\quad$CH₃CH₂—N—H$\quad$are isomers.
$\qquad$|$\qquad\qquad\qquad\qquad\qquad\qquad$|
$\qquad$H$\qquad\qquad\qquad\qquad\qquad\qquad$H

(c)

CH₃CH₂CH₂—O—CH₃$\quad$and$\quad$CH₃CH₂CH₂—C—CH₃$\quad$are unrelated.
$\qquad\qquad\qquad\qquad\qquad\qquad\qquad\qquad\qquad\qquad\qquad$‖
$\qquad\qquad\qquad\qquad\qquad\qquad\qquad\qquad\qquad\qquad\qquad$O

(d)

$\qquad$O$\qquad\qquad$CH₃$\qquad\qquad\qquad\qquad\qquad$O
$\qquad$‖$\qquad\qquad$|
CH₃—C—CH₂CH₂CHCH₃$\quad$and$\quad$CH₃CH₂—C—CH₂CH₂CH₂CH₃$\quad$are isomers.

(e)

$\qquad\qquad\qquad\qquad\qquad\qquad\qquad\qquad\qquad\qquad\qquad\qquad$O
$\qquad\qquad\qquad\qquad\qquad\qquad\qquad\qquad\qquad\qquad\qquad\qquad$‖
CH₃CH=CHCH₂CH₂—O—H$\quad$and$\quad$CH₃CH₂CH—C—H$\quad$are isomers.
$\qquad\qquad\qquad\qquad\qquad\qquad\qquad\qquad\qquad\qquad\quad$|
$\qquad\qquad\qquad\qquad\qquad\qquad\qquad\qquad\qquad\qquad\quad$CH₃

12.44 All three structures have a carbon atom with five bonds.

(a)$\qquad\qquad\qquad\qquad$(b)$\qquad\qquad\qquad\qquad\qquad$(c)$\qquad\qquad\qquad\qquad$CH₃
$\qquad\qquad\qquad\qquad\qquad\qquad\qquad\qquad$O
$\qquad\qquad\qquad\qquad\qquad\qquad\qquad\qquad$‖
CH₃=CHCH₂CH₂OH$\qquad$CH₃CH₂CH=CCH₃$\qquad$CH₂CH₂CH₂C≡CCH₃
$\qquad$↑$\qquad\qquad\qquad\qquad\qquad\qquad\qquad$↑$\qquad\qquad\qquad\qquad\quad$↑$\qquad\quad$↑
$\quad$5 bonds$\qquad\qquad\qquad\qquad\qquad$5 bonds$\qquad\qquad$3 bonds$\quad$5 bonds

Naming Alkanes

12.46

(a)

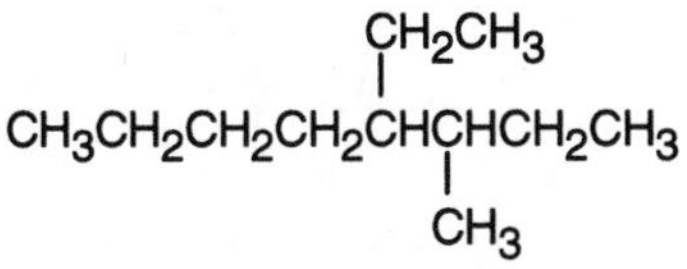

$$CH_2CH_3$$
$$CH_3CH_2CH_2CH_2CHCHCH_2CH_3$$
$$CH_3$$

4–Ethyl–3–methyloctane

(b)

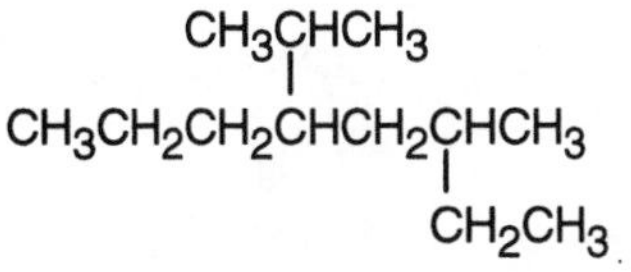

$$CH_3CHCH_3$$
$$CH_3CH_2CH_2CHCH_2CHCH_3$$
$$CH_2CH_3$$

5–Isopropyl–3–methyloctane

(c)

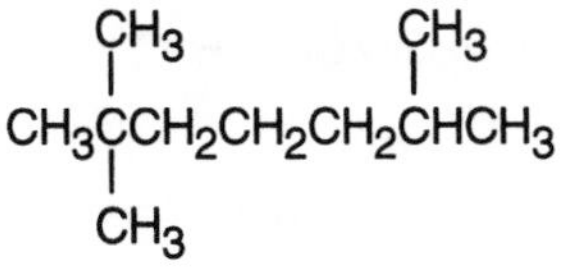

$$CH_3 \qquad CH_3$$
$$CH_3CCH_2CH_2CH_2CHCH_3$$
$$CH_3$$

2,2,6–Trimethylheptane

(d)

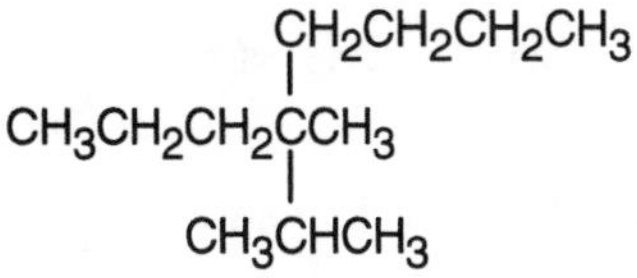

$$CH_2CH_2CH_2CH_3$$
$$CH_3CH_2CH_2CCH_3$$
$$CH_3CHCH_3$$

4–Isopropyl–4–methyloctane

(e)

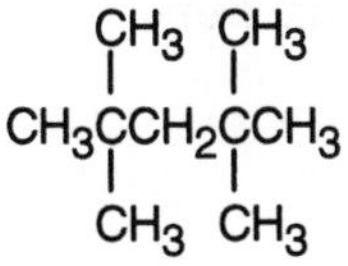

$$CH_3 \quad CH_3$$
$$CH_3CCH_2CCH_3$$
$$CH_3 \quad CH_3$$

2,2,4,4–Tetramethylpentane

(f)

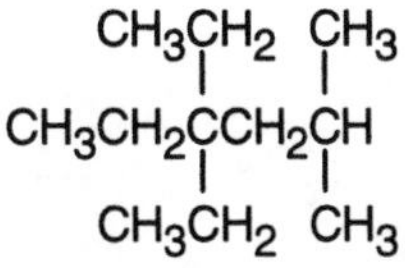

$$CH_3CH_2 \quad CH_3$$
$$CH_3CH_2CCH_2CH$$
$$CH_3CH_2 \quad CH_3$$

4,4–Diethyl-2–methylhexane

(g)

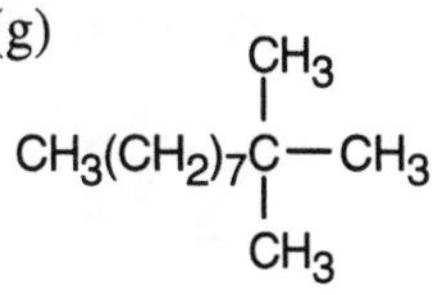

$$CH_3$$
$$CH_3(CH_2)_7C-CH_3$$
$$CH_3$$

2,2–Dimethyldecane

12.48

(a)

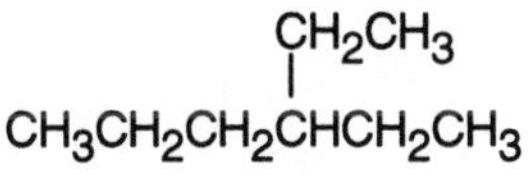

$$CH_2CH_3$$
$$CH_3CH_2CH_2CHCH_2CH_3$$

3–Ethylhexane

(b)

$$H_3C \quad CH_3$$
$$CH_3CH_2CHCCH_3$$
$$CH_3$$

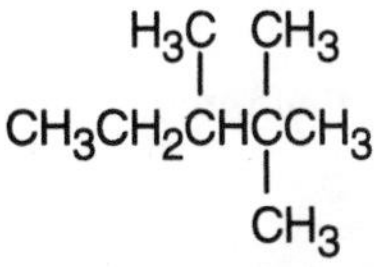

2,2,3–Trimethylpentane

(c)

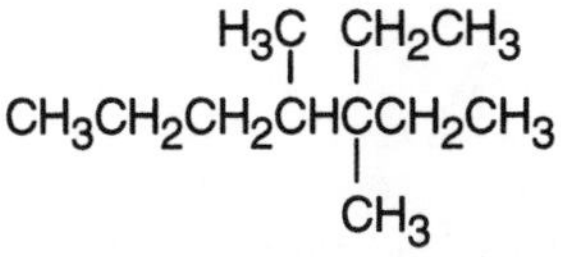

$$H_3C \quad CH_2CH_3$$
$$CH_3CH_2CH_2CHCCH_2CH_3$$
$$CH_3$$

3–Ethyl–3,4–dimethylheptane

(d)

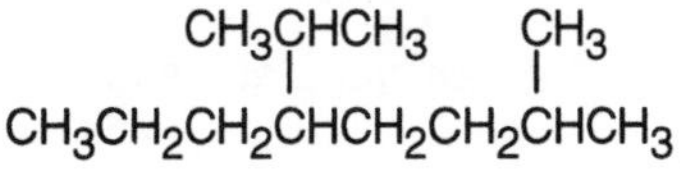

$$CH_3CHCH_3 \qquad CH_3$$
$$CH_3CH_2CH_2CHCH_2CH_2CHCH_3$$

5–Isopropyl–2-methyloctane

(e)

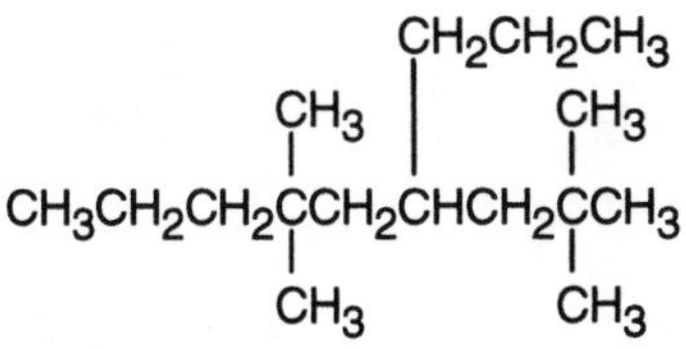

$$CH_2CH_2CH_3$$
$$CH_3 \qquad CH_3$$
$$CH_3CH_2CH_2CCH_2CHCH_2CCH_3$$
$$CH_3 \qquad CH_3$$

2,2,6,6–Tetramethyl–4–propylnonane

(f)

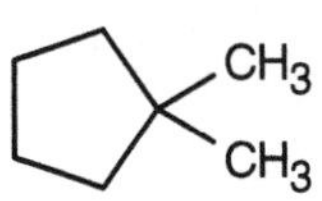

1,1–Dimethylcyclopentane

12.50

(a)

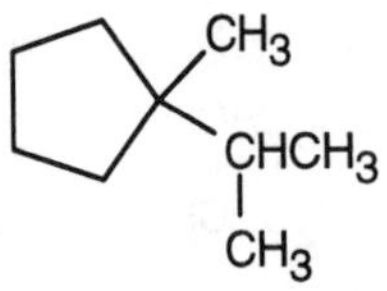

1–Isopropyl–1–methylcyclopentane

(b)

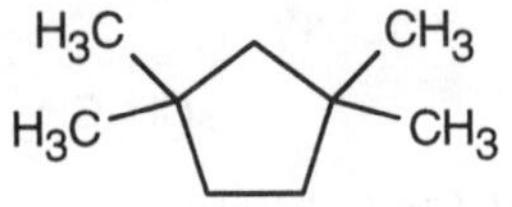

1,1,3,3–Tetramethylcyclopentane

(c)

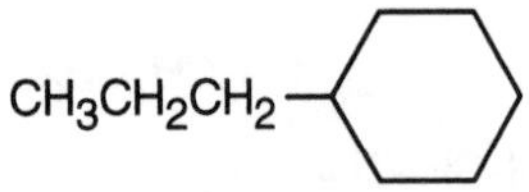

$CH_3CH_2CH_2$—⬡

Propylcyclohexane

(d)

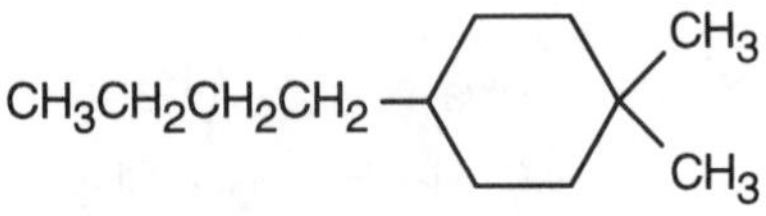

$CH_3CH_2CH_2CH_2$—⬡$\begin{smallmatrix}CH_3\\CH_3\end{smallmatrix}$

4–Butyl–1,1–dimethylcyclohexane

12.52

(a)

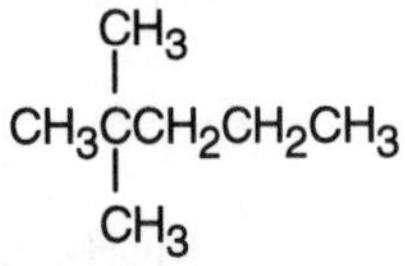

$$\underset{\underset{CH_3}{|}}{\overset{\overset{CH_3}{|}}{CH_3CCH_2CH_2CH_3}}$$

2,2–Dimethylpentane

The prefix "di-" must appear when two substituents are the same.

(b)

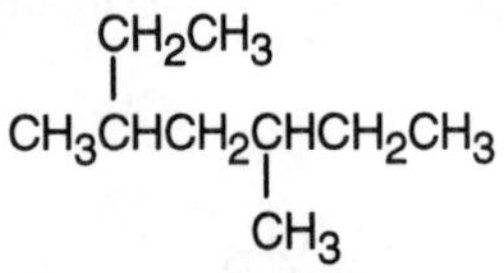

$$\underset{\underset{CH_3}{|}}{\overset{\overset{CH_2CH_3}{|}}{CH_3CHCH_2CHCH_2CH_3}}$$

3,5–Dimethylheptane

You must choose the longest carbon chain as the parent name.

(c)

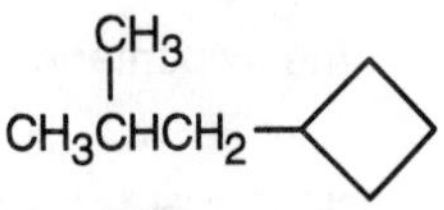

$$\overset{\overset{CH_3}{|}}{CH_3CHCH_2}\text{—}◇$$

sec–Butylcyclobutane

This compound is an alkyl-substituted cycloalkane.

12.54

$CH_3CH_2CH_2CH_2CH_2CH_2CH_3$

Heptane

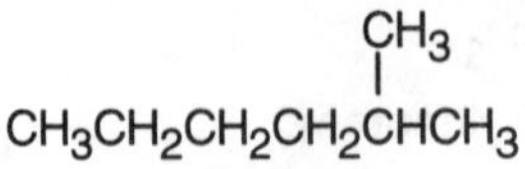

$\underset{}{\overset{\overset{CH_3}{|}}{CH_3CH_2CH_2CH_2CHCH_3}}$

2–Methylhexane

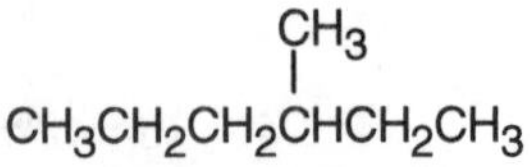

$\underset{}{\overset{\overset{CH_3}{|}}{CH_3CH_2CH_2CHCH_2CH_3}}$

3–Methylhexane

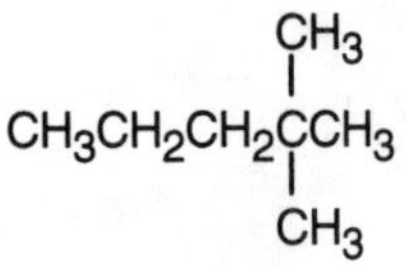

$\underset{\underset{CH_3}{|}}{\overset{\overset{CH_3}{|}}{CH_3CH_2CH_2CCH_3}}$

2,2–Dimethylpentane

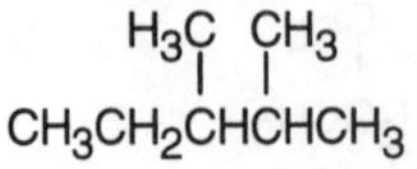

$\overset{\overset{H_3C\ \ CH_3}{|\ \ \ |}}{CH_3CH_2CHCHCH_3}$

2,3–Dimethylpentane

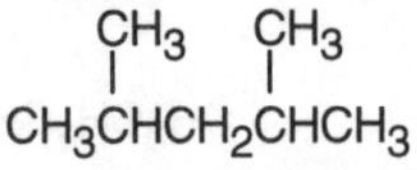

$\overset{\overset{CH_3\ \ \ CH_3}{|\ \ \ \ \ |}}{CH_3CHCH_2CHCH_3}$

2,4–Dimethylpentane

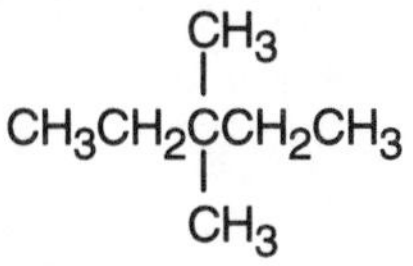

$$
\underset{\text{3,3–Dimethylpentane}}{CH_3CH_2\overset{\displaystyle CH_3}{\underset{\displaystyle CH_3}{C}}CH_2CH_3}
\qquad
\underset{\text{3–Ethylpentane}}{CH_3CH_2\overset{\displaystyle CH_2CH_3}{CH}CH_2CH_3}
\qquad
\underset{\text{2,2,3–Trimethylbutane}}{CH_3\overset{\displaystyle CH_3}{CH}-\overset{\displaystyle CH_3}{\underset{\displaystyle CH_3}{C}}CH_3}
$$

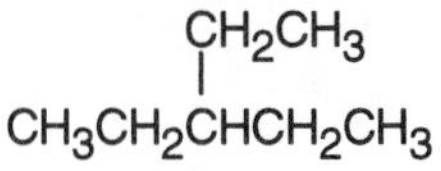

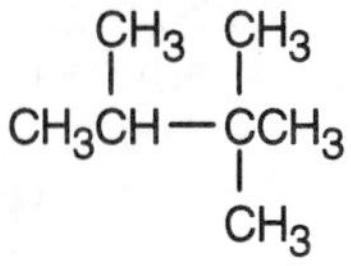

Reactions of Alkanes

12.56

$$CH_3CH_2CH_3 \;+\; 5\,O_2 \longrightarrow 3\,CO_2 \;+\; 4\,H_2O$$

12.58

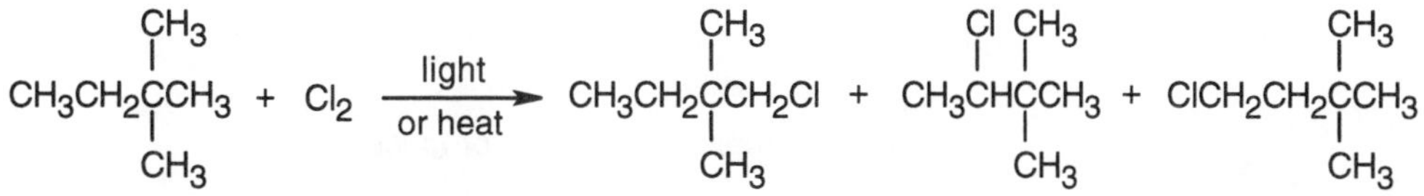

$$
CH_3CH_2\overset{\displaystyle CH_3}{\underset{\displaystyle CH_3}{C}}CH_3 \;+\; Cl_2
\xrightarrow[\text{or heat}]{\text{light}}
CH_3CH_2\overset{\displaystyle CH_3}{\underset{\displaystyle CH_3}{C}}CH_2Cl
\;+\;
CH_3\overset{\displaystyle Cl}{C}H\overset{\displaystyle CH_3}{\underset{\displaystyle CH_3}{C}}CH_3
\;+\;
ClCH_2CH_2\overset{\displaystyle CH_3}{\underset{\displaystyle CH_3}{C}}CH_3
$$

12.60 A synthetically produced version of a compound and a "natural" compound have the same properties because their chemical structures are identical.

12.62 Natural gas consists of $C_1 - C_4$ hydrocarbons and is a gas at room temperature. Petroleum consists of other alkanes, some of which are very high boiling.

General Questions and Problems

12.64

(a)

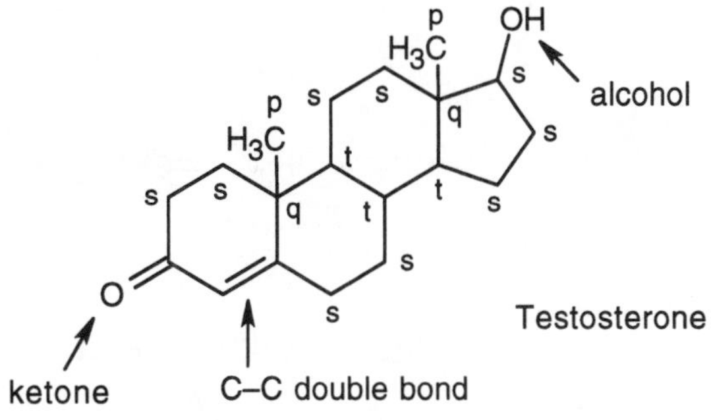

p = primary
s = secondary
t = tertiary
q = quaternary

(b)

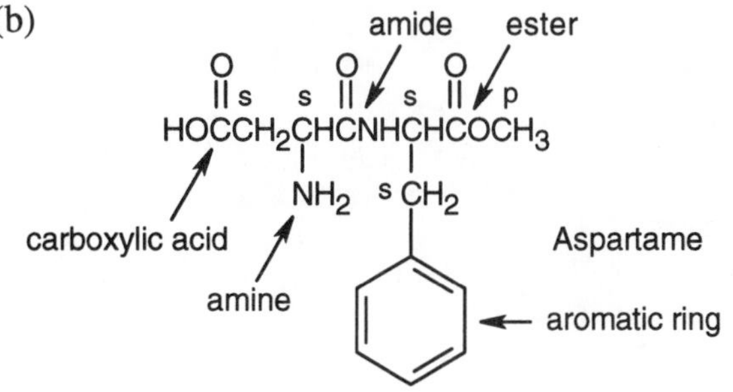

p = primary
s = secondary
t = tertiary
q = quaternary

12.66 Since carbon forms only four bonds, the largest number of hydrogens that can be bonded to three carbons is eight.

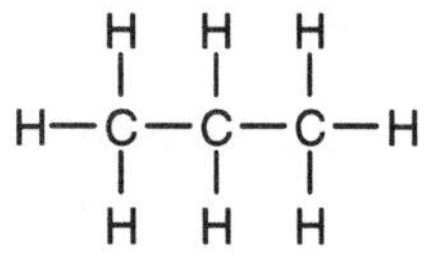

C_3H_8

12.68 Since "like dissolves like," lipstick, which is composed primarily of hydrocarbons, is more soluble in the hydrocarbon petroleum jelly than in water.

12.70

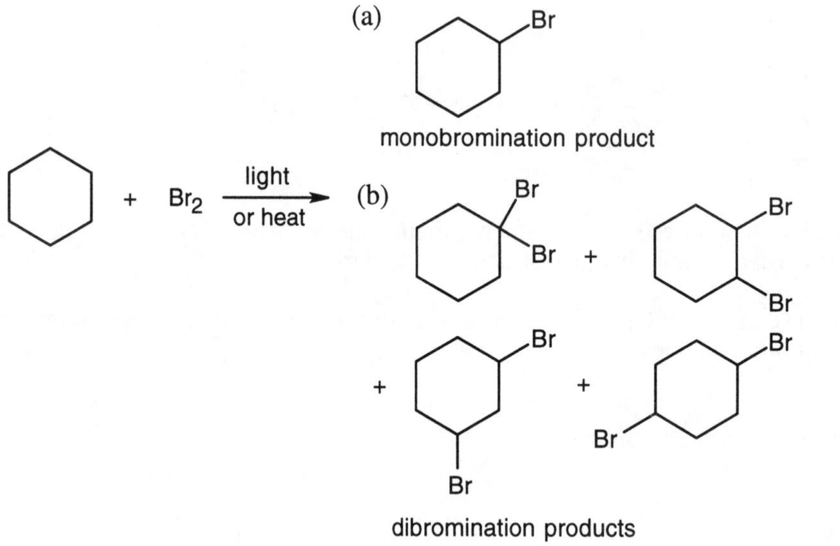

(a) monobromination product

(b) dibromination products

12.72

(a)

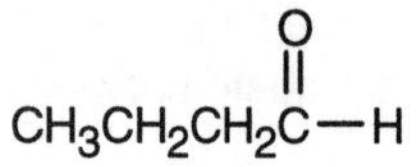

$$CH_3CH_2CH_2\overset{\overset{\displaystyle O}{\|}}{C}-H$$

(b)

$$CH_3CH_2CH_2CH=CHCH_2Br$$

(c)

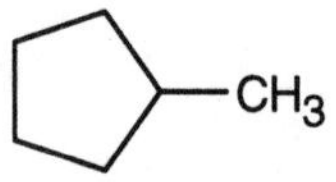

(d)

$$CH_3CH=CHCH=CH_2$$

Self-Test for Chapter 12

Multiple choice:

1. Which of the following functional groups doesn't contain a carbon–oxygen double bond?
   (a) ether   (b) aldehyde   (c) ketone   (d) ester

2. In which of the following alkanes are carbons not tetrahedral?
   (a) ethane   (b) propane   (c) cyclopropane   (d) cyclohexane

3. How many products can result from chlorination of ethane? (Include products with more than one chlorine.)
   (a) 2   (b) 4   (c) 6   (d) 9

4. How many branched-chain isomers of C_6H_{14} are there?
   (a) 2   (b) 3   (c) 4   (d) 5

5. Which of the following condensed structures doesn't represent a cycloalkane?
   (a) C_3H_6 (b) C_4H_{10} (c) C_5H_{10} (d) C_6H_{12}

6.

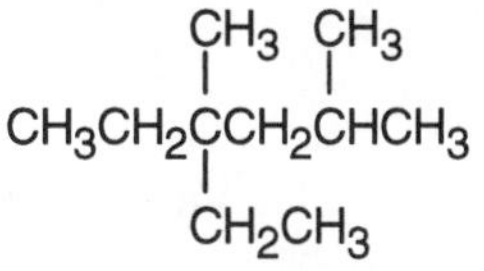

$$
\begin{array}{c}
\quad\; CH_3 \;\; CH_3 \\
\quad\;\; | \quad\;\; | \\
CH_3CH_2CCH_2CHCH_3 \\
\quad\;\; | \\
\quad\; CH_2CH_3
\end{array}
$$

   The correct name for the above structure is:
   (a) 3–ethyl–3,5–dimethylhexane   (b) 3–methyl–3–*sec*-butylpentane
   (c) 2,4–dimethyl–4–ethylhexane   (d) 4–ethyl–2,4–dimethylhexane

7. How many secondary carbons are in the structure shown in Problem 6?
   (a) 1   (b) 2   (c) 3   (d) 4

8. Which of the following structures is incorrectly drawn?

   (a) 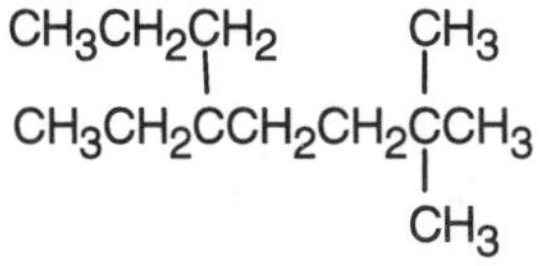 $CH_3CH_2CH_2 \qquad CH_3$
   $$CH_3CH_2CCH_2CH_2CCH_3$$
   $$CH_3$$

   (b) 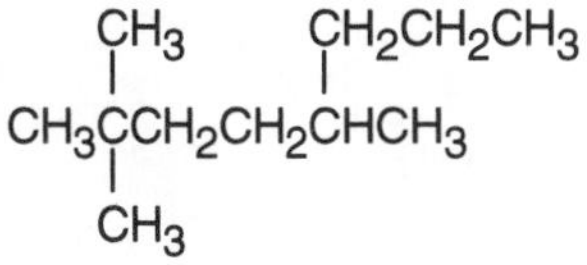 $CH_3 \qquad CH_2CH_2CH_3$
   $$CH_3CCH_2CH_2CHCH_3$$
   $$CH_3$$

   (c) 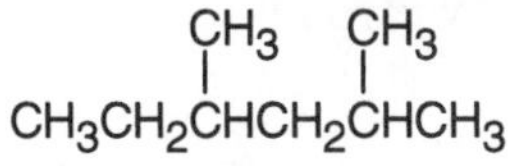 $CH_3 \;\; CH_3$
   $$CH_3CH_2CHCH_2CHCH_3$$

   (d) 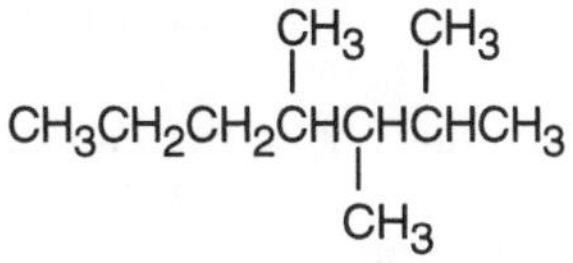 $CH_3 \;\; CH_3$
   $$CH_3CH_2CH_2CHCHCHCH_3$$
   $$CH_3$$

9. How many moles of O_2 are necessary for the complete combustion of one mole of C_6H_{12}?
   (a) 4   (b) 6   (c) 9   (d) 10

10. Which alkyl group has a quaternary carbon?
    (a) *tert*–butyl   (b) isobutyl   (c) *sec*–butyl   (d) *n*–butyl

Complete the following sentences:

1. C_{20} to C_{36} alkanes are known as _____.

2. Alkynes are compounds that contain _____ bonds.

3. Alcohols and ethers are functional groups that contain _____.

4. Mixtures of hydrocarbons can be separated by _____.

5. A _____ _____ is a shorthand way of drawing a chemical structure.

6. A _____ carbon is bonded to four other carbons.

7. Organic compounds generally have _____ melting points than inorganic compounds.

8. Cycloalkanes are compounds that contain carbon atoms joined together in a _____.

9. Organic molecules are named by the _____ system.

10. Compounds with the same formula but different structures are called _____.

11. _____ is the reaction of an alkane with oxygen.

12. A straight-chain alkane is _____ boiling than a branched-chain alkane.

Tell whether the following statements are true or false:

1. Cyclohexane and hexane are isomers.

2. A molecule with the formula C_5H_{12} can have the root name pentane, butane, or propane.

3. A cyclohexane ring is flat.

4. The correct name of the following alkane is 1,3–dimethylpentane.

$$\begin{array}{cc} CH_3 & CH_3 \\ | & | \\ \end{array}$$
$$CH_3CH_2CHCH_2CH_2$$

5. The compound 2,3–dimethylbutane has only primary and tertiary carbons.

6. Acyclic alkanes and cycloalkanes have similar chemical reactivity.

7. The C–Cl bond in CH_3Cl is ionic.

8. The compound 1,4–dimethylcyclohexane is correctly named.

9. Alkanes with one to four carbons exist as gases at room temperature.

10. Compounds with many functional groups are more reactive than compounds with few functional groups.

11.   2–Methylpentane and 3–methylpentane have nearly identical boiling points.

12.   At room temperature, an alkane exists in a single conformation.

Match the entries on the left with their partners on the right:

1. $RCH=O$ (a) Contains polar covalent bonds

2. C_5H_{12} (b) Butyl group

3. $CH_3CH(CH_3)_2$ (c) Ketone

4. $CH_3CH_2CH_2CH_3$ (d) Natural gas

5. $CH_3CH_2CH_2-$ (e) Formula of methylcyclobutane

6. $R_2C=O$ (f) Branched-chain alkane

7. CH_2Cl_2 (g) An alkene

8. $C_{30}H_{62}$ (h) Propyl group

9. C_5H_{10} (i) Aldehyde

10. $CH_3CH_2CH_2CH_2-$ (j) Formula of 2–methylbutane

11. $CH_3CH=CH_2$ (k) A solid

12. CH_4 (l) Straight-chain alkane

Chapter 13 – Alkenes, Alkynes, and Aromatic Compounds

Chapter Outline

I. Alkenes and alkynes (Sections 13.1–13.7).
  A. Introduction (Section 13.1).
    1. Alkenes are compounds that have double bonds (–C=C–).
    2. Alkynes are compounds that have triple bonds (–C≡C–).
  B. Naming alkenes and alkynes (Section 13.2).
    1. Find the longest chain containing the double or triple bond and name the parent compound by adding -ene or -yne to the root.
    2. Number the carbons in the main chain, beginning at the end nearer the multiple bond.
      a. If the bond is an equal distance from each end, begin numbering at the end nearer the first branch point.
      b. Cyclic alkenes are named cycloalkenes, and the double-bond carbons are carbons 1 and 2.
    3. Write out the full name.
      a. Number the substituents, and list them alphabetically.
      b. Indicate the position of the multiple bond by giving it the number of the first carbon in the bond.
      c. If more than one bond is present, use the endings -diene, -triene,-tetraene.
  C. Cis–trans isomerism in alkenes (Section 13.3).
    1. Atoms attached to a double bond lie in a plane.
    2. If each end of the bond is bonded to two different groups, isomerism can result.
      a. When the larger groups are on the same side of the bond, the isomer is cis.
      b. When the larger groups are on opposite sides of the bond, the isomer is trans.
  D. Properties of alkenes and alkynes (Section 13.4).
    1. Nonpolar, insoluble in water, flammable.
    2. Alkane-like in physical properties.
    3. Alkenes show cis–trans isomerism.
    4. Both alkenes and alkynes react at the multiple bond to form addition products.
  E. Organic reactions (Sections 13.5 – 13.7).
    1. Types of organic reactions (Section 13.5).
      a. Addition reactions occur when two reactants add to form a single product.
      b. Elimination reactions occur when a reactant splits into two products.
      c. Substitution reactions occur when two reactants exchange parts.
      d. Rearrangement reactions occur when a single reactant undergoes a rearrangement of bonds to yield an isomeric product.
    2. Reaction of alkenes and alkynes (Sections 13.6 – 13.7).
      a. Addition reactions (Section 13.6).
        i. Alkene + H_2 —> alkane
          Alkyne + 2 H_2 —> alkane
        ii. Alkene + X_2 —> dihaloalkane (X = halogen).
        iii. Alkene + HX —> alkyl halide
          Direction of addition: X is bonded to the more substituted carbon (Markovnikov's rule).
        iv. Alkene + H_2O —> alcohol
          Addition also follows Markovnikov's rule.
      b. Mechanism of addition reactions, using HBr addition as an example (Section 13.7)
        i. H^+ adds to the alkene to form a carbocation.
        ii. Br^- adds to the carbocation to form the product.

F. Alkene polymers (Section 13.8).
  1. Simple alkenes of the type $H_2C=CHZ$ (monomer) can add to each other in long chains.
  2. The reaction is started by an initiator, which adds to an alkene to form a reactive intermediate.
  3. The reactive intermediate starts the growth of the chain.
  4. The product is a chain-growth polymer.
  5. Varying –Z varies the properties of the polymer.
II. Aromatic compounds (Sections 13.9–13.11).
  A. Structure of benzene (Section 13.9).
    1. Benzene is a flat, six-membered ring containing three double bonds.
      a. All carbons in benzene are equivalent.
      b. The structure of benzene is an average of the two conventional structures.
      c. This phenomenon is known as resonance.
    2. Despite having double bonds, benzene is less reactive than alkenes.
    3. Aromatic compounds are nonpolar, water-insoluble, volatile and flammable.
    4. Some aromatic compounds are toxic and carcinogenic.
  B. Naming aromatic compounds (Section 13.10).
    1. Use "benzene" as the parent name.
    2. For monosubstituted benzenes, the name of the substituent is followed by -benzene (no number needed).
    3. For disubstituted benzenes:
      a. Ortho-disubstituted benzenes have substituents in the 1,2 positions of the ring.
      b. Meta-disubstituted benzenes have substituents in the 1,3 positions of the ring.
      c. Para-disubstituted benzenes have substituents in the 1,4 positions of the ring.
    4. Many aromatic compounds have trivial names.
  C. Reactions of aromatic compounds (Section 13.11).
    Aromatic compounds undergo substitution reactions.

    a. Aromatic ring + HNO_3 $\xrightarrow{H_2SO_4}$ Nitroaromatic ring

    b. Aromatic ring + X_2 $\xrightarrow{FeX_3}$ Haloaromatic ring

    c. Aromatic ring + SO_3 $\xrightarrow{H_2SO_4}$ Aromatic sulfonic acid

Solutions to Chapter 13 Problems

13.1

(a)
$$2\text{–methyl} \searrow CH_3$$
$$CH_3CH_2CH_2CH=CHCHCH_3$$
$$7 \quad 6 \quad 5 \quad 4 \quad\quad 3 \; 2 \; 1$$

      2–Methyl–3–heptene

(b)
$$6 \quad 5 \; 4 \quad 3 \; 2 \quad 1$$
$$H_2C=CHCH_2CH_2C=CH_2$$
$$2\text{–methyl} \longrightarrow CH_3$$

      2–Methyl–1,5–hexadiene

13.2

(a)
$$\overset{CH_3}{\underset{|}{}}$$
$$CH_3CH_2CH_2CH_2CHCH=CH_2$$

      3–Methyl–1-heptene

(b)
$$\overset{CH_3}{\underset{|}{}}$$
$$H_3C-\overset{|}{\underset{|}{C}}-C\equiv C-CH_3$$
$$\underset{CH_3}{}$$

      4,4–Dimethyl–2-pentyne

(c)

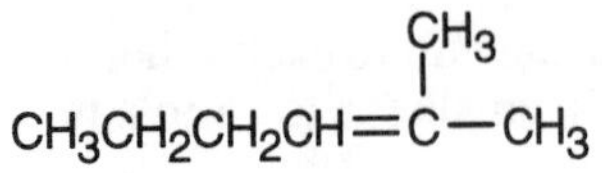

$$CH_3CH_2CH_2CH=\overset{\overset{\displaystyle CH_3}{|}}{C}-CH_3$$

2–Methyl–2–hexene

(d)

$$CH_3CH_2CH=\overset{\overset{\displaystyle CH_3CH_2}{|}}{C}-\overset{\overset{\displaystyle CH_3}{|}}{\underset{\underset{\displaystyle CH_3}{|}}{C}}-CH_3$$

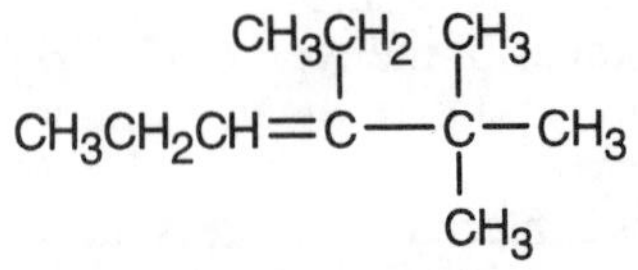

3–Ethyl–2,2–dimethyl–3–hexene

13.3   (a) Attached to C3: –H, –CH$_2$CH$_3$
Attached to C4: –H, –CH$_2$CH$_2$CH$_3$

Since each of the double-bond carbons has two different groups attached to it, 3-heptene exists as cis–trans isomers:

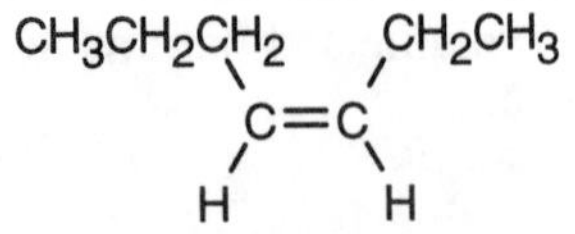

$$CH_3CH_2CH_2 \diagdown \diagup CH_2CH_3$$
$$C=C$$
$$\diagup \diagdown$$
$$H \qquad H$$

cis–3–Heptene

$$CH_3CH_2CH_2 \diagdown \diagup H$$
$$C=C$$
$$\diagup \diagdown$$
$$H \qquad CH_2CH_3$$

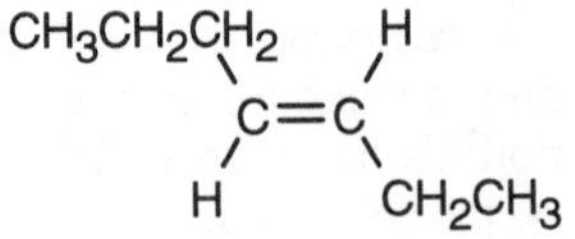

trans–3– Heptene

(b) Attached to C2: –CH$_3$, –CH$_3$
Attached to C3: –H, –CH$_2$CH$_2$CH$_3$

Since the two groups attached to C2 are identical, 2-methyl-2-hexene does not exist as cis–trans isomers:

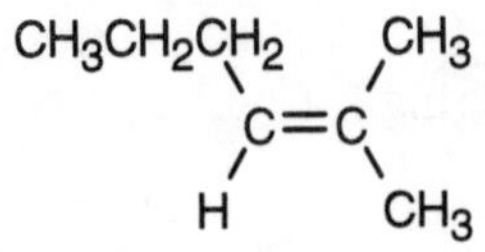

$$CH_3CH_2CH_2 \diagdown \diagup CH_3$$
$$C=C$$
$$\diagup \diagdown$$
$$H \qquad CH_3$$

2–Methyl–2–hexene

(c) Attached to C2: –H, –CH$_3$
Attached to C3: –H, –CH$_2$CH(CH$_3$)$_2$

Since each carbon has two different groups attached to it, 5-methyl-2-hexene exists as cis–trans isomers:

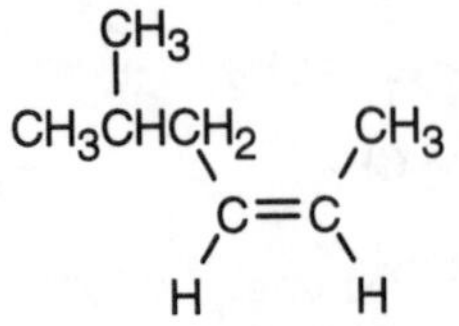

$$\overset{\overset{\displaystyle CH_3}{|}}{CH_3CHCH_2} \diagdown \diagup CH_3$$
$$C=C$$
$$\diagup \diagdown$$
$$H \qquad H$$

cis–5–Methyl–2–hexene

$$\overset{\overset{\displaystyle CH_3}{|}}{CH_3CHCH_2} \diagdown \diagup H$$
$$C=C$$
$$\diagup \diagdown$$
$$H \qquad CH_3$$

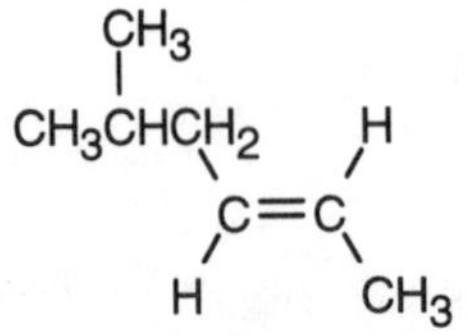

trans–5–Methyl–2–hexene

13.4

cis-3,4–Dimethyl–3–hexene   trans-3,4–Dimethyl–3–hexane

13.5

(a) CH_3Br + $NaOH$ ⟶ CH_3OH + $NaBr$

This reaction is a substitution because two reagents exchange parts to give two different products.

(b) $H_2C{=}CH_2$ + HCl ⟶ CH_3CH_2Cl

This reaction is an addition because two reactants combine to give one product.

(c) CH_3CH_2Br ⟶ $H_2C{=}CH_2$ + HBr

In this elimination reaction, two products are formed from one reactant.

13.6

(a) $CH_3CH_2CH{=}CH_2$ + H_2 $\xrightarrow{Pd}$ $CH_3CH_2CH_2CH_3$

(b)

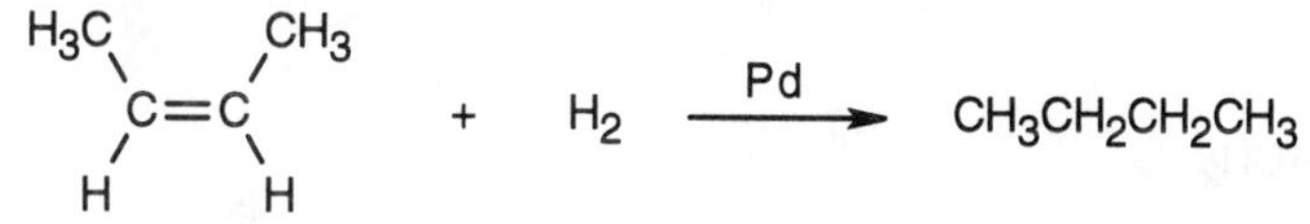

$+$ H_2 $\xrightarrow{Pd}$ $CH_3CH_2CH_2CH_3$

(c)

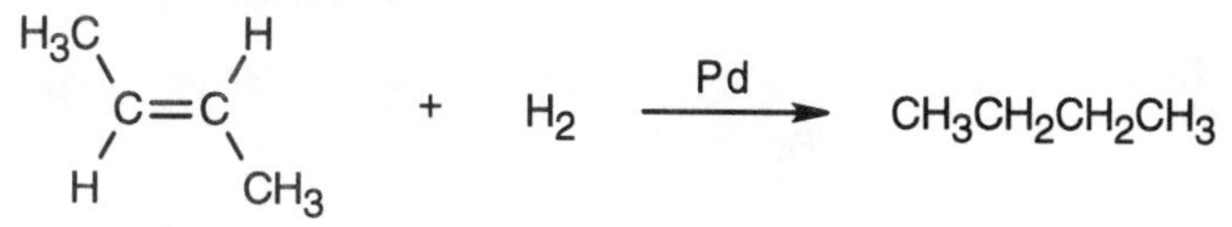

$+$ H_2 $\xrightarrow{Pd}$ $CH_3CH_2CH_2CH_3$

(d)

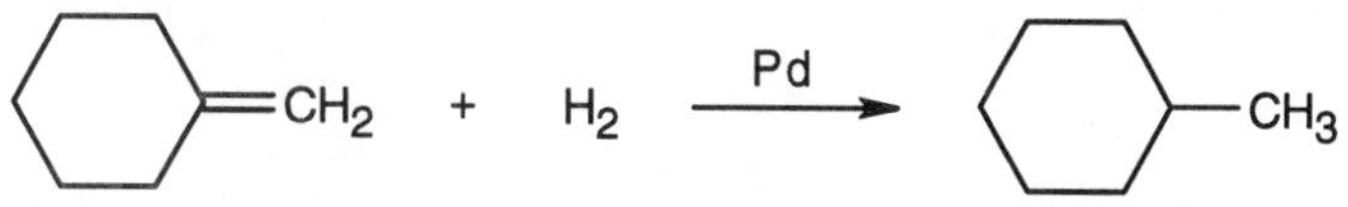

$+$ H_2 $\xrightarrow{Pd}$

13.7

(a)

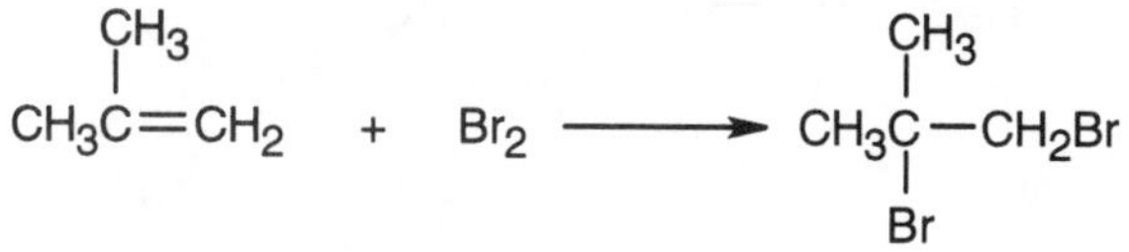

(b) $CH_3CH_2CH_2CH{=}CH_2$ + Cl_2 ⟶

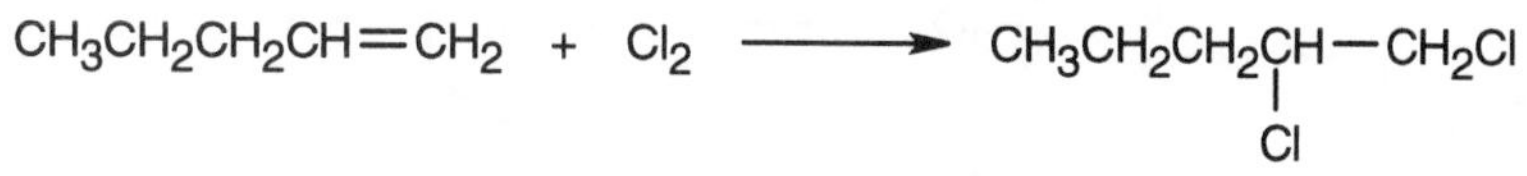

13.8

(a)

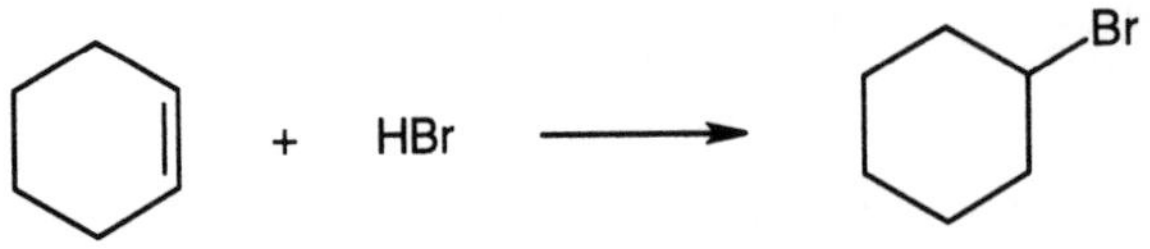

(b) $CH_3CH_2CH_2CH_2CH=CH_2$ + HCl $\longrightarrow$ $CH_3CH_2CH_2CH_2\underset{\underset{Cl}{|}}{CH}CH_3$

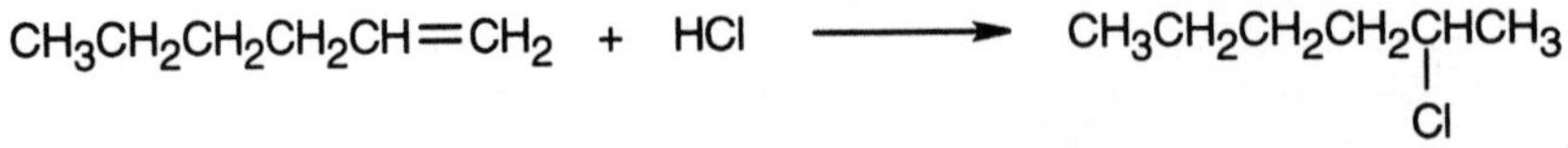

Chlorine attaches to the carbon that has fewer hydrogens.

(c)

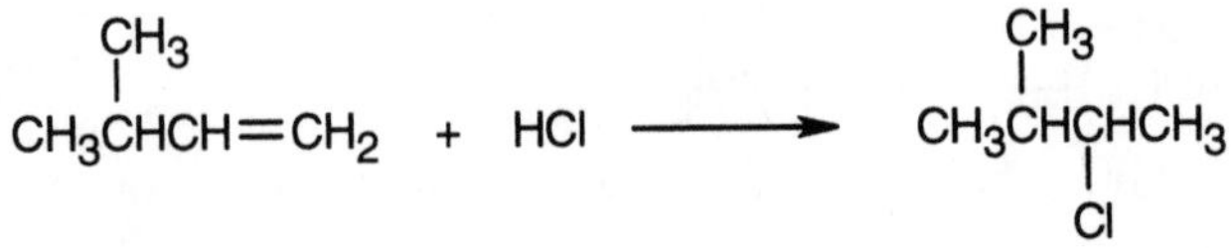

$CH_3\underset{\underset{CH_3}{|}}{CH}CH=CH_2$ + HCl $\longrightarrow$ $CH_3\underset{\underset{CH_3}{|}}{CH}\underset{\underset{Cl}{|}}{CH}CH_3$

13.9

(a)

$CH_3CH_2\underset{\underset{CH_2CH_3}{|}}{C}=CHCH_3$ + HCl $\longrightarrow$ $CH_3CH_2\underset{\underset{Cl}{\overset{CH_2CH_3}{|}}}{C}CH_2CH_3$

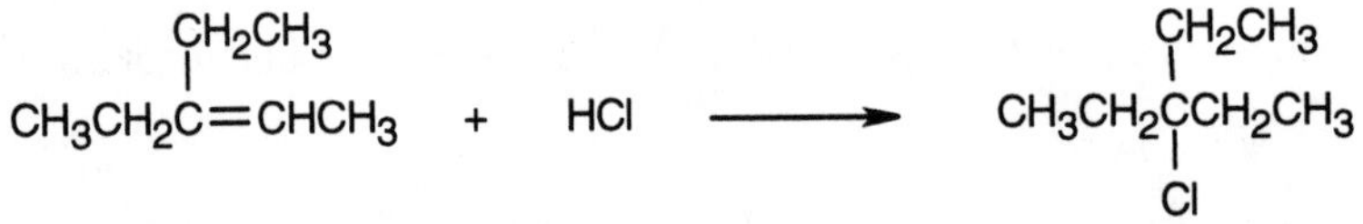

3-Ethyl-2-pentene   3-Chloro-3-ethylpentane

(b)

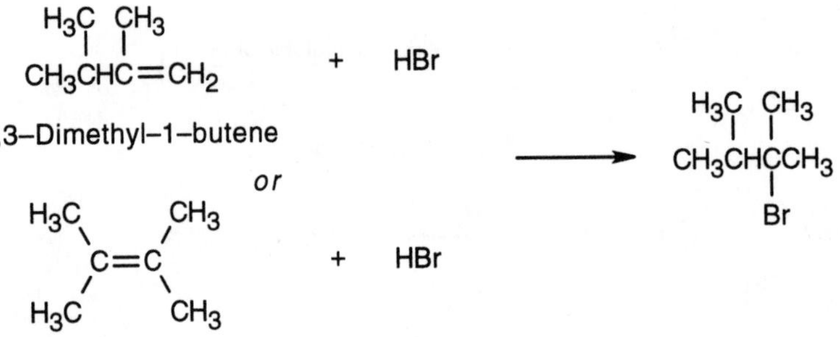

$CH_3\underset{\underset{}{\overset{H_3C\ CH_3}{|\ |}}}{CH}C=CH_2$ + HBr

2,3-Dimethyl-1-butene

or

$\underset{H_3C}{\overset{H_3C}{>}}C=C\underset{CH_3}{\overset{CH_3}{<}}$ + HBr

2,3-Dimethyl-2-butene

$\longrightarrow$ $CH_3\underset{\underset{Br}{\overset{H_3C\ CH_3}{|\ |}}}{CH}CCH_3$

13.10

(a)

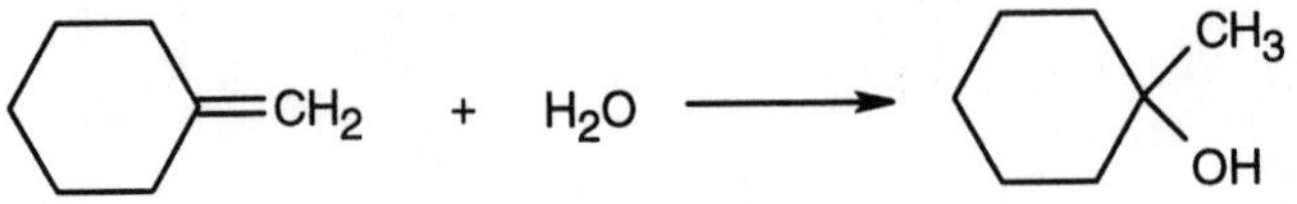

(b)

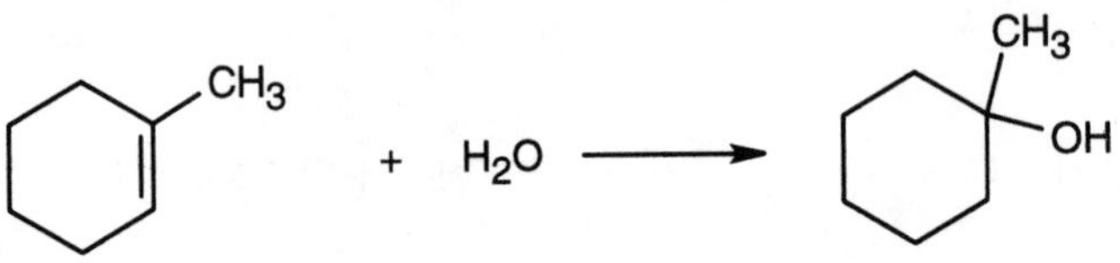

13.11

$$\underset{\text{3–Methyl–2–pentene}}{CH_3CH_2\overset{\overset{\displaystyle CH_3}{|}}{C}=CHCH_3}$$

or

$$+ \quad H_2O \longrightarrow \underset{\text{OH}}{CH_3CH_2\overset{\overset{\displaystyle CH_3}{|}}{\underset{|}{C}}CH_2CH_3}$$

$$\underset{\text{2–Ethyl–1–butene}}{CH_3CH_2\overset{\overset{\displaystyle CH_2}{||}}{C}CH_2CH_3}$$

13.12

$$\underset{\text{2–Methylpropene}}{CH_3\overset{\overset{\displaystyle CH_3}{|}}{C}=CH_2} + HCl \longrightarrow \left[\underset{+}{CH_3\overset{\overset{\displaystyle CH_3}{|}}{C}CH_3} \right] \longrightarrow \underset{\substack{\text{2–Chloro–2–} \\ \text{methylpropane}}}{CH_3\overset{\overset{\displaystyle CH_3}{|}}{\underset{\underset{\displaystyle Cl}{|}}{C}}CH_3}$$

carbocation
intermediate

13.13

(a)

Monomer	*Polymer*

$$\underset{\text{Tetrafluoroethylene}}{F_2C=CF_2} \qquad \underset{\text{Teflon}}{\left(\!\!-CF_2-CF_2-CF_2-CF_2-\!\!\right)}$$

(b)

$$\underset{\text{Acrylonitrile}}{H_2C=CH-C\equiv N}$$

$$\underset{\text{Polyacrylonitrile}}{\left(\!\!-CH_2-\overset{\overset{\displaystyle N}{\overset{\displaystyle |||}{\overset{\displaystyle C}{|}}}}{CH}-CH_2-\overset{\overset{\displaystyle N}{\overset{\displaystyle |||}{\overset{\displaystyle C}{|}}}}{CH}-\!\!\right)}$$

13.14

(a)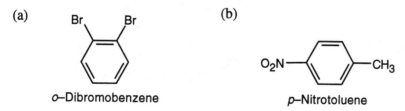

o–Bromochlorobenzene   Butylbenzene   *o*–Bromotoluene

13.15

(a)

(b)

o–Dibromobenzene   *p*–Nitrotoluene

(c)

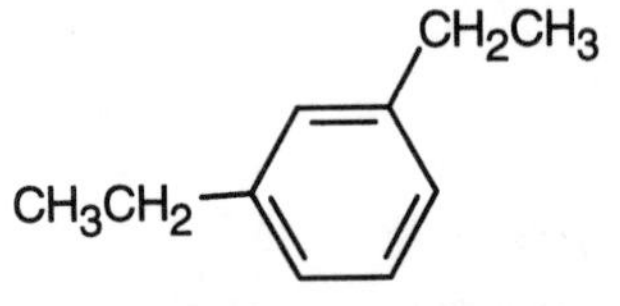

m–Diethylbenzene

(d)

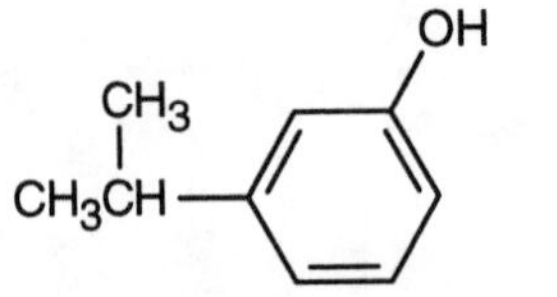

m–Isopropylphenol

13.16

(a)

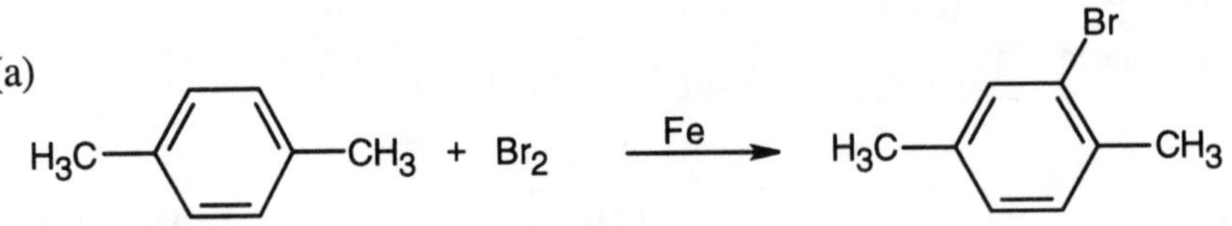

(b)

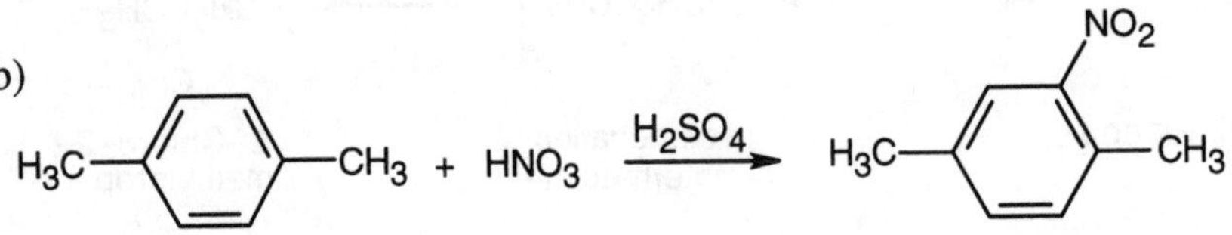

(c)

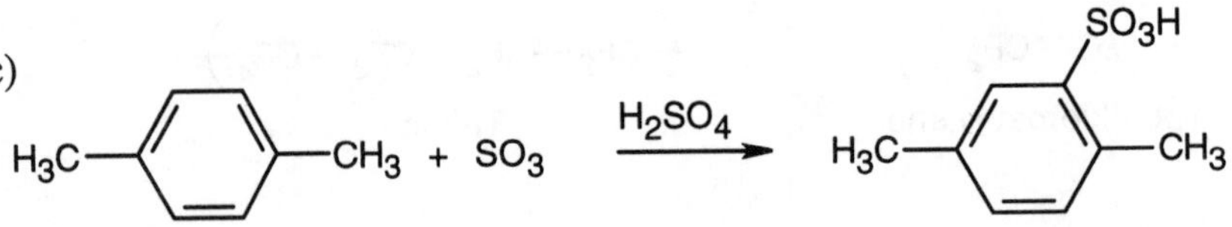

13.17

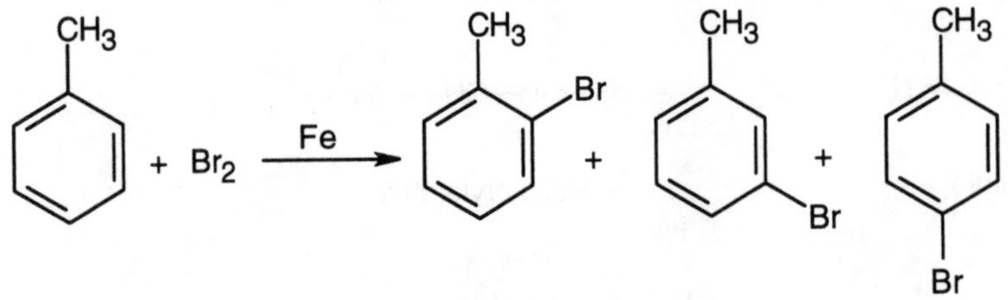

ortho   *meta*   *para*

Understanding Key Concepts

13.18

(a)

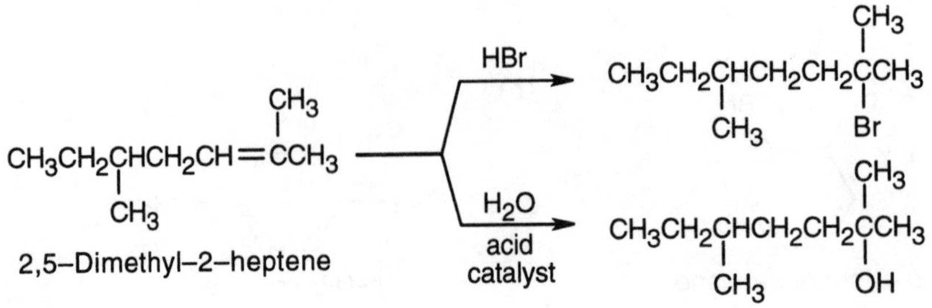

2,5–Dimethyl–2–heptene

(b)

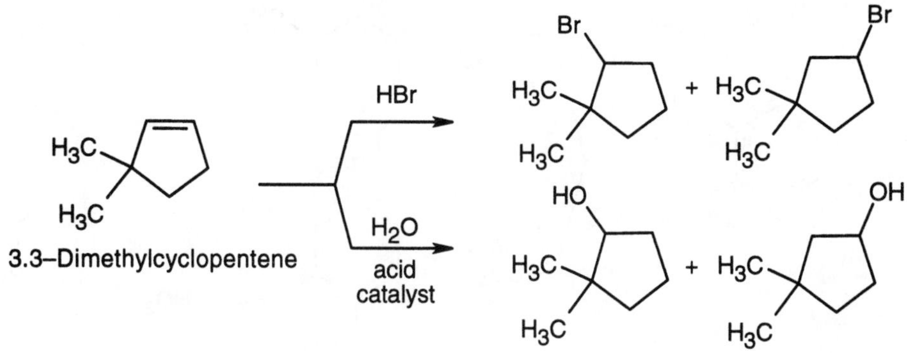

3.3–Dimethylcyclopentene

HBr

H_2O
acid
catalyst

13.19

(a)

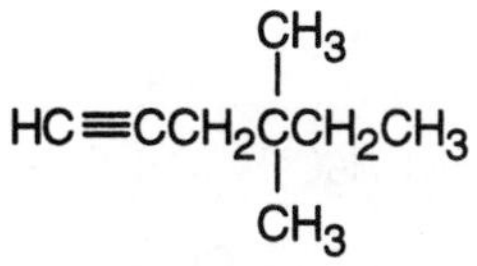

$HC\equiv CCH_2CCH_2CH_3$

with CH_3 groups

4,4–Dimethyl–1–hexyne

(b)

$CH_3CHCH_2C\equiv CCH_2CHCH_3$

with CH_3 groups

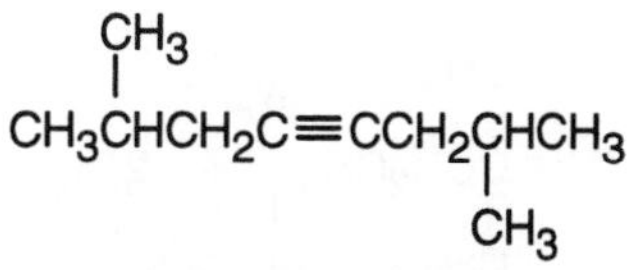

2,7–Dimethyl–4–octyne

13.20

(a)

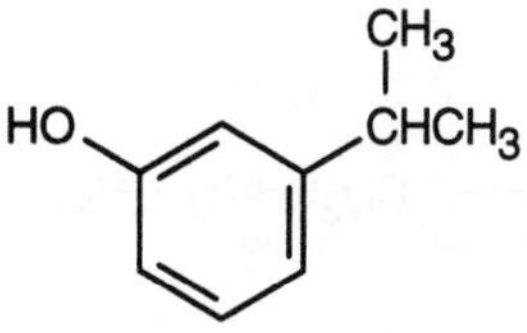

m–Isopropylphenol

(b)

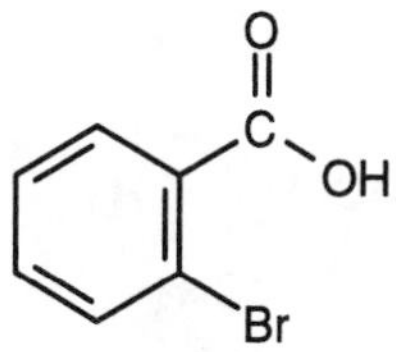

o–Bromobenzoic acid

13.21

(a)

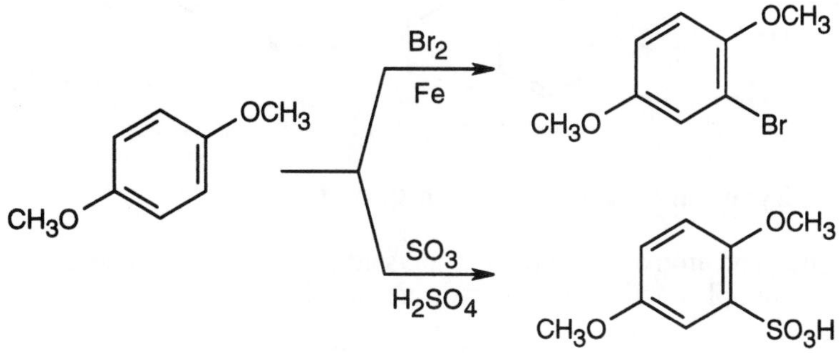

Br_2
Fe

SO_3
H_2SO_4

(b)

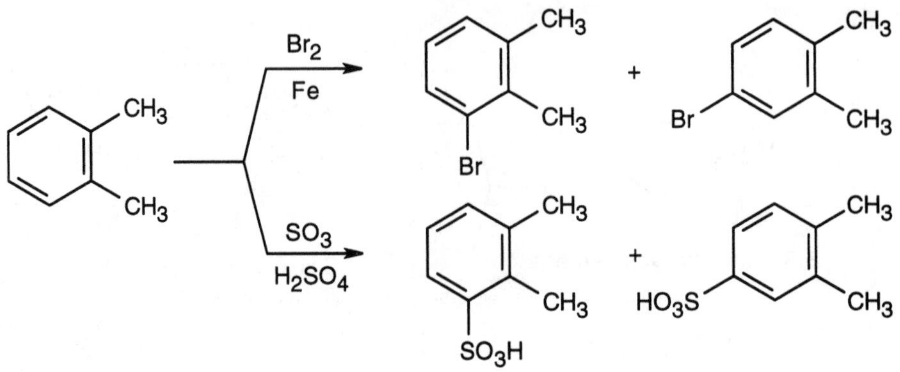

13.22

(a)

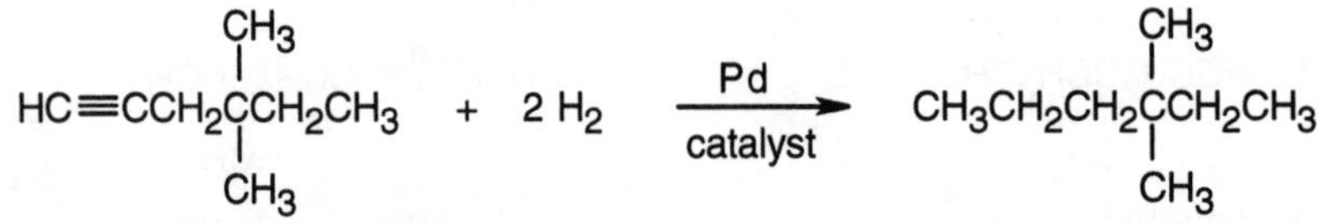

4,4–Dimethyl–1–hexyne   3,3–Dimethylhexane

(b)

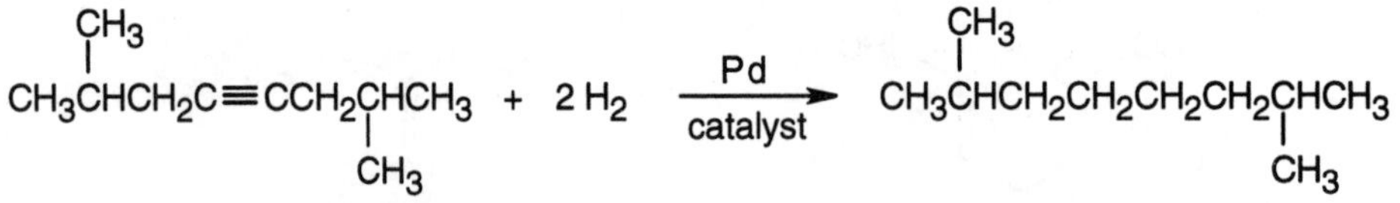

2,7–Dimethyl–4–octyne   2,7–Dimethyloctane

13.23

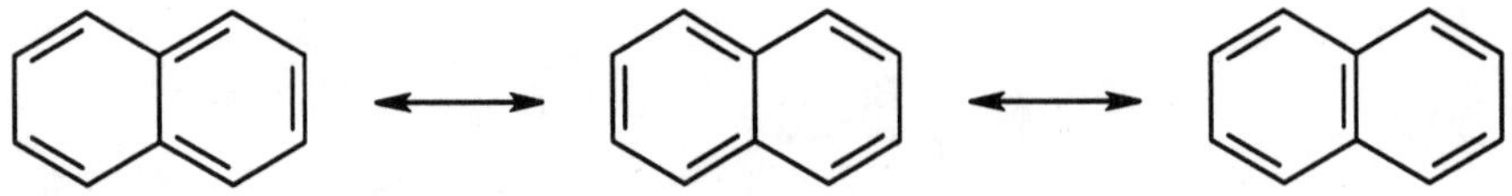

Naming Alkenes, Alkynes and Aromatic Compounds

13.24 Alkenes, alkynes, and aromatic compounds are said to be unsaturated because they have carbon–carbon multiple bonds to which hydrogen can be added.

13.26

Family:	Alkene	Alkyne	Aromatic Compound
Name Ending:	*-ene*	*-yne*	*-benzene*

13.28 There are many possible answers to this question. For example:

(a)   (b)   (c)

$CH_3CH_2CH_2CH=CH_2$ $CH_3CH_2C\equiv CH$

1–Pentene   1-Butyne

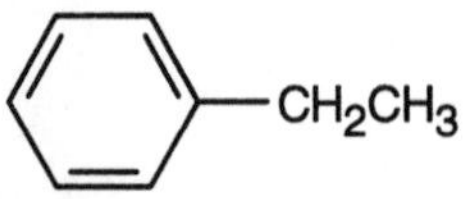

                                                Ethylbenzene

13.30

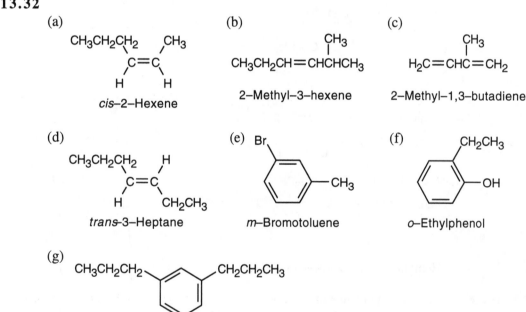

(a)

CH$_3$CH$_2$CH$_2$CH=CH$_2$

1–Pentene

(b)

CH$_3$CHCH$_2$C≡CCH$_3$ (with CH$_3$ on second carbon)

5–Methyl–2–hexyne

(c)

H$_3$C, CH$_3$ / C=C / H$_3$C, CH$_3$

2,3–Dimethyl–2–butene

(d)

CH$_3$CH=C–C=CH$_2$ (with CH$_3$ above and CH$_2$CH$_3$ below)

2–Ethyl–3–methyl–1,3–pentadiene

(e)

4–Ethyl–3,5–dimethylcyclohexene

(f)

3,3–Diethylcyclobutene (with CH$_2$CH$_3$ and CH$_2$CH$_3$)

13.32

(a)

CH$_3$CH$_2$CH$_2$, CH$_3$ / C=C / H, H

cis–2–Hexene

(b)

CH$_3$CH$_2$CH=CHCHCH$_3$ (with CH$_3$)

2–Methyl–3–hexene

(c)

H$_2$C=CHC=CH$_2$ (with CH$_3$)

2–Methyl–1,3–butadiene

(d)

CH$_3$CH$_2$CH$_2$, H / C=C / H, CH$_2$CH$_3$

trans–3–Heptane

(e) Br, CH$_3$

m–Bromotoluene

(f) CH$_2$CH$_3$, OH

o–Ethylphenol

(g)

CH$_3$CH$_2$CH$_2$ CH$_2$CH$_2$CH$_3$

m–Dipropylbenzene

13.34

CH$_3$CH$_2$CH$_2$C≡CH

1–Pentyne

CH$_3$CH$_2$C≡CCH$_3$

2–Pentyne

CH$_3$CHC≡CH (with CH$_3$)

3–Methyl–1–butyne

13.36

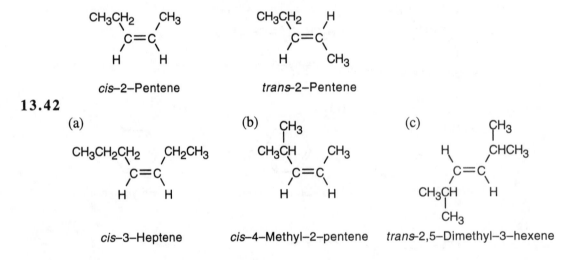

CH₃CH₂CH₂CH=CH₂

1–Pentene

CH₃CH₂CH=CHCH₃

2–Pentene

CH₃
|
CH₃CH₂C=CH₂

2–Methyl–1–butene

CH₃
|
CH₃CHCH=CH₂

3–Methyl–1–butene

CH₃
|
CH₃CH=CCH₃

2–Methyl–2–butene

Alkene Cis–Trans Isomers

13.38 For cis–trans isomers to exist, each carbon of the double bond must be bonded to two different groups.

13.40 Only 2-pentene exists as cis–trans isomers:

cis–2–Pentene

trans–2–Pentene

13.42

(a)

cis–3–Heptene

(b)

cis–4–Methyl–2–pentene

(c)

trans–2,5–Dimethyl–3–hexene

13.44 (a) These compounds are identical:

and

(b) These compounds are also identical:

and

Kinds of Reactions

13.46 In a substitution reaction, two reactants exchange parts to give two new products. In an addition reaction, two reactants add together to form a single product, with no atoms left over.

13.48 The conversion of 2–methyl–2–pentene to 1–hexene would be a rearrangement because it is the conversion of a single reactant into a single product by the reorganization of bonds.

13.50

(a)

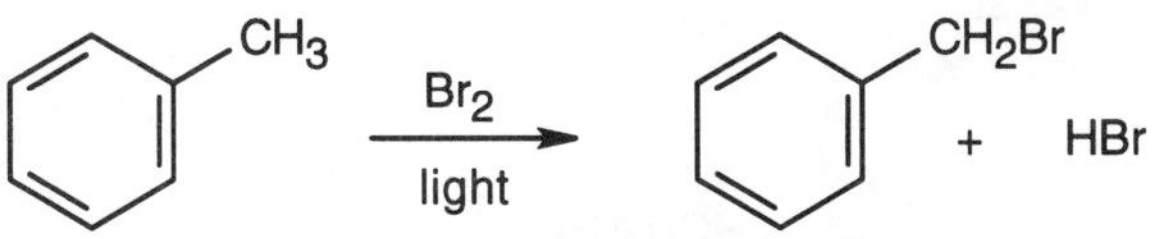

This reaction is a substitution because two reactants exchange parts to give two new products.

(b)

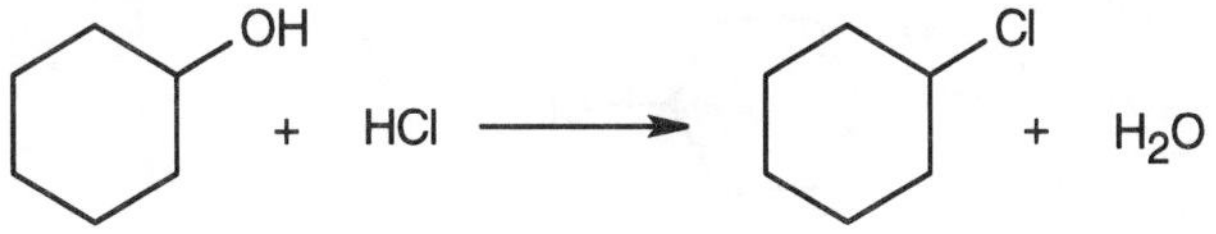

This reaction is also a substitution reaction.

Reactions of Alkenes and Alkynes

13.52

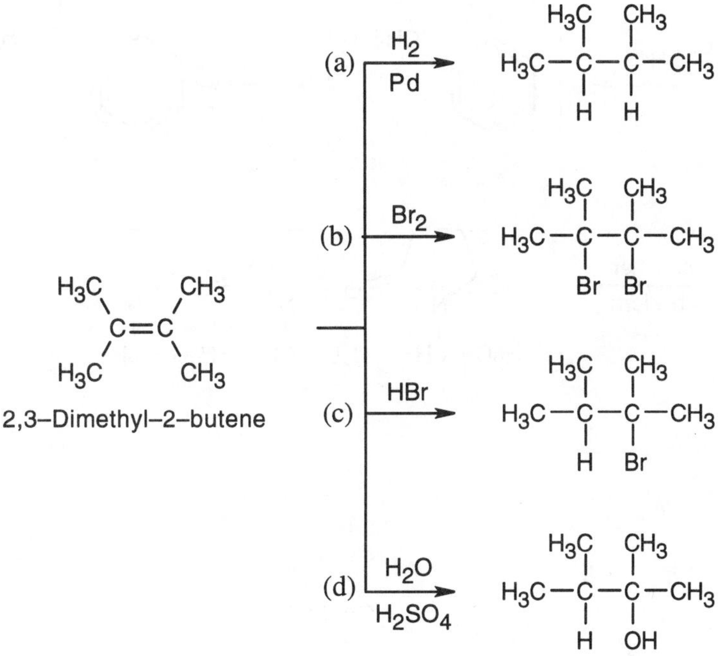

13.54

(a)

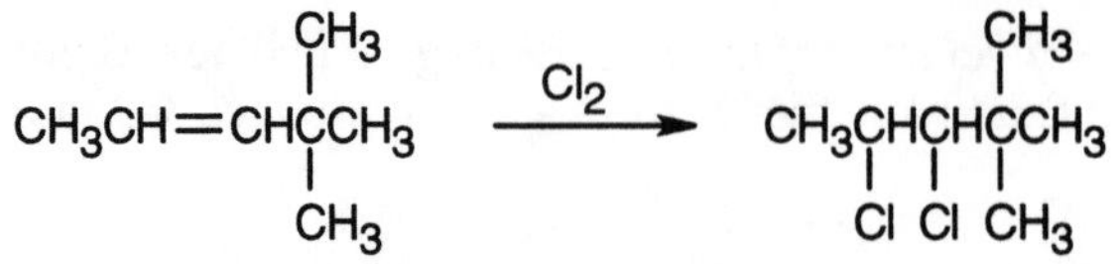
CH3
CH3CH=CHCCH3
CH3
Cl2
CH3
CH3CHCHCCH3
Cl Cl CH3

(b)

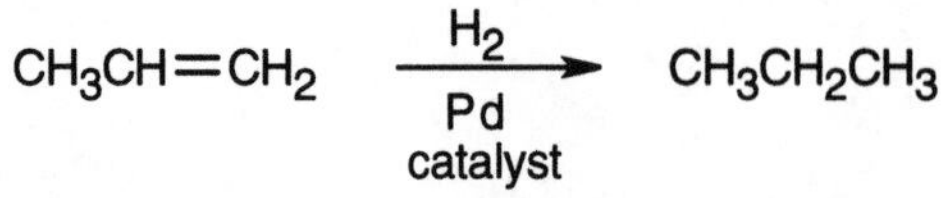
CH3CH=CH2
H2
Pd
catalyst
CH3CH2CH3

(c)

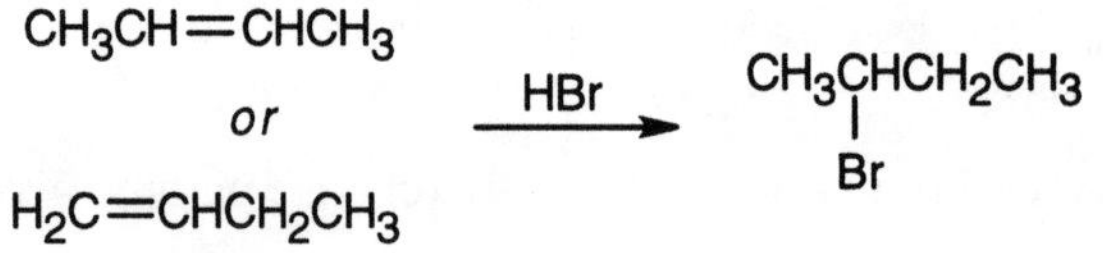
CH3CH=CHCH3
or
H2C=CHCH2CH3
HBr
CH3CHCH2CH3
Br

(d)

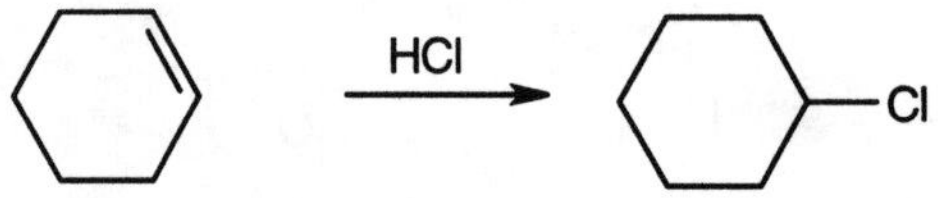
HCl
Cl

(e)

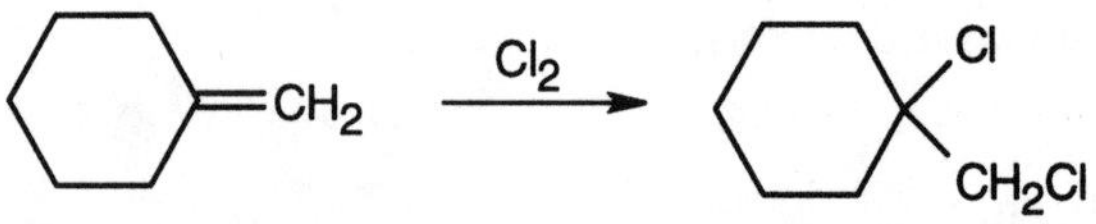
=CH2
Cl2
Cl
CH2Cl

13.56

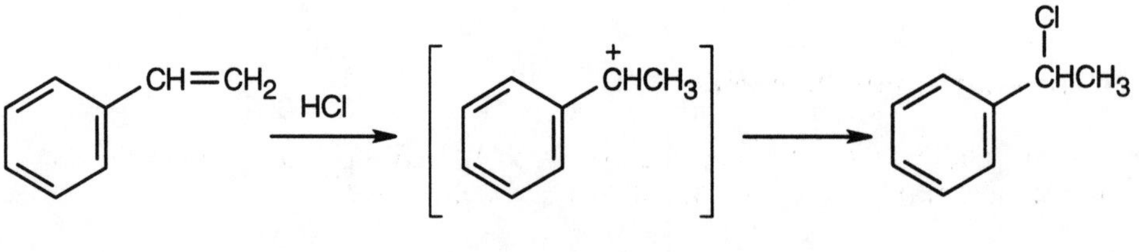
CH=CH2
HCl
+
CHCH3
Cl
CHCH3

13.58

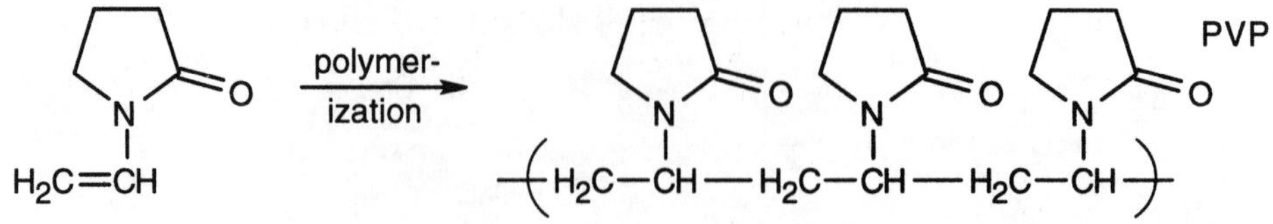
N
O
H2C=CH
polymer-
ization
PVP
H2C—CH—H2C—CH—H2C—CH

Reactions of Aromatic Compounds

13.60 Under conditions where an alkene would react with all four reagents, benzene reacts only with Br_2 (b) to give the product shown below.

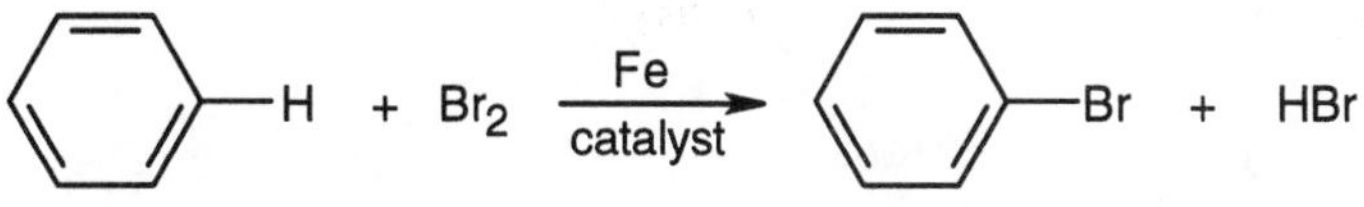

13.62

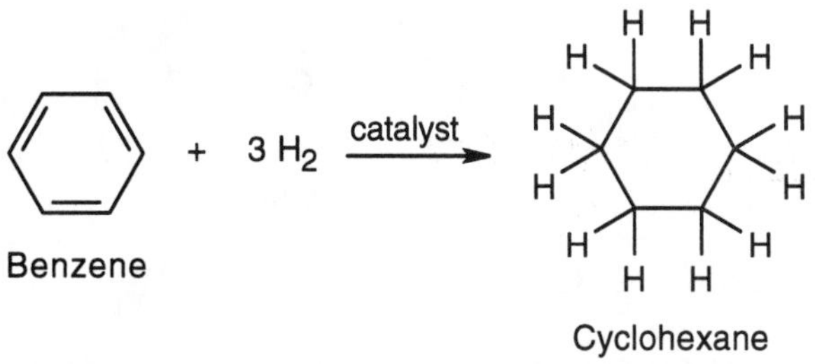

Benzene

Cyclohexane

Applications

13.64 The rod cells are responsible for vision in dim light, and the cone cells are responsible for vision in bright light and for color vision.

13.66 A polycyclic aromatic compound is a compound that has two or more benzene-like rings joined together to share a common bond.

13.68 Since naphthalene is white, it must absorb color in the ultraviolet range.

General Questions and Problems

13.70 A trans double bond is too strained to exist in a small ring like cyclohexene, but a large ring is more flexible and can include a trans double bond:

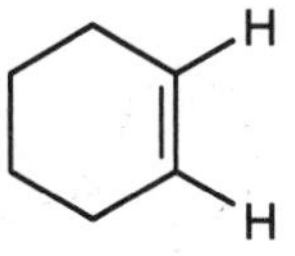

The double bond must be cis in this six-membered ring.

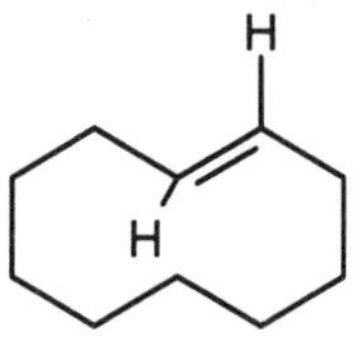

The double bond can be trans in this ten-membered ring.

13.72

$$2\ HC{\equiv}CH\ +\ 5\ O_2\ \longrightarrow\ 4\ CO_2\ +\ 2\ H_2O$$

13.74 None of the reagents that add to alkenes react with alkanes such as cyclohexane. Thus, you can mix a reagent such as Br_2 with a sample from each bottle. The mixture of cyclohexene and Br_2 turns from reddish-brown to colorless, but the mixture of cyclohexane and Br_2 remains colored.

13.76

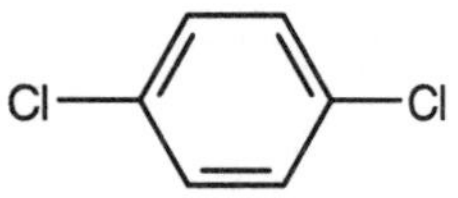

Cl—⬡—Cl   *p*–Dichlorobenzene

13.78

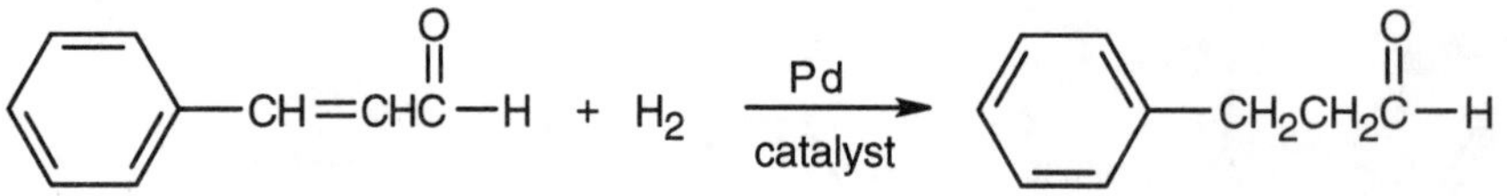

Cinnamaldehyde   3–Phenylpropanal

13.80

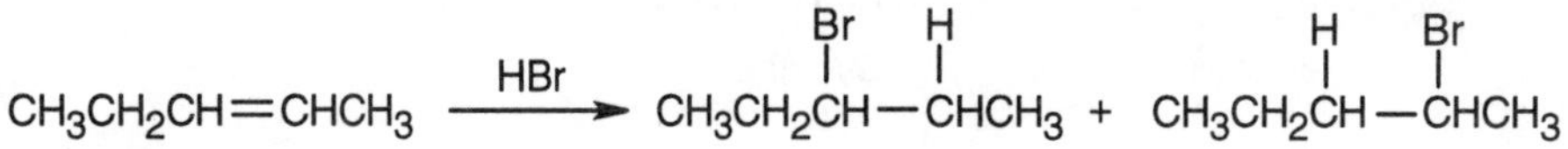

$CH_3CH_2CH{=}CHCH_3$ →(HBr)→ $CH_3CH_2CH{-}CHCH_3$ (Br H) + $CH_3CH_2CH{-}CHCH_3$ (H Br)

2–Pentene

The products are formed in equal amounts because each end of the double bond has the same number of hydrogens and the two intermediate carbocations are formed in approximately equal amounts.

13.82

(a)

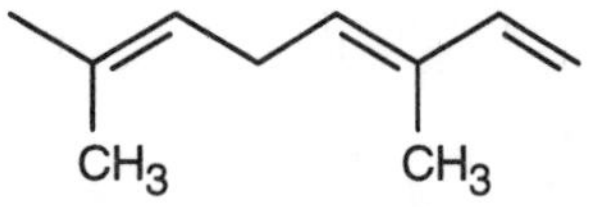

Ocimene   (3,7–Dimethyl–1,3,6–octatriene)

(b)

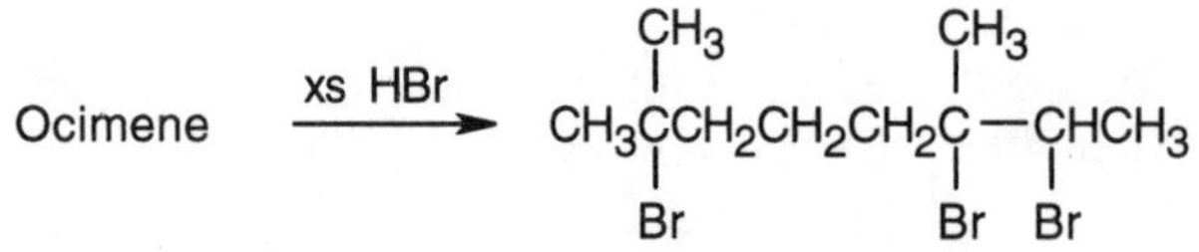

Ocimene →(xs HBr)→ $CH_3CCH_2CH_2CH_2C{-}CHCH_3$

13.84 Compound (b) does not exhibit cis–trans isomerism.

(a)

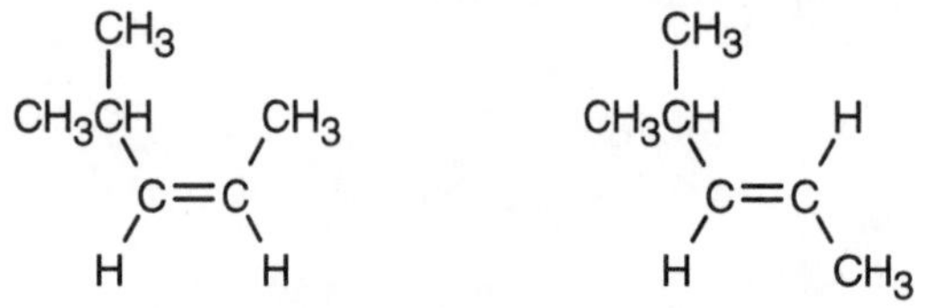

(c)

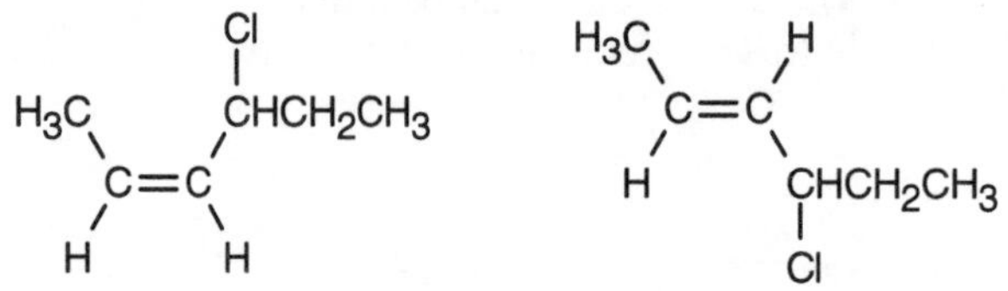

Self-Test for Chapter 13

Multiple choice:

1. Which of the following polymers is a hydrocarbon?
    (a) Teflon (b) poly(vinyl chloride) (c) Lucite (d) polystyrene

2. 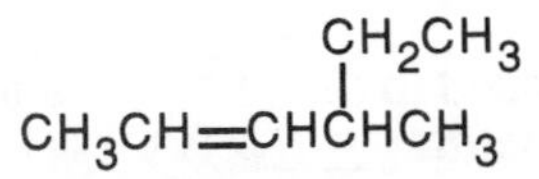 $$CH_3CH=CHCHCH_3$$ with CH_2CH_3 substituent

    The name of this compound is:
    (a) 3-methyl-4-hexene (b) 4-methyl-2-hexene (c) 2-ethyl-3-pentene (d) 3-ethyl-2-pentene

3. Which of the following statements about the reaction of benzene with Br_2 is true?
    (a) The reaction is catalyzed by iron. (b) The reaction is an addition reaction. (c) Two different products are formed. (d) When bromine is added to benzene, the bromine color disappears.

4. Reaction of a hydrocarbon with $2 H_2$ gives a product with the formula C_6H_{12}. Which of the following is the original hydrocarbon?
    (a) benzene (b) 3–methyl–1,3–pentadiene (c) 1,4–cyclohexadiene (d) 2–hexyne

5. Which of the following molecules shows cis–trans isomerism?
    (a) 2–hexene (b) 2–hexyne (c) 2–methyl–2–pentene (d) 2–ethyl–1–hexene

6. Which of the following statements about carbocations is true?
    (a) A carbocation has seven electrons in its outer shell. (b) Two different carbocations can be formed in the reaction of HBr with 3–hexene. (c) A carbocation is an intermediate in the reaction of HBr with an alkene. (d) Carbocations are stable ions.

7. How many isomers with the formula C_5H_8 can be drawn? (Don't include isomers with rings or cis–trans isomers.)
    (a) 5 (b) 7 (c) 9 (d) 11

8. Which of the following is probably not a monomer in a polymerization reaction?
    (a) $H_2C=CHCN$ (b) $H_2C=CHCH_3$ (c) $CH_3CH=C(CH_3)_2$ (d) $H_2C=CCl_2$

9. If toluene reacted with one mole of Cl_2, and each of the products of the reaction reacted with one mole of Cl_2, how many different products could be formed? (Not all of these can be formed in the laboratory.)
    (a) 3 (b) 4 (c) 5 (d) 6

10. Which of the following alkenes is not a starting material for 3-bromo-3-methylhexane?
    (a) 2-ethyl-1-pentene (b) 3-methyl-2-hexene (c) 3-methyl-3-hexene (d) 4-methyl-2-hexene

Complete the following sentences:

1. The name of $CH_3CH_2CH_2CH_2C{\equiv}CCH_3$ is _____.

2. Addition of hydrogen to an alkene or alkyne is known as _____.

3. A benzene ring with substituents at the 1 and 4 positions is said to be _____ disubstituted.

4. In the addition of HX to an alkene, the H becomes attached to the carbon that already has _____ H's, and the X becomes attached to the carbon that has _____ H's.

5. Ethanol can be produced by the _____ of ethylene.

6. In the nitration of benzene, H_2SO_4 is used as a _____.

7. The intermediate formed during the addition of HBr to an alkene is called a _____.

8. Compounds with double or triple bonds are said to be _____.

9. _____ is another name for methylbenzene.

10. The reaction of Br_2 with benzene is an example of a _____ reaction.

11. _____ _____ _____ are aromatic compounds consisting of two or more rings joined together by a common bond.

12. Simple alkenes are made by _____ _____ of natural gas and petroleum.

Tell whether the following statements are true or false:

1. Cis–trans isomers have identical physical properties.

2. Addition of one equivalent of H_2 to an alkyne yields an alkene.

3. Aromatic compounds are less reactive than alkenes.

4. The product of addition of HBr to 1–butene is 1–bromobutane.

5. The reaction of HBr with an alkene is known as halogenation.

6. A compound with the formula C_4H_6 can be either an alkyne or an alkene.

7. 1–Methylcyclohexene can exhibit cis–trans isomerism.

8. Mixing an alkene with water causes the hydration of the double bond.

9. Addition of HBr to an alkene is a two-step reaction.

10. Benzene and 1–butene react with Br_2 under the same reaction conditions.

11. Only aromatic compounds with more than one ring are carcinogenic.

12. Two different compounds result from the reaction of HBr with 2–pentene.

Match the entries on the left with their partners on the right:

1. HNO_3, H_2SO_4 (a) Does not have cis–trans isomers

2. H_2O, H_2SO_4 (b) Used to hydrogenate an alkene

3. $CH_3C{\equiv}CH$ (c) Polycyclic aromatic hydrocarbon

4. Hydroxybenzene   (d) Addition reaction

5. H_2, Pd   (e) Used to nitrate aromatic compounds

6. $(CH_3)_2CH^+$ (f) Substitution reaction

7. Propene + Br_2 (g) Exhibits cis–trans isomerism

8. Naphthalene   (h) Teflon monomer

9. 2–Methylpropene   (i) Alkyne

10. Benzene + Br_2 (j) Phenol

11. 2–Butene   (k) Used to hydrate an alkene

12. $CF_2{=}CF_2$ (l) Carbocation

Chapter 14 – Some Compounds with Oxygen, Sulfur, or a Halogen

Chapter Outline

I. Compounds containing oxygen (Sections 14.1–14.9).
  A. Introduction (Section 14.1).
    1. In all of these compounds, oxygen forms a single bond to either carbon or hydrogen.
    2. Alcohols (R–OH), phenols (Ar–OH) and ethers (R–O–R) are examples of these compounds.
      a. Many alcohols resemble water in their physical properties.
      b. Alcohols (and phenols) can form hydrogen bonds, which raise their boiling points.
  B. Alcohols (Sections 14.2–14.5).
    1. Common alcohols are methanol, ethanol, isopropanol, ethylene glycol and glycerol (Section 14.2).
    2. Naming alcohols (Section 14.3).
      a. Find the longest chain containing the hydroxyl group, and name the chain by replacing the -e ending of the corresponding alkane with -ol.
      b. Number the carbon atoms in the main chain, beginning at the end nearer the –OH group.
      c. Write the name.
        i. Place the number of the –OH group immediately before the parent compound name.
        ii. Number all other substituents according to their positions and list them alphabetically.
      d. Diols are often known as glycols.
      e. Alcohols can be classified according to the number of substituents bonded to the –OH carbon.
        i. If there is one substituent (RCH_2OH), the alcohol is primary.
        ii. If there are two substituents (R_2CHOH), the alcohol is secondary.
        iii. If there are three substituents (R_3COH), the alcohol is tertiary.
    3. Properties of alcohols (Section 14.4).
      a. Hydrogen bonding makes alcohols higher boiling than other compounds of similar mass.
      b. Hydrogen bonding also makes smaller alcohols miscible with water, as well as with organic solvents.
        i. Alcohols of higher mass aren't soluble.
        ii. Diols (glycols) are even more soluble than alcohols of similar mass.
      c. Alcohols are weak acids.
    4. Reactions of alcohols (Section 14.5).

      a. Dehydration: alcohol $\xrightarrow{\text{H}_2\text{SO}_4}$ alkene + H_2O
      If more than one product is possible, the product with the more substituted double bond will be favored.
      b. Oxidation:

        i. Primary alcohol $\xrightarrow{\text{[O]}}$ aldehyde $\xrightarrow{\text{[O]}}$ carboxylic acid

        ii. Secondary alcohol $\xrightarrow{\text{[O]}}$ ketone

        iii. Tertiary alcohol $\xrightarrow{\text{[O]}}$ no reaction

C. Phenols (Sections 14.6–14.7).
   1. Properties of phenols (Section 14.6).
      a. Phenols are named by replacing -benzene with -phenol.
      b. The properties of phenols are influenced by hydrogen bonding.
         i. Many phenols are water-soluble.
         ii. Phenols are higher boiling than alkylbenzenes.
      c. Phenols are commonly used as disinfectants.
   2. Acidity of alcohols and phenols (Section 14.7).
      a. Alcohols and phenols are weak acids.
         i. Methanol and ethanol are as acidic as water.
         ii. Dissociation of alcohols in water, or reaction of alcohols with sodium metal, produces an alkoxide anion (^-OR).
      b. Phenols are more acidic than water.
         i. K_a of phenol is 1.0×10^{-10}.
         ii. Phenols are soluble in dilute aqueous NaOH.
D. Ethers (Sections 14.8–14.9).
   1. Names and properties of ethers (Section 14.8).
      a. Ethers have two organic groups bonded to the same oxygen.
      b. Ethers are named by identifying the two groups and adding the word *ether*.
         i. Some cyclic ethers have common names (ethylene oxide, 1,4-dioxane).
         ii. An –OR group is an alkoxy group.
      c. Properties of ethers.
         i. Ethers are low-boiling and don't form hydrogen bonds.
         ii. Ethers are unreactive.
         iii. Ethers are good solvents for organic compounds.
         iv. Ethers are volatile and flammable.
         v. Ethers are only slightly soluble in water.
         vi. Ethers form explosive peroxides on standing.
   2. Some common ethers (Section 14.9).
      a. Diethyl ether is commonly used as a solvent but was formerly an anesthetic.
      b. Ether groups occur in many essential oils.
II. Thiols and disulfides (Section 14.10).
  A. Thiols.
     1. Thiols are the sulfur analogs of alcohols (R–SH).
     2. Naming thiols is similar to naming alcohols, except that the suffix –thiol is added to the parent name.
     3. Thiols are important biologically because they occur in proteins.
     4. Thiols stink!
  B. Disulfides.
     1. Reaction of a thiol with a mild oxidizing agent produces a disulfide (RS–SR).
     2. The reverse reaction occurs when a disulfide is treated with a reducing agent.
III. Halogen-containing compounds (Section 14.11).
  A. Haloalkanes are named by considering the halogen as a substituent on a parent alkane.
  B. A few haloalkanes are named by naming the alkyl group and then naming the halide.
  C. Haloalkanes don't occur frequently in nature but are widely used in industry and agriculture.

Solutions to Chapter 14 Problems

14.1

(a)

CH₃CH₂CHCH₃
|
OH

an alcohol

(b)

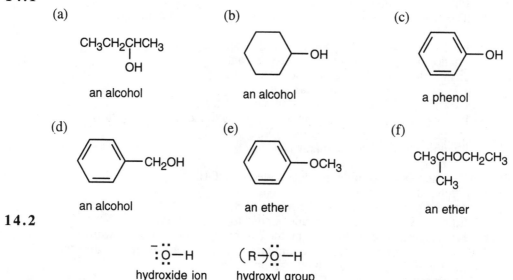

an alcohol

(c)

a phenol

(d)

an alcohol

(e)

an ether

(f)

CH₃CHOCH₂CH₃
|
CH₃

an ether

14.2

:Ö—H
hydroxide ion

(R→Ö—H)
hydroxyl group

A hydroxide ion has three lone electron pairs and a negative charge. A hydroxyl group is an –OH group that is part of an organic molecule.

14.3

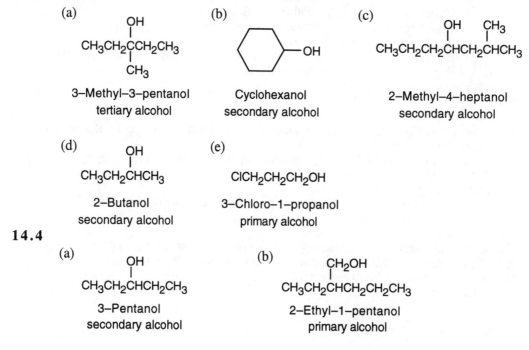

(a)

OH
|
CH₃CH₂CCH₂CH₃
|
CH₃

3–Methyl–3–pentanol
tertiary alcohol

(b)

—OH

Cyclohexanol
secondary alcohol

(c)

OH   CH₃
| |
CH₃CH₂CH₂CHCH₂CHCH₃

2–Methyl–4–heptanol
secondary alcohol

(d)

OH
|
CH₃CH₂CHCH₃

2–Butanol
secondary alcohol

(e)

ClCH₂CH₂CH₂OH

3–Chloro–1–propanol
primary alcohol

14.4

(a)

OH
|
CH₃CH₂CHCH₂CH₃

3–Pentanol
secondary alcohol

(b)

CH₂OH
|
CH₃CH₂CHCH₂CH₂CH₃

2–Ethyl–1–pentanol
primary alcohol

(c)

CH₂OH
|
CH₃CH₂CHCH₂CH₂CH₂Br

5–Bromo–2–ethyl–1–pentanol
primary alcohol

(d)

H₃C⟍   ⟍—OH
   ⟍
H₃C⟋

4,4–Dimethylcyclohexanol
secondary alcohol

14.5   See Problems 14.3 and 14.4.

14.6   CH₃CH₂CH₂OH has the highest boiling point because it's the only compound listed that can form hydrogen bonds.

14.7

(a)

CH₃(CH₂)₁₀CH₂OH

The hydrocarbon part
makes this alcohol
water–insoluble.

(b)

OH
|
CH₃CH₂CHCH₃

Water–soluble.

(c)

CH₃CH₂OCH₃

An ether – slightly
water–soluble.

14.8

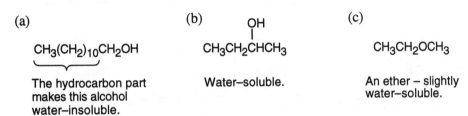

(a)

(H   OH)
 ┆ --- ┆
CH₃CH —CH₂   →$\xrightarrow{H_2SO_4}$ CH₃CH=CH₂ + H₂O

(b)

(H   OH)

⬡   →$\xrightarrow{H_2SO_4}$ ⬡   +   H₂O

(c)

(H (OH) H)CH₃
 ┆   ┆   ┆ |
CH₂—CH—CHCHCH₃   →$\xrightarrow{H_2SO_4}$

                    CH₃
                     |
H₂C=CHCH₂CHCH₃   +
     minor

                    CH₃
                     |
CH₃CH=CHCHCH₃   +   H₂O
     major

14.9

(a)

H   OH
| |
CH₃C —CCH₃   →$\xrightarrow{H_2SO_4}$
| |
H₃C CH₃

H₃C⟍   ⟋CH₃
    C=C   +   H₂O
H₃C⟋   ⟍CH₃

(b)

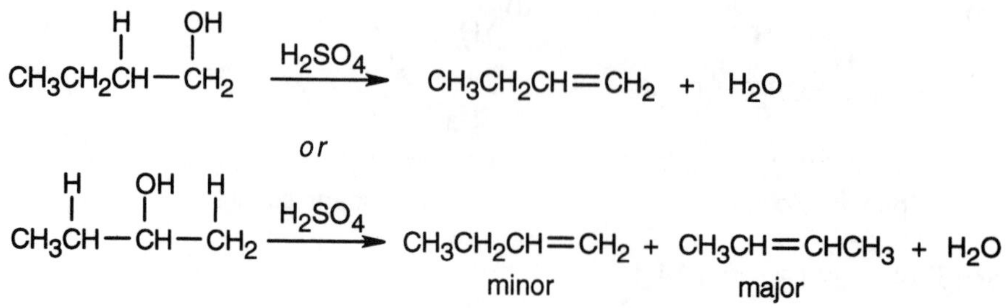

$$CH_3CH_2\overset{H}{\underset{|}{CH}}-\overset{OH}{\underset{|}{CH_2}} \xrightarrow{H_2SO_4} CH_3CH_2CH=CH_2 + H_2O$$

or

$$CH_3\overset{H}{\underset{|}{CH}}-\overset{OH}{\underset{|}{CH}}-\overset{H}{\underset{|}{CH_2}} \xrightarrow{H_2SO_4} CH_3CH_2CH=CH_2 + CH_3CH=CHCH_3 + H_2O$$

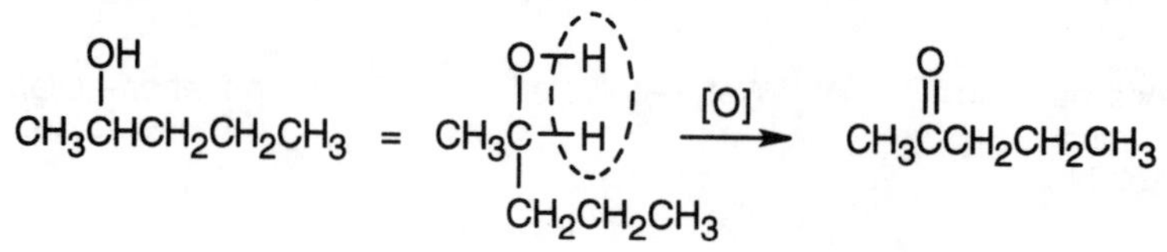

minor   major

14.10

(a)

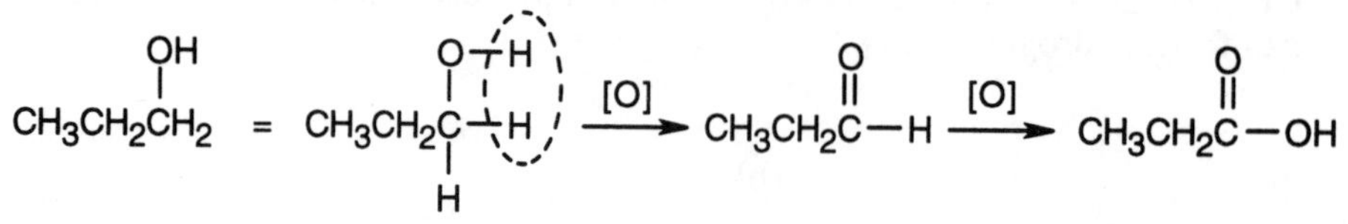

$$CH_3CH_2CH_2 \overset{OH}{\underset{|}{}} = CH_3CH_2\overset{O-H}{\underset{\underset{H}{|}}{C}}-H \xrightarrow{[O]} CH_3CH_2\overset{O}{\overset{\|}{C}}-H \xrightarrow{[O]} CH_3CH_2\overset{O}{\overset{\|}{C}}-OH$$

(b)

$$CH_3\overset{OH}{\underset{|}{CH}}CH_2CH_2CH_3 = CH_3\overset{O-H}{\underset{\underset{CH_2CH_2CH_3}{|}}{C}}-H \xrightarrow{[O]} CH_3\overset{O}{\overset{\|}{C}}CH_2CH_2CH_3$$

(c)

$$\underset{}{\bigcirc}\overset{OH}{\underset{|}{CHCH_3}} = \underset{}{\bigcirc}\overset{O-H}{\underset{\underset{CH_3}{|}}{C}}-H \xrightarrow{[O]} \underset{}{\bigcirc}\overset{O}{\overset{\|}{C}}CH_3$$

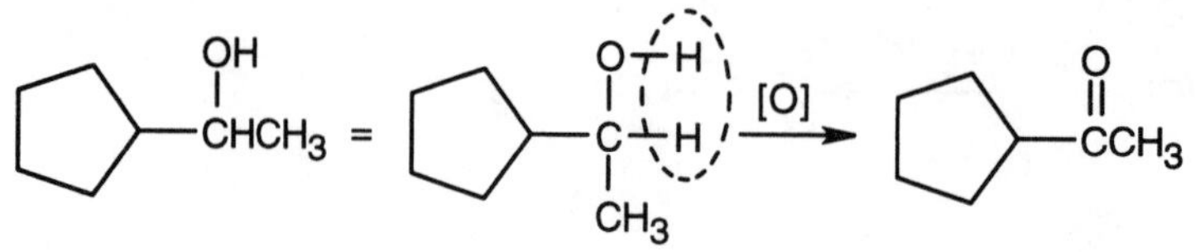

14.11

(a)

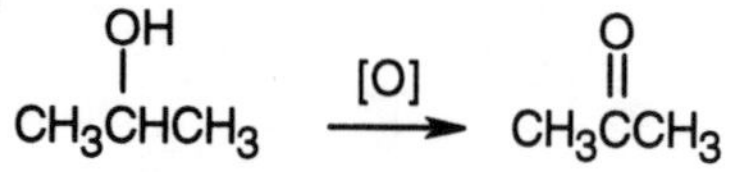

$$CH_3\overset{OH}{\underset{|}{CH}}CH_3 \xrightarrow{[O]} CH_3\overset{O}{\overset{\|}{C}}CH_3$$

(b)

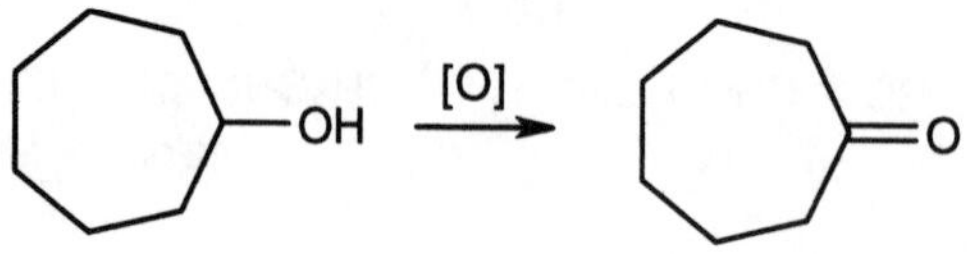

(c)

$$CH_3\overset{CH_3}{\underset{|}{CH}}CH_2CH_2OH \xrightarrow{[O]} CH_3\overset{CH_3}{\underset{|}{CH}}CH_2\overset{O}{\overset{\|}{C}}-H \xrightarrow{[O]} CH_3\overset{CH_3}{\underset{|}{CH}}CH_2\overset{O}{\overset{\|}{C}}-OH$$

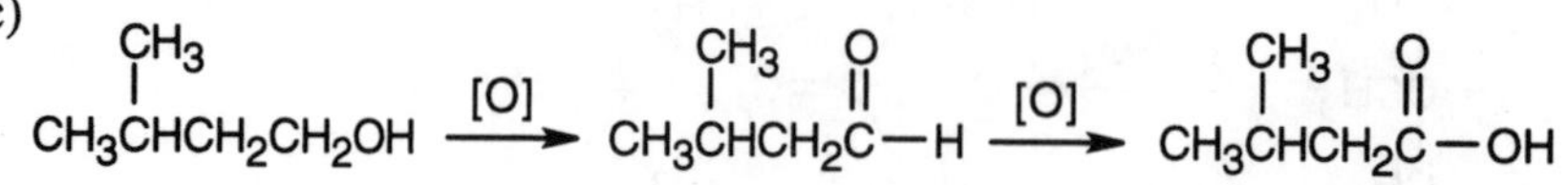

14.12

(a)

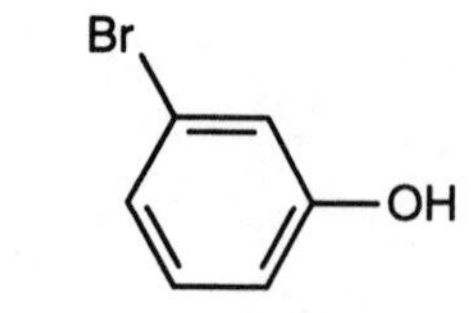

m–Bromophenol

(b)

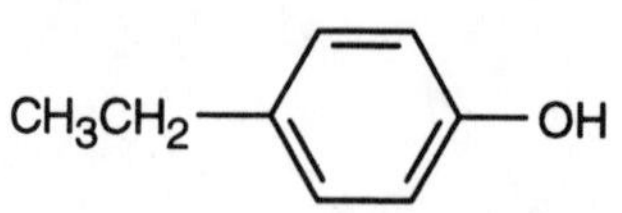

p–Ethylphenol

14.13

(a)

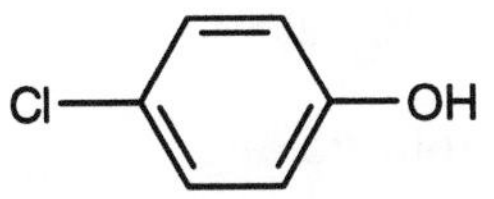

p–Chlorophenol

(b)

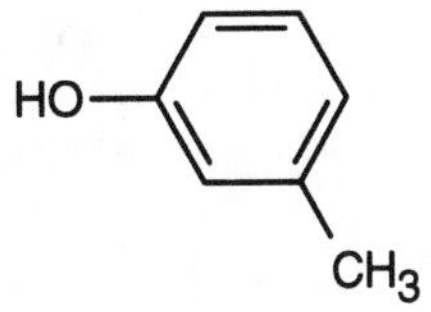

m–Methylphenol (m–Cresol)

14.14

(a)

$$2\ CH_3CH_2CH_2SH \xrightarrow{[O]} CH_3CH_2CH_2S-SCH_2CH_2CH_3 + H_2O$$

(b)

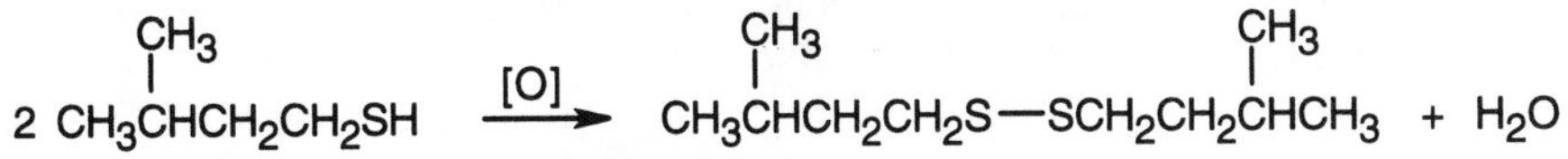

$$2\ CH_3\underset{\overset{|}{CH_3}}{CH}CH_2CH_2SH \xrightarrow{[O]} CH_3\underset{\overset{|}{CH_3}}{CH}CH_2CH_2S-SCH_2CH_2\underset{\overset{|}{CH_3}}{CH}CH_3 + H_2O$$

14.15

(a)

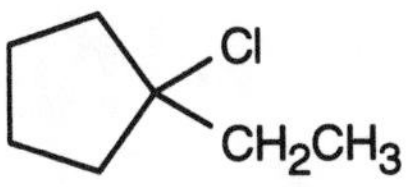

1–Chloro–1–ethylcyclopentane

(b)

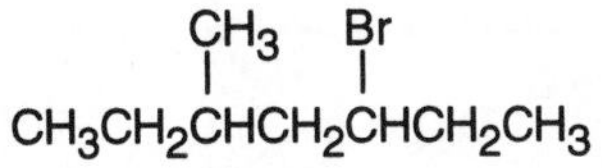

$$CH_3CH_2\underset{\overset{|}{CH_3}}{CH}CH_2\underset{\overset{|}{Br}}{CH}CH_2CH_3$$

3–Bromo–5–methylheptane

Understanding Key Concepts

14.16

(a)

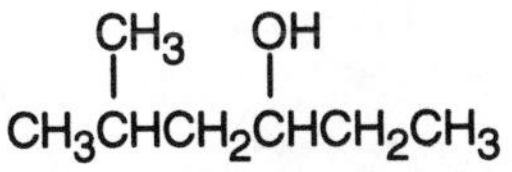

$$CH_3\underset{\overset{|}{CH_3}}{CH}CH_2\underset{\overset{|}{OH}}{CH}CH_2CH_3$$

5–Methyl–3–hexanol

(b)

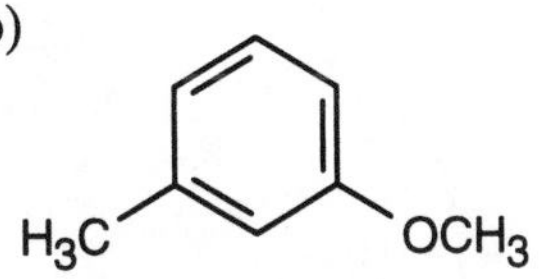

m–Methoxytoluene

(c)

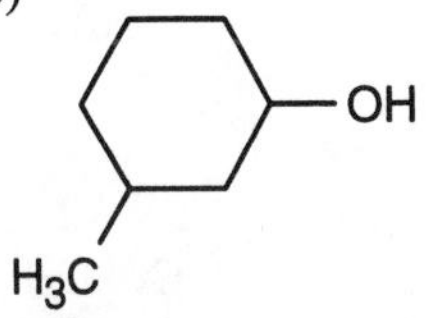

3–Methylcyclohexanol

14.17

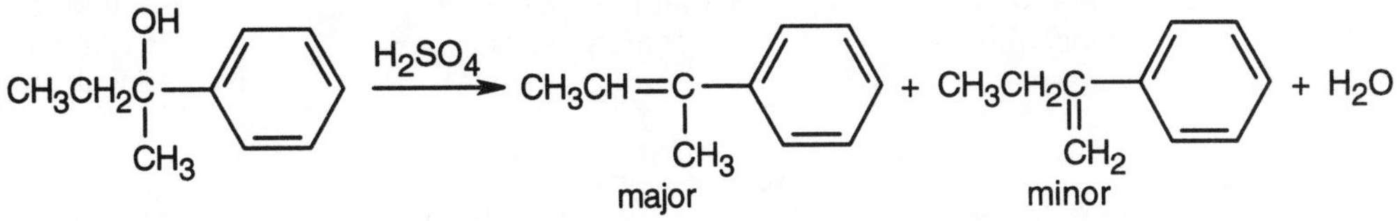

14.18

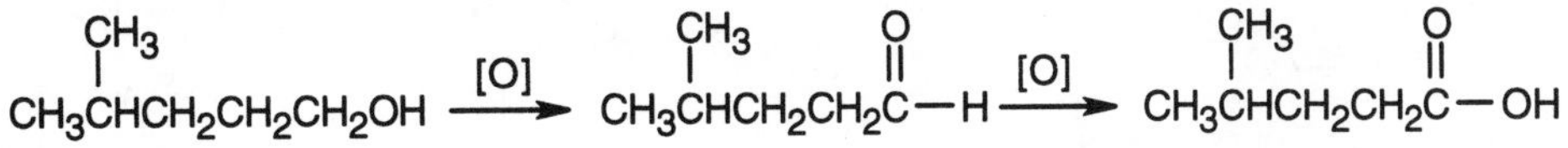

$$CH_3\underset{\overset{|}{CH_3}}{CH}CH_2CH_2CH_2OH \xrightarrow{[O]} CH_3\underset{\overset{|}{CH_3}}{CH}CH_2CH_2\overset{\overset{O}{\|}}{C}-H \xrightarrow{[O]} CH_3\underset{\overset{|}{CH_3}}{CH}CH_2CH_2\overset{\overset{O}{\|}}{C}-OH$$

14.19

$$2\ CH_3\underset{\overset{|}{CH_3}}{CH}CH_2\underset{\overset{|}{SH}}{CH}CH_3 \xrightarrow{[O]} CH_3\underset{\overset{|}{CH_3}}{CH}CH_2\underset{\overset{|}{CH_3}}{CH}S-S\underset{\overset{|}{CH_3}}{CH}CH_2\underset{\overset{|}{CH_3}}{CH}CH_3$$

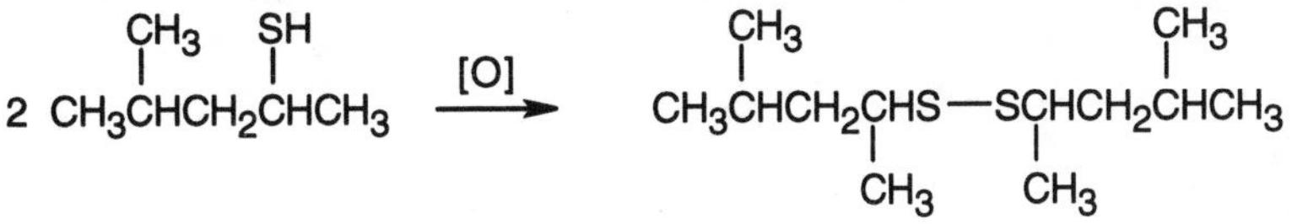

Alcohols, Ethers and Phenols

14.20 *Alcohols* have an –OH group bonded to an alkane-like carbon atom.
Ethers have an oxygen atom bonded to two carbon atoms.
Phenols have an –OH group bonded to a carbon of an aromatic ring.

—C—OH   —C—O—C—   ⬡—OH

an alcohol   an ether   a phenol

14.22 Alcohols contain –OH groups, which can form hydrogen bonds to each other. Since extra energy (heat) must be supplied to break these hydrogen bonds, alcohols are higher boiling than ethers, which can't hydrogen bond.

14.24

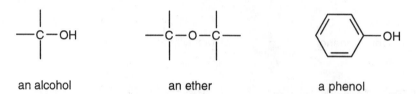

14.26, 14.30

(a)

$$CH_2OH$$
$$CH_3CH_2CHCH_2CH_2CH_3$$

2–Ethyl–1–pentanol
primary alcohol

(b)

$$CH_3$$
$$CH_3CHCH_2CH_2OH$$

3–Methyl–1–butanol
primary alcohol

(c)

OH
* *
HOCH₂CH₂CHCH₂OH

1,2,4–Butanetriol
*primary alcohol
secondary alcohol

(d)

$$CH_3$$
⬡—C—OH
$$CH_3$$

2–Phenyl–2–propanol
tertiary alcohol

(e)

CH₃
⬠—OH

2–Methylcyclopentanol
secondary alcohol

(f)

$$CH_2CH_3$$
$$CH_3CH_2CCH_2OH$$
$$CH_3$$

2–Ethyl–2–methyl–1–butanol
primary alcohol

14.28

(a)

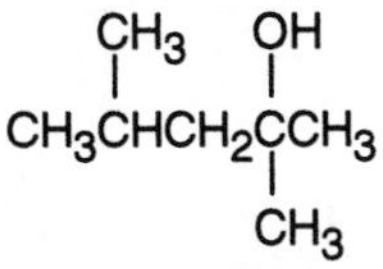

CH₃ OH
CH₃CHCH₂CCH₃
        CH₃

2,4–Dimethyl–2–pentanol

(b)

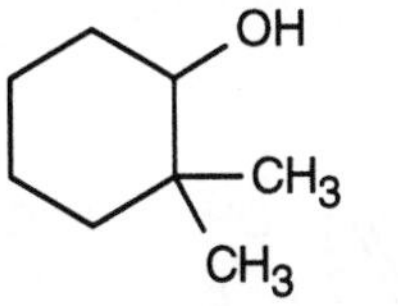

OH
CH₃
CH₃

2,2–Dimethylcyclohexanol

(c)

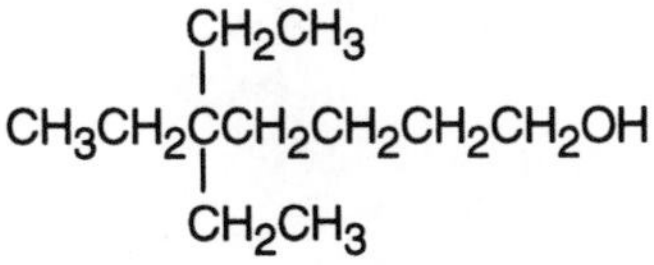

CH₂CH₃
CH₃CH₂CCH₂CH₂CH₂CH₂OH
CH₂CH₃

5,5–Diethyl–1–heptanol

(d)

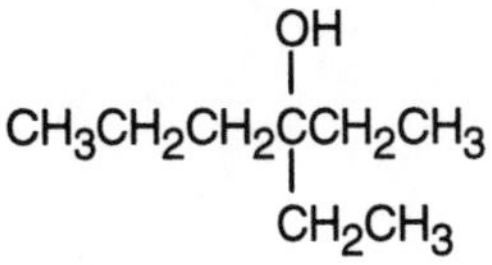

OH
CH₃CH₂CH₂CCH₂CH₃
        CH₂CH₃

3–Ethyl–3–hexanol

(e)

OH
H₃C
CH₃
CH₃

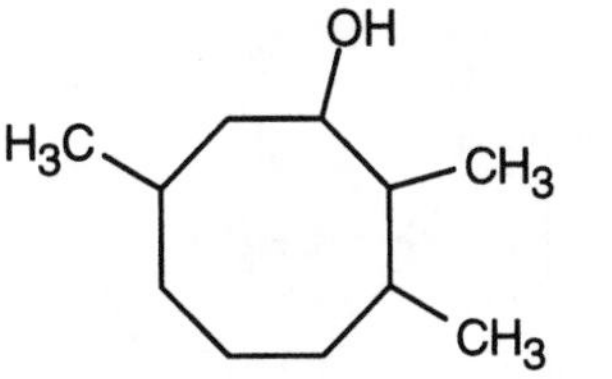

2,3,7–Trimethylcyclooctanol

(f)

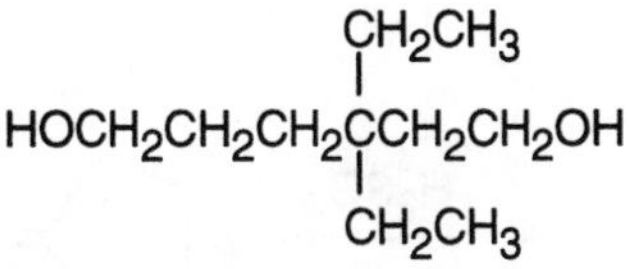

CH₂CH₃
HOCH₂CH₂CH₂CCH₂CH₂OH
CH₂CH₃

3,3–Diethyl–1,6–hexanediol

14.32

Compound	Boiling Point	Reason
Hexanol	Highest	Forms hydrogen bonds
Dipropyl ether	Middle	Polar, but doesn't form hydrogen bonds
Hexane	Lowest	Nonpolar

Reactions of Alcohols

14.34 A ketone is formed on oxidation of a secondary alcohol:

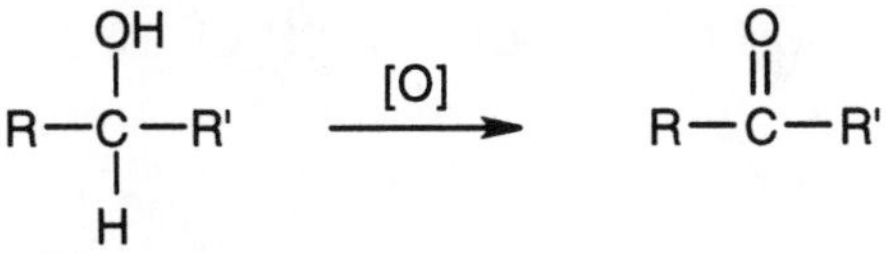

OH   O
| ||
R—C—R' $\xrightarrow{[O]}$ R—C—R'
|
H

A secondary alcohol   A ketone

14.36 Either an aldehyde or a carboxylic acid can be formed by oxidation of a primary alcohol:

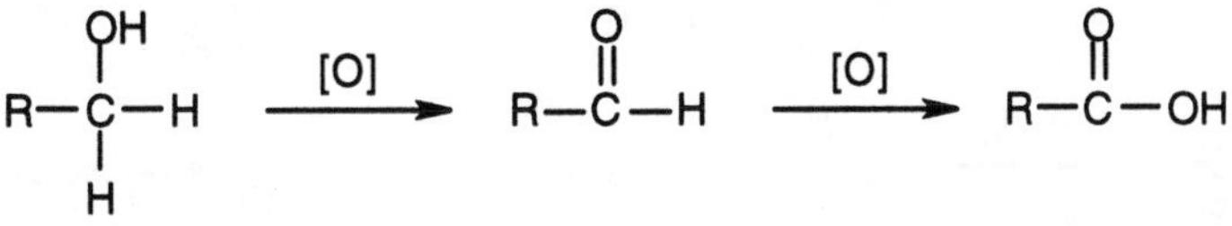

OH   O   O
| || ||
R—C—H $\xrightarrow{[O]}$ R—C—H $\xrightarrow{[O]}$ R—C—OH
|
H

a primary alcohol   an aldehyde   a carboxylic acid

14.38 Phenols are more acidic than alcohols and are converted into their sodium salts on reaction with NaOH. Thus, phenols dissolve in aqueous NaOH but alcohols do not.

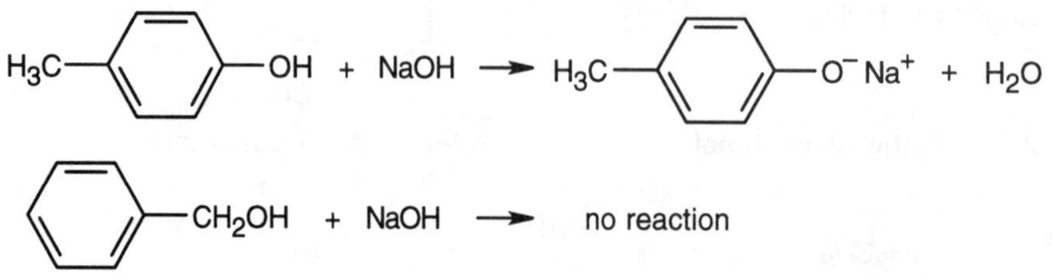

14.40

(a)

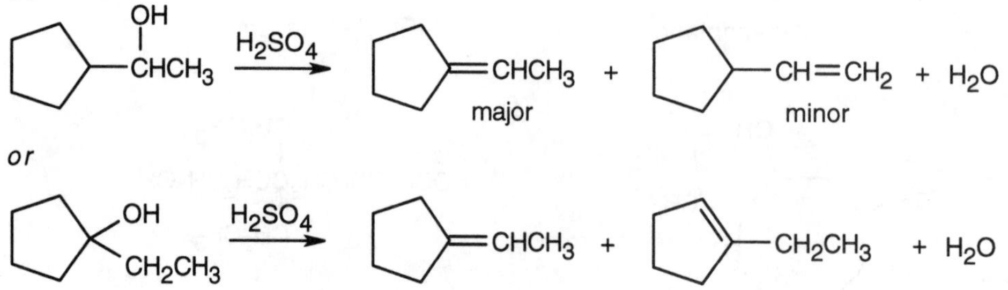

or

(b)

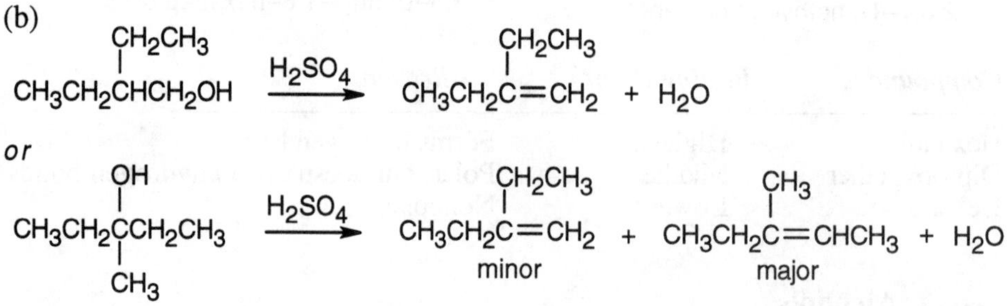

or

(c)

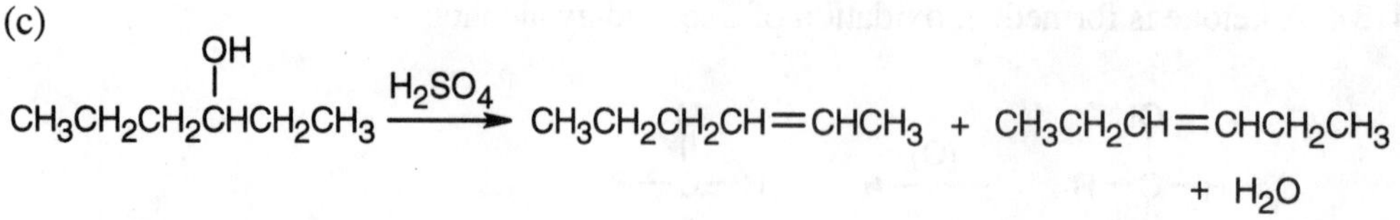

(d)

or

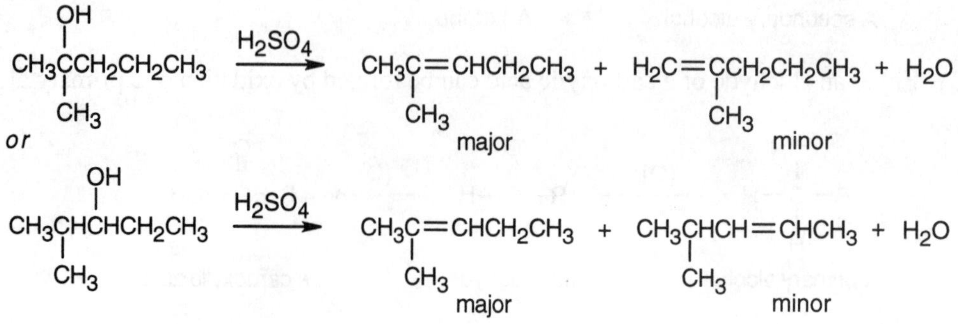

(e)

$$HOCH_2CH_2CH_2CH_2OH \xrightarrow{\text{xs } H_2SO_4} H_2C{=}CHCH{=}CH_2 + 2\ H_2O$$

or

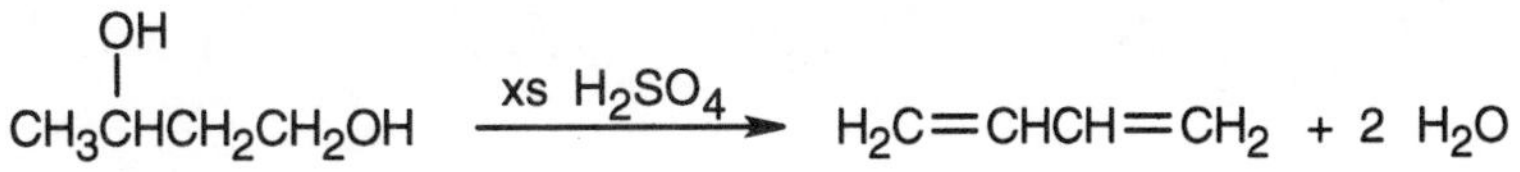

$$\underset{\overset{\displaystyle |}{OH}}{CH_3CHCH_2CH_2OH} \xrightarrow{\text{xs } H_2SO_4} H_2C{=}CHCH{=}CH_2 + 2\ H_2O$$

or

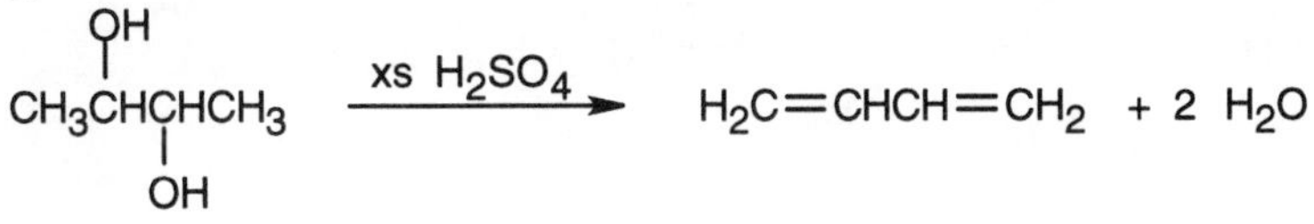

$$\underset{\overset{\displaystyle |}{OH}}{CH_3\underset{\overset{\displaystyle |}{OH}}{CHCHCH_3}} \xrightarrow{\text{xs } H_2SO_4} H_2C{=}CHCH{=}CH_2 + 2\ H_2O$$

(f)

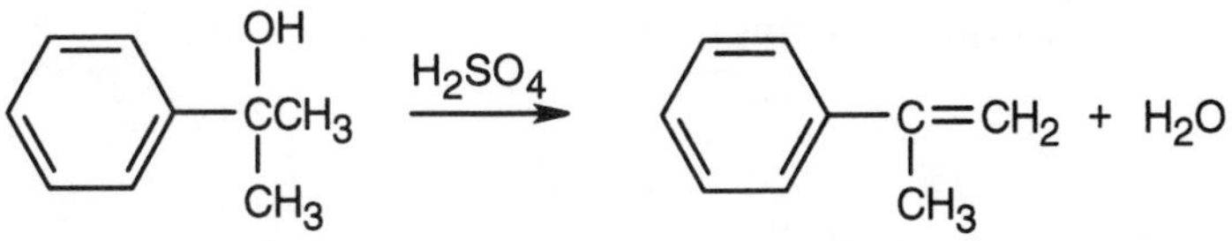

or

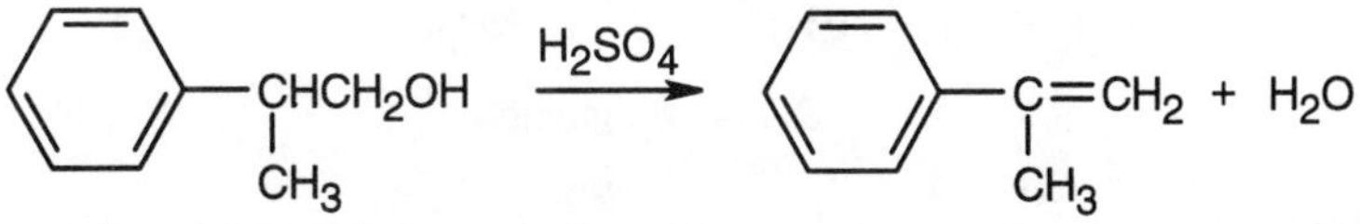

14.42

(a)

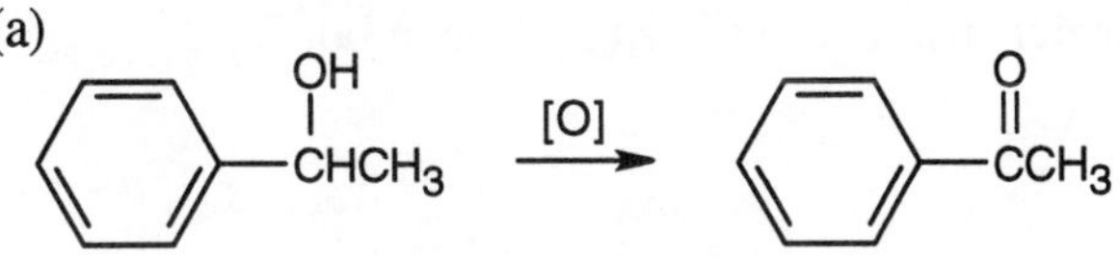

(b)

$$\underset{\overset{\displaystyle |}{\underset{\displaystyle}{}}}{\overset{\displaystyle H_3C}{CH_3CHCH_2OH}} \xrightarrow{[O]} \underset{\overset{\displaystyle |}{}}{\overset{\displaystyle H_3C}{CH_3CHC}}\overset{\displaystyle O}{\overset{\displaystyle \|}{C}}{-}H \xrightarrow{[O]} \underset{}{\overset{\displaystyle H_3C}{CH_3CHC}}\overset{\displaystyle O}{\overset{\displaystyle \|}{C}}{-}OH$$

(c)

$$\underset{\overset{\displaystyle |}{CH_3}}{CH_3CH_2\underset{\overset{\displaystyle |}{OH}}{C}CH_2CH_3} \xrightarrow{[O]} NR$$

(d)

(e)

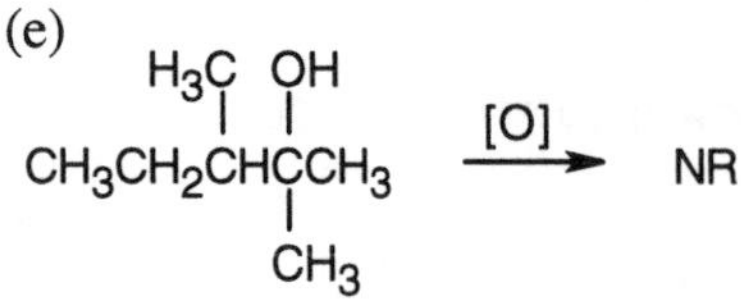

$$CH_3CH_2CHCCH_3 \quad \xrightarrow{[O]} \quad NR$$

(with H₃C and OH substituents above the carbon, and CH₃ below)

(f)

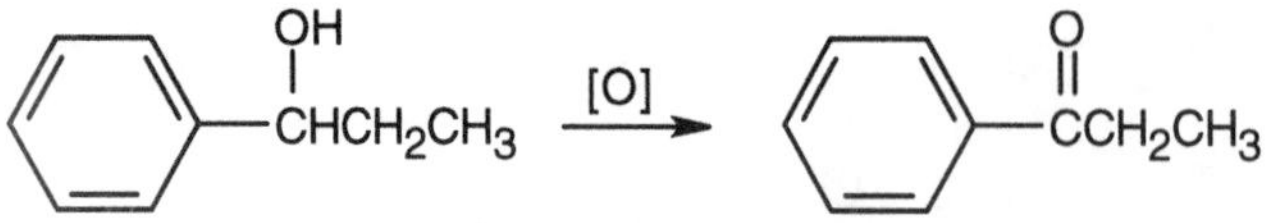

Thiols and Disulfides

14.44 The most noticeable characteristic of thiols is their vile stench.

14.46

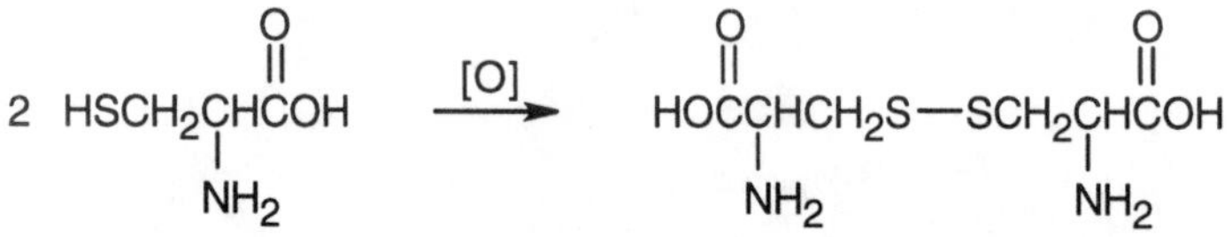

$$2 \; HSCH_2CHCOH \quad \xrightarrow{[O]} \quad HOCCHCH_2S-SCH_2CHCOH$$

(with NH₂ substituents; left structure labeled Cysteine, right structure labeled Cysteine disulfide)

Cysteine   Cysteine disulfide

14.48 Propanol is high-boiling because its –OH groups can form hydrogen bonds. The –SH groups of ethanethiol don't form hydrogen bonds, and thus ethanethiol has a lower boiling point, as does chloroethane, which also doesn't form hydrogen bonds.

Applications

14.50 Ethanol is a depressant. Its effects on the central nervous system are like those of anesthetics and other central nervous system depressants.

14.52 The liver is vulnerable to damage from alcohol because it is the principal site of alcohol metabolism, and toxic products of alcohol metabolism accumulate there.

14.54 A free radical is a reactive intermediate that contains an unpaired electron.

14.56 Ether was used as the first general anesthetic.

14.58 The ozone layer acts as a shield to protect the earth from intense solar radiation.

General Questions and Problems

14.60 Alcohol isomers of $C_4H_{10}O$:

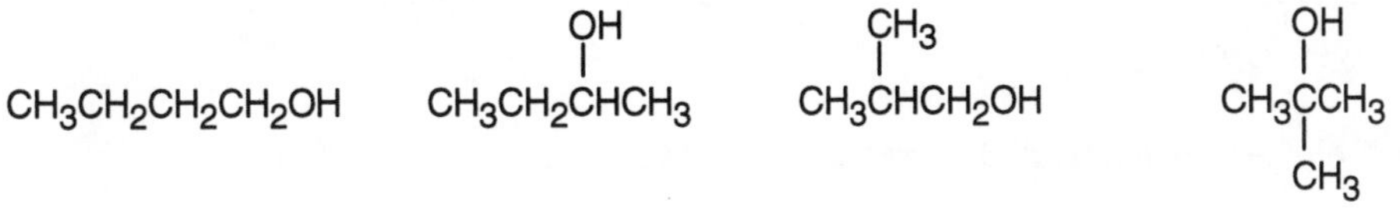

$$CH_3CH_2CH_2CH_2OH \qquad CH_3CH_2\overset{\overset{\displaystyle OH}{|}}{C}HCH_3 \qquad CH_3\overset{\overset{\displaystyle CH_3}{|}}{C}HCH_2OH \qquad CH_3\overset{\overset{\displaystyle OH}{|}}{\underset{\underset{\displaystyle CH_3}{|}}{C}}CH_3$$

| 1–Butanol | 2–Butanol | 2–Methyl–1–propanol | 2–Methyl–2–propanol |

Ether isomers of $C_4H_{10}O$:

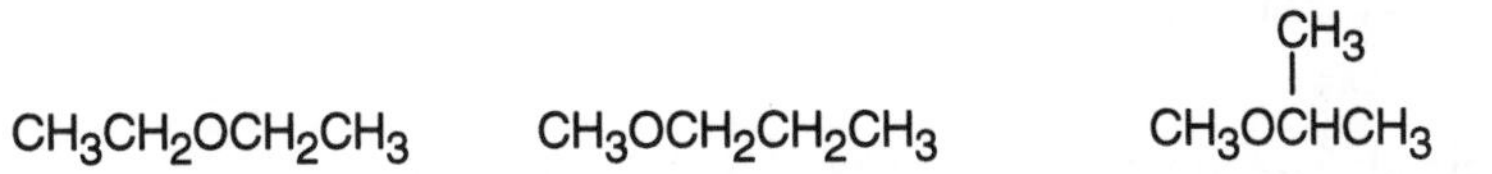

$$CH_3CH_2OCH_2CH_3 \qquad CH_3OCH_2CH_2CH_3 \qquad CH_3O\overset{\overset{\displaystyle CH_3}{|}}{C}HCH_3$$

| Diethyl ether | Methyl propyl ether | Isopropyl methyl ether |

14.62 $CH_3(CH_2)_8CH_3$ $CH_3(CH_2)_7CH_2OH$

Decane – a hydrocarbon   1-Nonanol – an alcohol

Insoluble in water because   Insoluble because its hydrocarbon,
hydrocarbons are insoluble   water-insoluble part, is much larger than
in water.   its polar hydroxyl group.

14.64 An antiseptic kills microorganisms on living tissue; a disinfectant is toxic and is used only to kill microorganisms on surfaces.

14.66

(a)

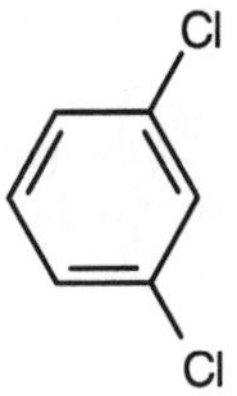

m–Dichlorobenzene

(b)

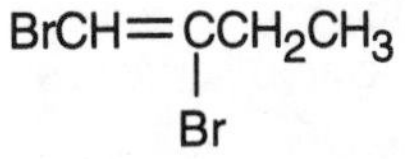

$$BrCH=\overset{\overset{\displaystyle Br}{|}}{C}CH_2CH_3$$

1,2–Dibromo–1–butene

(c)

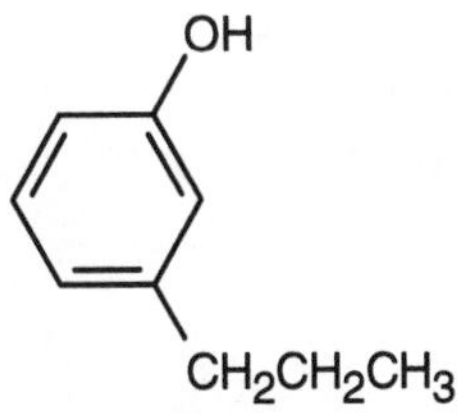

m–Propylphenol

(d)

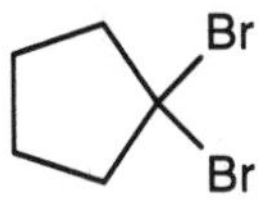

1,1–Dibromocyclopentane

(e)

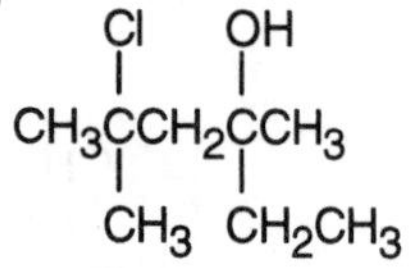

$$CH_3CCH_2CCH_3$$

with Cl and OH substituents, CH_3 and CH_2CH_3

5–Chloro–3,5–dimethyl–3–hexanol

(f)

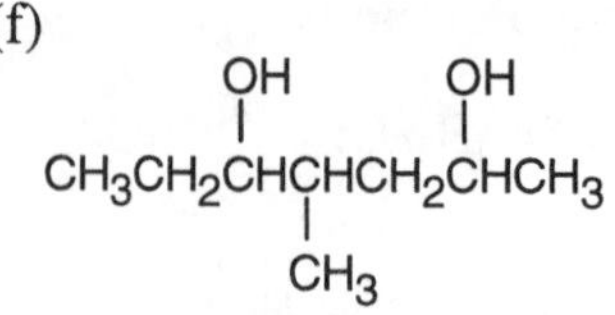

$$CH_3CH_2CHCHCH_2CHCH_3$$

with OH, OH substituents and CH_3

4–Methyl–2,5–heptanediol

(g)

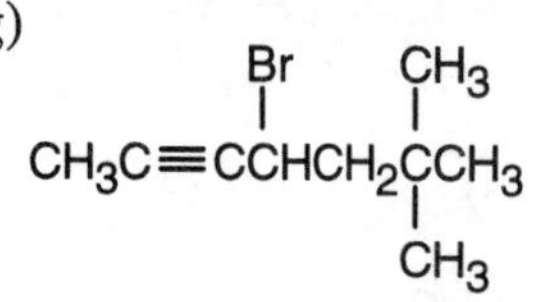

$$CH_3C\equiv CCHCH_2CCH_3$$

with Br and CH_3 substituents, CH_3

4–Bromo–6,6–dimethyl–2–heptyne

(h)

cyclopropane ring with Cl and Br

1–Bromo–2–chlorocyclopentane

14.68

$$CH_3C=CHCH_2CH_2C=CHCH_2OH \xrightarrow{[O]} CH_3C=CHCH_2CH_2C=CHC-H$$

3,7–Dimethyl–2,6–octadiene–1–ol   Citral

14.70

$$CH_3CH_2OH + 3 O_2 \longrightarrow 2 CO_2 + 3 H_2O$$

14.72

$$CH_3CH_2CH_2OH \underset{\longleftarrow}{\overset{H_2SO_4}{\longrightarrow}} CH_3CH=CH_2 + H_2O$$

The conversion of an alcohol, such as propanol, to the related alkene is an equilibrium process in which sulfuric acid serves as a catalyst for both the forward and the reverse reaction.

Self-Test for Chapter 14

Multiple choice:

1. Which of the following alcohols yields an aldehyde on oxidation?
   (a) 2-Hexanol (b) 2-Methyl-2-hexanol (c) 2-Methyl-1-hexanol (d) *p*–Chlorophenol

2. Which of the following compounds is least acidic?
   (a) *p*–Chlorophenol (b) 2–Butanol (c) HCl (d) Acetic acid

3. How many alcohols of the formula $C_4H_{10}O$ are primary alcohols?
   (a) 1 (b) 2 (c) 3 (d) 4

4. Which of the following is known as wood alcohol?
   (a) CH_3OH (b) CH_3CH_2OH (c) $CH_3CH_2CH_2OH$ (d) $HOCH_2CH_2OH$

5.   HO   CH$_2$CH$_2$CH$_3$
            | |
     CH$_3$CHCH$_2$CHCH$_2$CH$_3$

What is the name of the above compound?
(a) 4-Propyl-2-hexanol   (b) 4-Ethyl-6-heptanol   (c) 4-Ethylheptanol   (d) 4-Ethyl-2-heptanol

6. Which of the following is not a property of alcohols?
   (a) weakly acidic   (b) flammable   (c) react with acids   (d) low-boiling

7. Which of the following is not a product of dehydration of 2,3-dimethyl-3-pentanol?
   (a) 2,3-Dimethyl-1-pentene   (b) 2,3-Dimethyl-2-pentene   (c) 3,4-Dimethyl-2-pentene
   (d) 2-Ethyl-3-methyl-1-butene

8. Which of the following is a cyclic ether?
   (a) Enflurane   (b) Ethylene oxide   (c) Methoxybenzene (anisole)   (d) Methyl cyclohexyl ether

9. An alcohol of the formula C$_5$H$_{12}$O forms a carboxylic acid on oxidation yet can't be
   dehydrated by acid. What is its name?
   (a) 1-Pentanol   (b) 2-Methyl-2-butanol   (c) 2,2-Dimethyl-1-propanol   (d) 2-Methyl-1-butanol

10. Which reagent doesn't react with alcohols?
    (a) Na   (b) H$_2$SO$_4$ (c) KMnO$_4$ (d) NaOH

Complete the following statements:

1. The common name for methanol is _____.

2. Dialcohols are often called _____.

3. Aromatic compounds called _____ react with NaOH to give salts.

4. The dehydration of an alcohol yields an _____.

5. Compounds called _____ are noted for their foul odors.

6. _____ can be used to oxidize an alcohol.

7. Ethers are _____ boiling than alcohols of similar molecular weight.

8. _____ is a phenol used as a food additive.

9. The major product of alcohol dehydration has the _____ number of alkyl groups attached to
   the double bond carbons.

10. A _____ _____ is a reactive intermediate containing an unpaired electron.

11. On prolonged contact with air, an ether forms a _____.

12. _____ is another name for a chlorofluorocarbon.

Tell whether the following statements are true or false:

1. Phenols can form hydrogen bonds.

2. An aldehyde can be formed by oxidation of a secondary alcohol.

3. Two different alkenes result from dehydration of 2–pentanol.

4. Another name for phenol is carbonic acid.

5. Phenols are more acidic than alcohols.

6. Another name for a thiol is a mercaptan.

7. Phenol, isopropyl alcohol, and chloroethane are all antiseptics.

8. Oxidation is the removal of two hydrogen ions.

9. Several halogenated alkanes are used as anesthetics.

10. Under careful reaction conditions, a primary alcohol is oxidized to an aldehyde.

11. Isopropyl alcohol is more toxic than methyl alcohol.

12. Hydrogen bonding accounts for both boiling-point elevation and water solubility.

Match the entries on the left with their partners on the right:

1. CCl_3F (a) Peroxide

2. $(CH_3)_2CHS–SCH(CH_3)_2$ (b) Thiol

3. $CH_3CH(OH)CH_2CH_2CH_3$ (c) Phenol

4. $CH_3CH_2OCH_3$ (d) Alcohol that is not water soluble

5. CH_3OH (e) Tertiary alcohol

6. CH_3SH (f) Forms two alkenes on dehydration

7. $(CH_3)_3C–OH$ (g) Disulfide

8. $CH_3CH_2OOCH_3$ (h) Ether

9. $(CH_3)_3CCOCH_3$ (i) Glycol

10. $CH_3(CH_2)_{10}CH_2OH$ (j) Chlorofluorocarbon

11. $CH_3CH(OH)CH_2OH$ (k) Oxidation product of 3,3–dimethyl–2–butanol

12. C_6H_5OH (l) Formed from CO and H_2

Chapter Outline

I. General characteristics of amines (Sections 15.1–15.3).
  A. Classification of amines (Section 15.1).
    Amines are classified by the degree of substitution at nitrogen.
    a. Primary amines have the structure RNH_2.
    b. Secondary amines have the structure R_2NH.
    c. Tertiary amines have the structure R_3N.
    d. Quaternary ammonium salts have the structure $R_4N^+\ X^-$.
  B. Naming amines.
    1. Primary amines are named by identifying the alkyl group attached to nitrogen and adding the suffix *-amine*.
    2. Secondary and tertiary amines.
      a. If the groups are identical, the prefix *di-* or *tri-* is added to the name that would be given if the amine were primary.
      b. If the groups are different, the compound is named as an *N*-substituted derivative of a primary amine.
    3. The simplest aromatic amine is aniline.
    4. When the amino group is a substituent, the prefix *amino-* is used.
  C. Properties of amines (Section 15.2).
    1. Amines are basic.
    2. Primary and secondary amines form hydrogen bonds to each other.
    3. Amines can form hydrogen bonds with water.
    4. Simple amines are water-soluble.
    5. Amines have unpleasant odors.
    6. Amines are an important class of biomolecules.
  D. Heterocyclic amines (Section 15.3).
    1. In some nitrogen-containing compounds, nitrogen is part of a ring.
    2. Heterocyclic compounds may be aromatic or nonaromatic.
II. Reactions of amines (Sections 15.4–15.5).
  A. Acid–base reactions of amines (Section 15.4).
    1. Aqueous amines are weak bases that can accept a proton to form ammonium ions. Nonaromatic amines are stronger bases than aromatic amines.
    2. Amines can react with acids to form ammonium salts.
      a. Ammonium cations of alkylamines are named by replacing the ending *-amine* by the ending *-ammonium*.
      b. For cations of heterocyclic amines, *-e* is replaced by *-ium*.
    3. Ammonium salts react with hydroxide ion to yield an amine plus water.
    4. In the body, many amines are present as ammonium ions.
  B. Amine salts (Section 15.5).
    1. Amine salts are composed of an ammonium ion (the cation) and an anion.
    2. Most amine salts are much more soluble in water than the amines from which they were derived.
    3. Sometimes, amine salts are written as amine·HX.
    4. An amine can be regenerated from an amine salt by reaction with base.
    5. Amine salts can be formed by reaction of an amine with an alkyl halide.
    6. If four alkyl groups are bonded to nitrogen, the compound is a quaternary ammonium salt. Quaternary ammonium salts are neither acidic or basic.

III. Alkaloids: amines in plants (Section 15.6).
1. Many alkaloids are toxic and physiologically active.
2. Familiar alkaloids are coniine, atropine, solanine and morphine.

Solutions to Chapter 15 Problems

15.1

(a)

$CH_3CH_2CH_2NH_2$

primary amine

(b)

$CH_3CH_2NHCH_2CH_3$

secondary amine

(c)

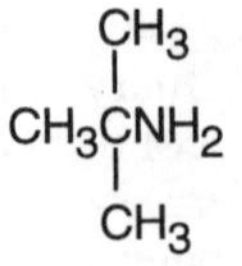

$$CH_3 \\ | \\ CH_3CNH_2 \\ | \\ CH_3$$

primary amine

(d)

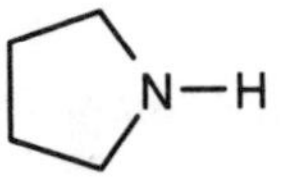

secondary amine

(e)

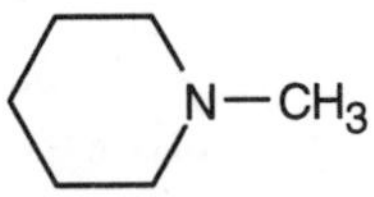

tertiary amine

15.2

(a)

$CH_3CH_2CH_2NH_2$

Propylamine

(b)

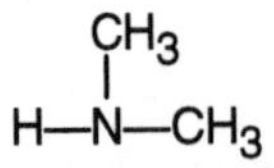

$$CH_3 \\ | \\ H-N-CH_3$$

Dimethylamine

(c)

—$NHCH_2CH_2CH_2CH_2CH_3$

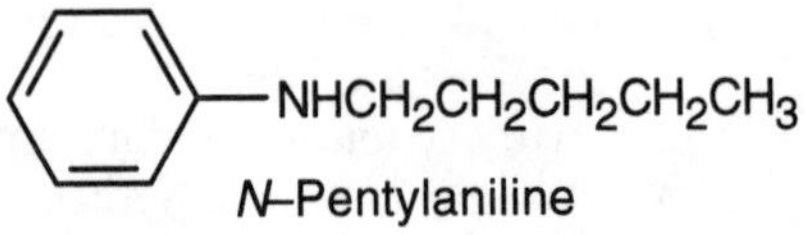

N–Pentylaniline

15.3

(a)

$CH_3CH_2CH_2CH_2NH_2$

Butylamine

(b)

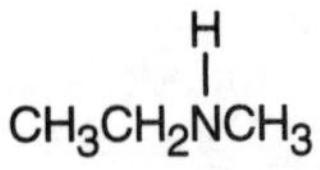

$$H \\ | \\ CH_3CH_2NCH_3$$

N–Methylethylamine

(c)

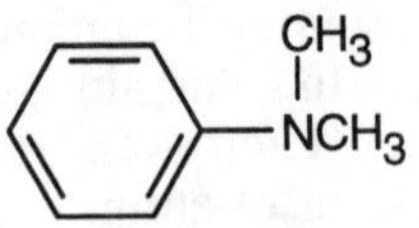

—NCH_3 with CH_3

N,N-Dimethylaniline

(d)

$$NH_2 \\ | \\ CH_3CH_2CHCH_2OH$$

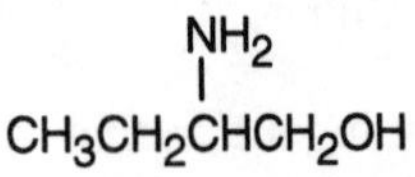

2–Aminobutanol

15.4

(a)

CH_3NH_2

Methylamine

$CH_3CH_2NH_2$

Ethylamine

CH_3NHCH_3

Dimethylamine

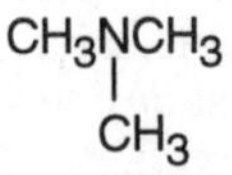

$$CH_3NCH_3 \\ | \\ CH_3$$

Trimethylamine

Amines that are gases at room temperature

(b)

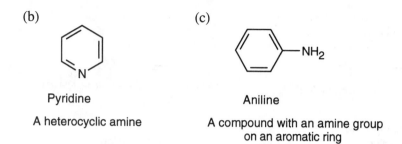

Pyridine

A heterocyclic amine

(c)

Aniline

A compound with an amine group
on an aromatic ring

15.5

$$CH_3\overset{\underset{\displaystyle |}{H}}{\underset{\underset{\displaystyle CH_3}{|}}{N}}: \quad + \quad H_2O \quad \rightleftarrows \quad CH_3\overset{\underset{\displaystyle |}{H}}{\underset{\underset{\displaystyle CH_3}{|}}{\overset{+}{N}}}-H \quad + \quad OH^-$$

base   acid   acid   base

15.6–15.7

(a)

$$CH_3CH_2\underset{\underset{\displaystyle CH_3}{|}}{C}HNH_2 \quad + \quad HBr(aq) \quad \longrightarrow \quad CH_3CH_2\underset{\underset{\displaystyle CH_3}{|}}{C}HNH_3{}^+ \; Br^-(aq)$$

sec–Butylamine   sec–Butylammonium bromide

(b)

$$-NH_2 \; + \; HCl(aq) \quad \longrightarrow \quad -NH_3{}^+ \; Cl^-(aq)$$

Aniline   Anilinium chloride

(c)

$$CH_3CH_2NH_2 \; + \; CH_3COOH(aq) \quad \longrightarrow \quad CH_3CH_2NH_3{}^+ \; CH_3COO^-(aq)$$

Ethylamine   Ethylammonium acetate

(d)

$$CH_3NH_3{}^+ \; Cl^-(aq) \; + \; NaOH(aq) \quad \longrightarrow \quad CH_3NH_2 \; + \; H_2O\,(l) \; + \; NaCl(aq)$$

Methylammonium chloride   Methylamine

15.8   Review Section 15.4 to choose the stronger base.

(a) Ethylamine is a stronger base than ammonia.
(b) Triethylamine (non-aromatic amine) is a stronger base than pyridine (aromatic amine).

15.9

(a)

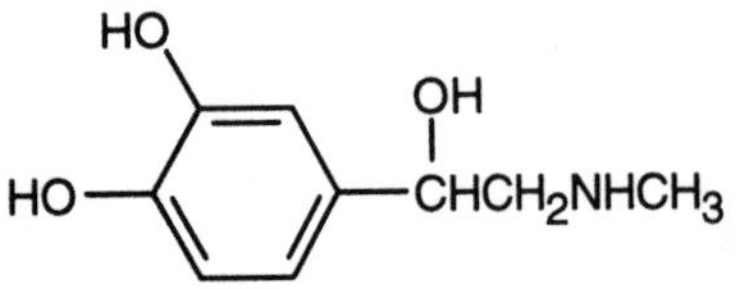

Epinephrine
amine

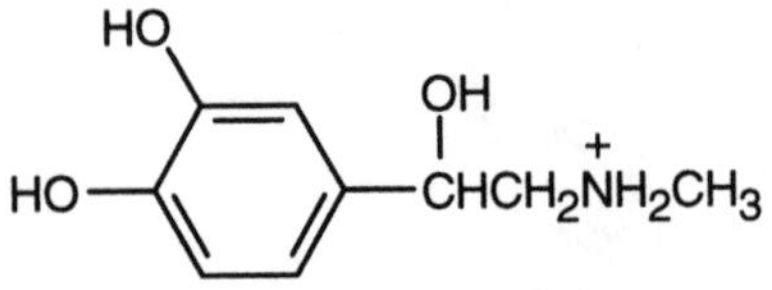

ammonium ion

(b)

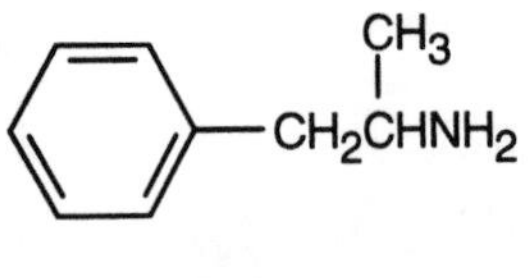

Amphetamine
amine

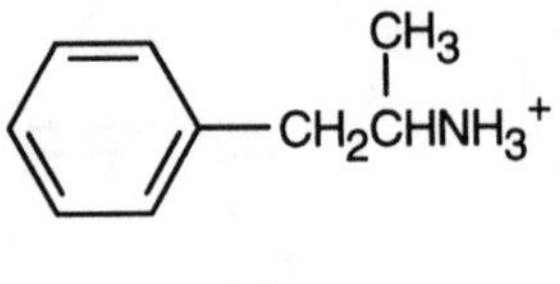

ammonium ion

15.10 – 15.11

(a)

$$CH_3CH_2CH_2CH_2CH_2CH_2\overset{\underset{|}{CH_3}}{\underset{|}{CH_3}}\overset{+}{N}H^+\ Cl^-$$

Hexyldimethylammonium chloride
*or N,N*Dimethylhexylammonium chloride
salt of a tertiary amine

(b)

$$CH_3CH_2NH_3^+\ Br^-$$

Ethylammonium bromide

salt of a primary amine

15.12

$$CH_3CH_2CH_2CH_2NH_3^+\ Cl^-(aq)\ +\ NaOH\ (aq) \longrightarrow CH_3CH_2CH_2CH_2NH_2\ +\ H_2O\ (l)\ +\ NaCl\ (aq)$$

15.13 Benadryl has the general antihistamine structure illustrated below. Attached to the central skeleton ($-Z-CH_2CH_2N-$) of Benadryl are two methyl groups bonded to nitrogen ($R = -CH_3$) and two phenyl groups ($R' = R'' = C_6H_5-$) bonded to Z ($Z = -CHO-$).

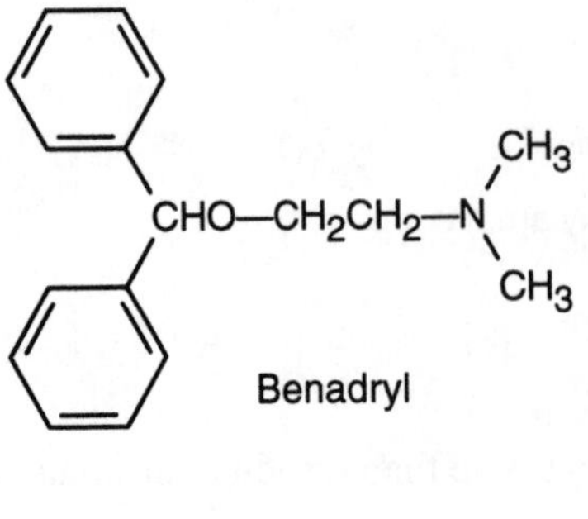

Benadryl

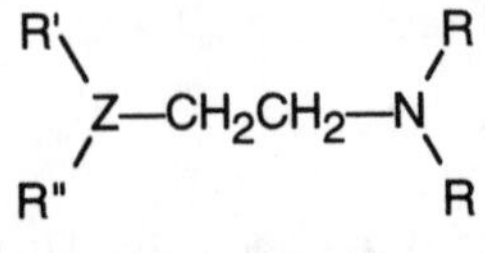

general antihistamine structure

15.14

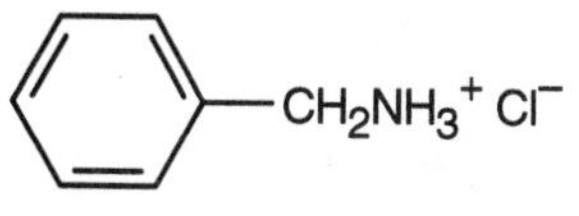

Benzylammonium chloride

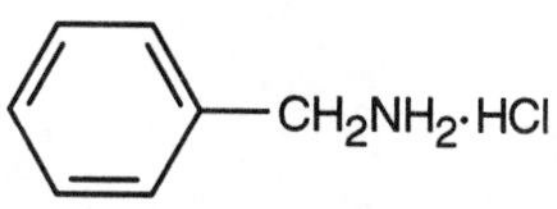

Understanding Key Concepts

15.15 (a)

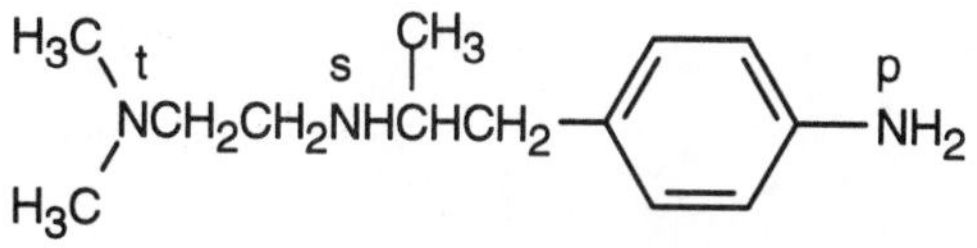

p = primary
s = secondary
t = tertiary

(b) The primary and secondary amine groups can participate in hydrogen bonding with nitrogens on other molecules of the above compound. The tertiary amine group can form hydrogen bonds with the primary and secondary amine groups but not with other tertiary amine groups. All amine groups can take part in hydrogen bonding between the above compound and water.

15.16

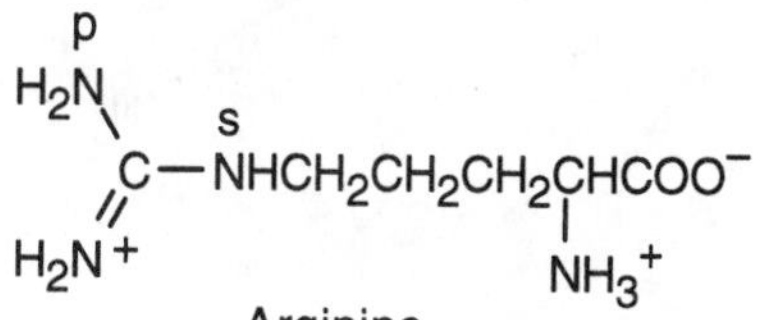

Arginine

(a) The amine groups labeled "p" and "s" can participate in hydrogen bonding because each has an unshared electron pair. Hydrogens on the $-NH_3^+$ group and the $=NH_2^+$ group can from hydrogen bonds with the electron pairs of other amino groups.
(b) Arginine is likely to be water-soluble because it is ionic and because it can form hydrogen bonds with water.

15.17

(a)

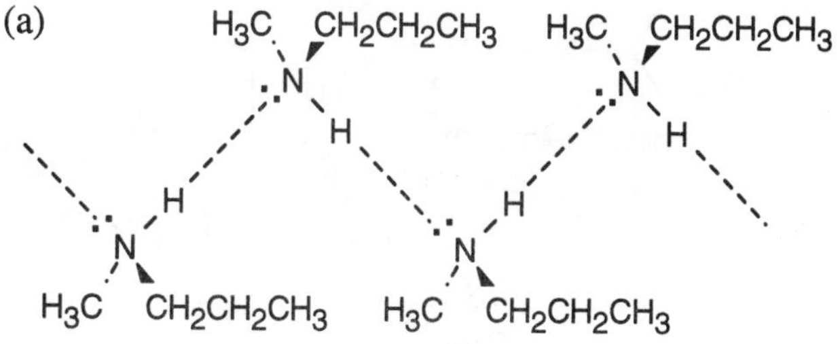

(b)

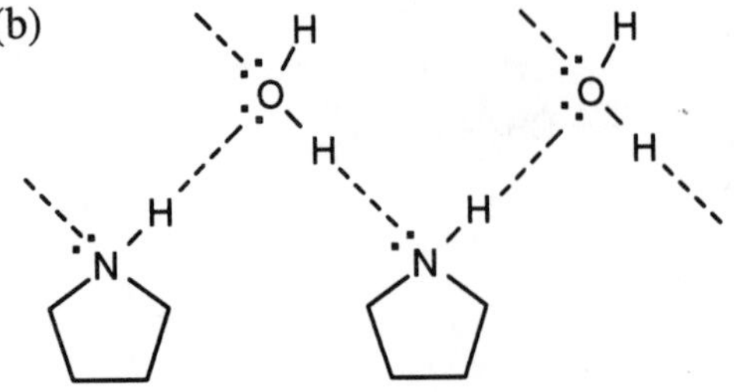

(c)

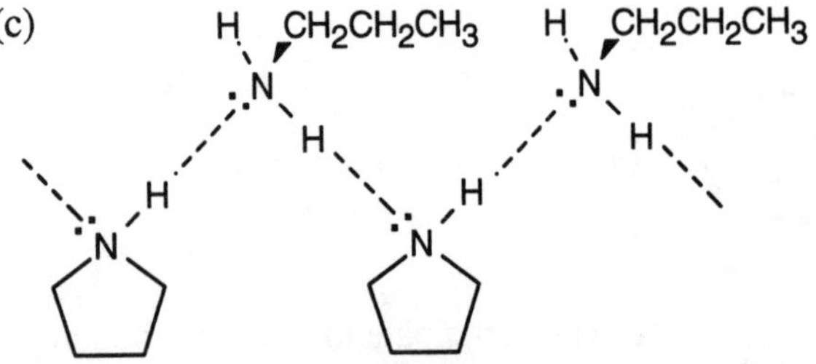
H CH2CH2CH3
H CH2CH2CH3

15.18

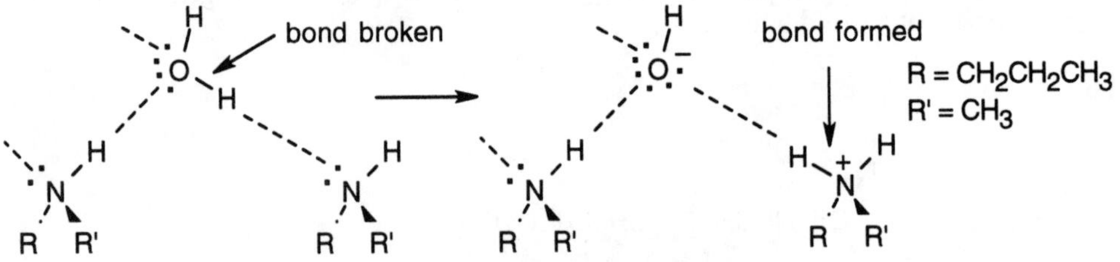
bond broken
bond formed
R = CH2CH2CH3
R' = CH3

An O–H bond of water is broken, and a N–H bond is formed in the reaction to form OH^-, an ammonium ion and an amine. The electrons remain with their original atoms.

Amines and Ammonium Salts

15.20

(a)

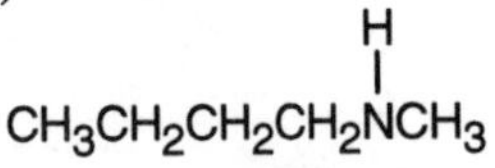
CH3CH2CH2CH2NCH3

N–Methylbutylamine

(b)

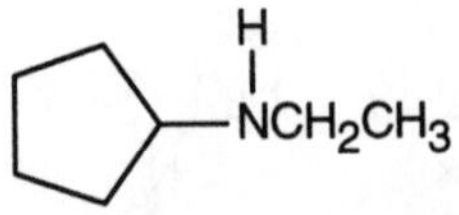
NCH2CH3

N–Ethylcyclopentylamine

(c)

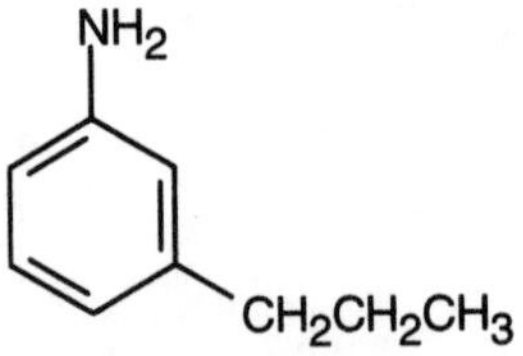
NH2
CH2CH2CH3

m–Propylaniline

15.22

(a)

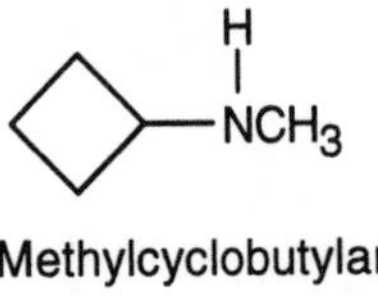
NCH3

N–Methylcyclobutylamine
secondary amine

(b)

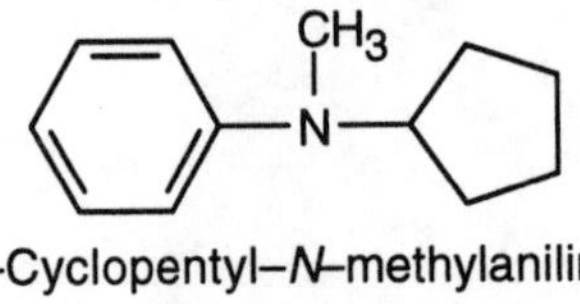
CH3

N–Cyclopentyl–*N*–methylaniline
tertiary amine

15.24 Diethylamine is a stronger base than diethyl ether because amines are more basic than ethers.

15.26

(a)

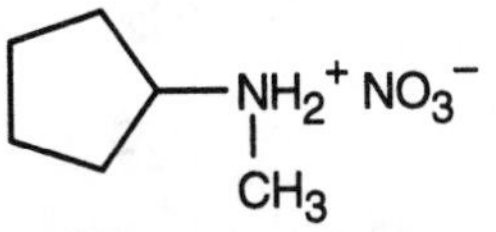

N–Methylcyclopentylammonium nitrate
(salt of a secondary amine)

(b)

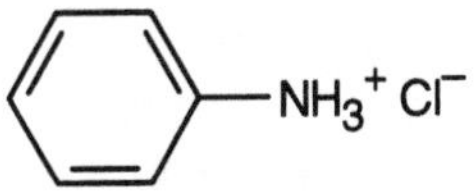

Anilinium chloride
(salt of a primary amine)

(c)

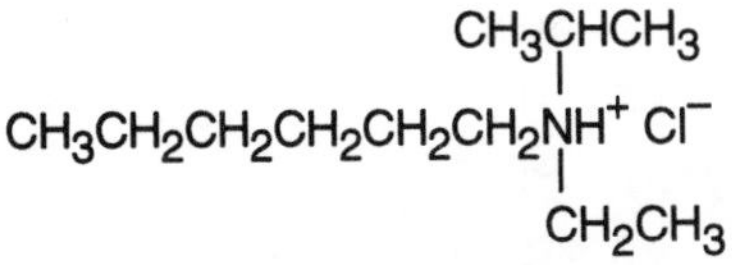

$$CH_3CHCH_3$$
$$CH_3CH_2CH_2CH_2CH_2CH_2NH^+ \; Cl^-$$
$$CH_2CH_3$$

N–Ethyl–N–isopropylhexylammonium chloride
(salt of a tertiary amine)

15.28

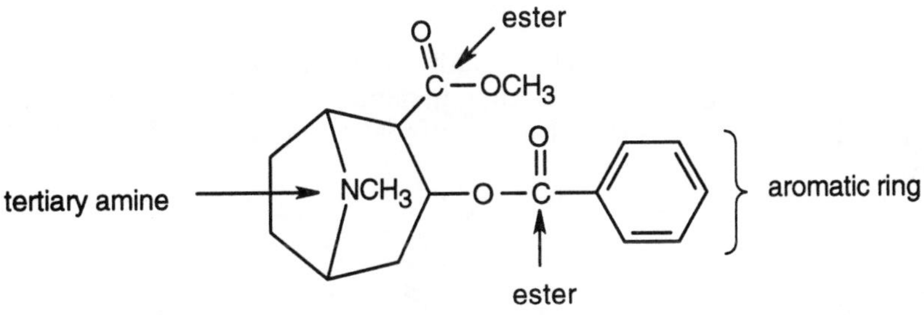

Cocaine

15.30

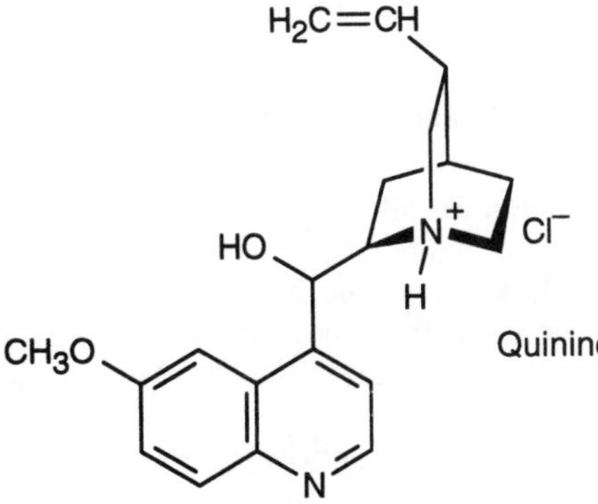

Quinine hydrochloride

The nonaromatic nitrogen is protonated because it is more basic.

Reactions of Amines

15.32

(a)

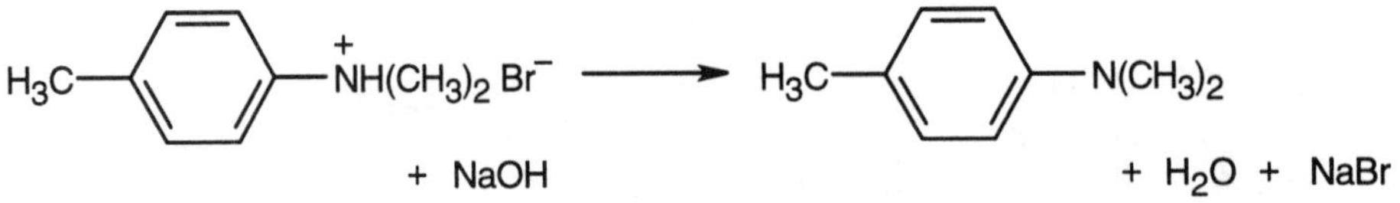

+ NaOH   + H₂O + NaBr

(b)

$$CH_3CHNH_2 + H_2O \rightleftharpoons CH_3CHNH_3^+ + OH^-$$
$$\quad\, |CH_3 \qquad\qquad\qquad\quad |CH_3$$

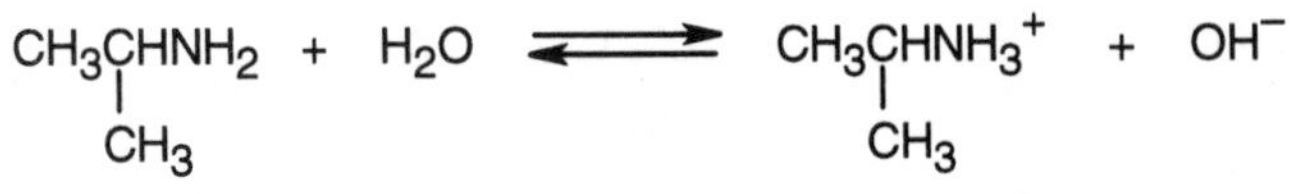

(c)

15.34 Choline doesn't react with HCl because its nitrogen atom isn't basic.

Applications

15.36 Functions that have been attributed to NO include: (1) lowering of blood pressure, (2) memory enhancement, (3) reduction of sickling in hemoglobin molecules of people affected with sickle-cell anemia, (4) destruction of malaria parasites, and (5) destruction of the tuberculosis bacterium.

15.38

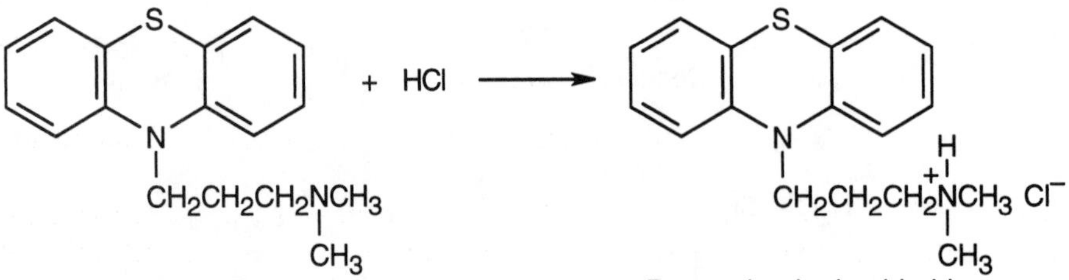

Promazine   Promazine hydrochloride

The nitrogen that is not part of a ring is protonated because it is more basic.

15.40 (a) Toxicologists work in three major areas. Clinical toxicologists are involved with the treatment of people harmed by toxic agents. Forensic toxicologists deal with the effects of toxic agents as they apply to criminal cases. Environmental toxicologists study the environmental impact of toxic substances.
(b) When working with a new toxin, a researcher needs to know the structure of the toxin, its mode of action at the molecular level, and a mechanism to reverse its effects.

General Questions and Problems

15.42 Decylamine is much less soluble in water than ethylamine because of its large hydrocarbon region, which is water-insoluble.

15.44

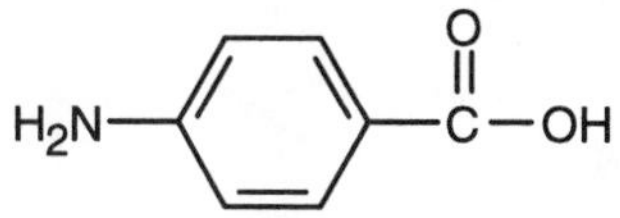

PABA

15.46

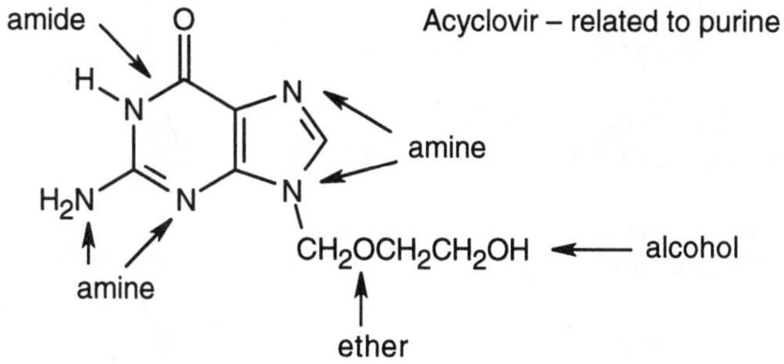

Acyclovir – related to purine

15.48 *Amines*

(a) foul smelling
(b) basic
(c) lower boiling, due to weaker hydrogen bonds, but higher boiling than ethers or alkyl halides

Alcohols

pleasant smelling
not basic
higher boiling, due to strong hydrogen bonds

15.50

(a)

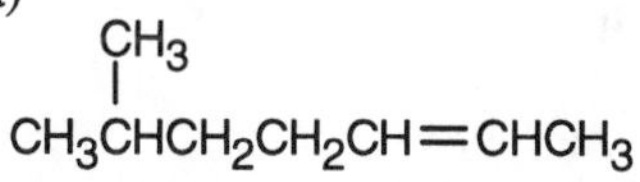

$CH_3CHCH_2CH_2CH=CHCH_3$
      |
      CH_3

6–Methyl–2–heptene

(b)

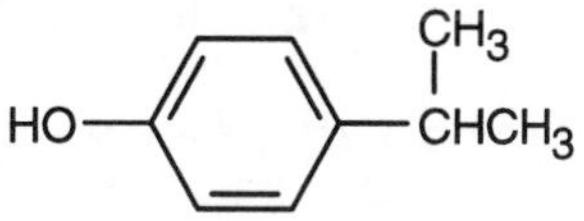

p–Isopropylphenol

(c)

$(CH_3CH_2CH_2CH_2)_2NH$

Dibutylamine

15.52 Molecules of hexylamine can hydrogen–bond to each other. Heat must be supplied to break these hydrogen bonds, and thus the boiling point of hexylamine is higher than that of triethylamine, a tertiary amine whose molecules don't hydrogen–bond to each other.

15.54

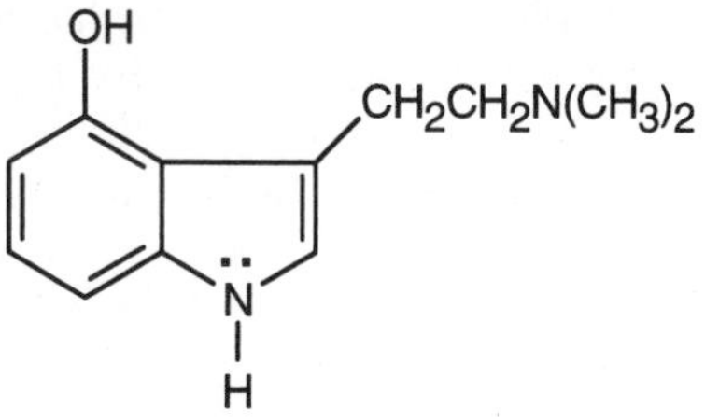

Psilocin

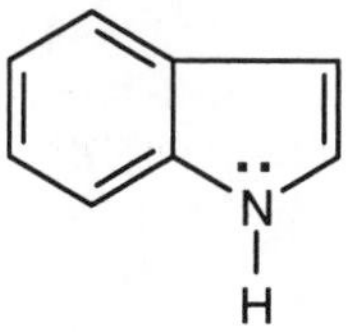

Indole

Psilocin is related to indole.

15.56 Pyridine is soluble in water because the ring nitrogen can form hydrogen bonds with water. No hydrogen bonding is possible for benzene.

Self-Test for Chapter 15

Multiple choice:

1. Which of the following amines is heterocyclic?
   (a) Aniline (b) Cyclohexylamine (c) Pyridine (d) Amphetamine

2. Which of the following amines is a secondary amine?
   (a) N–Methylaniline (b) Histamine (c) Triethylamine (d) Codeine

3. The name of the compound shown below is:
   (a) Ethylcyclopentylamine (b) Cyclopentylethylamine (c) N–Cyclopentylethylamine
   (d) N–Ethylcyclopentylamine

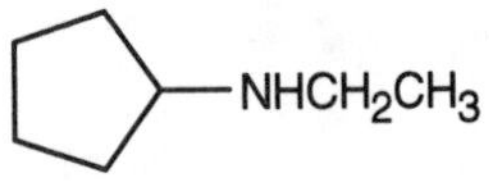

4. An amine and its ammonium salt differ in all respects except:
   (a) charge (b) solubility (c) carbon skeleton (d) basicity

5. Which of the following amines has the highest boiling point?
   (a) Triethylamine (b) Hexylamine (c) Tetramethylammonium chloride (d) Dipropylamine

6. Which of the following is an alkaloid?
   (a) Atropine (b) Amphetamine (c) Pyrimidine (d) Aniline

7. How many isomers of the formula $C_4H_{11}N$ are secondary amines?
   (a) 2 (b) 3 (c) 4 (d) 5

8. All of the following amines have a heterocyclic ring except:
   (a) Nicotine (b) Caffeine (c) Morphine (d) Aniline

9. Propylamine and triethylamine differ in all respects except:
   (a) formula weight (b) boiling point (c) solubility in water (d) melting point

10. Which of the following is a quaternary ammonium salt?
    (a) Anilinium chloride (b) Triethylpropylammonium chloride (c) Pyridinium chloride
    (d) Trimethylammonium chloride

Complete the following sentences:

1. When the $-NH_2$ group is a substituent, _____ is used as a prefix.

2. Tetramethylammonium bromide is a _____ amine salt.

3. _____ contains nitrogen heterocyclic rings derived from either purine or pyrimidine.

4. _____ is the science devoted to poisons.

5. A _____ has a nitrogen atom contained in a ring.

6. _____ are a class of amines derived from plants.

7. Simple amines are water-soluble because of _____ _____.

8. Most amines can be made water-soluble by conversion to _____ salts.

9. Nitric oxide is a molecule that is a ____ _____ because it has an unpaired electron.

10. Ammonia is less basic than _____ _____.

Tell whether the following statements are true or false:

1. Amine groups in biomolecules are usually protonated in body fluids.

2. Ammonium salts are water-soluble.

3. Tertiary amines are higher boiling than primary or secondary amines.

4. Morphine and codeine are alkaloids.

5. Quaternary ammonium salts are acidic.

6. Caffeine is a heterocyclic amine.

7. Heroin is a naturally occurring alkaloid.

8. The physical properties of low-molecular-weight amines and ammonia are similar.

9. NO is responsible for elevating blood pressure.

10. The correct name for $CH_3CH_2CH_2CH_2NHCH_3$ is methylbutylamine.

Match the item in the left column with its partner on the right:

1. Trimethylamine   (a) amino acid

2. Atropine   (b) vitamin

3. Piperidine   (c) primary aromatic amine

4. Tetramethylammonium chloride   (d) tertiary amine

5. Alanine   (e) aromatic heterocycle

6. Dimethylamine   (f) neurotransmitter

7. Pyridoxine   (g) primary amine

8. Putrescine   (h) nonaromatic heterocycle

9. Serotonin   (i) quaternary ammonium salt

10. Methylamine   (j) secondary amine

11. Pyridine   (k) diamine

12. Aniline   (l) alkaloid

Chapter Outline

I. Characteristics of aldehydes and ketones (Sections 16.1–16.4).
   A. The carbonyl group (Section 16.1).
      1. Carbonyl groups are polarized, with carbon having a partial positive charge and oxygen having a partial negative charge.
      2. Carbonyl groups are planar, with a 120° bond angle.
      3. Carbonyl compounds can be divided into two groups:
         a. In aldehydes and ketones, the carbonyl carbon is bonded to atoms that don't attract electrons strongly.
         b. In carboxylic acids, esters, anhydrides and amides, the carbonyl carbon is bonded to nitrogen or oxygen.
   B. Naming aldehydes and ketones (Section 16.2).
      1. Aldehydes are named by replacing the suffix of the parent compound with -al.
         a. For substituted aldehydes, the carbon chain is numbered with the aldehyde carbon as carbon 1.
         b. Aldehydes with common names are formaldehyde, acetaldehyde and benzaldehyde.
      2. Ketones are named by replacing the suffix of the parent compound with -one.
         a. Numbering starts at the end nearer the carbonyl carbon.
         b. Ketones with common names include acetone and acetophenone.
         c. Sometimes, ketones are named by naming the two alkyl groups, followed by the word ketone.
   C. Properties of aldehydes and ketones (Section 16.3).
      1. Aldehydes and ketones are polar.
      2. Aldehydes and ketones don't hydrogen-bond with each other.
      3. Aldehydes and ketones are soluble in organic solvents.
      4. Simple aldehydes and ketones are water-soluble because they can hydrogen-bond with water.
      5. Aldehydes and ketones have distinctive odors.
      6. Aldehydes and ketones are flammable.
   D. Common aldehydes and ketones (Section 16.4).
      1. Formaldehyde.
         a. Formaldehyde is an irritating component of smog.
         b. Formaldehyde is used as a disinfectant and as a preservative.
         c. Formaldehyde-containing polymers are used in building materials.
      2. Acetaldehyde.
      3. Acetone.
         a. Acetone is a commonly used organic solvent.
         b. Acetone is a product of fat metabolism.
II. Reactions of aldehydes and ketones (Sections 16.5–16.8).
   A. Oxidation (Section 16.5).
      1. Aldehydes can be oxidized to carboxylic acids.
         a. Tollens' reagent converts aldehydes to carboxylic acids and leaves a shiny silver residue on the flask.
         b. Benedict's reagent leaves a brick-red precipitate.
      2. Ketones don't react with most oxidizing agents.

B. Reduction (Section 16.6).
   1. Sodium borohydride reduces aldehydes to primary alcohols and ketones to secondary alcohols in a two-step reaction.
      a. Hydride ion adds to the carbonyl carbon.
      b. Hydrogen ion adds to the carbonyl oxygen.
   2. In the body, the coenzyme NADH is the reducing agent.
C. Formation of hemiacetals and acetals (Section 16.7).
   1. Hemiacetals.
      a. An alcohol can add to an aldehyde or ketone to form a hemiacetal.
         i. The negatively polarized alcohol oxygen adds to the positively polarized carbonyl carbon.
         ii. The reaction is reversible: Hemiacetals easily revert to an aldehyde or ketone.
      b. Although hemiacetals are often too unstable to isolate, the hemiacetals of sugars are stable.
   2. Acetals.
      a. Hemiacetals can react with a second molecule of an alcohol to form an acetal.
      b. Acetals are stable and can be isolated.
   3. Acetal hydrolysis.
      Aqueous acid reacts with acetals to regenerate the original aldehyde or ketone.
D. Aldol condensation (Section 16.8).
   1. Two molecules of aldehyde or ketone can react with each other in the presence of base to form a new carbon–carbon bond.
   2. In order for an aldol reaction to occur, the aldehyde or ketone must have a hydrogen atom bonded to the carbon next to the carbonyl group.

Solutions to Chapter 16 Problems

16.1

(a)   (b)   (c)

Aspirin   Testosterone   Vanillin

(d)   (e)   (f)

ketone   aldehyde   ester

16.2

(d)   (e)

16.3

(a)

$CH_3CH_2CH_2CH_2CH_2\overset{\displaystyle O}{\overset{\|}{C}}-H$

Hexanal

(b)

Methyl phenyl ketone

(c)

$CH_3CH_2\overset{\displaystyle CH_3}{\underset{|}{CH}}CH_2\overset{\displaystyle O}{\overset{\|}{C}}CH_3$

4–Methyl–2–hexanone

(d)

$CH_3\overset{}{\underset{|}{CH}}CH_2\overset{\displaystyle O}{\overset{\|}{C}}CH_3$
CH_3

Isobutyl methyl ketone

16.4

(a)

$CH_3CH_2CH_2CH_2\overset{\displaystyle O}{\overset{\|}{C}}H$

Pentanal

(b)

$CH_3CH_2\overset{\displaystyle O}{\overset{\|}{C}}CH_2CH_3$

3–Pentanone
or
Diethyl ketone

(c)

$CH_3CH_2\overset{\displaystyle CH_3}{\underset{|}{CH}}CH_2CH_2\overset{\displaystyle O}{\overset{\|}{C}}H$

4–Methylhexanal

(d)

$CH_3CH_2CH_2\overset{\displaystyle O}{\overset{\|}{C}}CH_2CH_2CH_3$

4–Heptanone
or
Dipropyl ketone

16.5

(a)

$CH_3\overset{\displaystyle CH_3}{\underset{|}{C}}... $

$CH_3\overset{CH_3}{\underset{|}{CH}}CH_2CH_2CH_2\overset{\displaystyle O}{\overset{\|}{C}}H$ $\xrightarrow[\text{2. H}_3\text{O}^+]{\text{1.Tollens' reagent}}$ $CH_3\overset{CH_3}{\underset{|}{CH}}CH_2CH_2CH_2\overset{\displaystyle O}{\overset{\|}{C}}OH$ + Ag(s)

(b)

$CH_3CH_2CH_2\overset{\displaystyle H_3C}{\underset{|}{C}}-\overset{\displaystyle O}{\overset{\|}{C}}H$
H_3C $\xrightarrow[\text{2. H}_3\text{O}^+]{\text{1.Tollens' reagent}}$ $CH_3CH_2CH_2\overset{\displaystyle H_3C}{\underset{|}{C}}-\overset{\displaystyle O}{\overset{\|}{C}}OH$ + Ag(s)
H_3C

(c)

$CH_3CH_2\overset{\displaystyle O}{\overset{\|}{C}}\overset{}{\underset{|}{CH}}CH_3$
CH_3 $\xrightarrow[\text{2. H}_3\text{O}^+]{\text{1.Tollens' reagent}}$ NR

16.6

(a)

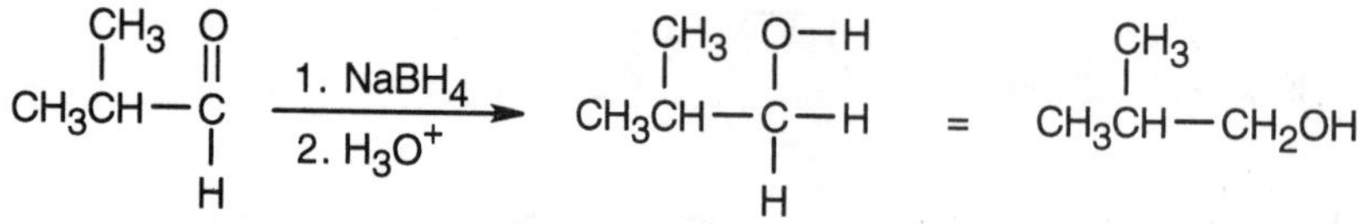

$$CH_3CH-\overset{\underset{|}{H}}{\underset{}{C}}\overset{O}{\underset{}{\parallel}} \xrightarrow[\text{2. } H_3O^+]{\text{1. } NaBH_4} CH_3CH-\overset{O-H}{\underset{|}{C}}-H \quad = \quad CH_3CH-CH_2OH$$

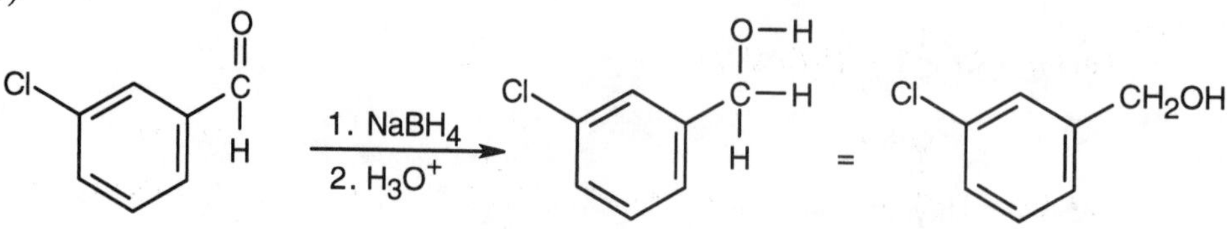

with CH_3 groups labeled on the left carbons

(b)

$$\xrightarrow[\text{2. } H_3O^+]{\text{1. } NaBH_4}$$

=

(c)

$$\xrightarrow[\text{2. } H_3O^+]{\text{1. } NaBH_4}$$

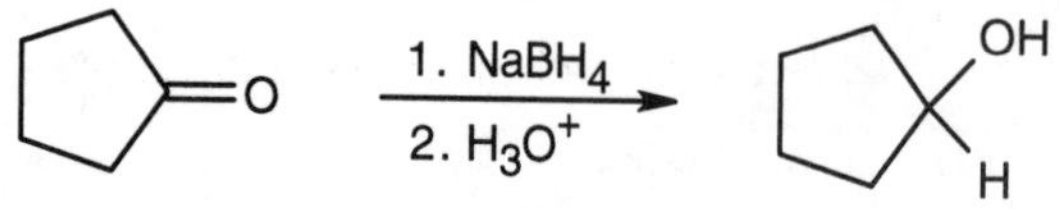

16.7

(a)

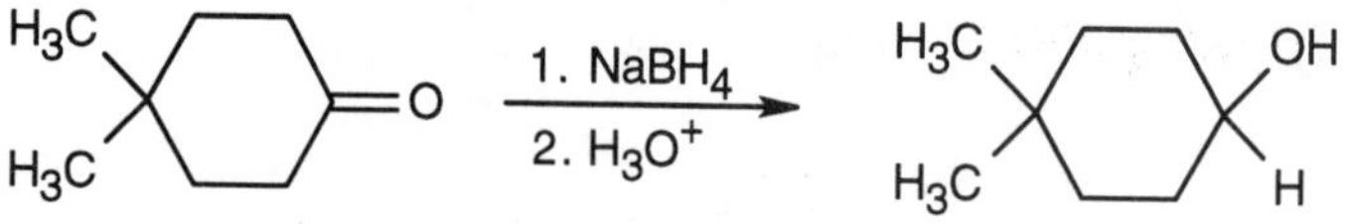

$$\xrightarrow[\text{2. } H_3O^+]{\text{1. } NaBH_4}$$

(b)

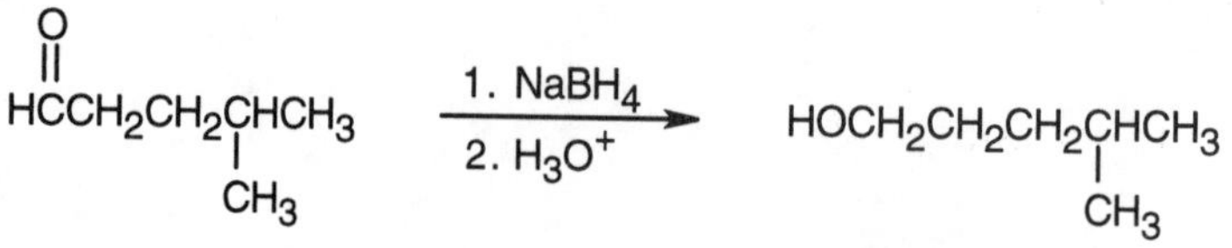

$$\overset{O}{\underset{\parallel}{}}HCCH_2CH_2\underset{\underset{CH_3}{|}}{CH}CH_3 \xrightarrow[\text{2. } H_3O^+]{\text{1. } NaBH_4} HOCH_2CH_2CH_2\underset{\underset{CH_3}{|}}{CH}CH_3$$

(c)

$$CH_3CH_2CH_2\underset{\underset{CH_3}{|}}{CH}\overset{O}{\underset{\parallel}{C}}H \xrightarrow[\text{2. } H_3O^+]{\text{1. } NaBH_4} CH_3CH_2CH_2\underset{\underset{CH_3}{|}}{CH}CH_2OH$$

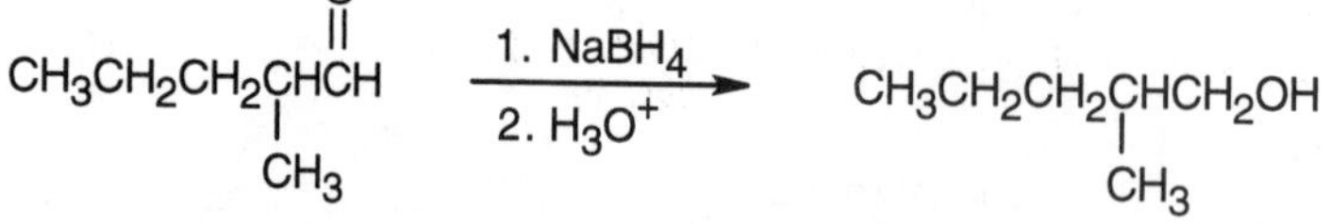

16.8 To identify a hemiacetal, look for a carbon with single bonds to two different oxygens. If one group bonded to the carbon is –OH and the other is –OR (R = organic group), the compound is a hemiacetal.

(a)

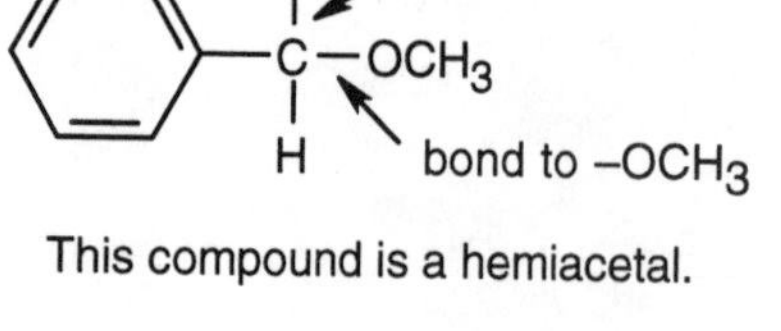

bond to –OH

bond to –OCH₃

This compound is a hemiacetal.

(b)

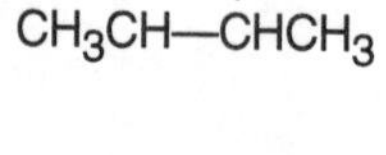

$$\underset{}{CH_3}\overset{OH}{\underset{|}{C}}H-\overset{OH}{\underset{|}{C}}HCH_3$$

This compound is not a hemiacetal.

(c)

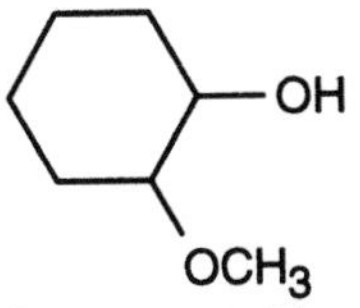

This compound is not a hemiacetal.

16.9

(a)

Redraw CH$_3$CH$_2$CH$_2$CHO as:

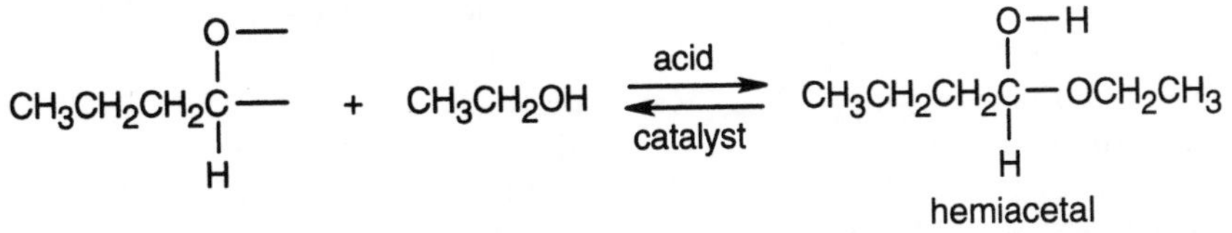

The hemiacetal is formed by adding –H to oxygen and –OCH$_2$CH$_3$ to carbon.

(b)

Redraw CH$_3$CH$_2$CCH$_2$CH(CH$_3$)$_2$ as:

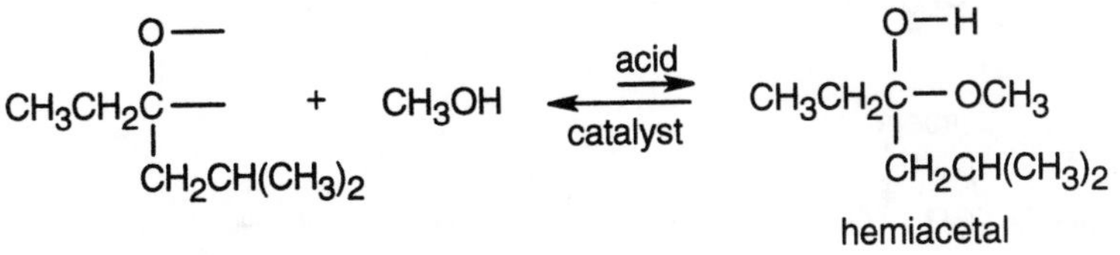

The equilibrium favors starting material.

16.10

(a)

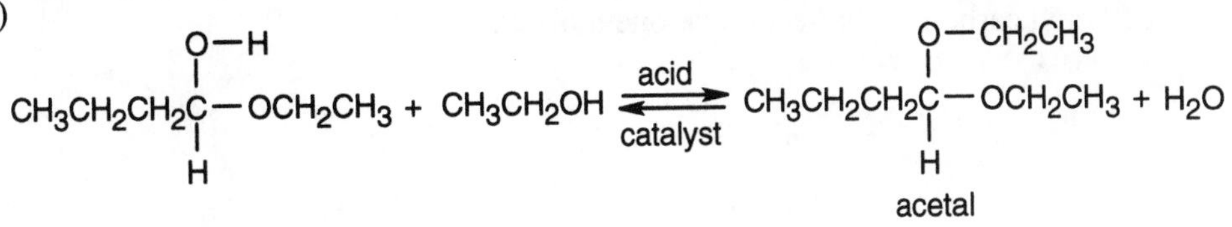

(b)

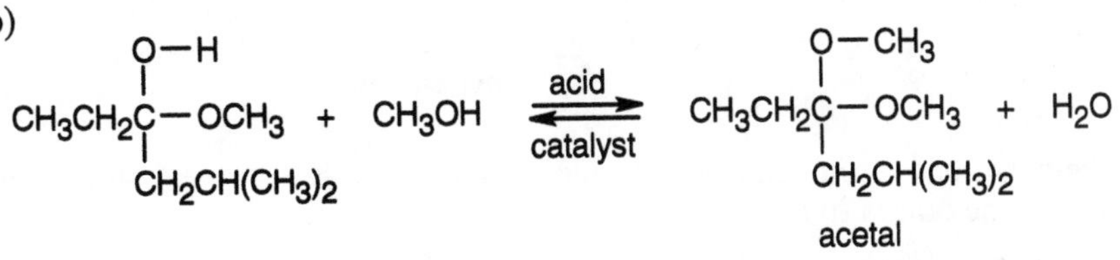

16.11 Follow the instructions for Practice Problem 16.8. If one carbon is bonded to two –OR groups, the compound is an acetal.

(a) 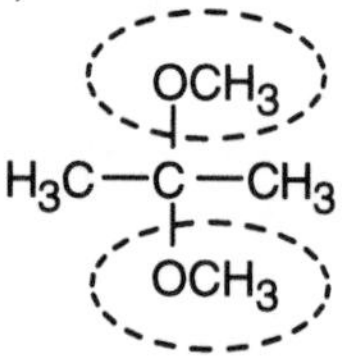   (b) 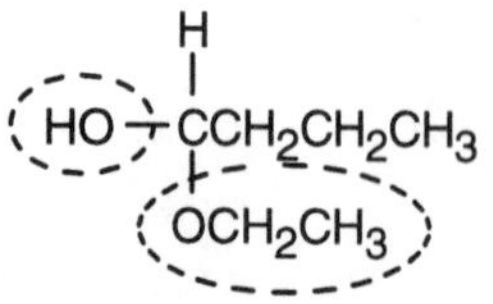   (c) 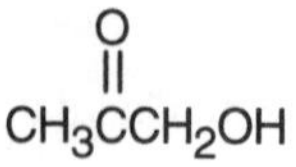   (d)

acetal   hemiacetal   neither acetal   acetal
                                        nor hemiacetal

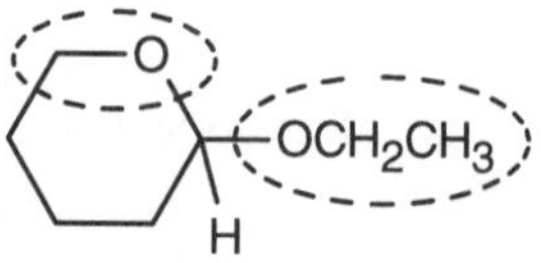

16.12 If the carbon that bears the –OH or –OR groups also has a –H *and* an –R group bonded to it, the original compound was an aldehyde. If the carbon has two –R groups bonded to it, the original compound was a ketone. Thus, hemiacetal (b) and acetal (d) were formed from aldehydes, and acetal (a) was formed from a ketone.

16.13

(a)

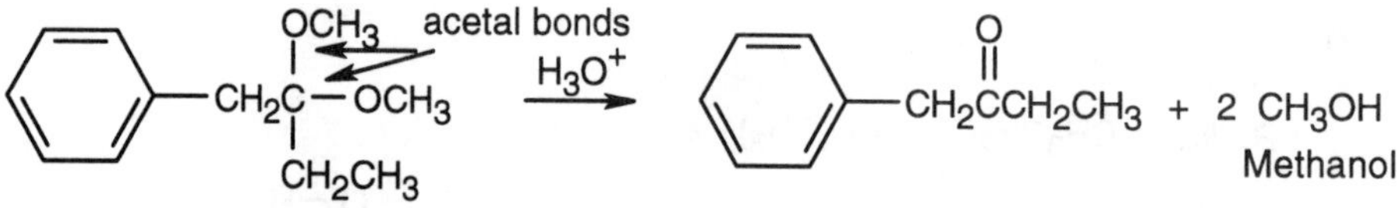

(b)

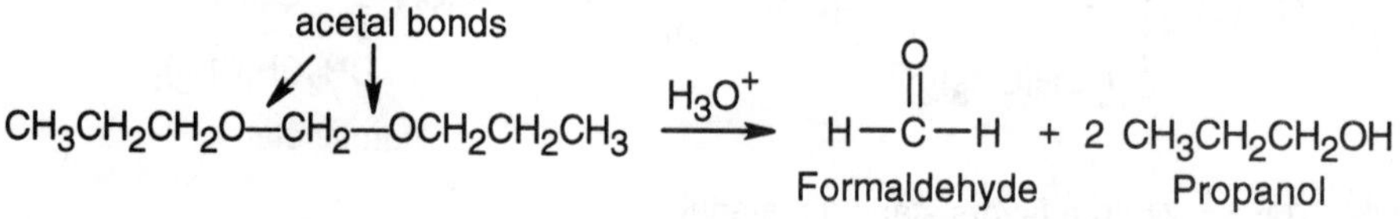

16.14

(a) Redraw the ketone to emphasize the position of the new bonds. The carbon–carbon bond connects the carbonyl carbon of one ketone molecule to the carbon next to the carbonyl carbon of the second ketone molecule.

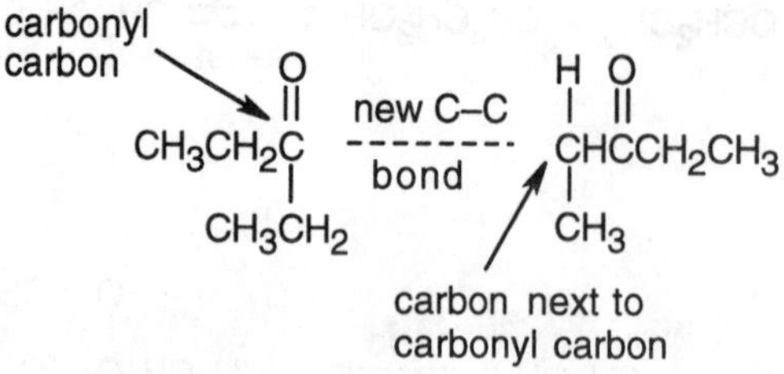

Draw the new bonds from the atoms on the ketone on the left, and attach the correct atoms from the ketone on the right.

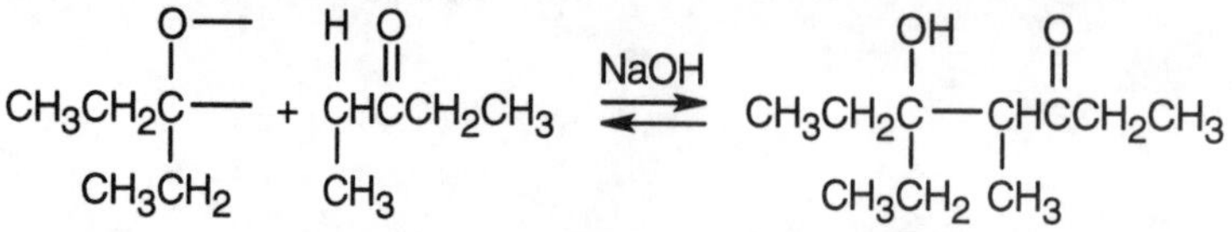

(b)

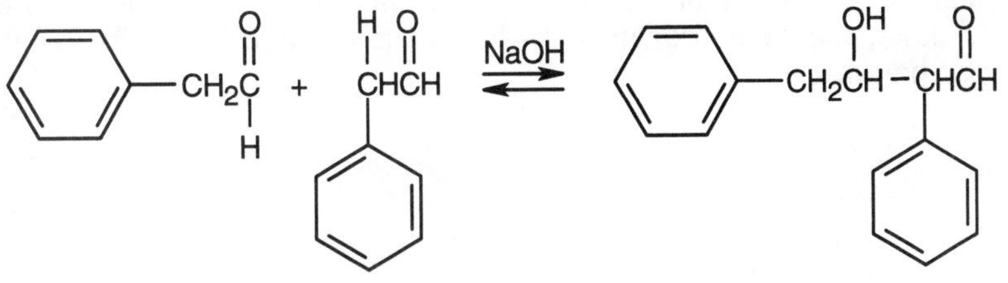

16.15 (a) This compound can't undergo an aldol reaction because it has only one carbon atom (and thus no hydrogens on a carbon atom next to the carbonyl group).
(b) This compound can't undergo an aldol reaction because it has no hydrogens on the carbon atom next to the carbonyl group.

no hydrogen bonded to this carbon

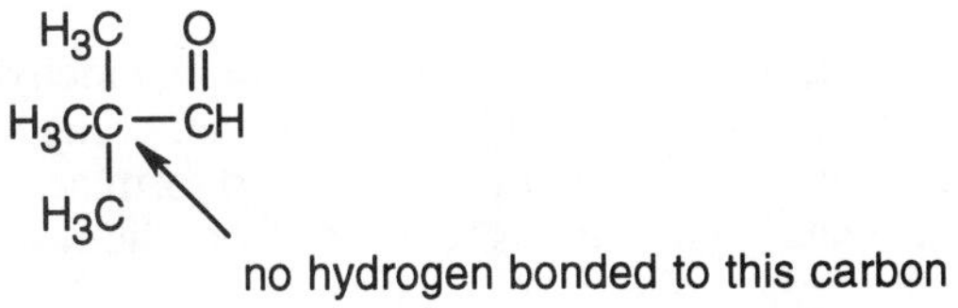

(c) This compound can undergo an aldol reaction:

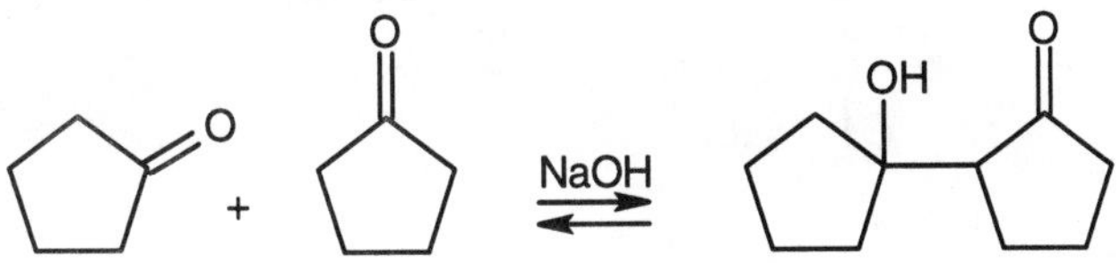

Understanding Key Concepts

16.16 (a) The hydride ion is added to the carbonyl carbon. The carbon end of the polar C=O bond has a partial positive charge, and thus reaction with negatively charged reagents occurs at carbon.
(b) The top arrow (reaction to the right) represents reduction, and the bottom arrow (reaction to the left) represents oxidation.

16.17 Aldehydes can be oxidized to carboxylic acids, but ketones cannot. Two tests that can distinguish aldehydes from ketones take advantage of selective aldehyde oxidation. Tollens' reagent produces a deposit of silver when it is mixed with an aldehyde, but no reaction takes place with a ketone. Benedict's reagent yields a red copper oxide precipitate when it reacts with an aldehyde, but no reaction occurs with a ketone.

16.18 In a solution of an aldehyde in water, hydrogen bonds form between the oxygen atoms of the aldehyde and the hydrogen atoms of water. Molecules of aldehyde don't hydrogen-bond with each other, and the hydrogen atoms bonded to the aldehyde carbon don't take part in hydrogen bonding.

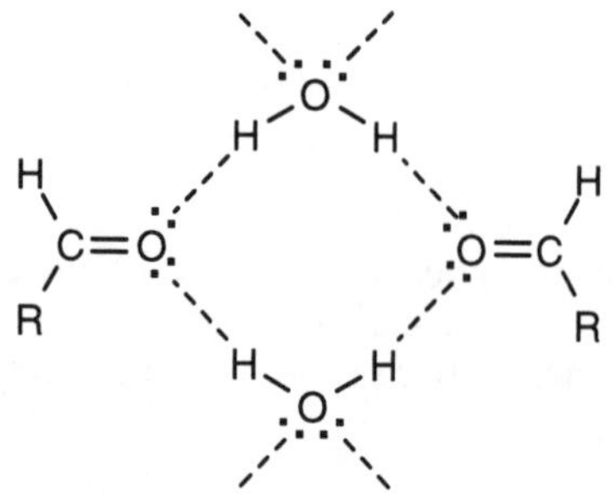

16.19 (a) Under acidic conditions, an alcohol adds to the carbonyl group of an aldehyde to form a hemiacetal. Although some hemiacetals are stable, most hemiacetals are either reconverted to aldehydes or further react with a second molecule of the alcohol to form acetals. The yield of acetal can be improved if the water byproduct is removed from the reaction mixture, driving the equilibrium to the right

(b)

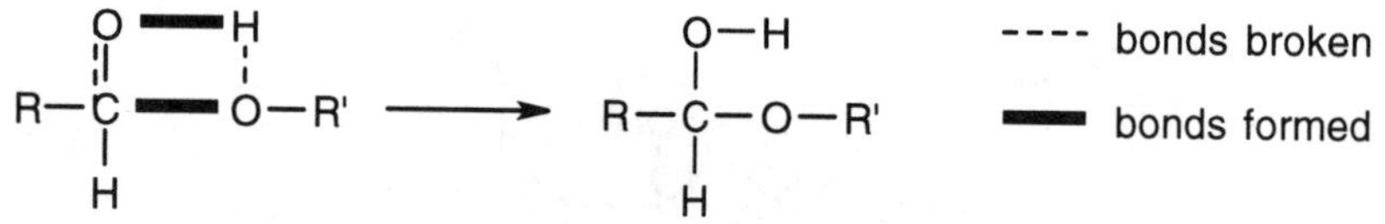

16.20 In an aldol condensation, a carbon–carbon bond is formed between two aldehydes or ketones. The new bond connects the carbonyl carbon of one molecule to the carbon next to the carbonyl carbon of a second molecule. Aldol condensations are catalyzed by base and require that at least one of the reacting partners have a hydrogen bonded to the carbon next to the carbonyl carbon.

(a)

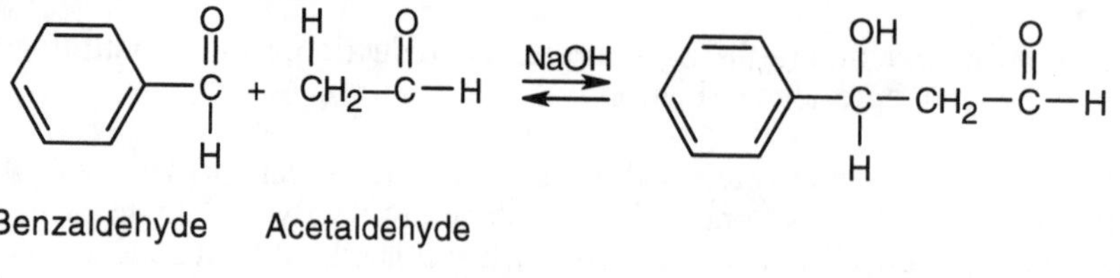

Benzaldehyde   Acetaldehyde

(b)

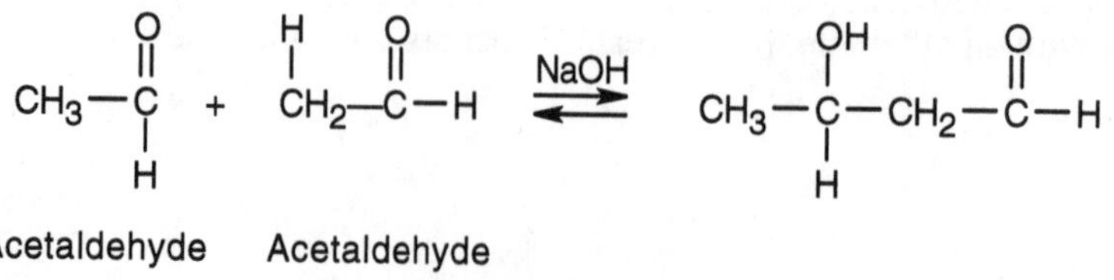

Acetaldehyde   Acetaldehyde

Acetaldehyde can react either with benzaldehyde (mixed condensation) or with another acetaldehyde (self-condensation). Two benzaldehydes can't react because no hydrogen is bonded to the carbon next to the carbonyl carbon.

16.21 In solution, glucose exists primarily in the cyclic hemiacetal form shown below because it is more stable in this form.

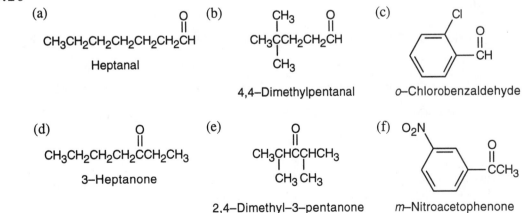

Aldehydes and Ketones

16.22

(a)

$$CH_3CCH_3$$
ketone (C_3H_6O)

(b)

$$CH_3CH_2CHCH_2CH$$
aldehyde ($C_6H_{12}O$)

(c)

$$CH_3CCH_2CH$$
ketoaldehyde ($C_4H_6O_2$)

(d)

$$HOCH_2CCH_3$$
hydroxyketone($C_3H_6O_2$)

16.24

(a)

$$CH_3CH_2C=O$$
aldehyde

(b)

$$O=CCH_2CH_2CHCH_3$$
amide

(c)

$$CH_3CH_2-O-CH=CH_2$$
no carbonyl group

(d)

$$CH_3CH_2C-OCH_3$$
no carbonyl group

(e)

$$CH_3CHCOH$$
carboxylic acid

(f)

$$CH_3CCH_2CH_2OH$$
ketone

Structure (a) is an aldehyde, and structure (f) is a ketone.

16.26

(a)

$$CH_3CH_2CH_2CH_2CH_2CH_2CH$$
Heptanal

(b)

$$CH_3CCH_2CH_2CH$$
4,4–Dimethylpentanal

(c)

o–Chlorobenzaldehyde

(d)

$$CH_3CH_2CH_2CH_2CCH_2CH_3$$
3–Heptanone

(e)

$$CH_3CHCCHCH_3$$
2,4–Dimethyl–3–pentanone

(f)

m–Nitroacetophenone

16.28

(a)

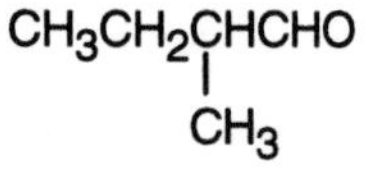

CH₃CH₂CHCHO
|
CH₃

2–Methylbutanal

(b)

CHO
|
CH₃CH₂CH₂CHCH₃

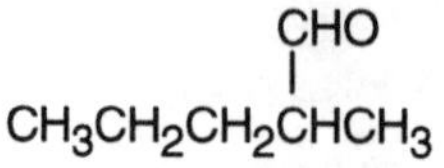

2–Methylpentanal

(c)

(CH₃)₃CCHO

2,2-Dimethylpropanal

(d)

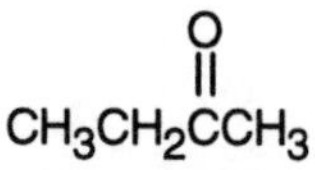

$$O$$
$$\|$$
CH₃CH₂CCH₃

2–Butanone

(e)

$$O \qquad CH_3$$
$$\| \qquad |$$
CH₃CCH₂CH₂CHCH₃

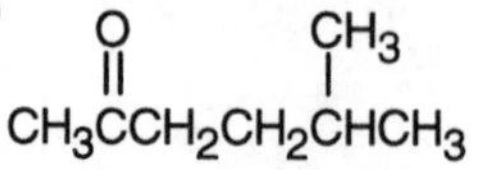

5–Methyl–2–hexanone

16.30 (a) (b)The name 1–butanone is incorrect because a ketone group can't occur at the end of a carbon chain.
(c) Numbering must start at the end of the carbon chain that is closer to the ketone functional group. Correct name: 2–Butanone.

Reactions of Aldehydes and Ketones

16.32 A *hemiacetal* is produced when an aldehyde reacts with an alcohol in a 1:1 ratio.

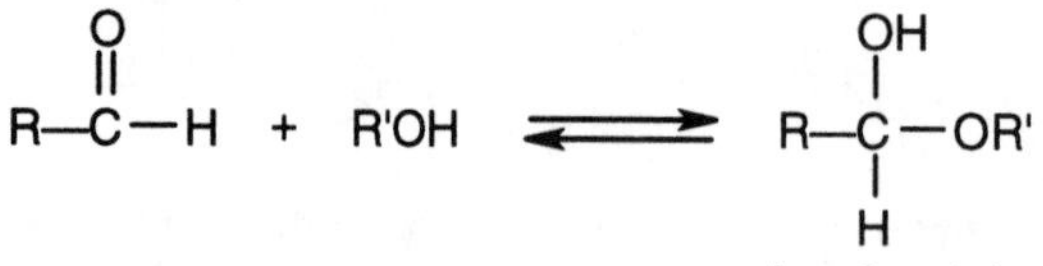

$$
\underset{\text{}}{\overset{O}{\overset{\|}{R-C-H}}} + R'OH \rightleftharpoons R-\overset{OH}{\underset{H}{\overset{|}{C}}}-OR'
$$

hemiacetal

16.34 Remember that only aldehydes react with Tollens' reagent. Ketones are not oxidized.

Compound	*Tollens' Product*	*NaBH₄ Product*
(a) cyclopentanone	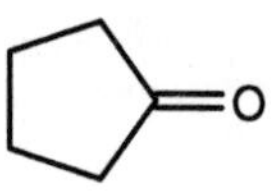 no reaction	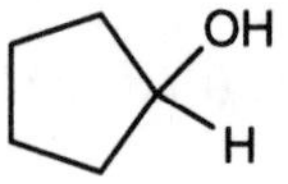 cyclopentanol (OH, H)
(b) CH₃CH₂CH₂CH₂CH₂CH(=O)	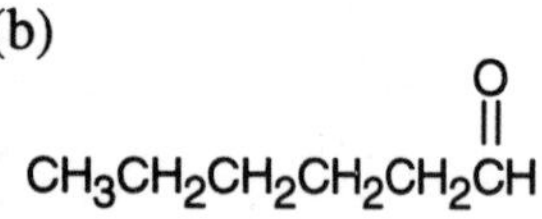 CH₃CH₂CH₂CH₂CH₂COH (=O)	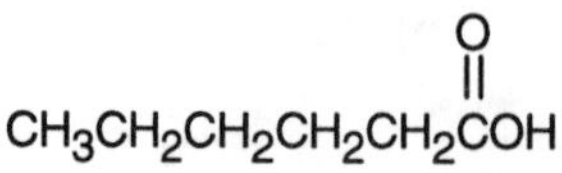 CH₃CH₂CH₂CH₂CH₂CH₂OH
(c) CHO / CH₃CH₂CH₂CHCH₂CH₃	COOH / CH₃CH₂CH₂CHCH₂CH₃	CH₂OH / CH₃CH₂CH₂CHCH₂CH₃

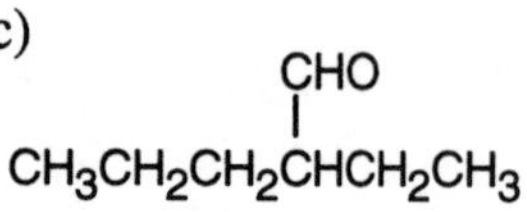

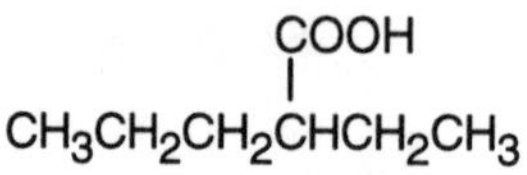

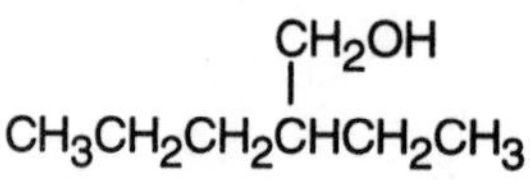

16.36

	Carboxylic acid	*Aldehyde*	*Primary alcohol*

(a)

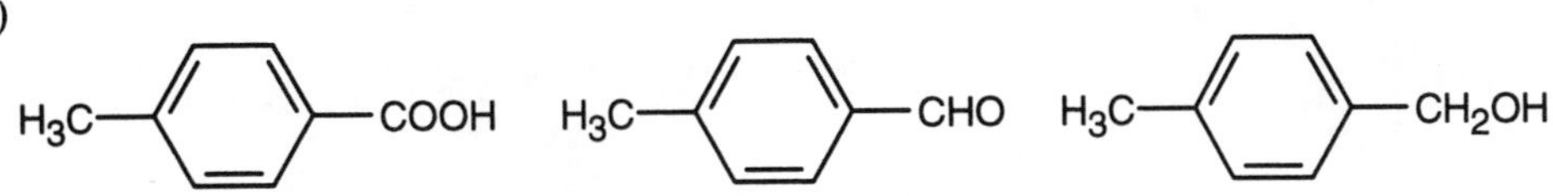

H_3C—⬡—COOH H_3C—⬡—CHO H_3C—⬡—CH_2OH

(b)

$$\underset{\underset{CH_3}{|}}{CH_3CH_2\overset{\overset{COOH}{|}}{C}HCH_2CHCH_3}$$

$$\underset{\underset{CH_3}{|}}{CH_3CH_2\overset{\overset{CHO}{|}}{C}HCH_2CHCH_3}$$

$$\underset{\underset{CH_3}{|}}{CH_3CH_2\overset{\overset{CH_2OH}{|}}{C}HCH_2CHCH_3}$$

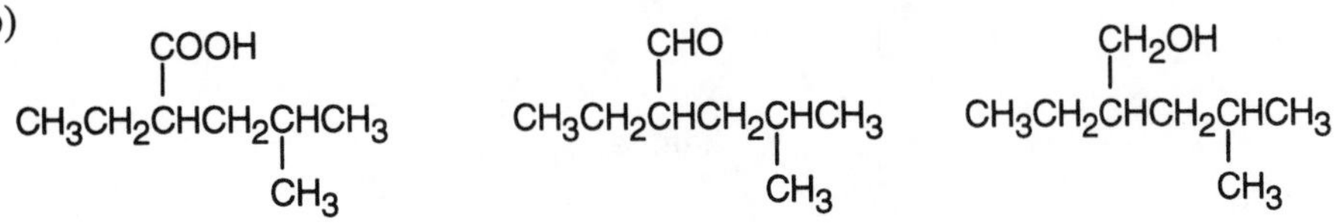

(c)

$CH_3CH{=}CHCOOH$ $CH_3CH{=}CHCHO$ $CH_3CH{=}CHCH_2OH$

16.38

(a)

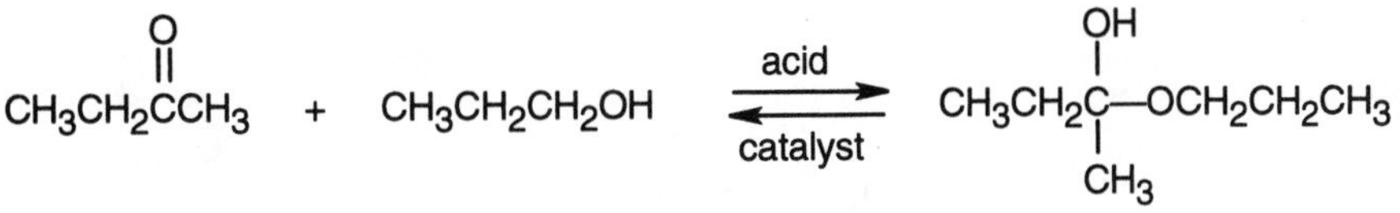

$$CH_3CH_2\overset{\overset{O}{\|}}{C}CH_3 \;+\; CH_3CH_2CH_2OH \;\underset{\text{catalyst}}{\overset{\text{acid}}{\rightleftharpoons}}\; CH_3CH_2\overset{\overset{OH}{|}}{\underset{\underset{CH_3}{|}}{C}}{-}OCH_2CH_2CH_3$$

(b)

$$CH_3CH_2CH_2\overset{\overset{O}{\|}}{C}H \;+\; (CH_3)_2CHOH \;\underset{\text{catalyst}}{\overset{\text{acid}}{\rightleftharpoons}}\; CH_3CH_2CH_2\overset{\overset{OH}{|}}{\underset{\underset{H}{|}}{C}}{-}OCH(CH_3)_2$$

(c)

$$CH_3CH_2CH_2\overset{\overset{O-CH_2CH_3}{|}}{C}H{-}OCH_3 \;\xrightarrow{H_3O^+}\; CH_3CH_2CH_2\overset{\overset{O}{\|}}{C}H \;+\; CH_3CH_2OH \;+\; CH_3OH$$

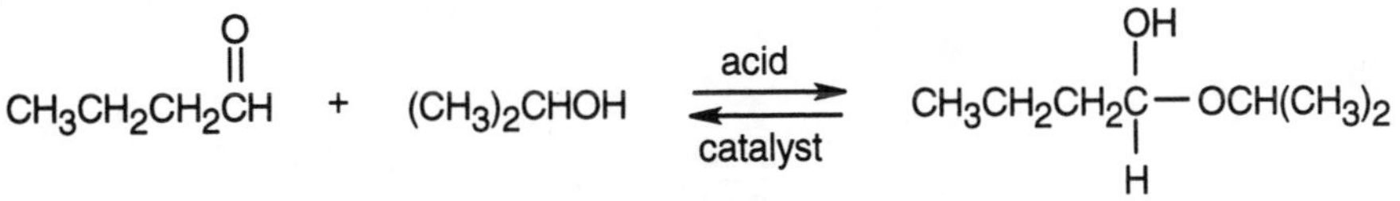

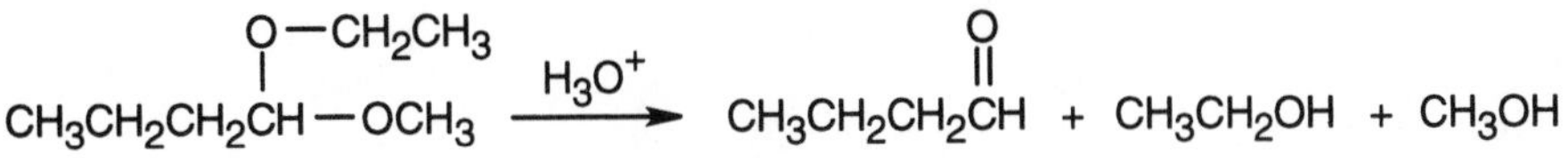

(d)

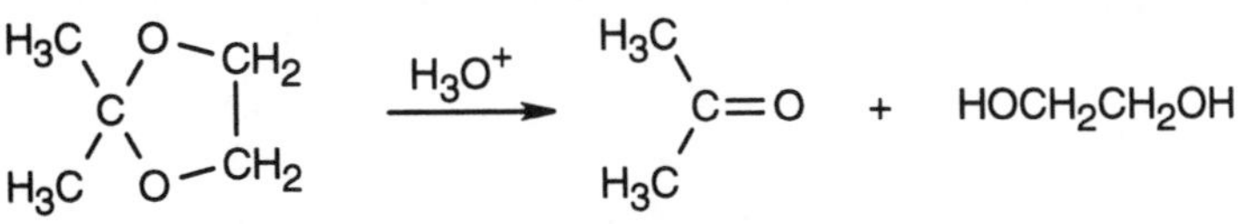

$$\underset{H_3C}{\overset{H_3C}{>}}\overset{\overset{O-CH_2}{\diagup}}{\underset{\underset{O-CH_2}{\diagdown}}{C}} \;\xrightarrow{H_3O^+}\; \underset{H_3C}{\overset{H_3C}{>}}C{=}O \;+\; HOCH_2CH_2OH$$

16.40

$$\underset{\underset{OH}{}}{\overset{\overset{O}{\|}}{CH}}\;\underset{\text{catalyst}}{\overset{\text{acid}}{\rightleftharpoons}}\;\overset{OH}{\diagdown}$$

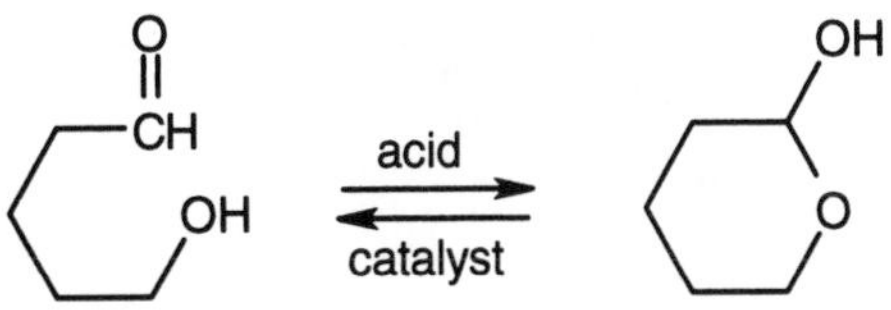

5–Hydroxypentanal

16.42

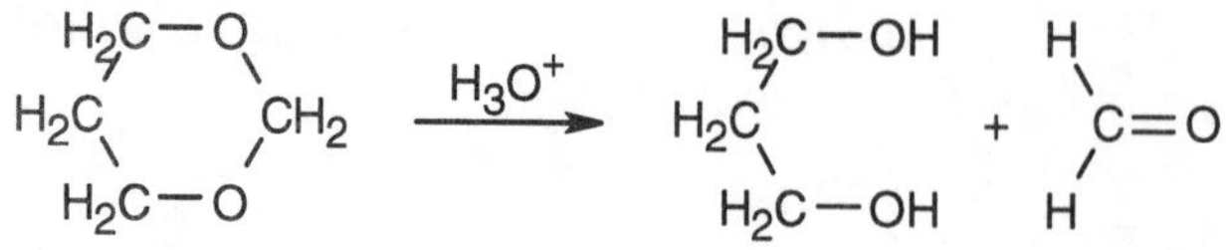

16.44

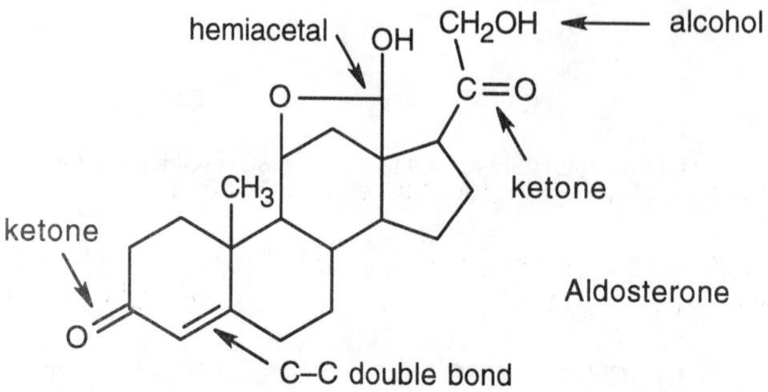

The hemiacetal group is derived from an aldehyde because the hemiacetal carbon has a hydrogen atom bonded to it.

16.46

(a)

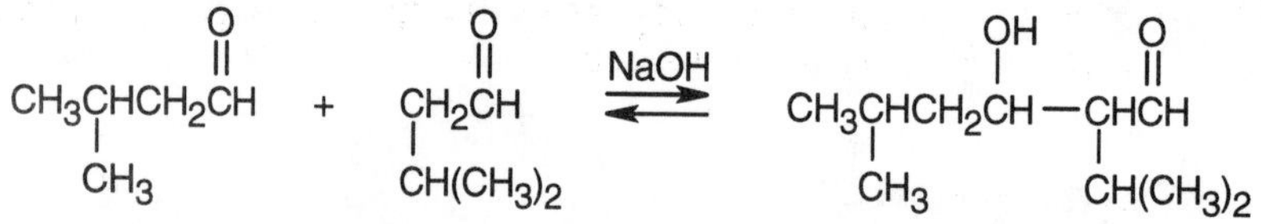

(b)

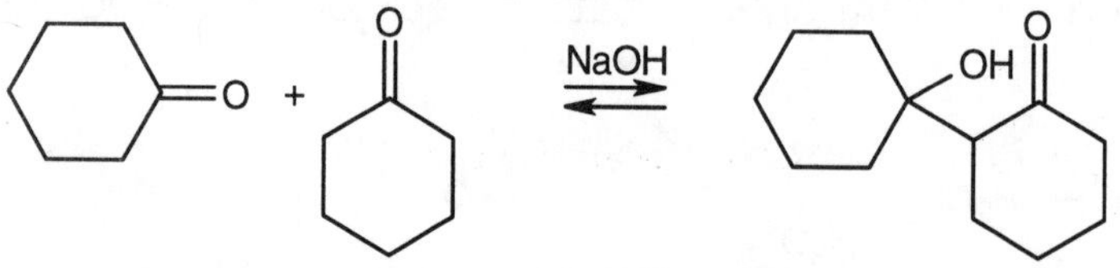

(c)

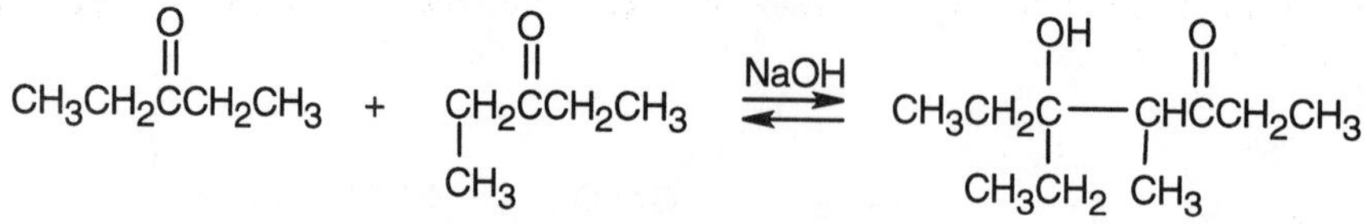

16.48 To solve this problem, locate and break the bond formed in the aldol reaction. Then, change the hydroxyl group to a carbonyl group and add a hydrogen to the carbon that was part of the broken bond. This series of steps is the reverse of the series used in Solved Problem 16.6 in the text.

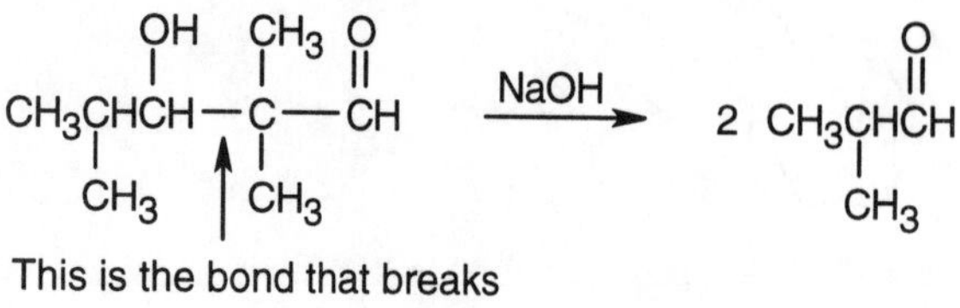

This is the bond that breaks

Applications

16.50

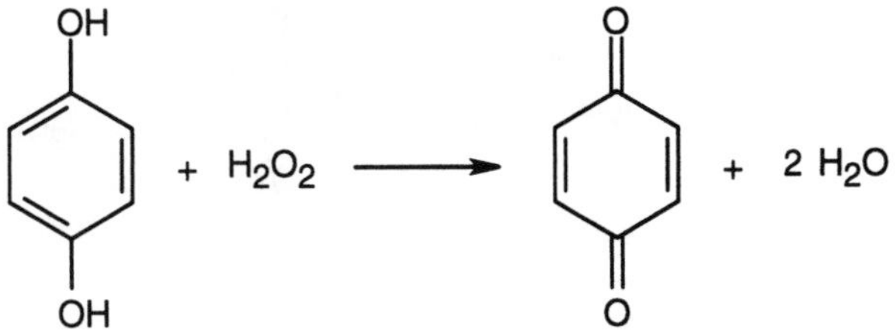

When *p*–dihydroxybenzene is oxidized, hydrogen peroxide is reduced.

16.52 Vanillin is an aromatic molecule with a polar hydroxyl group. The solvent of choice for extraction of vanillin from vanilla beans should also be polar, organic and nontoxic. Ethanol is a good choice.

16.54 (a) There are several advantages to using *in vitro* testing for acute toxicity. *In vitro* testing is relatively inexpensive, and many more tests can be performed for the same cost. In addition, animals don't have to be sacrificed for *in vitro* testing.
(b) Since *in vitro* testing is performed on cultured cells that are identical, the results of testing may not be reliable for organisms that have many different kinds of cells.

16.56 The peach pits contain a cyanide-containing compound that can release small amounts of HCN after being cleaved by digestive enzymes.

General Questions and Problems

16.58

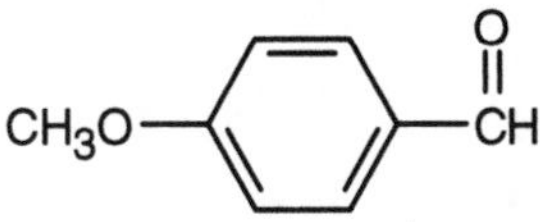

p–Methoxybenzaldehyde

16.60 The portion of the odor due to aldehyde is less stable because aldehydes are easily oxidized to carboxylic acids.

16.62

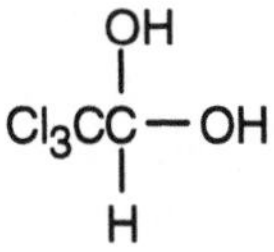

Chloral hydrate

16.64

(a)

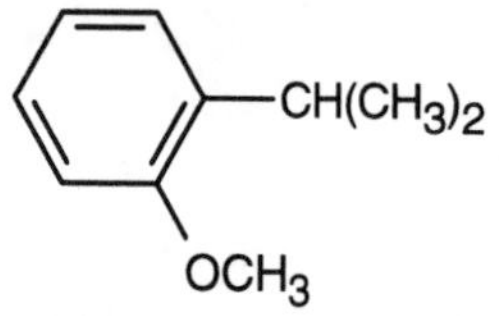

o–Isopropylmethoxybenzene
or
o–Isopropylanisole

(b)

$CH_3CH_2C≡CC(CH_2CH_3)_3$

5,5–Diethyl–3–heptyne

(c)

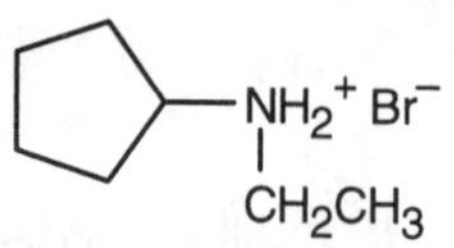

N–Ethylcyclopentyl-
ammonium bromide

(d)

$(CH_3CH_2)_2N(CH_2)_5CH_3$

N,N-Diethylhexylamine

16.66

(a)

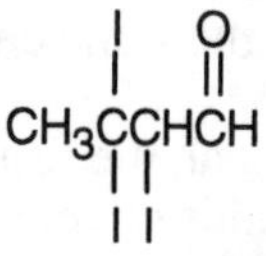

2,3,3–Triiodobutanal

(b)

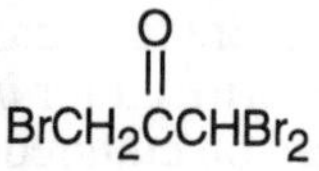

1,1,3–Tribromoacetone

(c)

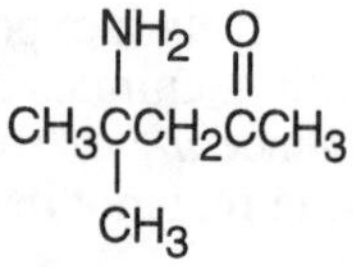

4–Amino–4–methyl–
2–pentanone

16.68

(a)

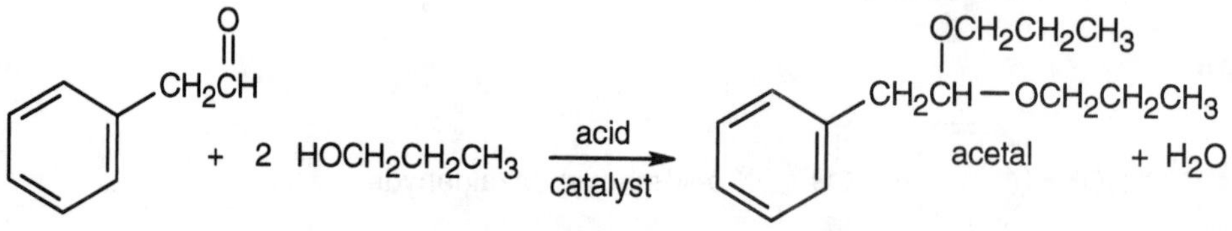

(b)

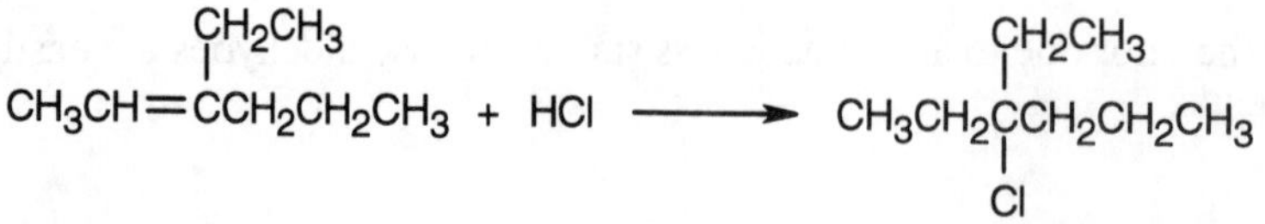

(c)

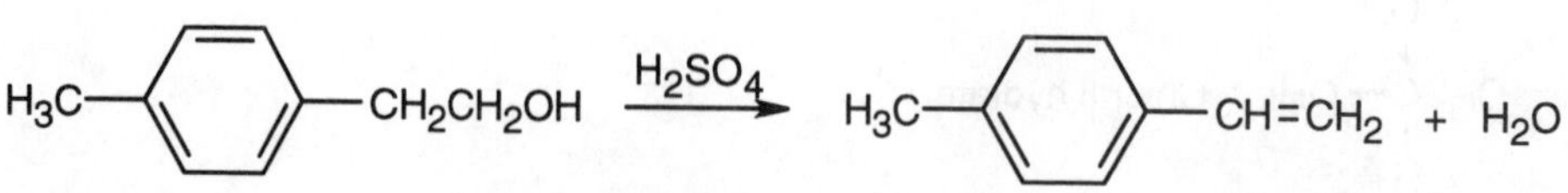

16.70 1-Butanol (bp 117°C) is the highest boiling of the three compounds because it forms stronger hydrogen bonds than does butylamine (bp 78°C). Butanal (bp 75°C) is polar but doesn't form hydrogen bonds.

Self-Test for Chapter 16

Multiple choice:

1. Which of the following alcohols can't be produced by reduction of an aldehyde or ketone?
   (a) 2–Pentanol   (b) Cyclohexanol   (c) 2–Methyl–2–pentanol   (d) 2–Methyl–1–butanol

2. The term LD_{50} refers to:
   (a) 50% of the amount of a substance that will kill a population   (b) the amount of a substance that will kill 50% of a population   (c) the name of a substance, 50% of which will kill a population   (d) none of the above

3. 3–Pentanone is unlikely to undergo which of the following reactions?
   (a) oxidation   (b) reduction   (c) acetal formation   (d) aldol condensation

4. Formaldehyde is unlikely to undergo which of the following reactions?
   (a) oxidation   (b) reduction   (c) acetal formation   (d) aldol condensation

5. How many ketone isomers of the formula $C_6H_{12}O$ are there?
   (a) 4   (b) 5   (c) 6   (d) 7

6. Which of the following aldehydes is least soluble in water?
   (a) Propanal   (b) Benzaldehyde   (c) Formaldehyde   (d) Acetaldehyde

7. Which of the following compounds undergoes reaction with Tollens' reagent?
   (a) 3-Pentanol   (b) Glucose   (c) Acetone   (d) Cyclohexanone dimethyl acetal

8. The main difference between aldehydes and ketones is:
   (a) reactivity   (b) solubility   (c) flammability   (d) polarity

9. Formaldehyde is used for all of the following except:
   (a) polymers   (b) disinfectant   (c) preservative   (d) food additive

10. Which of the following statements about 3–heptanone is true?
    (a) It undergoes reaction with Benedict's reagent.   (b) It forms a cyclic acetal with 1,3–propanediol.   (c) It is soluble in water.   (d) It doesn't undergo aldol condensation.

Complete the following statements:

1. Aldehydes, esters, and ketones are all _____ compounds.

2. The shiny product of oxidation of an aldehyde by Tollens' reagent is _____.

3. _____ is a reaction that converts an acetal to an aldehyde or a ketone.

4. A carbonyl group is polarized, with a partial _____ charge on carbon and a partial _____ charge on oxygen.

5. _____ is a ketone that is widely used as a solvent.

6. Aldol reactions are important because they result in the formation of ____ - _____ bonds.

7. Bonds to the carbonyl carbon of esters and amides are _____ polar than the bonds to the carbonyl carbon on ketones and aldehydes.

8. The conversion of an aldehyde or ketone into an alcohol is said to be a _____ reaction.

9. Formaldehyde is widely used as a _____.

10. The initial product of reaction between a ketone or aldehyde and an alcohol is called a _____.

11. _____ reagent is used to detect sugar in urine.

12. _____ can be detected on the breath during starvation.

Match the entries on the left with their partners on the right:

1. $AgNO_3$, NH_3, H_2O (a) Reagent used to form an acetal

2. $CH_3CH_2COCH_3$ (b) Reduces carbonyl groups to alcohols

3. CH_3CH_2COOH (c) An amide

4. CH_3OH, H^+ catalyst   (d) Product of an aldehyde plus Tollens' reagent

5. CH_3CH_2OH (e) Tollens' reagent

6. $CH_3CH_2COOCH_3$ (f) Catalyst for aldol reaction

7. $CH_3CH(OH)CH_3$ (g) Formaldehyde

8. $NaBH_4$ (h) Product of aldehyde reduction

9. CH_3CHO (i) Yields secondary alcohol when reduced

10. $NaOH$ (j) Ester

11. $HCHO$ (k) Can be oxidized to a ketone

12. CH_3CONH_2 (l) Product of primary alcohol oxidation

Tell whether the following statements are true or false:

1. Glucose contains an acetal link.

2. Many sugars are synthesized biochemically by aldol reactions.

3. Ketones are oxidized by Tollens' reagent to carboxylic acids.

4. The reduction of aldehydes and ketones is carried out by using NaOH.

5. An acetal is an alternative name for an ester.

6. Only aldehydes form acetals.

7. An aldehyde group always occurs at the end of a carbon chain.

8. Formaldehyde can't undergo an aldol reaction with itself.

9. 4–Hydroxybutanal can be made by an aldol reaction of acetaldehyde.

10. Acetaldehyde results from the oxidation of ethanol.

11. Both aldehydes and ketones can be reduced to alcohols.

12. Aldehydes and ketones are not capable of forming hydrogen bonds.

Chapter Outline

I. Properties and names of carboxylic acids and derivatives (Section 17.1).
  A. General characteristics.
    1. Groups bonded to the carbonyl carbon are electron-attracting.
      a. In carboxylic acids, –OH is bonded to the carbonyl carbon.
      b. In amides, –NH$_2$ is bonded to the carbonyl carbon.
      c. In esters, –OR is bonded to the carbonyl carbon.
    2. All of these functional groups undergo carbonyl group substitution reactions.
  B. Carboxylic acids.
    1. Properties
      a. All are high-boiling.
      b. Carboxylic acids can hydrogen-bond with each other.
      c. Smaller carboxylic acids are water-soluble.
      d. Volatile carboxylic acids have sharp odors
    2. Naming carboxylic acids
      a. For simple carboxylic acids, the -e of the corresponding alkane is replaced by -oic acid.
      b. Many simple carboxylic acids have common names.
      c. For dicarboxylic acids, -dioic acid replaces the -e of the corresponding alkane.
      d. The group remaining when a carboxylic acid loses -OH is an acyl group.
      e. Unsaturated carboxylic acids are named by using -enoic acid.
      f. In some cases, the carbon next to the –COOH group is referred to as the α carbon.
  C. Esters.
    1. Properties.
      a. Esters are lower boiling than carboxylic acids.
      b. Esters have pleasant odors.
      c. Simple esters are liquids.
    2. Naming esters
    Ester names have two parts.
      a. The –OR fragment has the name of the alkyl group R.
      b. The remaining portion is the name of the parent carboxylic acid, with -ate replacing -oic acid.
  D. Amides
    1. Properties.
      a. Amides are higher-boiling than carboxylic acids; most are solids.
      b. Amides are not basic.
    2. Naming amides.
      a. An amide has the name of the parent acid, with -amide replacing -oic acid.
      b. If nitrogen is substituted, the alkyl substituents are specified, preceded by N- (to indicate that the substituents are bonded to nitrogen).
II. Carboxylic acids (Sections 17.2–17.4).
  A. Common carboxylic acids (Section 17.2).
    1. Acetic acid.
      a. Acetic acid is a common laboratory solvent.
      b. Acetic acid is formed from fermentation of fruit in the presence of ample O$_2$.
    2. Citric acid.

B. Acidity of carboxylic acids(Section 17.3).
  1. Carboxylic acids are weak acids, with $pK_a \sim 10^{-5}$.
  2. Carboxylate anions are given the name of the parent carboxylic acid, with *-ate* replacing *-oic acid.*
  3. Carboxylic acids react with base to give carboxylic acid salts.
    a. The amount of salt or acid present depends on pH.
    b. Carboxylic acid salts are much more soluble in water than the parent acids.
C. Reactions of carboxylic acids (Section 17.4).
  1. Ester formation.
    a. carboxylic acid + alcohol $\underset{\text{catalyst}}{\overset{H^+}{\rightleftharpoons}}$ ester + H_2O
    b. Esterification reactions are reversible.
  2. Amide formation.
    a. Carboxylic acid + ammonia (or an amine) $\longrightarrow$ amide + H_2O
    b. Acid anhydride + ammonia (or an amine) $\longrightarrow$ amide + carboxylic acid
III. Esters, amides, and carboxylic acid anhydrides (Sections 17.5–17.7).
  A. Aspirin and other over-the-counter carboxylic acid derivatives.(Section 17.5).
    1. Aspirin.
      a. Aspirin is a salicylic acid ester.
      b. Aspirin causes pain relief, reduces fever and reduces inflammation.
      c. Aspirin's side effects include gastric bleeding and gastric upset.
    2. Acetaminophen is an amide that can be used in place of aspirin.
    3. Benzocaine and lidocaine are amides that are used as topical anesthetics.
  B. Hydrolysis of esters and amides (Section 17.6).
    1. Esters.
      a. Ester + H_2O $\xrightarrow{\text{acid catalyst}}$ carboxylic acid + alcohol
      b. Ester + H_2O $\xrightarrow{\text{base}}$ carboxylate anion + alcohol
    2. Amides.
      amide + H_2O $\xrightarrow{\text{acid or base}}$ carboxylic acid + amine (or ammonia)
  C. Polyesters and polyamides (Section 17.7).
    1. Nylons are polyamides formed in the reaction of a diacid with a diamine.
    2. Polyesters result from the reaction of a diacid with a dialcohol.
IV. Phosphoric acid derivatives (Section 17.8).
  A. Structure of phosphate esters.
    1. Phosphoric acid has three ionizable hydrogens and can form three different anions.
    2. Phosphates can react with alcohols at 1, 2 or 3 oxygens.
    3. Mono- and diphosphate esters are present as anions.
  B. Phosphate esters in the body.
    1. In the body, phosphate esters exist as anions.
    2. In the body, phosphate esters can form anhydrides.
      a. Diphosphates and triphosphates are the anhydrides that occur in living things.
      b. Triphosphate esters are used for energy storage in the body.

Solutions to Chapter 17 Problems

17.1

(a)

$$CH_3CH_2CH_2CHCH_2COH$$

with CH_3 on carbon 3 and $\overset{O}{\overset{\|}{C}}$ at carbon 1

6 5 4 3 2 1

3–Methylhexanoic acid

(b)

benzene ring with $-COH$ ($\overset{O}{\overset{\|}{}}$) group and NO_2 group ortho

o–Nitrobenzoic acid

17.2

$$H-O-\overset{O}{\overset{\|}{C}}-\overset{\overset{H}{|}}{\underset{\underset{H}{|}}{C}}-\overset{O}{\overset{\|}{C}}-O-H$$

Malonic acid

17.3

$$H_2C=CH-\overset{O}{\overset{\|}{C}}-OH + H_2 \xrightarrow{Pd} CH_3CH_2\overset{O}{\overset{\|}{C}}-OH$$

Acrylic acid   Propionic acid
(Propenoic acid)   (Propanoic acid)

17.4

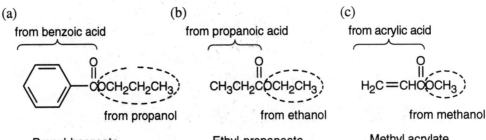

(a) from benzoic acid / from propanol — Propyl benzoate

(b) from propanoic acid / from ethanol — Ethyl propanoate

(c) from acrylic acid / from methanol — Methyl acrylate

17.5 (a) CH_3OCH_3 (b) CH_3COOH (c) $CH_3CH_2CH_3$

Low boiling   Highest boiling   Lowest boiling
Polar, but doesn't   Forms strongest
form hydrogen bonds hydrogen bonds

17.6

More soluble	*Less soluble*	*Reason*
(a) $CH_3CH_2CH_2COOH$	$C_8H_{17}COOH$	The large hydrocarbon part of $C_8H_{17}COOH$ makes it insoluble in water.
(b) $(CH_3)_2CHCOOH$	$CH_3CH_2COOCH(CH_3)_2$	Carboxylic acids form hydrogen bonds with water.

17.7 *N*–Methyl amides are illustrated:

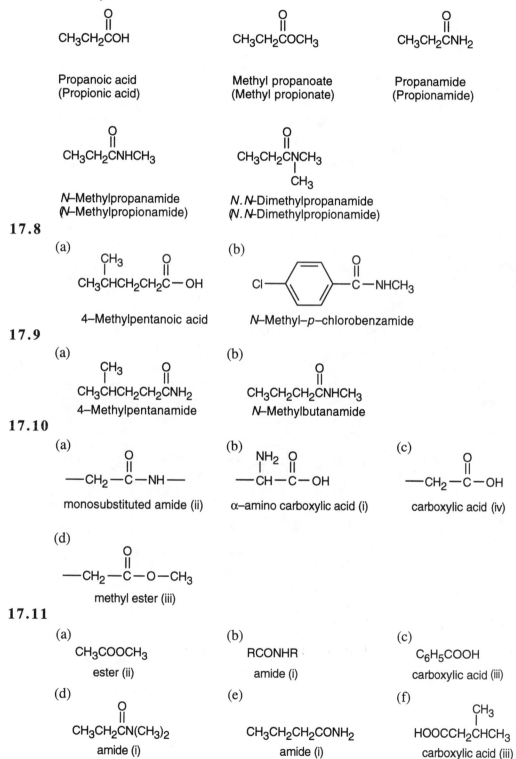

CH₃CH₂COH

Propanoic acid
(Propionic acid)

CH₃CH₂COCH₃

Methyl propanoate
(Methyl propionate)

CH₃CH₂CNH₂

Propanamide
(Propionamide)

CH₃CH₂CNHCH₃

N–Methylpropanamide
(*N*–Methylpropionamide)

CH₃CH₂CNCH₃
|
CH₃

N.*N*-Dimethylpropanamide
(*N*.*N*-Dimethylpropionamide)

17.8

(a)

CH₃CHCH₂CH₂C—OH
|
CH₃

4–Methylpentanoic acid

(b)

Cl—⟨ ⟩—C—NHCH₃

N–Methyl–*p*–chlorobenzamide

17.9

(a)

CH₃CHCH₂CH₂CNH₂
|
CH₃
4–Methylpentanamide

(b)

CH₃CH₂CH₂CNHCH₃

N–Methylbutanamide

17.10

(a)

—CH₂—C—NH—

monosubstituted amide (ii)

(b)

NH₂
|
—CH—C—OH

α–amino carboxylic acid (i)

(c)

—CH₂—C—OH

carboxylic acid (iv)

(d)

—CH₂—C—O—CH₃

methyl ester (iii)

17.11

(a)

CH₃COOCH₃

ester (ii)

(b)

RCONHR

amide (i)

(c)

C₆H₅COOH

carboxylic acid (iii)

(d)

CH₃CH₂CN(CH₃)₂

amide (i)

(e)

CH₃CH₂CH₂CONH₂

amide (i)

(f)

CH₃
|
HOOCCH₂CHCH₃

carboxylic acid (iii)

17.12

(a)

$$CH_3CH_2CH_2\overset{\overset{O}{\|}}{C}-OH + KOH \longrightarrow CH_3CH_2CH_2\overset{\overset{O}{\|}}{C}-O^-K^+ + H_2O$$

(b)

$$2\ CH_3CH_2CH_2\underset{\underset{CH_3}{|}}{CH}\overset{\overset{O}{\|}}{C}-OH + Ba(OH)_2 \longrightarrow \left[CH_3CH_2CH_2\underset{\underset{CH_3}{|}}{CH}\overset{\overset{O}{\|}}{C}-O^- \right]_2 Ba^{2+} + 2\ H_2O$$

17.13

$$\left[H-\overset{\overset{O}{\|}}{C}-O^- \right]_2 Ca^{2+} \qquad H_2C=CH\overset{\overset{O}{\|}}{C}-O^-\ Na^+$$

Calcium formate   Sodium acrylate

17.14 When sodium acetate and disodium glutarate are dissolved in water, acetate ion, glutarate ion and sodium ion are present.

$$CH_3\overset{\overset{O}{\|}}{C}-O^- \qquad\qquad ^-O-\overset{\overset{O}{\|}}{C}CH_2CH_2CH_2\overset{\overset{O}{\|}}{C}-O^- \qquad\qquad Na^+$$
acetate ion   glutarate ion   sodium ion

17.15 Redraw the structures so that the alcohol hydroxyl group and the –OH group of the carboxylic acid are pointing toward each other. Remove water, and draw the ester bond.

$$H-\overset{\overset{O}{\|}}{C}-(OH\ +\ H)-O-CH_2\underset{\underset{CH_3}{|}}{CH}CH_3 \underset{catalyst}{\overset{H^+}{\rightleftarrows}} H-\overset{\overset{O}{\|}}{C}-O-CH_2\underset{\underset{CH_3}{|}}{CH}CH_3 + H_2O$$

17.16

(a)

$$\bigcirc-O-(H\ +\ HO)-\overset{\overset{O}{\|}}{C}CH_2CH_2\underset{\underset{CH_3}{|}}{CH}CH_3 \underset{catalyst}{\overset{H^+}{\rightleftarrows}} \bigcirc-O-\overset{\overset{O}{\|}}{C}CH_2CH_2\underset{\underset{CH_3}{|}}{CH}CH_3 + H_2O$$

Cyclohexanol   4–Methylpentanoic acid

(b)

$$CH_3CH_2CH_2CH_2\overset{\overset{O}{\|}}{C}-(OH\ +\ H)-O-\underset{\underset{CH_3}{|}}{CH}CH_3 \underset{catalyst}{\overset{H^+}{\rightleftarrows}} CH_3CH_2CH_2CH_2\overset{\overset{O}{\|}}{C}-O-\underset{\underset{CH_3}{|}}{CH}CH_3 + H_2O$$

Pentanoic acid   2–Propanol
(Isopropanol)

17.17 Use the technique shown in Problem 17.15 to draw the amide product.

(a)

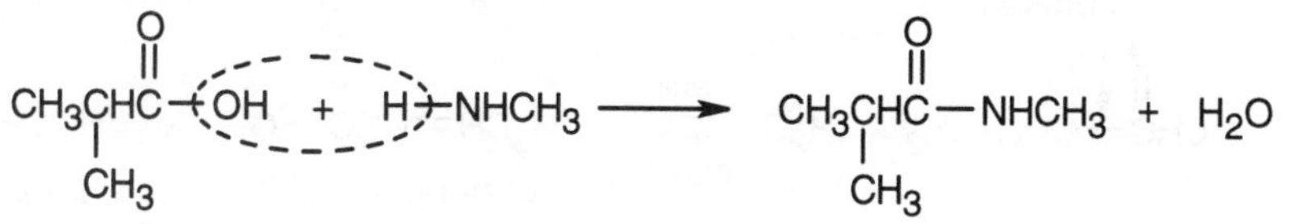

$$CH_3CHC\underset{\underset{CH_3}{|}}{\overset{\overset{O}{\|}}{}}\!\!-\!\!(OH\ +\ H)\!\!-\!\!NHCH_3 \longrightarrow CH_3CHC\underset{\underset{CH_3}{|}}{\overset{\overset{O}{\|}}{}}\!\!-\!\!NHCH_3\ +\ H_2O$$

(b)

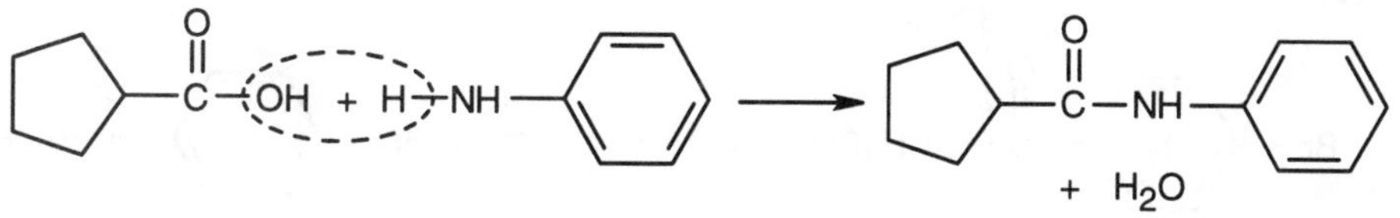

[cyclopentane ring]—C(=O)—(OH + H)—NH—[benzene ring] ⟶ [cyclopentane ring]—C(=O)—NH—[benzene ring] + H₂O

17.18

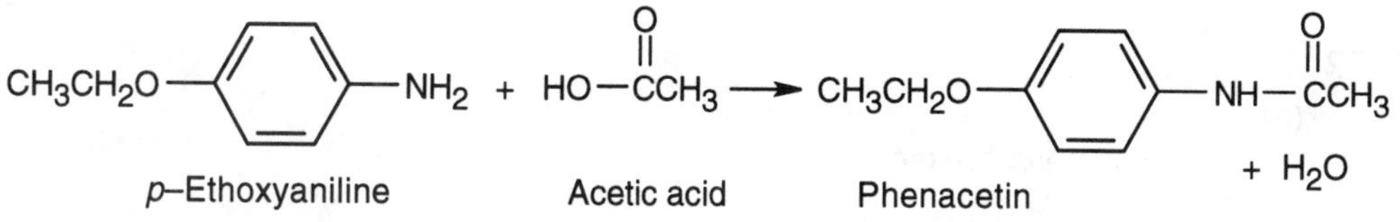

CH₃CH₂O—[benzene ring]—NH₂ + HO—C(=O)CH₃ ⟶ CH₃CH₂O—[benzene ring]—NH—C(=O)CH₃

+ H₂O

p–Ethoxyaniline   Acetic acid   Phenacetin

17.19

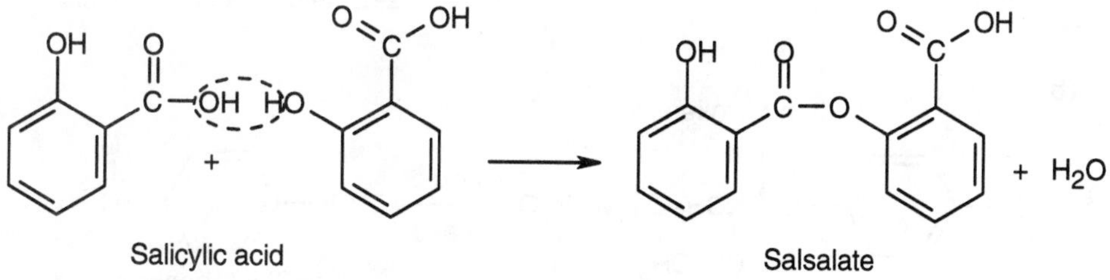

[salicylic acid structure] + [structure] ⟶ [salsalate structure] + H₂O

Salicylic acid   Salsalate

17.20 Moisture in the air causes hydrolysis of the ester bond of aspirin.

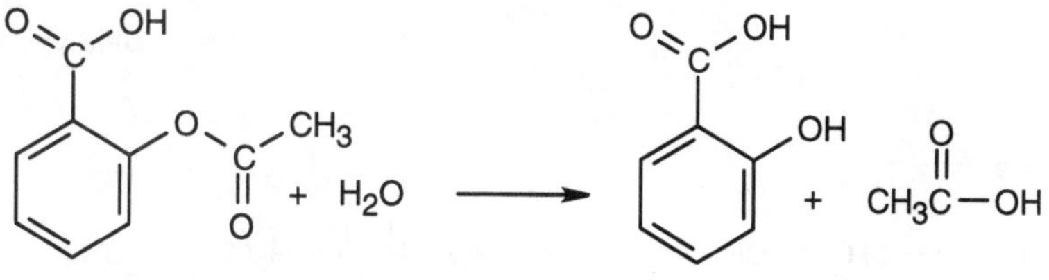

[aspirin structure] + H₂O ⟶ [salicylic acid structure] + CH₃C(=O)—OH

17.21

(a)

bond broken

$$CH_3CH\!-\!\underset{\underset{}{}}{\overset{\overset{CH_3\ O}{|\ \ \|}}{C}}\!-\!O\!-\!CHCH_3\ +\ H_2O \underset{catalyst}{\overset{acid}{\rightleftarrows}} CH_3CH\!-\!\overset{\overset{CH_3\ O}{|\ \ \|}}{C}\!-\!OH\ +\ HO\!-\!CHCH_3$$

2–Methylpropanoic   2–Propanol
acid

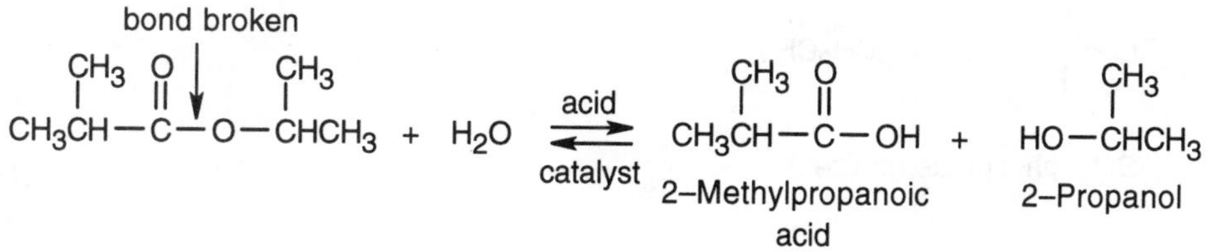

(b)

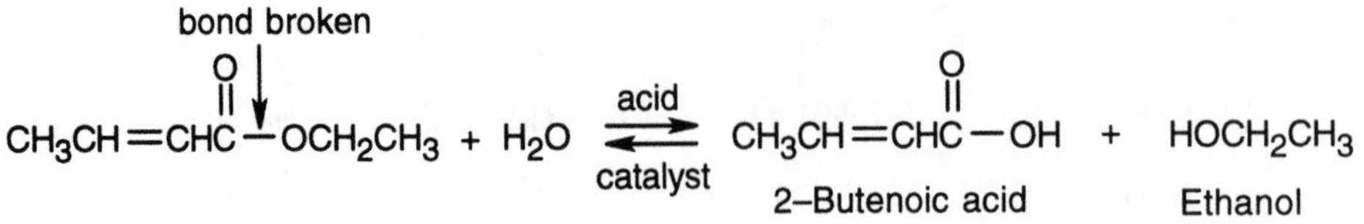

bond broken

CH₃CH=CHC—OCH₂CH₃ + H₂O ⇌(acid catalyst) CH₃CH=CHC—OH + HOCH₂CH₃

2–Butenoic acid   Ethanol

(c)

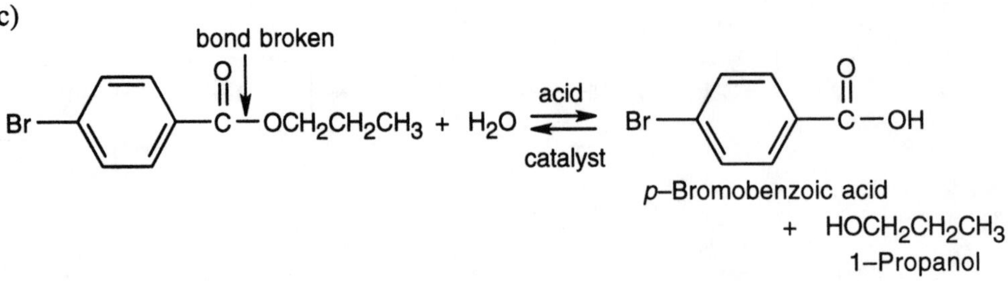

bond broken

Br—⟨benzene⟩—C—OCH₂CH₂CH₃ + H₂O ⇌(acid catalyst) Br—⟨benzene⟩—C—OH

p–Bromobenzoic acid
+ HOCH₂CH₂CH₃
1–Propanol

17.22

(a)

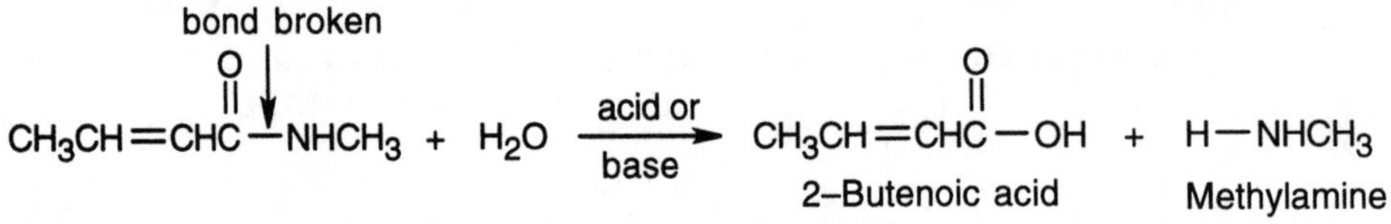

bond broken

CH₃CH=CHC—NHCH₃ + H₂O →(acid or base) CH₃CH=CHC—OH + H—NHCH₃

2–Butenoic acid   Methylamine

(b)

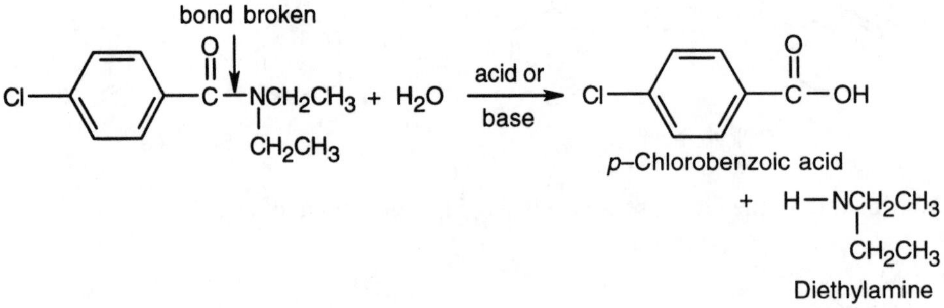

bond broken

Cl—⟨benzene⟩—C—NCH₂CH₃ (CH₂CH₃) + H₂O →(acid or base) Cl—⟨benzene⟩—C—OH

p–Chlorobenzoic acid
+ H—NCH₂CH₃
CH₂CH₃
Diethylamine

17.23

HO—P(=O)(OH)—OH + HO—CH₂CH₂CH₂CH₃ → HO—P(=O)(OH)—OCH₂CH₂CH₂CH₃ + H₂O

Butyl phosphate (unionized)

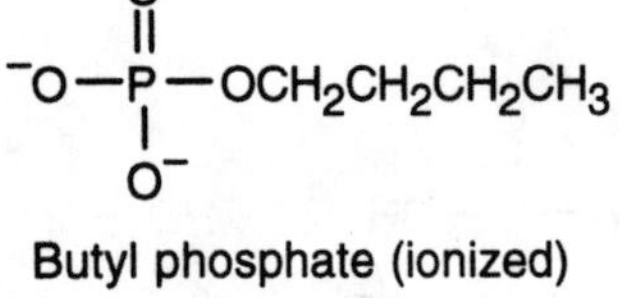

⁻O—P(=O)(O⁻)—OCH₂CH₂CH₂CH₃

Butyl phosphate (ionized)

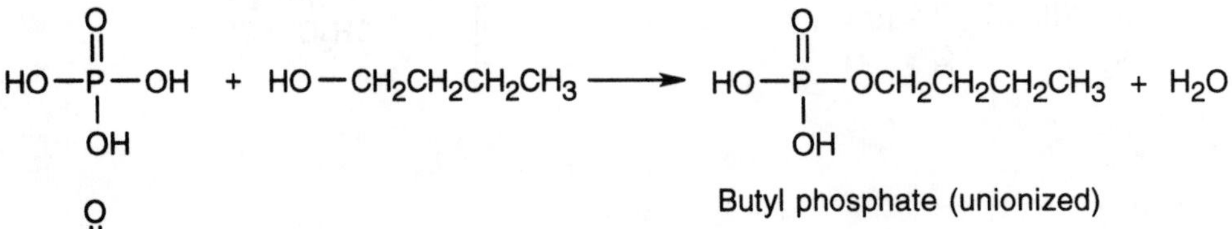

17.24

(a)

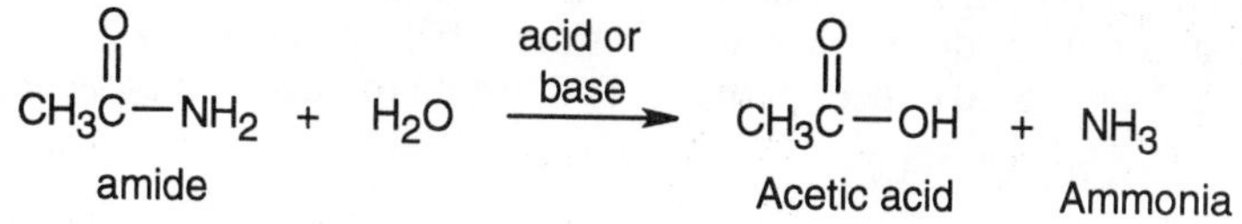

$$CH_3\overset{\displaystyle O}{\overset{\displaystyle \|}{C}}-NH_2 \ + \ H_2O \ \xrightarrow[\text{base}]{\text{acid or}} \ CH_3\overset{\displaystyle O}{\overset{\displaystyle \|}{C}}-OH \ + \ NH_3$$

amide   Acetic acid   Ammonia

(b)

$$CH_3CH_2OPO_3{}^{2-} \ + \ H_2O \ \longrightarrow \ CH_3CH_2OH \ + \ HOPO_3{}^{2-}$$

phosphate monoester   Ethanol   Hydrogen phosphate anion

(c)

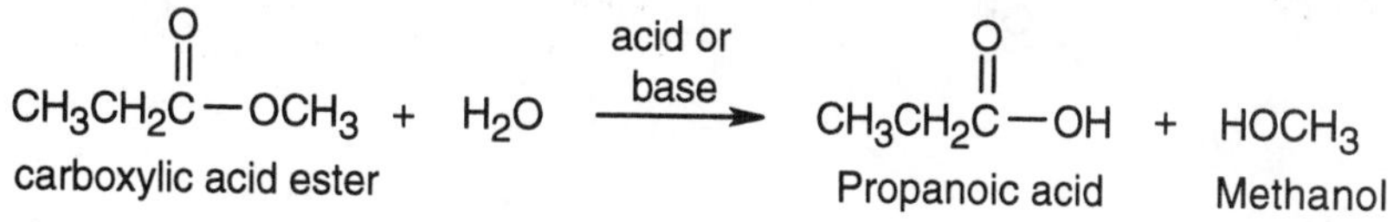

$$CH_3CH_2\overset{\displaystyle O}{\overset{\displaystyle \|}{C}}-OCH_3 \ + \ H_2O \ \xrightarrow[\text{base}]{\text{acid or}} \ CH_3CH_2\overset{\displaystyle O}{\overset{\displaystyle \|}{C}}-OH \ + \ HOCH_3$$

carboxylic acid ester   Propanoic acid   Methanol

17.25

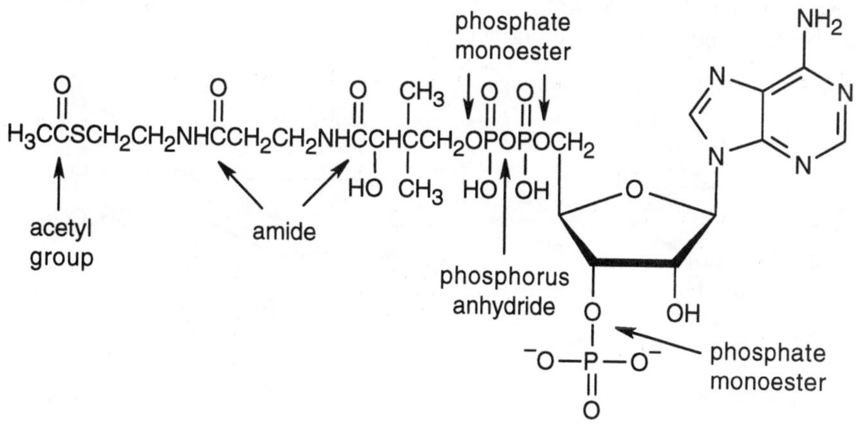

acetyl group   amide   phosphate monoester   phosphorus anhydride   phosphate monoester

Understanding Key Concepts

17.26 (a) At physiological pH (7.4), pyruvic acid exists as the pyruvate anion, and lactic acid exists as the lactate anion.

(b)

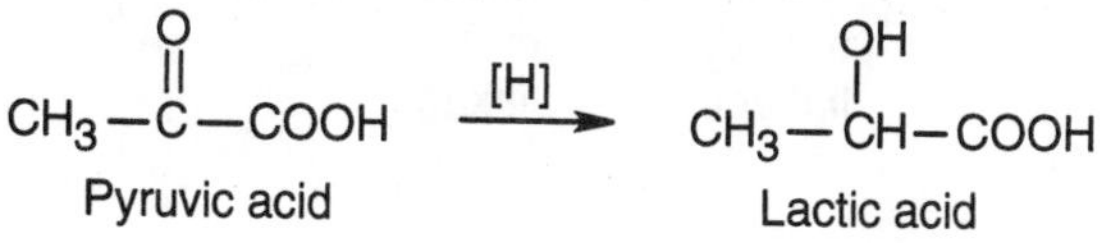

$$CH_3-\overset{\displaystyle O}{\overset{\displaystyle \|}{C}}-COOH \ \xrightarrow{[H]} \ CH_3-\overset{\displaystyle OH}{\overset{\displaystyle |}{C}H}-COOH$$

Pyruvic acid   Lactic acid

(c) Hydrogen bonds between the carboxylate oxygen and water are shown. In addition, the carbonyl oxygens can also hydrogen-bond with water. For lactate, hydrogen bonding takes place between the hydroxyl hydrogen and water (shown below), as well as between molecules of lactate. You would expect pyruvate and lactate to have comparable solubility in water.

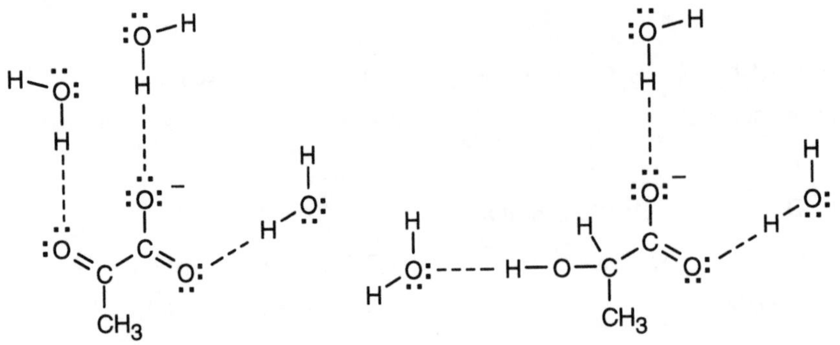

17.27 (a) Under conditions that favor amide hydrolysis (H₂O, plus either acid or base), the acetyl group can be removed from *N*–acetylglucosamine.

(b)

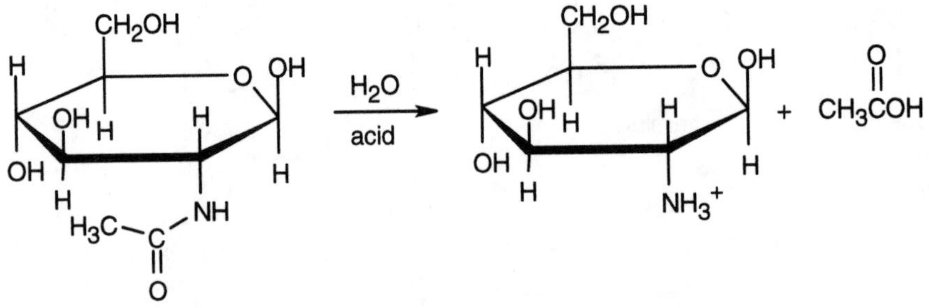

17.28 (a) Glycerate and phosphate are connected by an ester linkage.
(b)

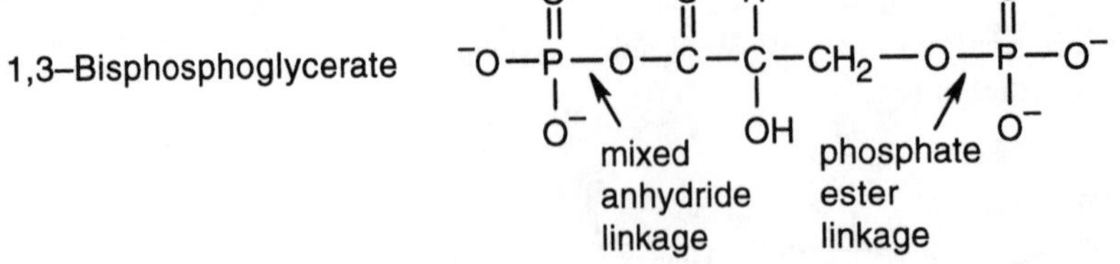

1,3–Bisphosphoglycerate

17.29

Oxalate   Malonate   Succinate   Glutarate

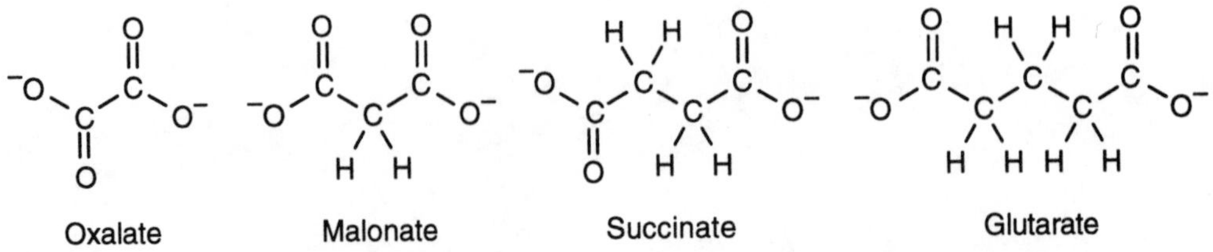

17.30

(a)

$$\underset{\substack{\\ \text{2–Amino–4–hydroxybutanoic acid} \\ \text{2–Amino–4–hydroxybutyric acid}}}{\overset{\overset{\displaystyle O}{\|} \quad \overset{\displaystyle NH_2}{|}}{HOC-CH-CH_2-CH_2-OH}} \longrightarrow \underset{\text{Homoserine lactone}}{\begin{array}{c} H_2N \\ CH-CH_2 \\ O=C \quad CH_2 \\ O \end{array}}$$

(b)

$$2 \ \overset{\overset{\displaystyle O}{\|} \quad \overset{\displaystyle NH_2}{|}}{HOC-CH-CH_2-CH_2OH} \longrightarrow \overset{\overset{\displaystyle O}{\|} \quad \overset{\displaystyle NH_2}{|} \qquad\qquad \overset{\displaystyle O}{\|} \quad \overset{\displaystyle NH_2}{|}}{HOC-CH-CH_2-CH_2O-C-CH-CH_2-CH_2OH}$$
$$+ \ H_2O$$

(c)

$$2 \ \overset{\overset{\displaystyle O}{\|} \quad \overset{\displaystyle NH_2}{|}}{HOC-CH-CH_2-CH_2OH} \longrightarrow \underset{\substack{| \\ CH_2CH_2OH}}{\overset{\overset{\displaystyle O}{\|} \quad \overset{\displaystyle H}{|} \quad \overset{\displaystyle H}{|} \quad \overset{\displaystyle O}{\|} \quad \overset{\displaystyle NH_2}{|}}{HOC-C-N-C-CH-CH_2-CH_2OH}} \ + \ H_2O$$

17.31

$$\overset{OH}{\underset{|}{CH_3CHCH}}=CHCH_2CH=CHCH_2CH=CH(CH_2)_7\overset{\overset{\displaystyle O}{\|}}{C}-\overset{\overset{\displaystyle H}{|}}{N}-\overset{\overset{\displaystyle COOH}{|}}{CHCH_2CH_2}\overset{\overset{\displaystyle O}{\|}}{C}-NH_2$$

$$\downarrow \begin{array}{c} H_2O \\ \text{acid} \end{array}$$

$$\underset{\text{17–Hydroxylinolenic acid}}{\overset{OH}{\underset{|}{CH_3CHCH}}=CHCH_2CH=CHCH_2CH=CH(CH_2)_7\overset{\overset{\displaystyle O}{\|}}{C}OH} \ + \ \underset{\text{Glutamic acid}}{H_2N\overset{\overset{\displaystyle COOH}{|}}{CHCH_2CH_2}\overset{\overset{\displaystyle O}{\|}}{C}OH} \ + \ \underset{\text{Ammonia}}{NH_3}$$

Carboxylic Acids

17.32

$$\begin{array}{c} \text{C}_6\text{H}_5-\overset{\overset{\displaystyle O}{\|}}{C}-OH \end{array} + \ H_2O \ \rightleftharpoons \ \begin{array}{c} \text{C}_6\text{H}_5-\overset{\overset{\displaystyle O}{\|}}{C}-O^- \end{array} + \ H_3O^+$$

17.34

$$CH_3CH_2CH_2CH_2\overset{\overset{\displaystyle O}{\|}}{C}-OH$$

Pentanoic acid

$$CH_3CH_2\overset{\overset{\displaystyle H_3C}{|}}{CH}\overset{\overset{\displaystyle O}{\|}}{C}-OH$$

2–Methylbutanoic acid

$$CH_3\overset{\overset{\displaystyle CH_3}{|}}{CH}CH_2\overset{\overset{\displaystyle O}{\|}}{C}-OH$$

3–Methylbutanoic acid

$$CH_3\overset{\overset{\displaystyle H_3C}{|}}{\underset{\underset{\displaystyle H_3C}{|}}{C}}-\overset{\overset{\displaystyle O}{\|}}{C}-OH$$

2,2–Dimethylpropanoic acid

17.36

(a)

$$CH_3CH_2CH_2CH_2CH_2\overset{\overset{\displaystyle O}{\|}}{C}OH$$

Hexanoic acid

(b)

$$CH_3CH_2CH_2\underset{\underset{\displaystyle COOH}{|}}{CH}CH_3$$

2–Methylpentanoic acid

(c)

$$CH_3CH_2\overset{\overset{\displaystyle COOH}{|}}{CH}CH_2CH_3$$

2–Ethylbutanoic acid

(d)

$$\triangleright-CH_2CH_2\overset{\overset{\displaystyle O}{\|}}{C}OH$$

3–Cyclopropylpropanoic acid

17.38

(a)

$$CH_3CH_2\underset{\underset{\displaystyle CH_2CH_3}{|}}{CH}CH_2\overset{\overset{\displaystyle O}{\|}}{C}O^-\ K^+$$

Potassium 3–ethylpentanoate

(b)

$$\text{benzene ring}-\overset{\overset{\displaystyle O}{\|}}{C}O^-\ NH_4^+$$

Ammonium benzoate

(c)

$$\left[CH_3CH_2\overset{\overset{\displaystyle O}{\|}}{C}O^-\right]_2 Ca^{2+}$$

Calcium propanoate

17.40

(a)

$$CH_3\overset{\overset{\displaystyle CH_3}{|}}{CH}\underset{\underset{\displaystyle CH_3}{|}}{CH}CH_2\overset{\overset{\displaystyle O}{\|}}{C}OH$$

3,4–Dimethylpentanoic acid

(b)

$$\overset{\overset{\displaystyle O}{\|}}{C}-COH$$

Triphenylacetic acid

(c)

$$CH_3CH_2-\text{benzene ring}-\overset{\overset{\displaystyle O}{\|}}{C}OH$$

m–Ethylbenzoic acid

(d)

$$CH_3CH_2CH_2\overset{\overset{\displaystyle O}{\|}}{C}O^-\ ^+NH_3CH_3$$

Methylammonium butanoate

17.42

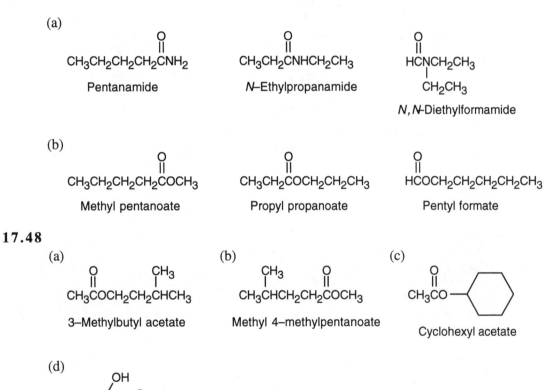

O   OH   O
‖ | ‖
HOCCH₂CH—COH   Malic acid

17.44

O   OH   O
‖ | ‖
Na⁺ ⁻OCCH₂CH—CO⁻ Na⁺   Disodium malate

Esters and Amides

17.46 There are many answers to this question. Here are some possibilities:

(a)

O
‖
CH₃CH₂CH₂CH₂CNH₂

Pentanamide

O
‖
CH₃CH₂CNHCH₂CH₃

N–Ethylpropanamide

O
‖
HCNCH₂CH₃
|
CH₂CH₃

N,N–Diethylformamide

(b)

O
‖
CH₃CH₂CH₂CH₂COCH₃

Methyl pentanoate

O
‖
CH₃CH₂COCH₂CH₂CH₃

Propyl propanoate

O
‖
HCOCH₂CH₂CH₂CH₂CH₃

Pentyl formate

17.48

(a)

O   CH₃
‖ |
CH₃COCH₂CH₂CHCH₃

3–Methylbutyl acetate

(b)

CH₃   O
| ‖
CH₃CHCH₂CH₂COCH₃

Methyl 4–methylpentanoate

(c)

O
‖
CH₃CO—⟨cyclohexyl⟩

Cyclohexyl acetate

(d)

OH
O
‖
CO—⟨phenyl⟩

Phenyl o–hydroxybenzoate

17.50

(a)

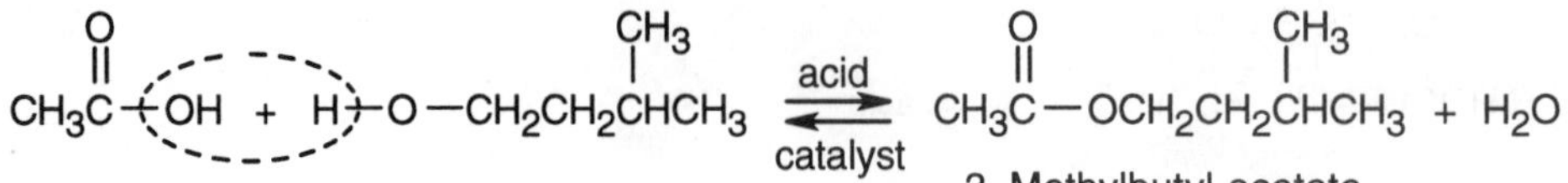

$$CH_3C \overset{O}{\underset{}{\parallel}} \!\!\!(OH + H)O-CH_2CH_2CHCH_3 \;\overset{acid}{\underset{catalyst}{\rightleftharpoons}}\; CH_3C-OCH_2CH_2CHCH_3 + H_2O$$

with CH_3 groups on the $CHCH_3$ carbons

3–Methylbutyl acetate

(b)

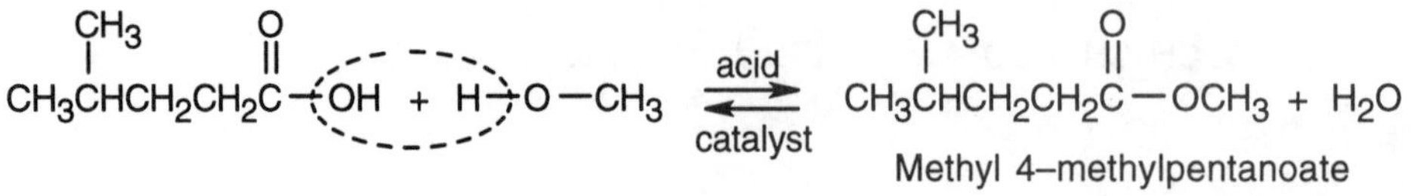

$$CH_3CHCH_2CH_2C \!\!\!(OH + H)O-CH_3 \;\overset{acid}{\underset{catalyst}{\rightleftharpoons}}\; CH_3CHCH_2CH_2C-OCH_3 + H_2O$$

with CH_3 substituents

Methyl 4–methylpentanoate

(c)

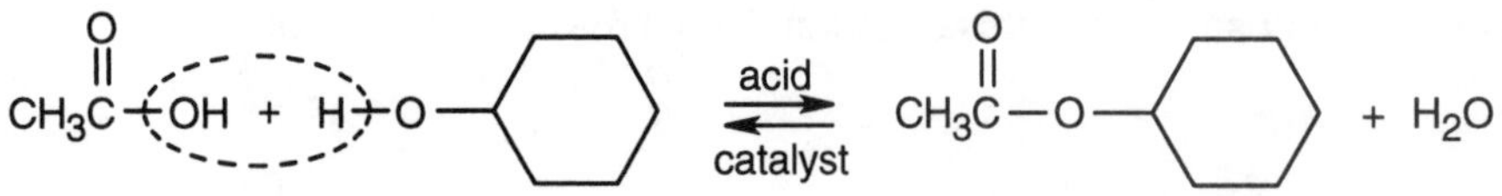

$$CH_3C \!\!\!(OH + H)O-\bigcirc \;\overset{acid}{\underset{catalyst}{\rightleftharpoons}}\; CH_3C-O-\bigcirc + H_2O$$

Cyclohexyl acetate

(d)

$$\underset{OH}{\bigcirc}C \!\!\!(OH + H)O-\bigcirc \;\overset{acid}{\underset{catalyst}{\rightleftharpoons}}\; \underset{OH}{\bigcirc}C-O-\bigcirc$$

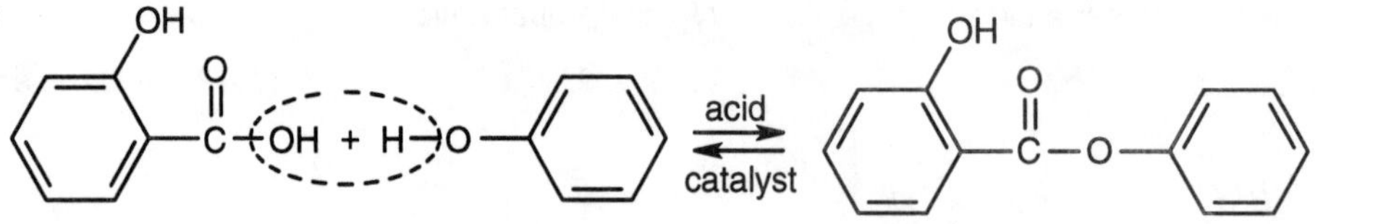

Phenyl *o*–hydroxybenzoate + H_2O

17.52

(a)

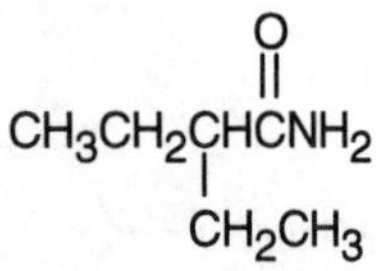

$$CH_3CH_2CHCNH_2$$
$$CH_2CH_3$$

2–Ethylbutanamide

(b)

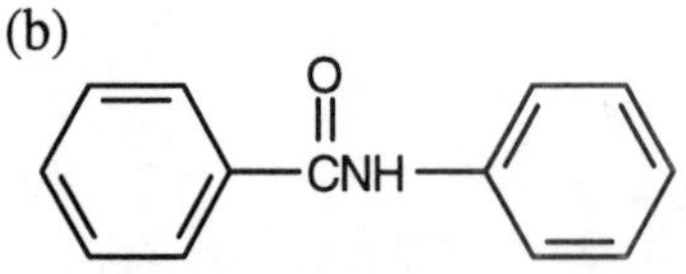

N–Phenylbenzamide

(c)

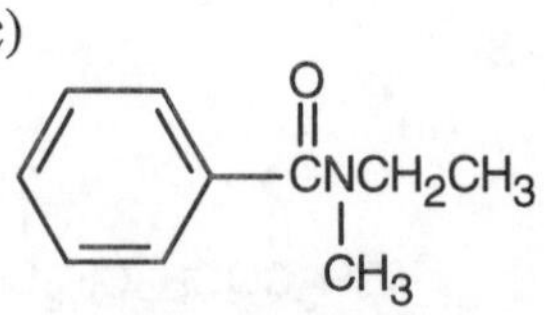

N–Ethyl–N–methylbenzamide

(d)

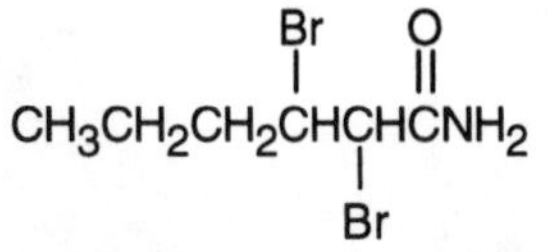

$$\overset{Br}{\underset{Br}{CH_3CH_2CH_2CHCHCNH_2}}$$

2,3–Dibromohexanamide

17.54

(a)

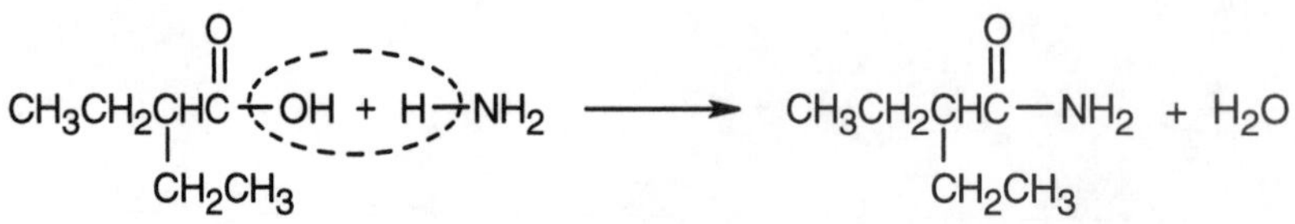

$$CH_3CH_2CHC \!\!\!(OH + H)NH_2 \;\longrightarrow\; CH_3CH_2CHC-NH_2 + H_2O$$
$$CH_2CH_3 \qquad\qquad\qquad CH_2CH_3$$

2–Ethylbutanamide

(b)

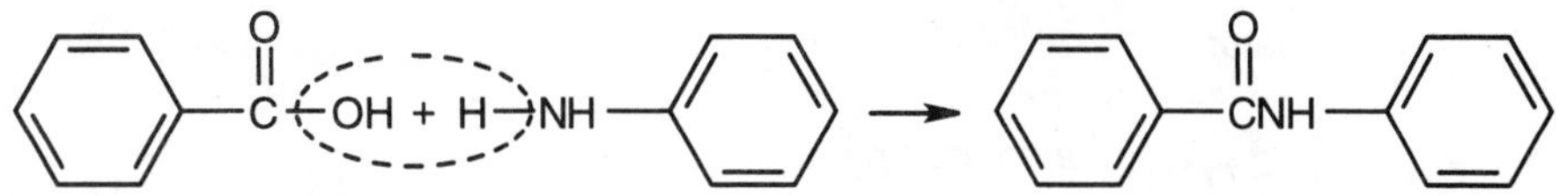

N-Phenylbenzamide + H_2O

(c)

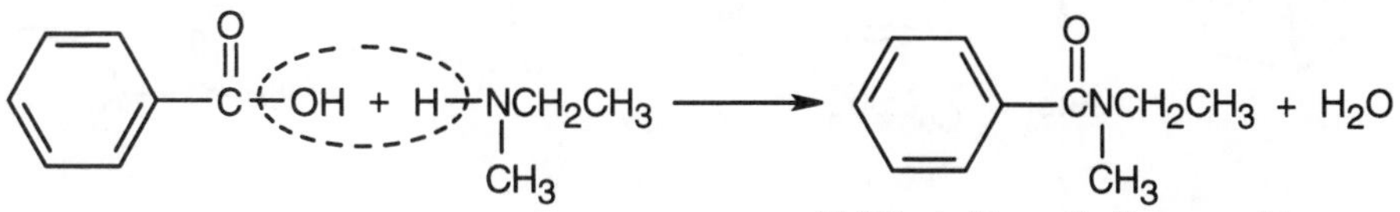

N-Ethyl-*N*-methylbenzamide

(d)

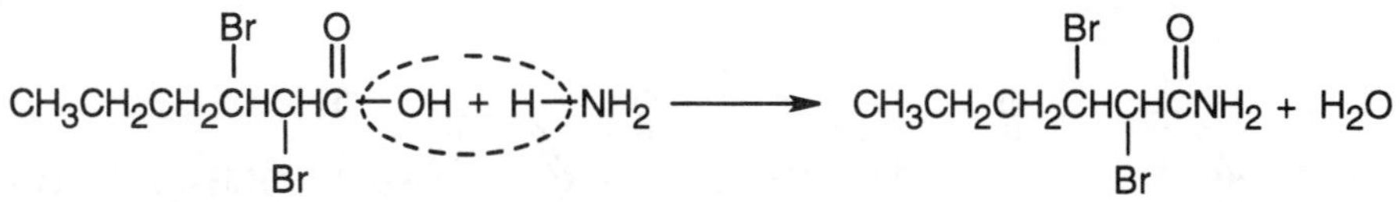

2,3-Dibromohexanamide

Reactions of Carboxylic Acids and their Derivatives

17.56

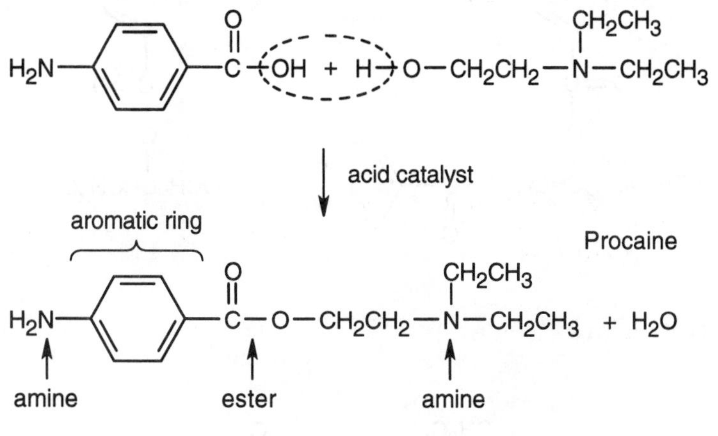
acid catalyst
aromatic ring
Procaine
amine
ester
amine

17.58

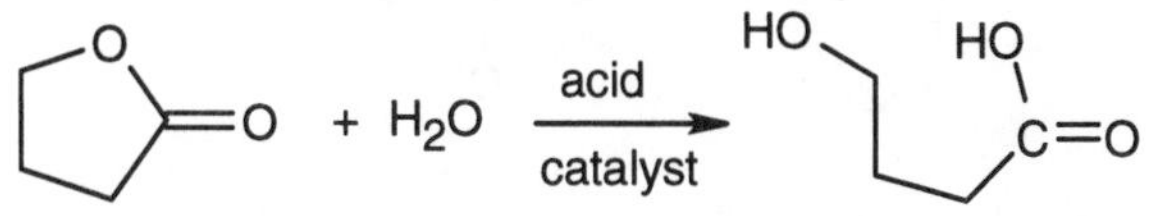
acid
catalyst

Butyrolactone 4-Hydroxybutanoic acid

17.60

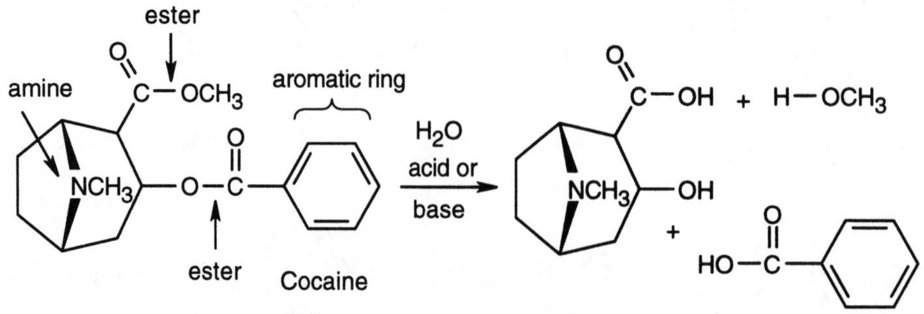

Polyesters and Polyamides

17.62

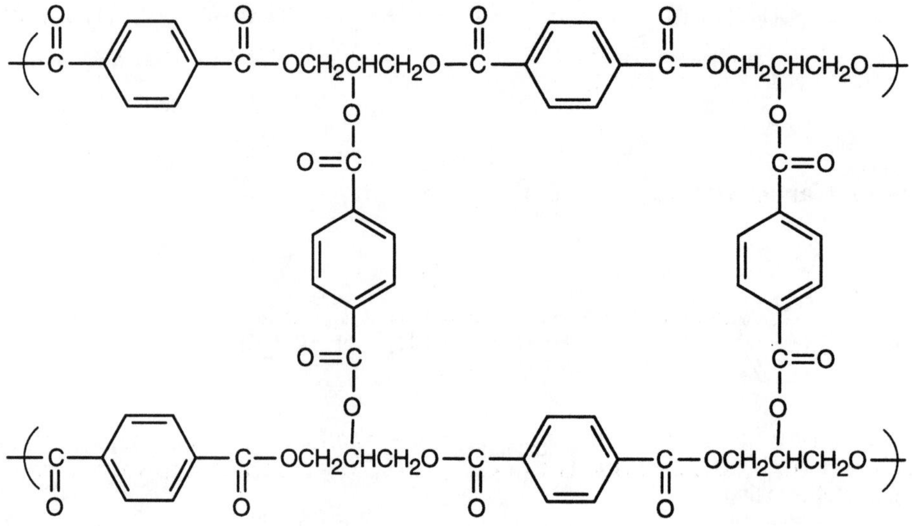

Phosphate Esters and Anhydrides

17.64

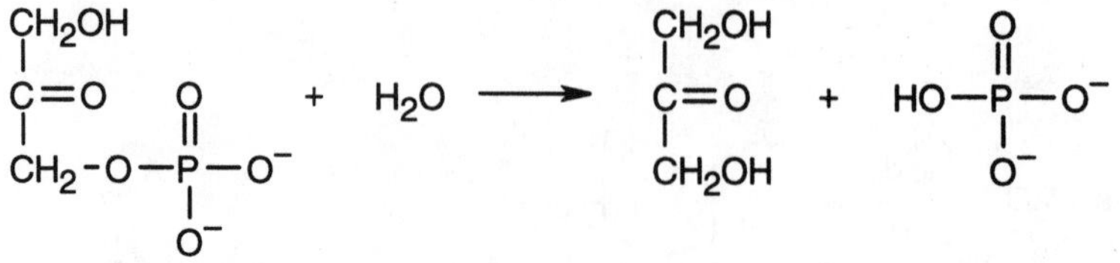

The products of hydrolysis are dihydroxyacetone and hydrogen phosphate anion.

17.66

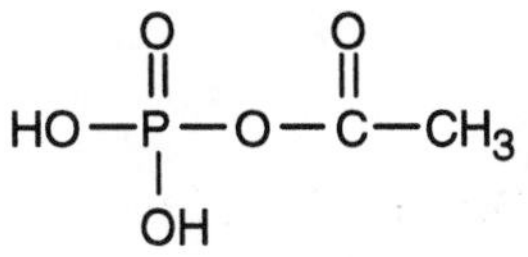

Acetyl phosphate

17.68

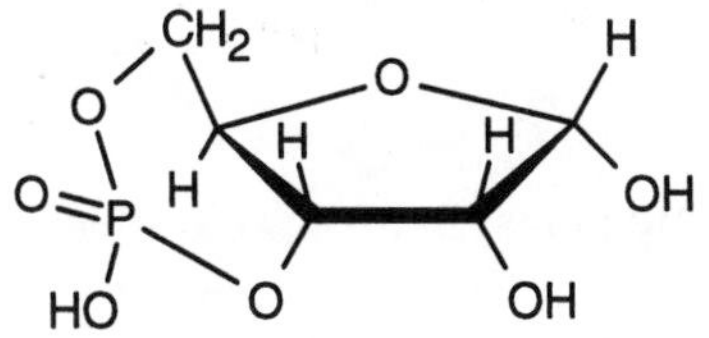

A cyclic phosphate diester

A cyclic phosphate diester is formed when one phosphate forms ester bonds with two hydroxyl groups in the same molecule.

Applications

17.70

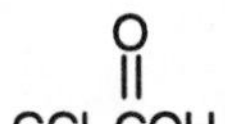

Trichloroacetic acid   Lactic acid

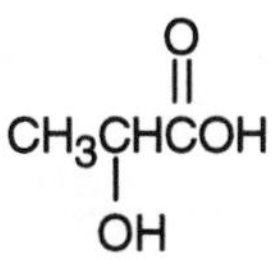

Trichloroacetic acid is a strong acid used for chemical peeling of the skin, and for removing scars and wrinkles. Lactic acid is a weaker acid used for wrinkle removal and skin moisturizing.

17.72

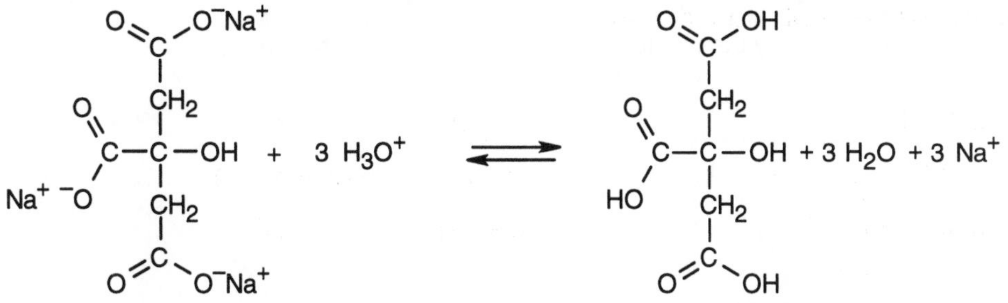

Trisodium citrate   Citric acid

17.74 Kevlar is a polyamide formed from p–benzenedicarboxylic acid and p–diaminobenzene. Because it is an amide, it can be hydrolyzed by strong acids and bases.

General Questions and Problems

17.76

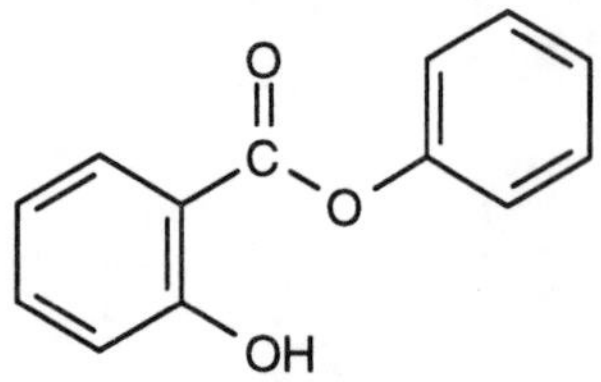

Salol (Phenyl salicylate)

17.78 (1) Measure the pH of solutions of the two compounds. Benzoic acid is acidic ; benzaldehyde is non-acidic.

(2) Benzaldehyde reacts with Tollens' reagent to form a silver mirror; benzoic acid doesn't react with Tollens' reagent.

17.80

(a)

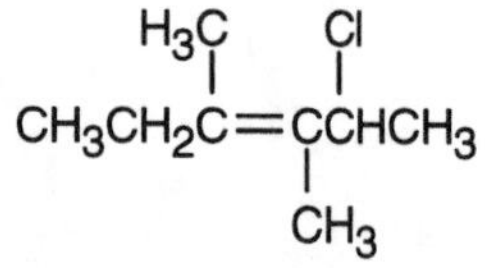

2–Chloro–3,4–dimethyl–3–hexene

(b)

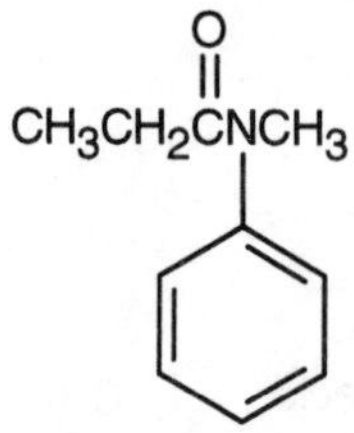

N–Methyl–N–phenylpropanamide

(c)

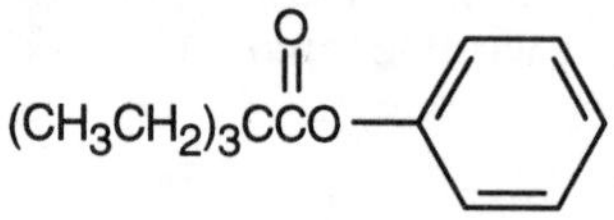

Phenyl 2,2–diethylbutanoate

(d)

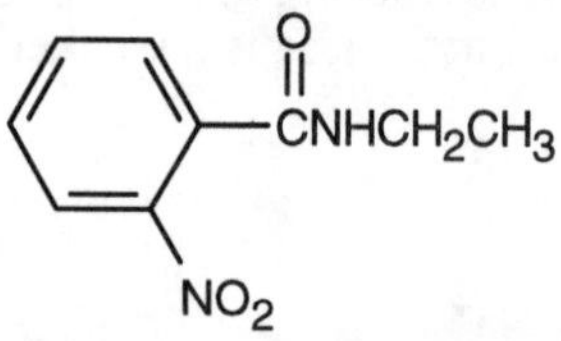

N–Ethyl–o–nitrobenzamide

Self-Test for Chapter 17

Multiple choice:

1. Which of the following amides does not form hydrogen bonds?
    (a) Benzamide   (b) Formamide   (c) *N*–Methylformamide   (d) *N,N*–Dimethylformamide

2. Which of the following statements about phosphoric acid anhydrides is untrue?
    (a) Energy is released when triphosphate anhydrides react with water.
    (b) Both mono- and dianhydrides occur in the body.
    (c) Hydrolysis of phosphate ester anhydrides yields caustic products.
    (d) Two molecules of water are necessary to completely hydrolyze a triphosphate anhydride.

3. Which class of compounds is lowest boiling?
    (a) carboxylic acid esters   (b) amides   (c) carboxylic acids   (d) carboxylic acid salts

4. The common name of an -enoic acid is:
    (a) succinic acid   (b) benzoic acid   (c) oxalic acid   (d) acrylic acid

5. Amide bonds occur in all of the following except:
    (a) Nylon   (b) Dacron   (c) urea   (d) proteins

6. In the reaction $CH_3COOH + CH_3OH \rightleftharpoons CH_3COOCH_3 + H_2O$, the yield of CH_3COOCH_3 can be improved by :
    (a) distilling off the CH_3COOCH_3 (b) removing the water   (c) using more CH_3COOH and CH_3OH (d) all of the above

7. Reaction of methanol with oxalic acid in the presence of an acid catalyst forms:
    (a) methyl oxalate   (b) dimethyl oxalate   (c) methyl acetate   (d) reaction doesn't occur

8. Polypropylene and Nylon resemble each other in which respect?
    (a) They are both polymers.   (b) They are both hydrocarbons.   (c) Concentrated acid will dissolve them.   (d) An initiator is needed for polymerization to occur.

9. Which of the following compounds is an α-amino acid?

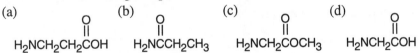

10. How many amides of the formula C_3H_7NO can be drawn?
    (a) 3   (b) 4   (c) 5   (d) 6

Complete the following sentences:

1. The most common general reaction of carboxylic acids, esters, and amides is called a _____ _____ reaction.

2. Kevlar is a type of _____.

3. A carboxylic acid can be dissolved in water by converting it into its _____ ____.

4. The reaction of a carboxylic acid with an alcohol in the presence of an acid catalyst is called an _____ reaction.

5. In carboxylic acids, esters, and amides, the carbonyl-group carbon is bonded to an atom that strongly _____ electrons.

6. Carboxylic acids are named by using the family-name ending ___ ____.

7. $CH_3CH_2COOCH_2CH_2CH_3$ is named _____ _____.

8. Many flavors and fragrances are due to _____.

9. _____ is the transfer of a —PO_3^{2-} group from one molecule to another.

10. Long-chain carboxylic acids can be found in nature as components of _____.

11. The reaction of an ester with aqueous NaOH to yield a salt and an alcohol is called a _____ reaction.

12. Malonic acid is also known as _____ acid.

Tell whether the following statements are true or false:

1. A carboxylic acid salt is more soluble in water than a carboxylic acid.

2. A *saponification* reaction is the acid-catalyzed hydrolysis of an ester.

3. Amides and amines are both basic.

4. A carboxylic acid is higher boiling than an ester of the same molecular weight.

5. Basic hydrolysis of ethyl acetate yields acetic acid and ethanol.

6. The compound $HCON(CH_3)_2$ is named dimethylformamide.

7. Nitrate esters are important in living systems.

8. Acetic acid is about 1% dissociated in a 1 M aqueous solution.

9. Carboxylic acids are either solids or liquids at room temperature.

10. Esterification can be brought about by treating a carboxylic acid with an alcohol in the presence of NaOH.

11. Pyrophosphoric acid is a phosphate ester.

12. Propanamide is higher boiling than methyl acetate.

Match the entries on the left with their partners on the right:

1. $CH_3COOH + CH_3OH + HCl$

2. $HOOCCH_2COOH$

3. $(CH_3COO^-)_2Mg^{2+}$

4. $CH_3COOCH_3 + NaOH, H_2O$

5. $HCOOH$

6. $CH_3CH=CHCOOH$

7. $CH_3CONH_2 + NaOH, H_2O$

8. CH_3OPO_3H

9. Nylon

10. Dacron

11. Acetyl–SCoA

12. Benzocaine

(a) Amide hydrolysis

(b) Ester hydrolysis

(c) Thioester

(d) -enoic acid

(e) Phosphate ester

(f) a dioic acid

(g) an amide

(h) Polyester

(i) Formic acid

(j) Ester formation

(k) Acid salt

(l) Polyamide

Chapter 18 – Amino Acids and Proteins

Chapter Outline

I. Introduction to biochemistry and proteins (Sections 18.1–18.2).
   A. Biochemistry (Section 18.1).
      1. Biochemistry is the study of the structure and function of biomolecules.
      2. The principal classes of biomolecules are proteins, carbohydrates, lipids and nucleic acids.
      3. Biomolecules range in size from small organic molecules to polymers with millions of subunits.
      4. The three-dimensional shape of biomolecules is critical to their ability to function.
   B. Proteins (Section 18.2).
      1. Proteins are polymers of amino acids.
      2. The bonds that form between amino acids are amide bonds (peptide bonds).
         a. Two amino acids bond together to form a dipeptide.
         b. Three amino acids bond together to form a tripeptide.
         c. A chain with 10–100 amino acids is a polypeptide.
         d. The atoms that form a peptide bond have a planar relationship.
      3. There are four levels of protein structure.
         a. Primary structure refers to the sequence of amino acids that form peptide bonds.
         b. Secondary structure refers to the organization of polypeptide chains into a regular pattern.
         c. Tertiary structure refers to the overall shape of the protein molecule.
         d. Quaternary structure refers to the organization of proteins composed of several polypeptide chains.
      4. Proteins have numerous functions in living things.
         Among these functions are structure, support, storage, transport, and control of biochemical reactions.
II. Amino acids (Sections 18.3–18.6).
   A. Structure of amino acids (Section 18.3).
      1. Twenty amino acids commonly occur in nature.
         a. All twenty are α-amino acids.
         b. Nineteen of the twenty amino acids are primary amines.
      2. Each amino acid is represented by a three-letter code.
      3. Amino acids are classified as neutral, acidic or basic.
         Of the common amino acids, fifteen are neutral, three are basic, and two are acidic.
      4. Amino acid side chains are classified as hydrophilic (polar) or hydrophobic (nonpolar).
         a. Hydrophobic side chains cluster in the middle of a protein.
         b. Hydrophilic side chains are positioned on the surface of the protein.
   B. Acid–base properties of amino acids (Section 18.4).
      1. Amino acids exist as dipolar zwitterions.
         a. Amino acids have properties similar to salts: they are high-melting and soluble in water.
         b. Amino acids can react as acids or bases.
      2. The pH at which the number of positive charges on an amino acid equals the number of negative charges is called the isoelectric point (pI).
         a. Neutral amino acids have pIs in the range 5.0–6.5.
         b. Acidic amino acids are negatively charged at physiological pH.

C. Chirality and amino acids (Sections 18.5–18.6).
  1. Chirality (Section 18.5).
    a. Chirality is the property of handedness.
    b. An object that lacks a plane of symmetry is chiral.
  2. Molecular handedness (Section 18.6).
    a. A carbon that is bonded to four different atoms or groups of atoms is a chiral carbon atom.
    b. The two mirror-image forms of a chiral molecule are enantiomers, or optical isomers.
      i. Optical isomers are one kind of stereoisomer.
      ii. Optical isomers are identical in all properties except for their effect on polarized light.
    c. All amino acids except for glycine are chiral.
    d. Only one of a pair of enantiomeric amino acids occurs naturally.
III. Proteins (Sections 18.7–18.12).
  A. Primary protein structure (Sections 18.7–18.8).
    1. The repeating chain of peptide bonds and α-carbons is known as the protein backbone (Section 18.7).
      a. The atoms that form the peptide bond lie in a plane.
      b. The amino-terminal end of the peptide is written on the left, and the carboxy-terminal end is on the right.
      c. A peptide is named by citing the residues in order, from left to right.
    2. Protein function is dependent on the exact sequence of amino acids in protein primary structure.
    3. Primary structure is responsible for the shape of a protein molecule.
    4. Several types of interactions determine protein shape (Section 18.8).
      a. Noncovalent interactions.
        i. Hydrogen bonds can occur between atoms on the protein backbone
        ii. Hydrogen bonds can occur between side-chains of amino acids or between side-chain amino acids and the polypeptide backbone.
        iii. Ionic interactions can occur between ionized acidic and basic amino acids; these are called salt bridges.
        iv. Hydrophobic interactions occur between nonpolar side chains.
      b. Covalent interactions. The thiol groups of cysteine residues form disulfide bonds.
  B. Secondary protein structure (Section 18.9).
    1. Secondary structure refers to the ordered relationships of backbone atoms resulting from hydrogen bonding.
    2. There are two types of secondary structures.
      a. The α-helix is a right-handed coil formed by hydrogen bonds between an N–H group and a carbonyl group four amino acids away.
      b. The β–sheet occurs when polypeptide chains line up next to each other, and hydrogen bonds form between adjacent chains.
    3. Fibrous and globular proteins show examples of secondary structure.
      a. Some fibrous proteins are composed almost entirely of α–helices.
      b. Globular proteins have smaller regions of α-helix and β–sheet secondary structure.
    4. The parts of the polypeptide chain not involved in a secondary structural element are called random coil segments.
  C. Tertiary protein structure (Section 18.10).
    1. Tertiary structure.
      a. Tertiary structure describes the overall shape of proteins.
      b. The interactions responsible for tertiary structure may be between amino acids many units apart.
      c. Interactions described in Section 18.7 give each protein its unique three-dimensional shape.

2. Examples.
   a. Ribonuclease — a globular protein.
      Hydrophobic side-chains congregate in the middle, and hydrophilic side chains are distributed on the outside.
   b. Myoglobin — a globular protein.
      i. Myoglobin has eight α-helix segments.
      ii. A heme group is embedded within the polypeptide chain.
D. Quaternary structure (Section 18.11).
   1. Quaternary structure describes the noncovalent interactions between the polypeptide chains of proteins that consist of more than one chain.
   2. Examples.
      a. Collagen is formed by several tropocollagen strands overlapping lengthwise.
      b. Hemoglobin consists of four polypeptide chains held together by hydrophobic interactions.
   3. Classification of proteins.
      a. Proteins can be classified as simple or conjugated.
      b. Proteins can be classified as fibrous or globular.
F. Chemical properties of proteins (Section 18.12).
   1. Hydrolysis.
      Polypeptide amide bonds can be cleaved by acid or enzymes to yield amino acids.
   2. Denaturation.
      a. Denaturation disturbs a protein's shape without disrupting primary structure.
      b. Denaturation changes the properties of proteins.
      c. Denaturation can be caused by various agents.
         i.   Heat disturbs side-chain interactions.
         ii. Mechanical agitation.
         iii Detergents disrupt the interactions of hydrophobic side chains.
         iv. Organic compounds.
         v.   pH changes disrupt salt bridges.
         vi. Inorganic salts disrupt salt bridges.
   3. Occasionally, denatured proteins can undergo renaturation.

Solutions to Chapter 18 Problems

18.1 Amino acids containing an aromatic ring: phenylalanine, tyrosine, tryptophan

Phenylalanine   Tyrosine   Tryptophan

Amino acids containing sulfur: cysteine, methionine

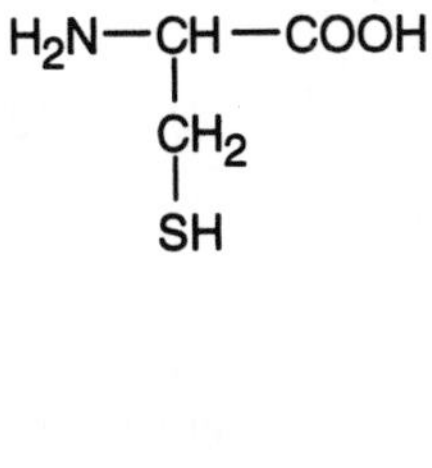

H₂N—CH—COOH
    |
    CH₂
    |
    SH

Cysteine

H₂N—CH—COOH
    |
    CH₂
    |
    CH₂
    |
    S
    |
    CH₃

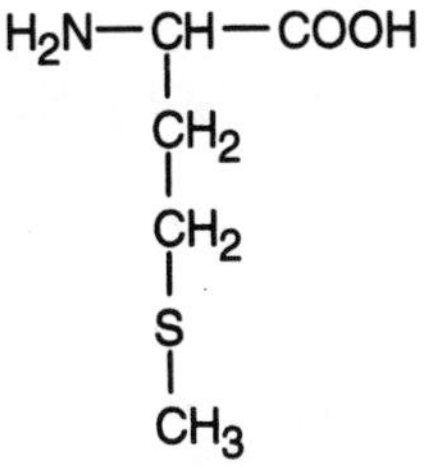

Methionine

Amino acids that are alcohols: serine, threonine, tyrosine (a phenol)

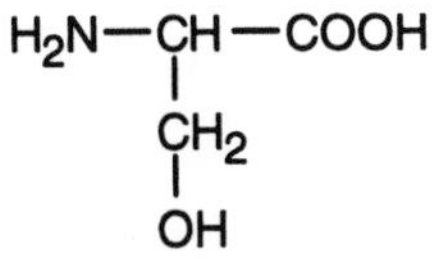

H₂N—CH—COOH
    |
    CH₂
    |
    OH

Serine

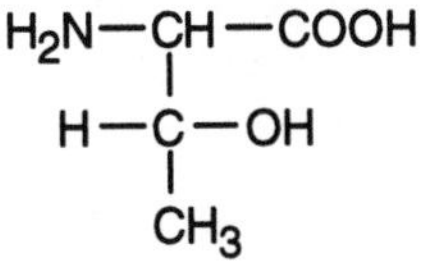

H₂N—CH—COOH
    |
 H—C—OH
    |
    CH₃

Threonine

H₂N—CH—COOH
    |
    CH₂
    |
  (benzene ring)
    |
    OH

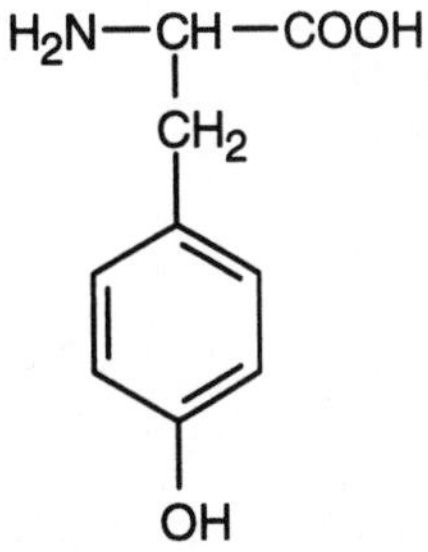

Tyrosine

Amino acids with alkyl group side chains: alanine, valine, leucine, isoleucine

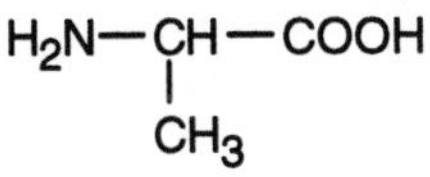

H₂N—CH—COOH
    |
    CH₃

Alanine

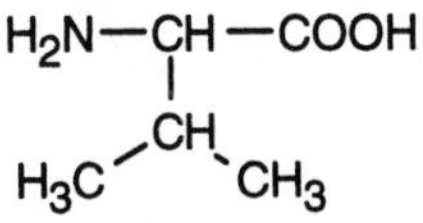

H₂N—CH—COOH
    |
    CH
   / \
 H₃C   CH₃

Valine

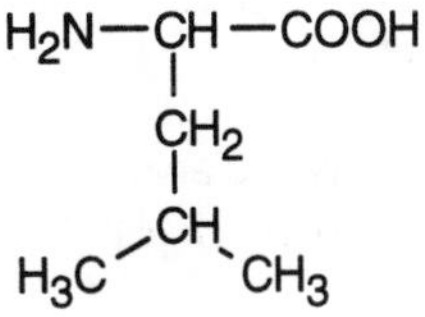

H₂N—CH—COOH
    |
    CH₂
    |
    CH
   / \
 H₃C   CH₃

Leucine

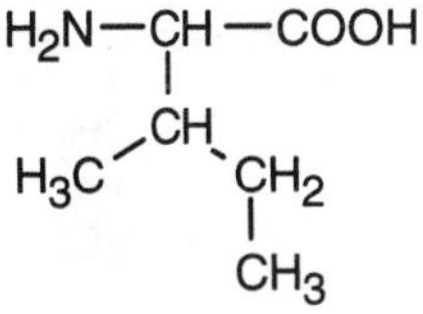

H₂N—CH—COOH
    |
    CH
   / \
 H₃C   CH₂
         |
         CH₃

Isoleucine

18.2

COOH
 |
 C
/|\
H NH₂
H₃C

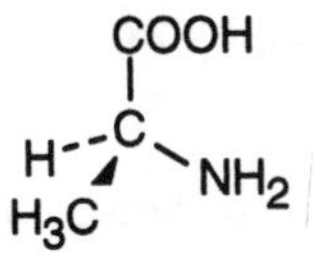

Alanine

18.3 Two dipeptides of alanine and serine can be drawn.

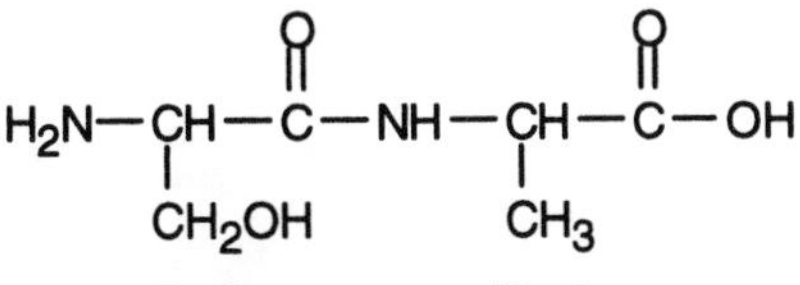

        O   O
        ‖   ‖
H₂N—CH—C—NH—CH—C—OH
    | |
    CH₂OH   CH₃

  Serine   Alanine

        O   O
        ‖   ‖
H₂N—CH—C—NH—CH—C—OH
    | |
    CH₃   CH₂OH

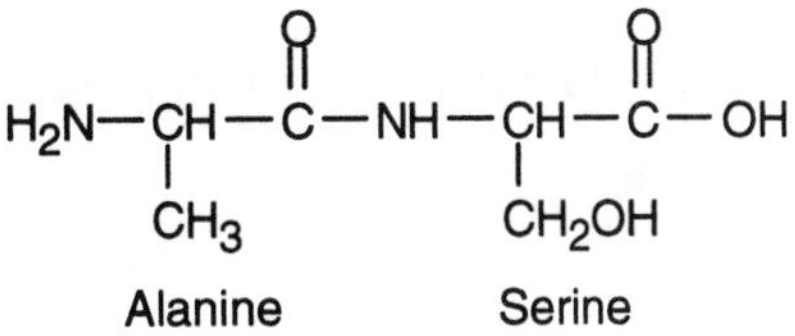

  Alanine   Serine

18.4

(a)

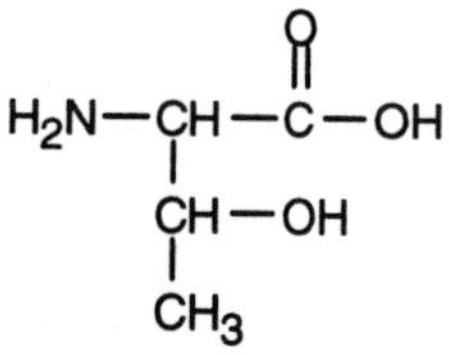

$$H_2N-CH-\overset{\overset{\displaystyle O}{\|}}{C}-OH$$
$$|$$
$$CH-OH$$
$$|$$
$$CH_3$$

α–amino acid
(Threonine)

(b)

$$H_2N-\overset{\overset{\displaystyle O}{\|}}{C}-CH_2CH_2CH_3$$

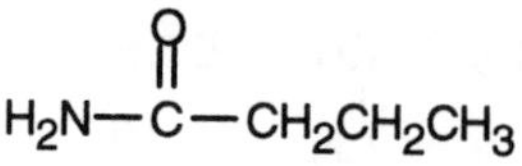

not an α–amino acid
(amide)

(c)

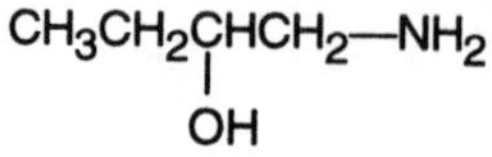

$$CH_3CH_2CHCH_2-NH_2$$
$$|$$
$$OH$$

not an α–amino acid
(amino alcohol)

(d)

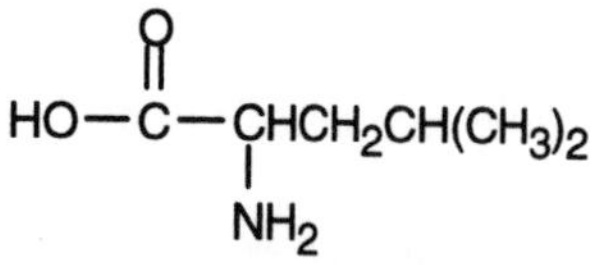

$$HO-\overset{\overset{\displaystyle O}{\|}}{C}-CHCH_2CH(CH_3)_2$$
$$|$$
$$NH_2$$

α–amino acid
(Leucine)

18.5

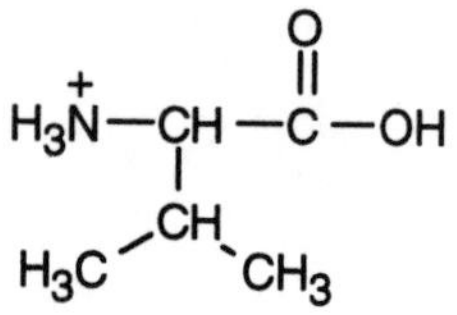

$$H_3\overset{+}{N}-CH-\overset{\overset{\displaystyle O}{\|}}{C}-OH$$
$$|$$
$$\underset{H_3C\quad CH_3}{CH}$$

At low pH

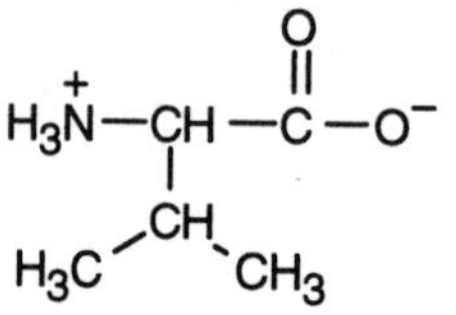

$$H_3\overset{+}{N}-CH-\overset{\overset{\displaystyle O}{\|}}{C}-O^-$$
$$|$$
$$\underset{H_3C\quad CH_3}{CH}$$

At pI

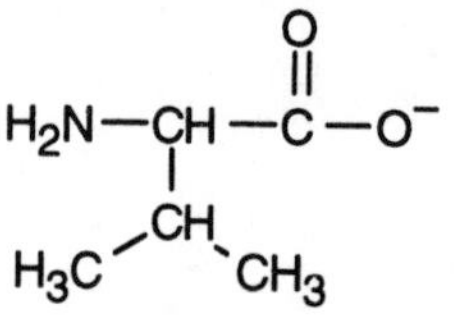

$$H_2N-CH-\overset{\overset{\displaystyle O}{\|}}{C}-O^-$$
$$|$$
$$\underset{H_3C\quad CH_3}{CH}$$

At high pH

18.6

$$H_3\overset{+}{N}-CH-\overset{\overset{\displaystyle O}{\|}}{C}-O^-$$
$$|$$
$$CH_2$$
$$|$$
$$CH_2$$
$$|$$
$$C-O^-$$
$$\|$$
$$O$$

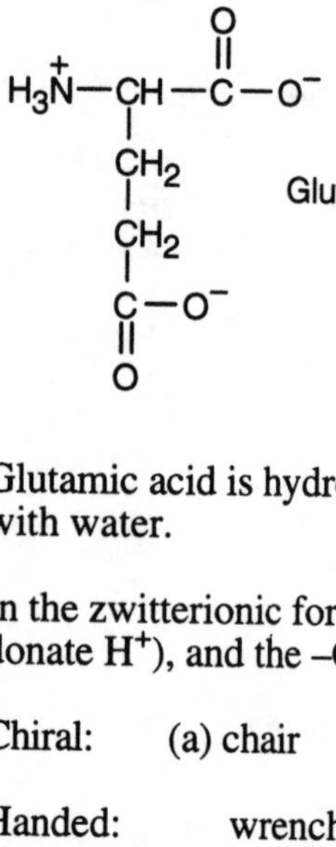

Glutamic acid

Glutamic acid is hydrophilic because its side-chain carboxyl group can hydrogen-bond with water.

18.7   In the zwitterionic form of an amino acid, the $-NH_3^+$ group is an acid (because it can donate H^+), and the $-COO^-$ group is a base (because it can accept H^+).

18.8   Chiral: (a) chair   (b) jar   (d) scissors   (e) glove   (g) wood screw

18.9   Handed: wrench, beanstalk, bottle cap
Not handed: thumb tack, pencil, eraser

18.10

2-Aminopropane

2-Aminobutane

2-Aminopropane is achiral because no carbon has four different groups bonded to it. 2-Butanol is chiral because four different groups are bonded to carbon 2 (–H, –CH$_3$, –NH$_2$ and –CH$_2$CH$_3$).

18.11

(a)

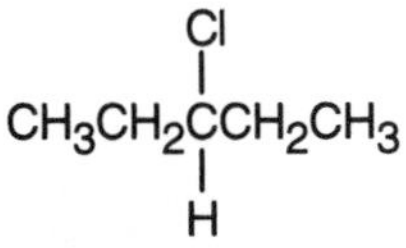

achiral

(b)

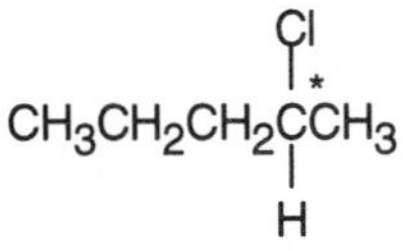

chiral

(c)

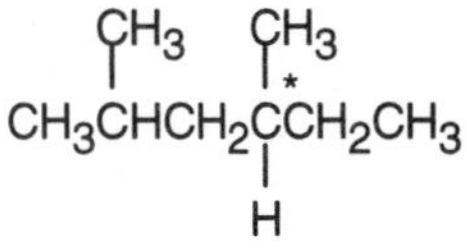

chiral

The starred carbon atoms in (b) and (c) each have four different groups bonded to them.

18.12 Threonine and isoleucine each have two chiral carbon atoms (starred in the following structures).

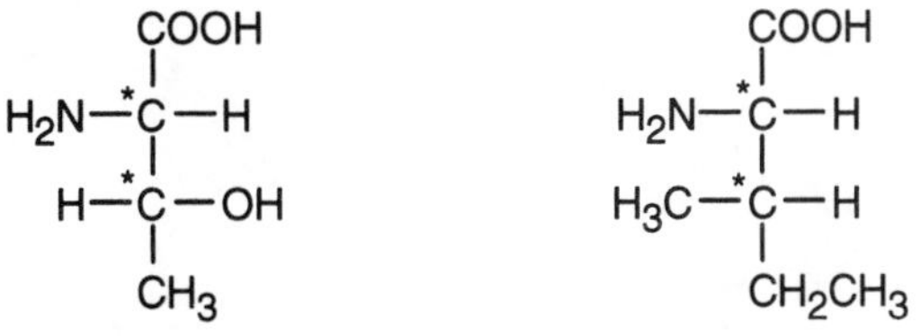

Threonine

Isoleucine

18.13

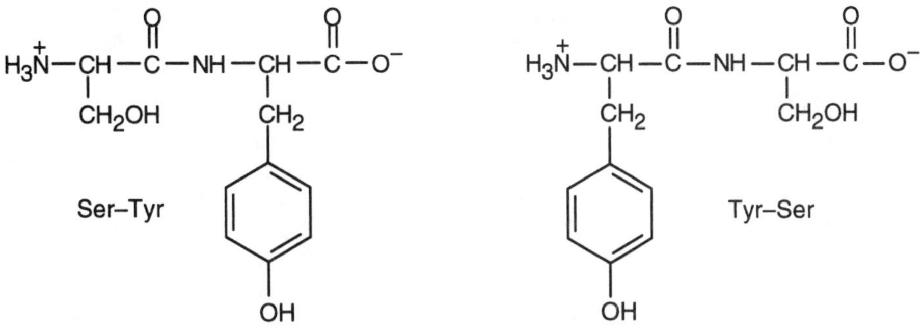

Ser–Tyr

Tyr–Ser

18.14 Val–Tyr–Gly Tyr–Gly–Val Gly–Tyr–Val
Val–Gly–Tyr Tyr–Val–Gly Gly–Val–Tyr

18.15

(a)

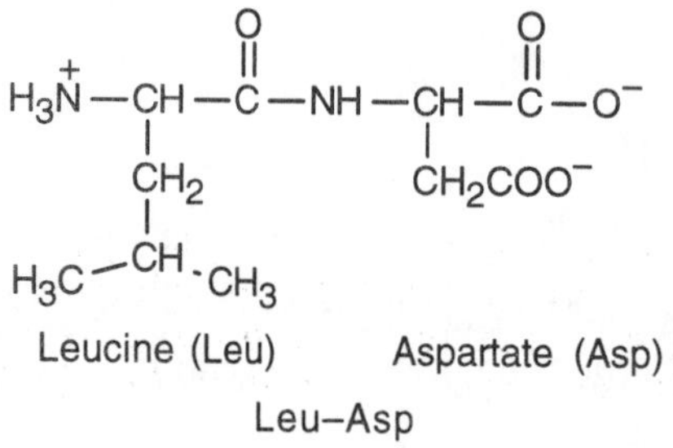

Leucine (Leu)   Aspartate (Asp)

Leu–Asp

(b)

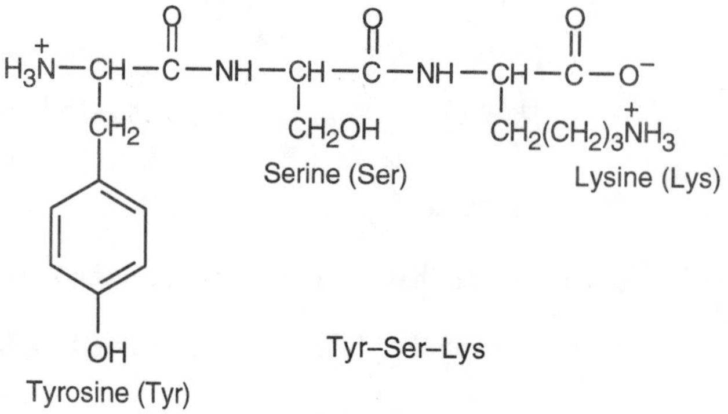

Serine (Ser)   Lysine (Lys)

Tyrosine (Tyr)   Tyr–Ser–Lys

18.16

Tyr–Ser–Lys

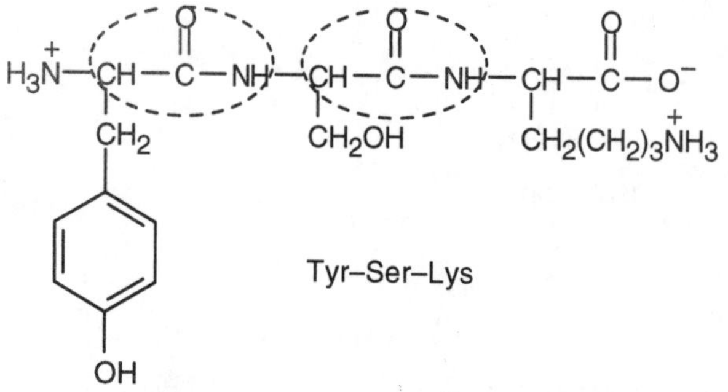

18.17 (a) Glutamine and tyrosine interact through *hydrogen bonds* between the terminal $-NH_2$ group of glutamine and the $-OH$ of tyrosine.
(b) Leucine and proline are pulled together through *hydrophobic interactions* between the alkyl side chain of leucine and the ring portion of proline.
(c) A *salt bridge* occurs between the negatively charged aspartate carboxyl group and the positively charged terminal group of arginine.
(d) The alkyl side chain of isoleucine and the aromatic ring of phenylalanine are held together by *hydrophobic interactions*.

18.18 (a) Hydrogen bonds from side chains: tyrosine, asparagine, serine
(b) Hydrophobic group interactions: alanine, isoleucine, valine, leucine

18.19 In an α–helix, a carbonyl oxygen forms a hydrogen bond with an amide hydrogen twelve atoms away. Thus, 11 backbone atoms lie between the atoms that take part in an α–helix hydrogen bond.

Understanding Key Concepts

18.20 Peptides that contain neither acidic nor basic amino acids have a net charge of +1 at pH = 1 because both the N–terminal amino group and the C–terminal carboxylic acid group are protonated. At pH = 11, these peptides have a net charge of –1, because the N–terminal group is uncharged and the C–terminal group is a carboxylate anion. At pH = 7, these peptides have a net charge of zero.

(a)

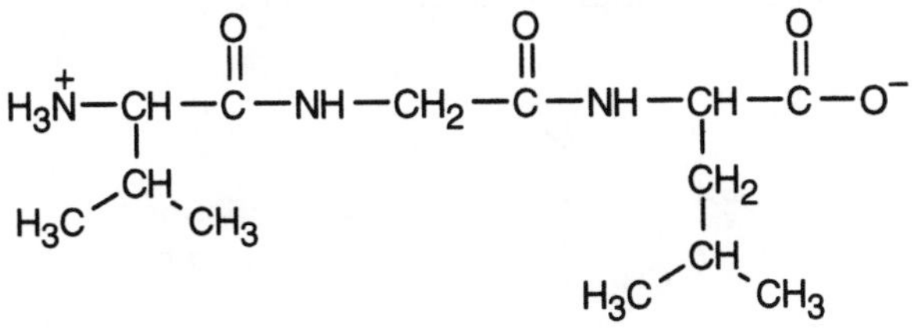

Val–Gly–Leu at pH = 7.0

Net charge at pH = 1: +1   Net charge at pH = 7: 0   Net charge at pH = 11: –1

(b)

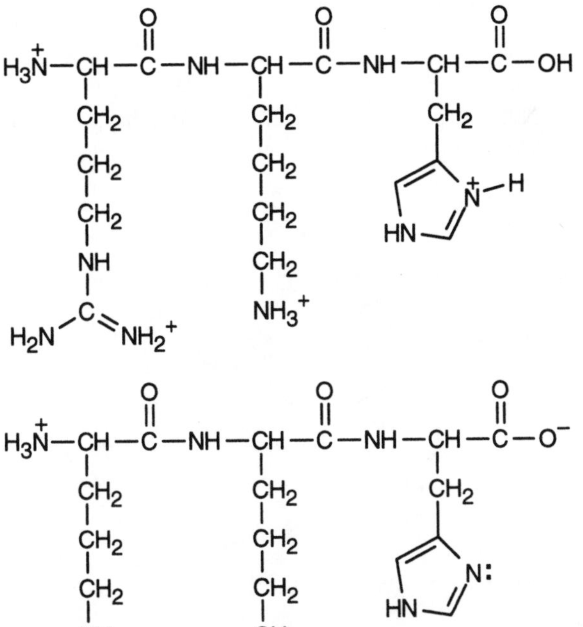

Arg–Lys–His at pH = 1.0

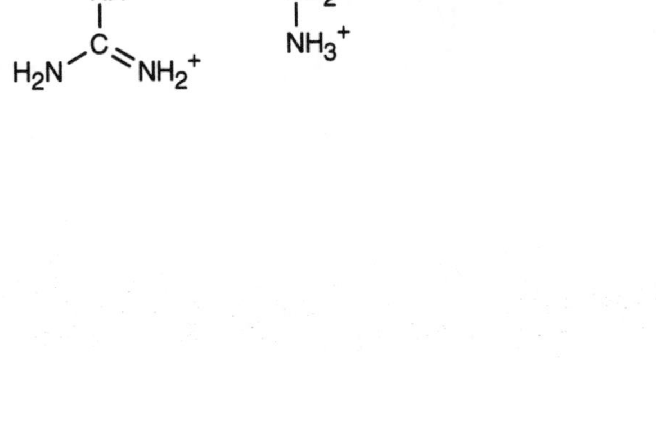

at pH = 7.0

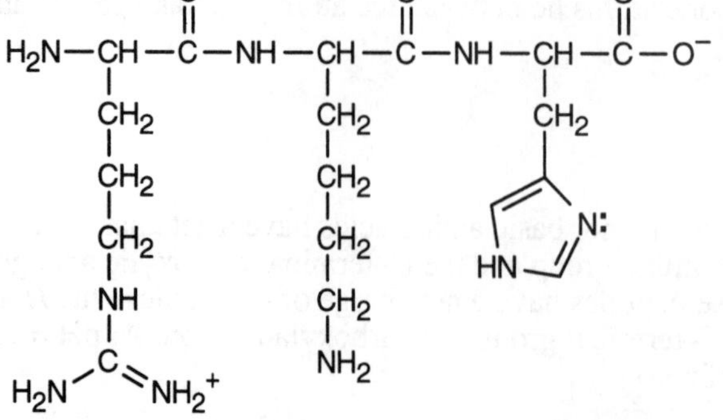

at pH = 11.0

Net charge at pH = 1: +4   Net charge at pH = 7: +2   Net charge at pH = 11: 0

(c)

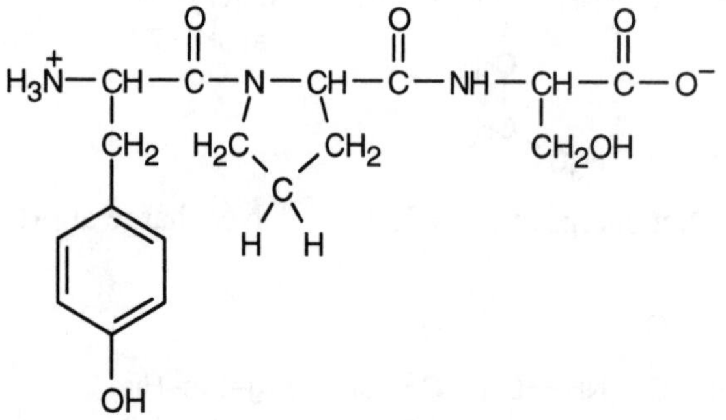

Tyr–Pro–Ser
at pH = 7.0

Net charge at pH = 1: +1   Net charge at pH = 7: 0   Net charge at pH = 11: –2
At pH = 11, the phenol –OH group is ionized and is anionic.

(d)

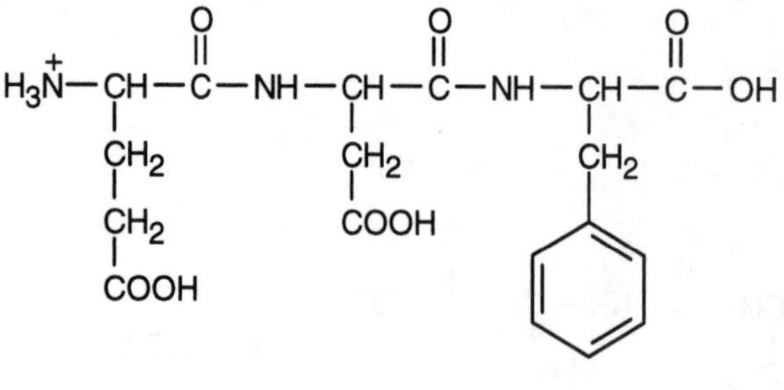

Glu–Asp–Phe
at pH = 1.0

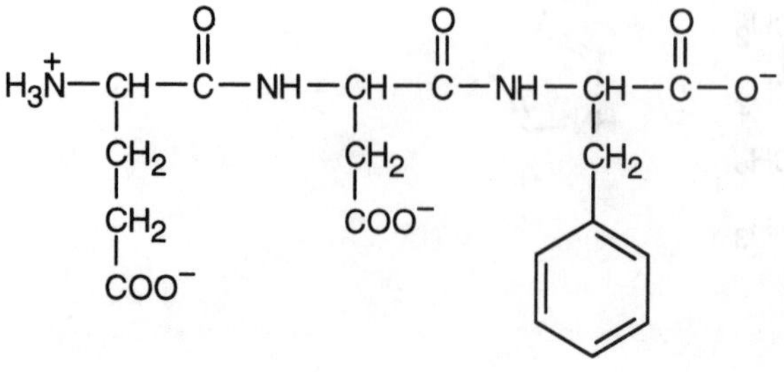

at pH = 7.0

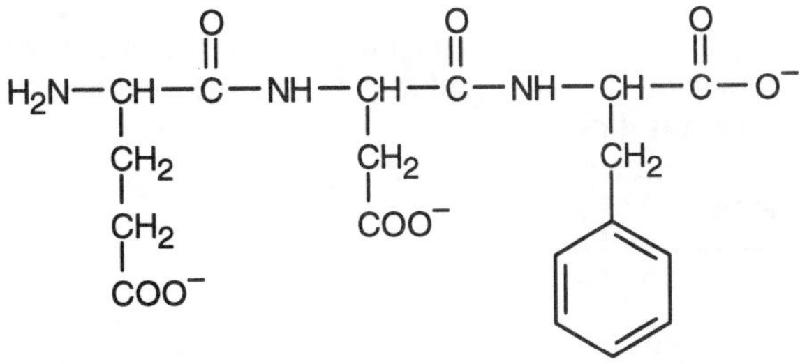

at pH = 11.0

Net charge at pH = 1: +1   Net charge at pH = 7: −2   Net charge at pH = 11: −3

(e)

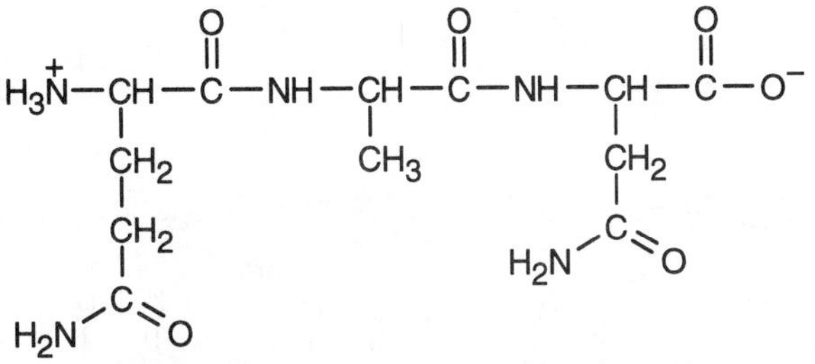

Gln–Ala–Asn
at pH = 7.0

Net charge at pH = 1: +1   Net charge at pH = 7: 0   Net charge at pH = 11: −1

(f)

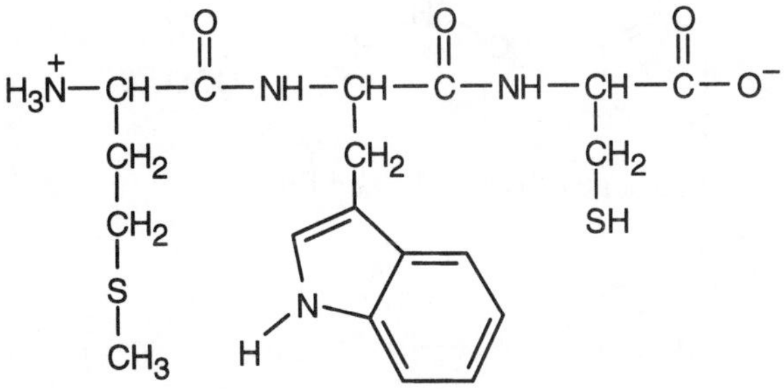

Met–Trp–Cys
at pH = 7.0

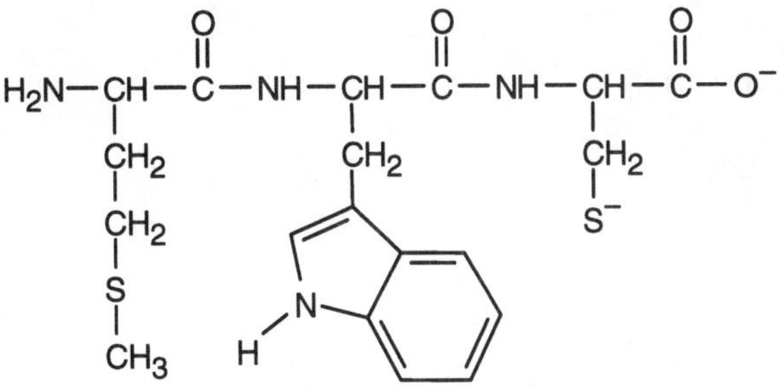

at pH = 11.0

Net charge at pH = 1: +1   Net charge at pH = 7: 0   Net charge at pH = 11: −2

18.21 In order for two amino acids to interact, they must both be of the same type (both polar or both nonpolar, for example).
  (a) The pairs Pro...Leu and Ile...Val show hydrophobic interactions because they are both nonpolar. Tyr ...Phe also shows hydrophobic interactions.
  (b) Arg...Asp and His...Glu show ionic interactions because they are both charged.
  (c) Thr...Glu form hydrogen bonds.

18.22 You need to remember these facts to answer this question.
   (1) In a peptide, the acidic and basic amino acids determine the charge of the peptide.
   (2) An amino acid that is acidic is negatively charged at a neutral pH, and a basic amino acid is positively charged at a neutral pH.
   (3) A positively charged molecule migrates to the cathode (–), and a negatively charged molecule migrates to the anode (+).

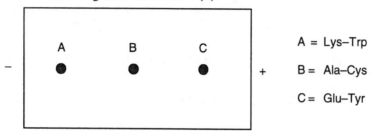

18.23

Hydrogen bonds in an α–helix are indicated by the dashed lines.

18.24

Phe–Glu–Phe
    Glu–Phe
    Glu–Phe–Asp
          Asp–His–Tyr
               His–Tyr
                    Tyr–Glu–His
The complete peptide:
Phe–Glu–Phe–Asp–His–Tyr–Glu–His

18.25

	Fibrous protein	*Globular protein*
Biological function:	Structural proteins	Enzymes, hormones, transport
Water solubility:	Water-insoluble	Usually water-soluble
Amino acid composition:	Contains many Gly and Pro residues	Varies; hydrophilic groups on the outside account for solubility
Secondary structure:	Large regions of α–helix or β–sheet	Smaller regions of α–helix or β–sheet
Tertiary Structure:	Few interactions between side chains on the same backbone	Complex: determined by hydrophobic and hydrophilic groups on side chains, as well as by disulfide bonds.
Examples:	Collagen (connective tissue) α–Keratin (hair) Fibroin (silk)	Ribonuclease (enzyme) Hemoglobin (oxygen transport) Insulin (hormone)

Amino Acids

18.26 When referring to an amino acid, the prefix "α" means that the amino group is bonded to the carbon next to the –COOH carbon. In other words, the –NH$_2$ and –COOH groups are bonded to the same carbon.

18.28

(a) Serine (Ser)   (b) Threonine (Thr)   (c) Proline (Pro)

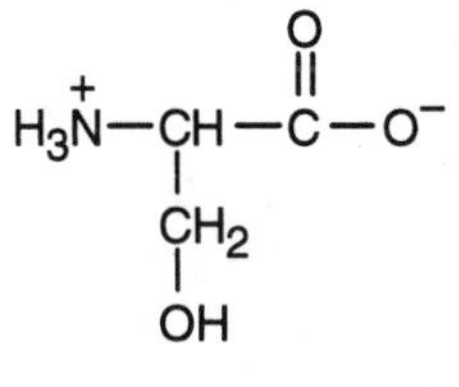

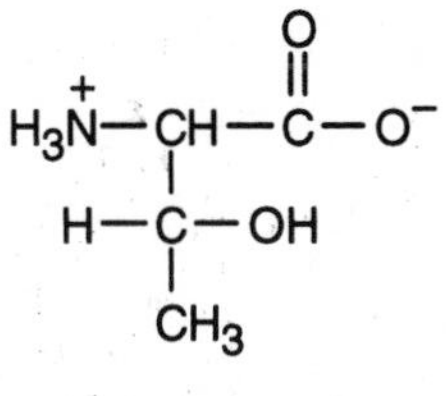

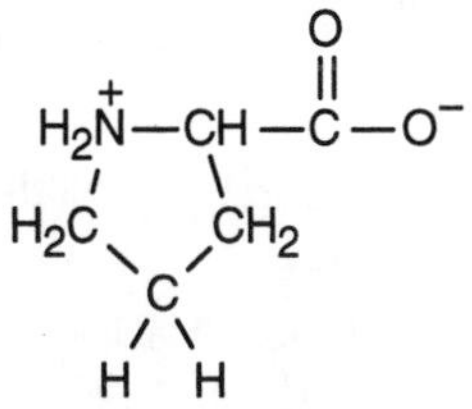

18.30

(a) Valine (Val)   (b) Threonine (Thr)

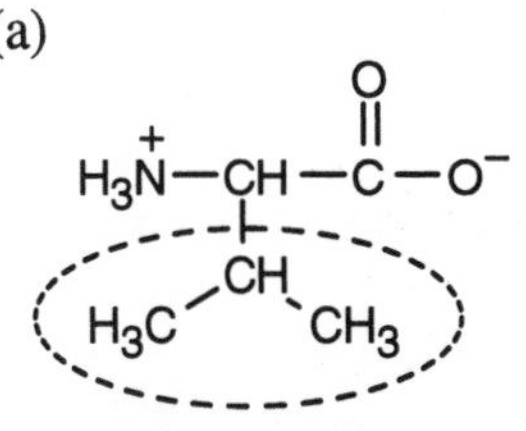

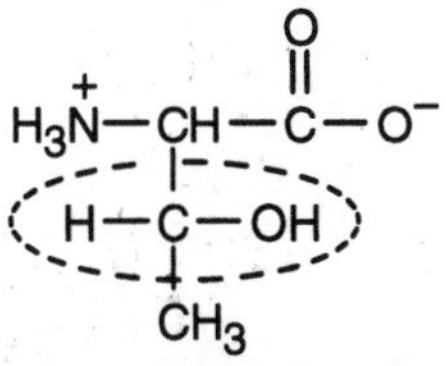

18.32 At a neutral pH (pH = 5 – 8), an amino acid with a pI less than 5 is negatively charged, and an amino acid with a pI greater than 8 is positively charged. Otherwise, an amino acid has no net charge at neutral pH and is neutral.
(a) Lysine (pI = 9.7) is positively charged. (b) (c) Phenylalanine (pI = 5.5) and leucine (pI = 6.0) are neutral.

18.34

(a)

$$HO-\overset{\overset{\textstyle O}{\|}}{C}-CH_2-\underset{\underset{\textstyle +NH_3}{|}}{CH}-\overset{\overset{\textstyle O}{\|}}{C}-O^-$$

This structure represents aspartic acid at pH = 3, its isoelectric point.

(b)

$$^-O-\overset{\overset{\textstyle O}{\|}}{C}-CH_2-\underset{\underset{\textstyle NH_2}{|}}{CH}-\overset{\overset{\textstyle O}{\|}}{C}-O^-$$

This structure represents aspartic acid at pH = 13.

18.36 A chiral object is one that has handedness. Examples include a glove and a car.

18.38 Chiral: (a) shoe   (c) light bulb (because of screw threads)
Achiral: (b) bed

18.40 2-Bromo-2-chloropropane has a symmetry plane and is achiral. 2-Bromo-2-chlorobutane and 2-bromo-2-chloro-3-methylbutane don't have a symmetry plane and are chiral because each has a carbon atom bonded to four different atoms or groups of atoms. A star indicates a chiral carbon atom.

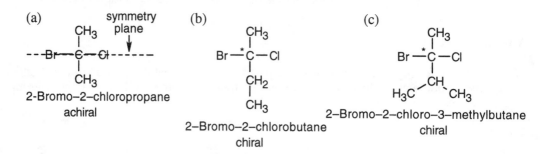

(a)   symmetry plane

2-Bromo–2–chloropropane
achiral

(b)

2–Bromo–2–chlorobutane
chiral

(c)

2–Bromo–2–chloro–3–methylbutane
chiral

18.42

chiral   achiral

$$CH_3CHCH_2CH_3$$

F

achiral

Peptides and Proteins

18.44 A simple protein is composed only of amino acids. A conjugated protein consists of a simple protein associated with one or more nonprotein molecules.

18.46

Type of protein	Function	Example
Enzymes:	Catalyze biochemical reactions	Ribonuclease
Hormones:	Regulate body functions	Insulin
Storage proteins:	Store essential substances	Myoglobin
Transport proteins:	Transport substances through body fluids	Serum albumin
Structural proteins:	Provide shape and support	Collagen
Protective proteins:	Defend the body against foreign matter	Immunoglobulins
Contractile proteins	Do mechanical work	Myosin and actin

18.48 The disulfide bonds that cysteine forms help to stabilize a protein's tertiary or quaternary structure.

18.50 (a) *Hydrophobic interactions* occur between hydrocarbon side chains of amino acids. In a protein, these side chains cluster in the center of the molecule to exclude water, and are responsible for the nearly spherical tertiary shape of globular proteins. Alanine and isoleucine take part in hydrophobic interactions.
(b) *Salt bridges* occur between negatively charged and positively charged amino acid side chain groups. They can stabilize the tertiary structure of a protein by connecting two distant parts of a polypeptide chain or by pulling the protein backbone together in the middle of the chain. They can also stabilize quaternary structure by bringing together two polypeptide chains. Lysine and aspartate can form salt bridges.

18.52 When a protein is denatured, its three-dimensional structure is disrupted, and its ability to catalyze reactions is impaired. Primary structure is not affected by denaturation.

18.54 Met—Ile—Lys   Ile—Met—Lys   Lys—Met—Ile
Met—Lys—Ile   Ile—Lys—Met   Lys—Ile—Met

18.56 Amino acids with polar side chains (aspartate and asparagine, for example) are likely to be found on the outside of a globular protein, where they can form hydrogen bonds with water and with each other. Amino acids with nonpolar side chains (valine and leucine, for example) are likely to be found on the inside of globular proteins, where they can escape from water.

18.58 If a diabetic took insulin orally, digestive enzymes would catalyze its hydrolysis, and the individual amino acids would be absorbed as food.

18.60

N–terminal amino acid   Tyr – Gly – Gly – Phe – Met   C–Terminal amino acid

Properties and Reactions of Amino Acids and Proteins

18.62

(a)

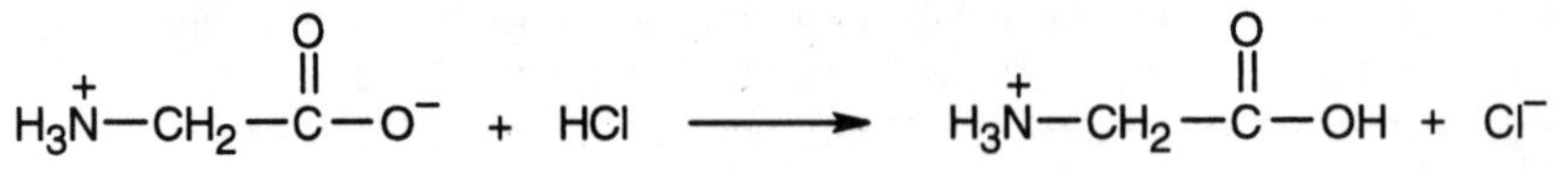

$$H_3\overset{+}{N}-CH_2-\overset{O}{\overset{\|}{C}}-O^- + HCl \longrightarrow H_3\overset{+}{N}-CH_2-\overset{O}{\overset{\|}{C}}-OH + Cl^-$$

(b)

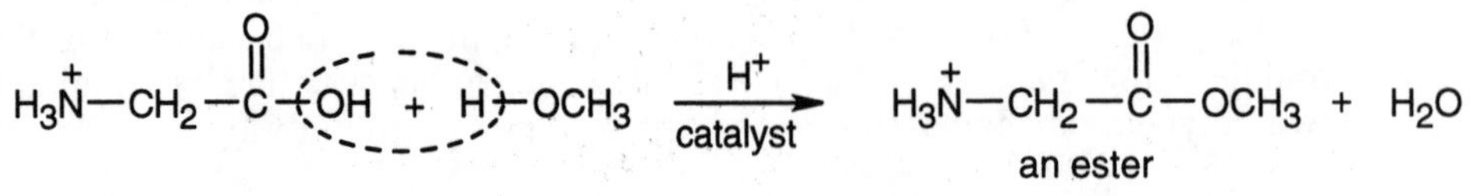

$$H_3\overset{+}{N}-CH_2-\overset{O}{\overset{\|}{C}}-(OH + H)-OCH_3 \xrightarrow[\text{catalyst}]{H^+} H_3\overset{+}{N}-CH_2-\overset{O}{\overset{\|}{C}}-OCH_3 + H_2O$$

an ester

18.64

N–terminal
amino acid

C–terminal
amino acid

$$H_3\overset{+}{N}-CH-\overset{O}{\overset{\|}{C}}-N-CH_2-\overset{O}{\overset{\|}{C}}-N-CH-\overset{O}{\overset{\|}{C}}-N-CH-\overset{O}{\overset{\|}{C}}-N-CH-\overset{O}{\overset{\|}{C}}-O^-$$

Valine   Glycine   Serine   Alanine   Aspartate

$$H_3\overset{+}{N}-CH-\overset{O}{\overset{\|}{C}}-O^- \ + \ H_3\overset{+}{N}-CH_2-\overset{O}{\overset{\|}{C}}-O^- \ + \ H_3\overset{+}{N}-CH-\overset{O}{\overset{\|}{C}}-O^- \ +$$

$$H_3\overset{+}{N}-CH-\overset{O}{\overset{\|}{C}}-O^- \ + \ H_3\overset{+}{N}-CH-\overset{O}{\overset{\|}{C}}-O^-$$

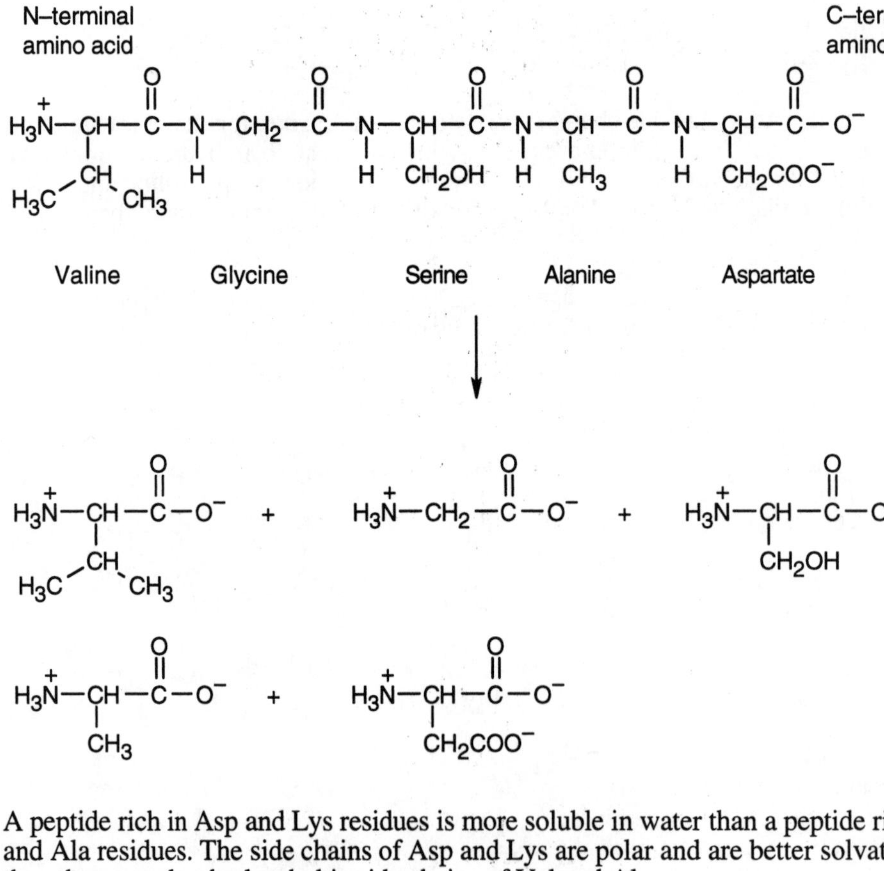

18.66 A peptide rich in Asp and Lys residues is more soluble in water than a peptide rich in Val and Ala residues. The side chains of Asp and Lys are polar and are better solvated by water than the nonpolar, hydrophobic side chains of Val and Ala.

Applications

18.68

(a)

Tyrosine → Tyramine + CO_2

Decarboxylation is the elimination of CO_2 from a molecule.

(b)

Phenelzine   Tyramine

Like tyramine, phenelzine has an amino group on a two-carbon chain that is bonded to an aromatic ring. Phenelzine resembles tyramine, and it inhibits the enzyme that removes the amino group from tyramine.

18.70 An incomplete protein lacks one or more of the nine essential amino acids.

18.72 Casein and egg white protein are well-balanced proteins because they must provide complete nutrition to newborn and embryonic organisms. It is thus not surprising that they are also well-balanced proteins for human growth and development.

18.74 If an aspartate residue were substituted for a glutamate residue, a health problem might not occur because both amino acids have similar physical properties and chemical behavior.

General Questions and Problems

18.76 In α-keratin, pairs of α–helixes twist together into small fibrils that are twisted into larger bundles. In tropocollagen, three coiled chains wrap around each other to form a triple helix.

18.78 Hydrophobic interactions: (b) methionine, (f) phenylalanine, (h) valine
Hydrogen bonding: (a) glutamate, (c) glutamine, (d) threonine, (e) histidine
Salt bridges: (a) glutamate, (e) histidine
Covalent bonding: (g) cysteine

18.80 Denaturation disrupts a protein's shape without disrupting its primary structure: hydrolysis breaks bonds and thus destroys a protein's primary structure.

18.82 The sulfur in methionine is a sulfide ($-SCH_3$) sulfur instead of a thiol ($-SH$) sulfur and can't form disulfide bridges.

Self-Test for Chapter 18

Multiple choice:

1. Which level of protein structure doesn't involve hydrogen bonds?
   (a) primary (b) secondary (c) tertiary (d) quaternary

2. Which of the following amino acids has a hydrophobic side chain?
   (a) Asparagine (b) Threonine (c) Histidine (d) Phenylalanine

3. The isoelectric point of an amino acid is 7.6. Which of the following statements about it is untrue?
   (a) At pH = 7.6, the number of positive charges equals the number of negative charges.
   (b) It is a basic amino acid.
   (c) At pH = 5.5, both the carboxylic acid group and the amine group are protonated.
   (d) It forms salt bridges when it is part of a polypeptide chain.

4. Which of the following organic molecules is chiral?
   (a) 1-Pentanol (b) 2-Pentanol (c) 3-Pentanol (d) 2-Methyl-2-butanol

5. How many tetrapeptides can be formed from alanine, lysine, and two valines?
   (a) 6 (b) 12 (c) 18 (d) 24

6. Which of the following is an amino acid with a nitrogen heterocyclic ring?
   (a) Histidine (b) Threonine (c) Tyrosine (d) Cysteine

7. Addition of heavy metal ions to a protein disrupts which structural element?
   (a) hydrogen bonds (b) primary structure (c) hydrophobic interactions (d) disulfide bonds

8. A table in which proteins are described as collagens and immunoglobulins classifies them by:
   (a) size (b) shape (c) function (d) the type of non-protein associated with them

9. In a nucleoprotein, the protein is conjugated with:
   (a) carbohydrate (b) metal ions (c) RNA (d) lipids

10. Substitution of one amino acid for another in a polypeptide chain disrupts;
   (a) secondary structure (b) tertiary structure (c) isoelectric point (d) all or none of the above, depending on the amino acids involved

Complete the following sentences:

1. The isoelectric point of a neutral amino acid is near pH = _____.

2. Two molecules that differ only in the arrangement of groups around a chiral carbon atom are called _____.

3. Amino acids exist as dipolar ions called _____.

4. The repeating chain of amide bonds in a peptide is called the _____.

5. A disulfide bond between two cysteines in the same chain produces a _____ in the peptide.

6. A protein bonded to a carbohydrate is called a _____.

7. _____ structure refers to how the entire protein is folded and coiled into a specific three-dimensional shape.

8. In the secondary structure called a _____ _____, polypeptide chains line up in a parallel arrangement held together by hydrogen bonds.

9. The tripeptide Ser-Gln-Lys contains side chains that are _____.

10. The amino acids methionine and cysteine are the only two that contain the element _____.

11. A chain with fewer than 50 amino acids is called a _____.

12. _____ interactions pull nonpolar side chains together to exclude water.

Tell whether the following statements are true or false:

1. All amino acids have at least one chiral carbon atom.

2. Tyrosine and valine can react to form a dipeptide.

3. Protein denaturation disrupts the primary structure of a protein.

4. Lysylalanine is identical to alanyllysine.

5. Some amino acids have an isoelectric point near 10.

6. Simple proteins are more common than conjugated proteins.

7. β–sheets and α-helices occur mostly in fibrous proteins.

8. Amino acids are quite water-soluble.

9. Proteins, as well as amino acids, have isoelectric points.

10. Both fibrous and globular proteins are water-soluble.

11. Proteins may be classified by biological function.

12. 2–Butanol has a chiral carbon atom.

Match the entries on the left with their partners on the right:

1. Isoleucine

2. Insulin

3. Glycylglycine

4. Glycine

5. β–sheet

6. Aspartic acid

7. Collagen

8. Cysteine

9. Albumin

10. Arginine

11. Proline

12. Tryptophan

(a) Achiral amino acid

(b) Secondary structure

(c) Fibrous protein

(d) Amino acid that is a secondary amine

(e) Amino acid with hydrocarbon side-chain

(f) Globular protein

(g) Peptide hormone

(h) Basic amino acid

(i) Aromatic amino acid

(j) Dipeptide

(k) Acidic amino acid

(l) Can form disulfide bridges

Chapter 19 – Enzymes and Vitamins

Chapter Outline

I. Introduction to enzymes (Sections 19.1–19.3).
  A. Catalysis by enzymes (Section 19.1).
     1. Enzymes are globular proteins that catalyze biochemical reactions.
        a. The active site is the region of the enzyme where catalysis takes place.
        b. The reactant in an enzyme-catalyzed reaction is called the substrate.
        c. Some enzymes are specific for one particular substrate, whereas others catalyze reactions involving a number of substrates.
        d. Most enzymes are specific with respect to stereochemistry.
     3. Enzymes affect only the rate of reaction and not the position of equilibrium.
     4. The catalytic efficiency of an enzyme is measured by its turnover number.
  B. Enzyme cofactors (Section 19.2).
     1. Many enzymes include protein portions and nonprotein portions that are called cofactors.
        The cofactors, called coenzymes, are either metal ions or small organic molecules.
     2. Enzymes can obtain from cofactors chemically reactive groups not available as side chains.
     3. Some cofactors are covalently bonded: others serve as cosubstrates.
  C. Enzyme classification (Section 19.3).
     1. Classes of enzymes.
        a. Oxidoreductases catalyze oxidation–reduction reactions.
        b. Transferases catalyze the transfer of a specific group from one substrate to another.
        c. Hydrolases catalyze the hydrolysis of substrates.
        d. Isomerases catalyze the isomerization of substrates.
        e. Lyases catalyze the addition or elimination of small molecules.
        f. Ligases catalyze the bonding of two substrate molecules.
     2. Naming enzymes.
        a. The first part of the name identifies the substrate.
        b. The second part of the name identifies the enzyme subclass.
II. Enzyme function (Sections 19.4–19.6).
  A. How enzymes work (Section 19.4).
     1. Models for representing enzyme action.
        a. The shape of the active site is complementary to the shape of the substrate.
           This description of enzyme–substrate is called the lock-and-key model.
        b. A more modern interpretation of enzyme–substrate interaction is the induced-fit model.
           i. In this model, an enzyme is flexible enough to change shape to fit the spatial requirement of the substrate.
           ii. The enzyme and substrate induce each other to change shape.
     2. Mechanism of enzyme catalysis.
        a. An enzyme–substrate complex is formed when the substrate migrates to the active site, and atoms that will take part in the reaction are held in place (proximity effect).
        b. Reactants are positioned at the exact distance necessary for reaction to occur (orientation effect).
        c. The active site provides the kinds of functional groups necessary for catalysis (catalytic effect).
        d. The activation energy for reaction is lowered by introducing strain into the bonds of the substrate (energy effect).

    C. Influence of temperature and pH on enzymes (Section 19.5).
        1. Temperature.
            a. All enzymes have an optimum temperature for greatest catalytic efficiency. In the human body, this temperature is 37°C.
            b. At temperatures above 50–60°C, enzymes denature.
        2. pH.
            a. Enzymes also have an optimum pH.
            b. If pH is too high or too low, enzymes lose their ability to catalyze reactions.
    D. Effect of enzyme and substrate concentration (Section 19.6).
        1. When substrate concentration is high, and enzyme concentration varies:
            a. Additional enzyme increases the reaction rate.
            b. The increase in reaction rate is directly proportional to enzyme concentration.
        2. When substrate concentration varies, and enzyme concentration remains constant:
            a. Additional substrate increases the rate until all active sites are occupied.
            b. At this point, reaction rate becomes constant.
            c. The enzyme is said to be saturated.
        3. Under most conditions, reaction rate is controlled by enzyme efficiency.
            The upper limit to reaction rate is about 10^8 collisions per mole per second.
III. Enzyme regulation (Sections 19.7–19.9).
    A. General strategies of control (Section 19.7).
        1. Activation is any process that increases the action of an enzyme.
        2. Inhibition is any process that slows or stops the action of an enzyme.
    B. Feedback and allosteric control .
        1. Feedback control.
            a. The product of a series of reactions is an inhibitor for the first reaction.
            b. This strategy keeps excessive amounts of products from accumulating.
        2. Allosteric control.
            a. Most enzymes are regulated by allosteric control.
            b. Allosteric enzymes have more than one polypeptide chain.
            c. Allosteric enzymes have catalytic sites and regulatory sites.
            d. Binding of a positive regulator increases reaction rate.
            e. Binding of a negative regulator decreases reaction rate.
    C. Enzyme inhibition (Section 19.8).
        1. Noncompetitive inhibition.
            a. An inhibitor binds to the enzyme at a site other than the active site and changes the shape of the enzyme.
            b. The enzyme is a less effective catalyst , and reaction rate is slowed.
            c. The inhibitor doesn't compete with the substrate.
        2. Competitive inhibition.
            a. In competitive inhibition, a substrate that resembles the normal substrate occupies the enzyme's active site.
            b. Competitive inhibition is reversible.
               i. The degree of inhibition can be regulated by controlling the amounts of substrate and inhibitor.
               ii. Increasing the concentration of substrate displaces inhibitor from the active site.
        3. Irreversible inhibition.
            The inhibitor bonds covalently to the active site, and the enzyme is irreversibly inhibited.
    D. Covalent modification and genetic control (Section 19.9).
        1. Zymogens.
            a. Some enzymes(zymogens) are synthesized in a form that differs from their catalytic form.
            b. Zymogens are activated by enzymatic addition or removal of a part of the zymogen.

c. Enzymes that might injure the body if constantly present in their active form are synthesized as zymogens.
2. Phosphorylation/dephosphorylation.
Phosphate groups can be added to serine and threonine side chains to activate certain enzymes
3. Genetic control.
a. Synthesis of some enzymes is regulated by genes.
b. Genetic control is used for enzymes needed only at certain stages of development.
IV. Vitamins (Section 19.10).
A. Vitamins are small organic molecules that must be supplied in the diet.
B. Vitamins are classified by solubility.
1. Water-soluble vitamins are either coenzymes or precursors to coenzymes.
Water-soluble vitamins include vitamin C and the B vitamins.
2. Fat-soluble vitamins are stored in the body's fatty tissues.
a. Vitamin A is important for vision.
b. Vitamin D regulates calcium absorption.
c. Vitamin E is an antioxidant.
d. Vitamin K is involved in blood-clotting.

Solutions for Chapter 19 Problems

19.1 Both acetylcholinesterase and kinases catalyze 1000 (10^3) reactions per second.

19.2 Most vitamin/mineral supplements contain the listed metal ion cofactors (iron, zinc, copper, manganese, molybdenum, vanadium, cobalt, and nickel), as well as containing selenium and boron.

19.3 (a) Retinal isomerase catalyzes the isomerization of retinal.
(b) Squalene oxidase catalyzes the oxidation of squalene.
(c) Glucose kinase catalyzes the transfer of a phosphate group to glucose.
(d) Cellulose hydrolase catalyzes the hydrolysis of cellulose.

19.4 Pyruvate decarboxylase is a lyase and catalyzes the elimination of CO_2 from pyruvate.

19.5 In an isomerization catalyzed by triose phosphate isomerase, a terminal hydroxyl group is converted to an aldehyde group, and the adjacent ketone group is converted to a hydroxyl group.

19.6 The rate of the reaction shown in Figure 19.5a is faster at 30°C than at 20°C.
The rate is slightly faster at 40°C than at 25°C.

19.7 The rate of the reaction catalyzed by trypsin is about the same at pH = 7 as it is at pH = 9.

19.8 If enzyme concentration is halved, the rate of reaction is also halved because the rate is directly proportional to enzyme concentration.

19.9

(a)   (b)

H_2N—◯—$\overset{\overset{O}{\|}}{C}$—$O^-$ H_2N—CH_2CH_3 H_2N—◯—$\overset{\overset{O}{\|}}{\underset{\overset{\|}{O}}{S}}$—$NH_2$

p–Aminobenzoate

Structure (b) is a possible competitive inhibitor for the enzyme that has *p*–aminobenzoate (PABA) as a substrate because it resembles PABA both in shape and in the type of functional groups present.

19.10 A product of an enzyme-catalyzed reaction that resembles the substrate might be a competitive inhibitor for the enzyme.

19.11 (a) *Covalent modification*, either by activation of a zymogen or by phosphorylation–dephosphorylation, is a type of enzyme regulation that occurs when an enzyme must be quickly activated.
(b) *Competitive inhibition* by use of a drug can regulate an overactive enzyme.
(c) *Genetic control* regulates enzymes that are needed only during certain stages of development.
(d) *Covalent modification* by phosphorylation–dephosphorylation can regulate enzymes that are needed for quick energy. Alternatively, *feedback control* can regulate glucose production. When glucose levels are adequate, glucose inhibits the enzyme that catalyzes its formation. When glucose levels drop, the enzyme is no longer inhibited, and glucose is formed.

19.12 Vitamin A is fat-soluble because it has a long hydrocarbon chain. Vitamin C is water-soluble because it has polar hydroxyl groups.

19.13 The difference among these compounds occurs at the functional group at the end of the hydrocarbon chain. In retinal, an aldehyde replaces the –CH$_2$OH group; in retinoic acid, the –CH$_2$OH group becomes a –COOH group.

Understanding Key Concepts

19.14

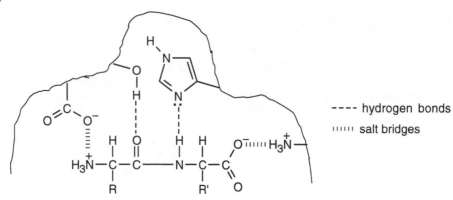

---- hydrogen bonds

⅋⅋⅋ salt bridges

19.15

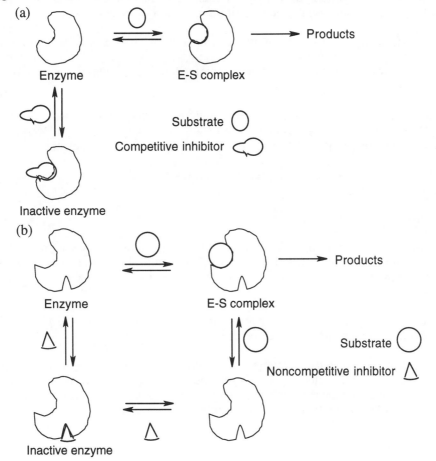

(a) The enzyme that catalyzes the above reaction is an oxidoreductase.
(b) The enzyme belongs to the dehydrogenase subclass.
(c) L-Lactate is the substrate for the above enzyme.
(d) The enzyme is named L-lactate dehydrogenase.

19.16 The above enzyme will most likely not use D-lactate as a substrate because most enzymes are handed and catalyze the reaction of only one enantiomer of a pair of enantiomers. It is possible that D-lactate could act as a competitive inhibitor of the enzyme.

19.17 The coenzyme needed for the above reaction is NAD^+ (nicotinamide adenine dinucleotide), which is an oxidizing agent and includes the vitamin niacin.

19.18

19.19 (a) *Allosteric regulation* (either positive or negative) occurs when a regulator binds to the enzyme at a site other than the active site. This binding changes the shape of the enzyme and alters the catalytic ability of the enzyme.

(b) In *covalent modification*, the activity of an enzyme is influenced by the addition or removal of a group that is covalently bonded to the enzyme.

(c) *Inhibition* is any process that stops or slows down an enzyme's ability to catalyze a reaction. Noncompetitive inhibition can be a type of allosteric regulation (see part (a)). Competitive inhibition occurs when an inhibitor reversibly occupies an enzyme's active site. Irreversible inhibition results when an inhibitor covalently binds to an enzyme and destroys its ability to catalyze a reaction.

(d) In *genetic control*, hormones control the synthesis of enzymes.

Structure and Classification of Enzymes

19.20 (a) A *hydrolase* catalyzes the hydrolysis (bond-breaking by addition of water) of a substrate.

(b) An *isomerase* catalyzes the isomerization of a substrate.

(c) A *lyase* catalyzes the addition of a small molecule to a double bond of a substrate, or the elimination of a small molecule from a substrate to form a double bond.

19.22 An enzyme is a large three-dimensional molecule with a catalytic site into which a substrate can fit. Enzymes are specific in their action because only one or a few molecules have the appropriate shape and functional groups to fit into the catalytic site.

19.24 (a) A *hydrolase* catalyzes this reaction, which is the hydrolysis of a peptide bond.

(b) A *lyase* catalyzes this reaction.

(c) An *oxidoreductase* catalyzes the introduction of a double bond into a molecule by removal of H_2.

19.26 (a) A *protease* catalyzes the hydrolysis of peptide (amide) bonds in proteins.

(b) A *DNA ligase* catalyzes the formation of a new bond between two small DNA chains.

(c) A *transmethylase* catalyzes the transfer of a methyl group between substrates.

19.28 A urease is a hydrolase, since it catalyzes the hydrolysis of urea.

Enzyme Function and Regulation

19.30 In the lock-and-key model of enzyme action, the active site of an enzyme has a specific shape (lock) into which only a specific substrate (key) can fit. In the induced-fit model, an enzyme can change its shape slightly to fit the different spatial requirements of a number of substrates.

19.32 The amino acid residues involved in the active site can be brought close to each other by protein folding without being near each other in the polypeptide chain.

19.34 To function in the very acidic environment of the stomach, an enzyme operates best at a low pH. To function in the intestine, an enzyme must have high catalytic activity at a pH near neutral. Each enzyme has an optimum pH for catalysis, and an enzyme that is most active at neutral pH will not be active in a strongly acidic environment.

19.36

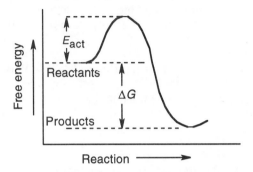

19.38 The rate of reaction increases as the substrate concentration increases, up to a point where all enzyme catalytic sites are occupied. The reaction rate then levels off, and adding more substrate doesn't increase the reaction rate.

19.40 (a) Lowering the temperature of the enzyme-catalyzed reaction from 37°C to 27°C decreases the rate of reaction.
(b) Raising the pH of the enzyme-catalyzed reaction from 7.5 to 10.5 will probably decrease the rate of reaction, since most enzymes have their optimum rates at close to neutral pH. However, if the enzyme has a rate optimum near 10.5, then the increase in pH from 7.5 to 10.5 will increase the rate of reaction.
(c) Adding a heavy-metal salt could either stop the reaction or decrease the rate of the enzyme-catalyzed reaction because heavy metals bind to enzymes, causing irreversible inhibition.

19.42 *Competitive inhibition* occurs when the structure of a second substrate closely resembles that of the normal substrate for an enzyme. The second substrate can occupy the active site and thereby inhibit binding at the active site of the usual substrate. Competitive inhibition is usually reversible.

Noncompetitive inhibition occurs when an inhibitor binds to the enzyme at a location other than the active site. The conformation of the enzyme changes, and the enzyme is inactivated or its catalytic ability is reduced.

Irreversible inhibition occurs when a molecule covalently bonds to the active site of an enzyme. The active site is thus irreversibly inactivated, and enzyme activity stops.

In competitive inhibition, the inhibitor bonds noncovalently to the active site. In noncompetitive inhibition, the inhibitor binds noncovalently with a group away from the active site. In irreversible inhibition, the inhibitor forms a covalent bond at the active site.

19.44 Papain is effective as a meat tenderizer because it catalyzes the hydrolysis of peptide bonds and partially digests the proteins in the meat and softens tough connective tissue.

19.46 Allosteric enzymes have two types of binding sites — one site is for catalysis of the enzymatic reaction and one site is for regulation of the reaction. Having two kinds of sites allows for greater regulation and control of enzyme activity.

19.48 Feedback inhibition occurs when the end product of a series of reactions is an inhibitor for an earlier reaction. When this product accumulates, it inhibits an enzyme that catalyzes an earlier step in the series. When the amount of product drops, inhibition stops, and product formation is resumed.

19.50 A zymogen is an enzyme that is synthesized in a form different from its active form and is activated when needed. Some enzymes are secreted as zymogens because they would digest or otherwise injure the body if they were secreted in their active form.

Vitamins

19.52 Vitamins are small organic molecules that the body can't manufacture and that must be present in trace amounts in the diet.

19.54 Vitamin C (water-soluble) is excreted in the urine and must be replenished daily, whereas vitamin A (fat-soluble) can be stored in fatty tissue.

Applications

19.56 Enzyme activity must be monitored under standard conditions because activity is affected by pH, temperature and substrate concentration. The standard is the unit (u) which is the amount of enzyme that converts one micromole of substrate to product at defined standard conditions of pH, temperature and substrate concentration.

19.58 Isoenzymes are enzymes that catalyze the same reaction but differ slightly in structure and that are active in different types of tissue.

19.60 The body excretes excess water-soluble vitamins, but fat-soluble vitamins accumulate in tissues.

19.62 Listings for vitamin A, vitamin C, iron and calcium are mandatory on food labels because they are considered to be of greatest importance in maintaining good health.

General Questions and Problems

19.64

$$1.6 \text{ mg riboflavin} \times \frac{100 \text{ mL apple juice}}{0.014 \text{ mg riboflavin}} = 11,000 \text{ mL} = 11 \text{ L apple juice}$$

19.66 Because competitive inhibition is reversible, addition of a large amount of the normal substrate will reverse the binding of the inhibitor, and the rate of reaction of the normal substrate will return to its usual value. The effects of noncompetitive inhibition can't be reversed by addition of excess substrate.

Self-Test for Chapter 19

Multiple choice:

1. A subclass of enzyme that catalyzes cleavage of peptide bonds is a:
   (a) lipase   (b) dehydrase   (c) protease   (d) reductase

2. Which of the following is an enzyme cofactor?
   (a) thiamine   (b) tocopherol   (c) hexokinase   (d) trypsin

3. The ability of enzymes to bring reactants together is known as the:
   (a) orientation effect   (b) catalytic effect   (c) proximity effect   (d) energy effect

4. Fat-soluble vitamins serve all of the following functions except:
   (a) promotion of bone growth   (b) antioxidant   (c) aiding night vision
   (d) anemia prevention

5. Which of the following enzymes probably requires a coenzyme that is reduced during reaction?
   (a) transferase   (b) oxidase   (c) isomerase   (d) dehydrase

6. The most likely control mechanism for reactions that occur during embryonic development is:
   (a) feedback control   (b) genetic control   (c) zymogens   (d) allosteric control

7. Snake venom probably causes its effects by:
   (a) noncompetitive inhibition   (b) competitive inhibition   (c) allosteric control
   (d) irreversible inhibition

8. Why does the rate of enzymatic reactions decrease as temperature is lowered?
   (a) Salt bridges are disrupted.   (b) The shape of the active site is changed.   (c) Reaction rate is
   slowed as temperature is lowered.   (d) The enzyme begins to denature.

9. If an enzyme is saturated, adding more substrate will:
   (a) increase reaction rate   (b) have no effect on reaction rate   (c) decrease reaction rate
   (d) have varying effects, depending on the enzyme

10. In which of the following types of enzyme regulation can adding large amounts of substrate
    restore an enzyme's reaction rate to its maximum value?
    (a) feedback inhibition   (b) irreversible inhibition   (c) noncompetitive inhibition
    (d) competitive inhibition

Complete the following sentences:

1. An enzyme called a _____ catalyzes the isomerization of a chiral center.

2. _____ are enzymes that have slightly different structures but that catalyze the same reaction.

3. Vitamin __ is necessary for the synthesis of blood-clotting factors.

4. In the _____ - _____ model of enzyme action, an enzyme can change its shape slightly to fit
   different substrates.

5. In _____ inhibition, an inhibitor changes the shape of an enzyme by binding at a location other than the active site.

6. If the temperature becomes too high, enzymes begin to _____.

7. The catalytic activity of an enzyme is measured by its _____ _____.

8. A type of covalent modification of an enzyme involves addition or removal of a _____ group.

9. The _____ effect is responsible for bringing substrate and catalytic sites together.

10. The upper limit of any enzyme's rate of reaction is ___collisions per mole per second.

11. An _____ enzyme has more than one chain and has binding sites for both substrate and regulator.

12. An enzyme that is synthesized in a form different from its active form is called a _____.

Tell whether the following statements are true or false:

1. 98.6°F is the optimum temperature for most enzymes.

2. In an enzyme-substrate complex, the substrate is in its lowest energy shape.

3. Noncompetitive inhibition is irreversible.

4. A dehydrogenase catalyzes the loss of H_2O from a substrate.

5. At the active site, the enzyme and substrate are held together by covalent bonds.

6. Vitamins may be small organic molecules or inorganic ions.

7. Chymotrypsinogen is a zymogen.

8. β-Carotene is the active form of vitamin A.

9. Copper, cobalt, and selenium are essential enzyme cofactors.

10. Heavy metals cause irreversible inhibition of enzymes.

11. As enzyme concentration is increased, the reaction rate eventually levels off.

12. The side chains of serine and threonine are sites of covalent modification.

Match the entries on the left with their partners on the right:

1. Papain

2. Vitamin D

3. Competitive inhibition

4. Kinase

5. Alanine transaminase

6. Cofactor

7. Noncompetitive inhibition

8. Vitamin B_6

9. Lipase

10. Vitamin C

11. Active enzyme

12. Lyase

(a) Deficiency causes anemia

(b) Occurs away from an enzyme's active site

(c) Nonspecific enzyme

(d) Catalyzes hydrolysis of ester groups in lipids

(e) Protein part of enzyme, plus cofactor

(f) Deficiency causes scurvy

(g) Transfers a phosphate group between substrates

(h) Fat-soluble vitamin

(i) Occurs at an enzyme's active site

(j) Metal ion or small organic molecule

(k) Specific enzyme

(l) Catalyzes loss of small molecule from substrate

Chapter 20 – Chemical Messengers

Chapter Outline

I. Introduction to chemical messengers (Section 20.1).
   A. Control of vital functions is accomplished by chemical messengers.
      1. The messengers interact with the cells of a target tissue.
      2. The message is delivered by interaction between the chemical messengers and receptors.
      3. Noncovalent interactions draw messengers and receptors together.
      4. The results of the interaction are chemical changes within the target cell.
   B. Two kinds of chemical messengers are important in the body.
      1. Hormones are the chemical messengers of the endocrine system.
        a. Hormones travel through the bloodstream.
        b. The responses produced by hormones are slow but long-lasting.
      2. The chemical messengers of the nervous system are neurotransmitters.
        a. Signals travel very quickly along nerve fibers.
        b. Neurotransmitters carry the message of the signal across the gap that separates one nerve fiber from the next fiber.
        c. The effects of neurotransmitters are very short-lived.
II. Hormones (Sections 20.2–20.5).
   A. Hormones and the endocrine system (Section 20.2).
      1. The endocrine system consists of all the glands that secrete hormones.
      2. The endocrine glands are managed by the hypothalamus in three different ways.
        a. Direct neural control by a nervous system pathway from the hypothalamus.
        b. Direct release of hormones from the hypothalamus.
        c. Indirect control by release of regulatory hormones.
      3. There are three types of hormones.
        a. Polypeptide hormones.
        b. Steroid hormones.
        c. Amino acid derivatives.
      4. The signal of a hormone enter cells in either of two ways.
        a. Steroid hormones pass through the hydrophobic cell membrane.
        b. Other hormones bind with receptors in the cell wall.
   B. How hormones work: epinephrine (Section 20.3).
      1. Epinephrine carried in the bloodstream binds to a receptor on the surface of a cell.
      2. The hormone–receptor complex interacts with a nearby G protein, causing it to bind GTP.
      3. This complex activates the enzyme adenylate cyclase, which resides in the cell membrane.
      4. Adenylate cyclase catalyzes production within the cell of the second messenger, cyclic AMP.
      5. Cyclic AMP initiates reactions that activate glycogen phosphorylase, which catalyzes release of glucose from storage.
      6. After the emergency, a phosphodiesterase catalyzes hydrolysis of cyclic AMP to AMP.
   C. Types of hormones (Sections 20.4–20.6).
      1. Polypeptide hormones (Section 20.4).
        a. TRH and TSH control the thyroid gland.
        b. Vasopressin and oxytocin are small cyclic polypeptides.
        c. Insulin regulates glucose metabolism.

    2. Steroid hormones (Section 20.5).
       a. Mineralocorticoids (such as aldosterone) regulate ionic balance in cellular fluid.
       b. Glucocorticoids (such as cortisone) regulate inflammation.
       c. Sex hormones.
          i. Androgens (male hormones) include testosterone and androsterone.
          ii. Female hormones include estrogens and progestins.
          iii. There are also hundreds of synthetic hormones of all types.
    3. Amino acid derivatives (Section 20.6).
       a. Many amino acid derivatives are also neurotransmitters.
         Examples include epinephrine, dopamine and norepinephrine.
       b. Thyroxine is an iodine-containing hormone that regulates the synthesis of various enzymes.

III. Neurotransmitters (Sections 20.7–20.12).
  A. General features of neurotransmitters (Section 20.7).
    1. A nerve impulse is transmitted along a neuron by variations in electric potential.
    2. Neurotransmitters convey the impulse across the synaptic cleft from a presynaptic neuron to a postsynaptic neuron.
    3. The impulse is transmitted down the next neuron, and the above process is repeated.
    4. Neurotransmitters are synthesized and stored in vesicles in the presynaptic neuron.
    5. After transmission, the neurotransmitter is inactivated in one of two ways.
       a. A chemical change inactivates the neurotransmitter.
       b. The neurotransmitter is returned to the presynaptic neuron.
    6. Most neurotransmitters are amines.
    7. Some neurotransmitters act directly, and others rely on second messengers.
  B. How neurotransmitters work: acetylcholine (ACh) (Section 20.8).
    1. Events of neurotransmission.
       a. An impulse arrives at the presynaptic neuron.
       b. The vesicles move to the cell membrane, fuse with it, and release ACh.
       c. ACh crosses the synaptic cleft and binds to receptors on the postsynaptic neuron.
       d. A change in the permeability of the postsynaptic neuron initiates the nerve impulse in that neuron.
       e. Acetylcholinesterase in the synaptic cleft catalyzes the decomposition of ACh.
       f. Choline is reabsorbed into the presynaptic neuron, and new ACh is synthesized.
    2. Interactions of drugs at ACh synapses.
       a. To have an effect a drug must connect with a receptor.
       b. Drugs that are agonists prolong the biochemical response of a receptor.
         Nicotine at a low dose is an example of an agonist.
       c. Drugs that are antagonists block the normal response of a receptor.
         Antagonists can be either competitive (tubocurarine) or irreversible (nerve gas).
  C. Histamine and antihistamines (Section 20.9).
    1. Histamine is the neurotransmitter responsible for the symptoms of allergic reactions.
    2. Antihistamines are drugs that are histamine receptor antagonists.
  D. Monoamines (Sections 20.10–20.11).
    1. Serotonin, norepinephrine, and dopamine are neurotransmitters active in the brain (Section 20.10).
    2. Since these neurotransmitters affect mood, drugs have been created to affect the concentration of these neurotransmitters at synapses.
       a. Tricyclic antidepressants (Elavil) prevent the reuptake of serotonin and norepinephrine from the synaptic cleft.
       b. MAO inhibitors (Nardil) inhibit the enzyme that breaks down monoamine neurotransmitters.
       c. SSRI antidepressants (Prozac) inhibit only the reuptake of serotonin.

3. Dopamine (Section 20.11).
   a. Dopamine plays a role in emotion, thought and behavior through interactions with five different kinds of receptors in the brain.
   b. Dopamine levels are responsible for many types of behaviors.
      i.   An oversupply of dopamine is associated with schizophrenia.
      ii. An undersupply of dopamine is responsible for Parkinson's disease.
      iii. An ample supply of dopamine is responsible for a feeling of well-being.
   c. Drugs such as heroin, cocaine, marijuana, and alcohol increase dopamine levels.
E. Neuropeptides (Section 20.12).
   The brain has receptors for small polypeptides (enkephalins) that also act as receptors for opiates.
IV. Drug discovery and drug design (Section 20.13).
   A. Plants were the first source of drugs.
      Today, ethnobotanists seek new plant sources of drugs in remote regions.
   B. In the 19th century, simple drugs (benzocaine, phenacetin) were synthesized in chemical laboratories.
   C. Combinatorial chemistry generates large masses of related compounds and screens them for possible effectiveness as drugs.
   D. Supercomputers and molecular graphics are increasingly used in drug design.

Solutions to Chapter 20 Problems

20.1

If you redraw the reaction shown in Figure 20.4, you can see the anion that is a byproduct of the conversion of ATP to cyclic AMP. The anion (PP$_i$) is P$_2$O$_7^{4-}$.

20.2

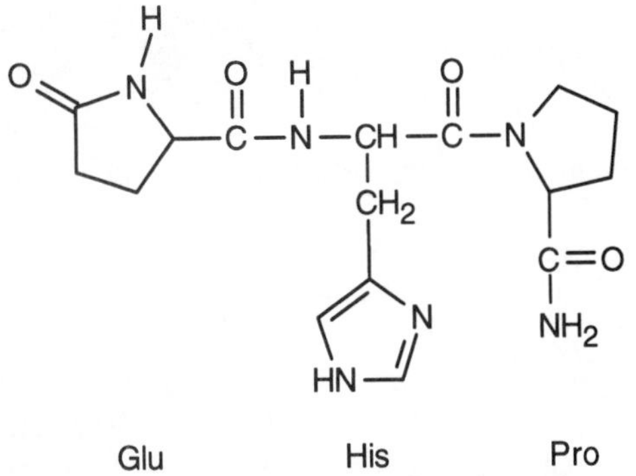

Glu　　　　　　His　　　　　Pro

The tripeptide is Glu–His–Pro.

20.3

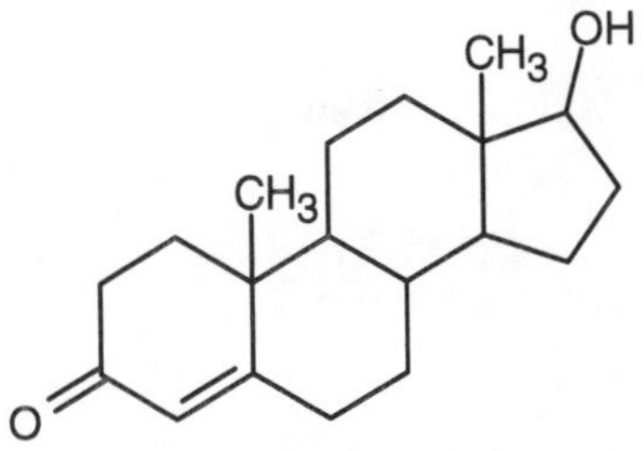

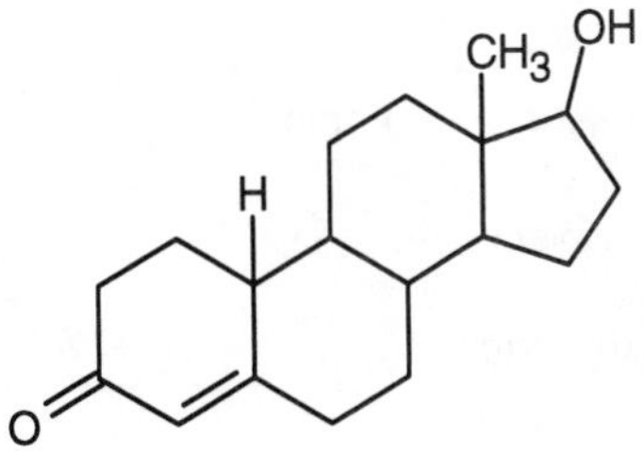

Testosterone　　　　　　　　　　　Nandrolone

Nandrolone and testosterone are identical except for the presence in testosterone of a methyl group between the first two rings that is absent in nandrolone.

20.4

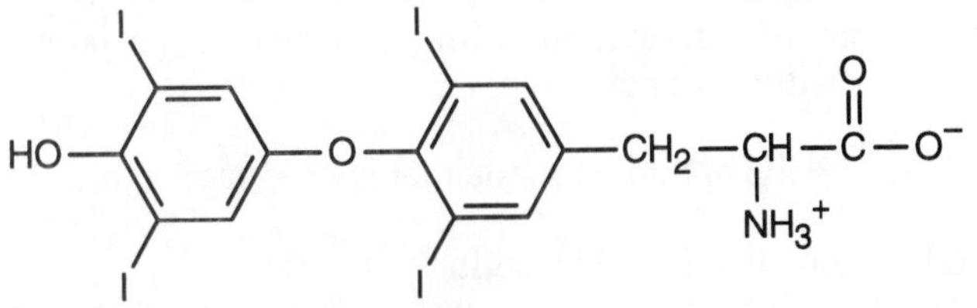

Thyroxine

Thyroxine is hydrophobic because its aromatic, hydrophobic part is larger than its zwitterionic, hydrophilic part.

20.5

5–Hydroxytryptophan

Serotonin

N–Acetylserotonin

Melatonin

(a) decarboxylation (2)
(b) acetylation (3)
(c) methylation (1)

Understanding Key Concepts

20.6 (a) Insulin, a polypeptide hormone, is involved in type I diabetes.
   (b) In unaffected individuals, insulin is released by the pancreas. The pancreas fails to produce insulin in individuals with type I diabetes.
   (c) Insulin is transported through the bloodstream to cells that need it.
   (d) Insulin doesn't enter cells because it is a polypeptide hormone and can't pass through the hydrophobic cell membrane. Instead, it binds with a cell surface receptor, which generates a second messenger within the cell.

20.7 (a) Luteinizing hormone (LH) is a polypeptide hormone that is produced in the anterior pituitary gland.
   (b) Progesterone is a steroid hormone that is produced in the ovaries.
   (c) LH doesn't enter progesterone-producing cells because it is a polypeptide hormone. Instead, LH interacts on the cell surface with LH receptors that generate second messengers, which carry out the function of LH.
   (d) Progesterone enters the cell directly because it is a steroid hormone and can pass through the hydrophobic cell membrane.

20.8 Since a small amount of epinephrine produces a massive response, at least one step in the sequence that results in the release of glucose must be amplified many fold. Although amplification occurs in all steps of the sequence of events, two steps have the greatest amplification. (1) Adenylate cyclase is capable of catalyzing the production of a great number of cAMP molecules. (2)The kinase enzymes phosphorylated by cAMP (Section 19.9), quickly catalyze the breakdown of glycogen to release large amounts of glucose.

20.9 The transmission of a nerve impulse may be terminated by an enzyme that converts the neurotransmitter to an inactive form. It is also possible for the neurotransmitter to be returned to the presynaptic neuron.

Chemical Messengers

20.10 Hormones are molecules of different sizes and types that travel through the bloodstream and regulate the rates of biochemical reactions without directly taking part in the reactions. A hormone is detected by a receptor, either at a cell surface or within the cell.

20.12 A vitamin is usually an enzyme cofactor, whereas a hormone regulates enzyme activity.

20.14 Like allosteric regulation, hormone binding is noncovalent and serves to control the rate of a reaction, rather than to take part in a reaction.

Hormones and the Endocrine System

20.16 The three major classes of hormones are polypeptide hormones, steroid hormones and hormones that are derivatives of amino acids.

20.18 The body's endocrine system manufactures and secretes hormones, which regulate the rates of biochemical reaction pathways.

20.20 Enzymes are proteins, whereas hormones vary greatly in structure. Some hormones are polypeptides, some are proteins, some are steroids, and some are derivatives of amino acids.

20.22 Polypeptide hormones travel through the bloodstream and bind to cell receptors, which are on the outside of a cell. The receptors cause production within cells of "second messengers" that activate enzymes.

How Hormones Work: Epinephrine

20.24 Epinephrine is produced in the adrenal cortex and released as a result of a nervous system signal from the hypothalamus. It is produced when the body needs an instant response to danger. At target tissues, epinephrine stimulates the production of glucose as a source of energy to deal with whatever stress is at hand.

20.26 The second messenger initiates reactions that activate glycogen phosphorylase, the enzyme responsible for releasing glucose from storage.When the message is ready to be terminated, the enzyme phosphodiesterase converts cyclic AMP to AMP.

Hormones

20.28 Insulin is a polypeptide hormone that contains 51 amino acids in two chains that are linked by disulfide bridges. It is stored in the pancreas and is released in response to high glucose levels in the blood. The hormone stimulates cells to take up glucose for use or storage.

20.30 *Mineralocorticoids* include aldosterone.
Glucocorticoids include hydrocortisone and cortisone.
Sex hormones include testosterone, androsterone, estrone, estradiol and progesterone.

20.32 Both thyroxine and steroid hormones have large nonpolar regions and can cross a cell membrane to activate the synthesis of enzymes.

20.34

Hormone	*Class*
(a)	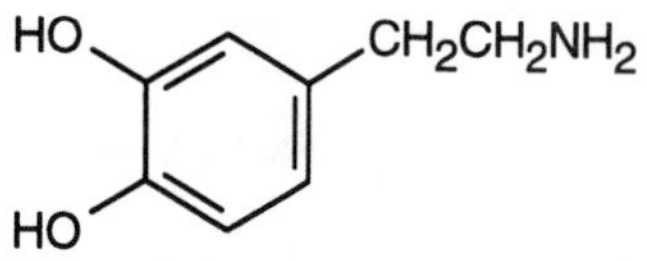 amino acid derivative

Dopamine

(b) Insulin	polypeptide hormone

| (c) | 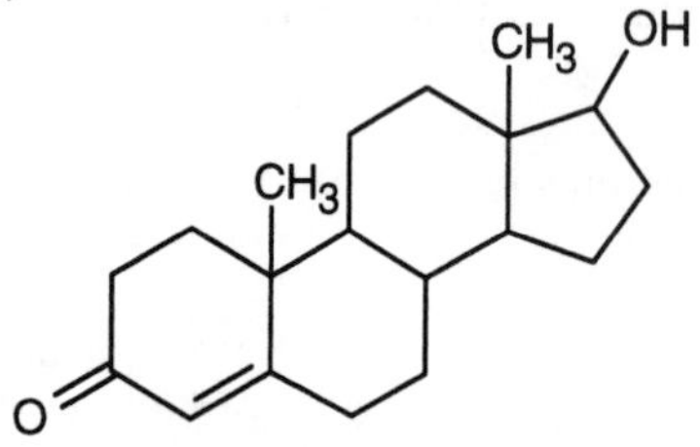 steroid hormone |

Testosterone

Neurotransmitters

20.36 A synapse is the gap between two nerve cells (neurons). Neurotransmitters released by one neuron cross the synapse to receptors on a second neuron and transmit the nerve impulse.

20.38 The signal from a neurotransmitter might be received by another nerve cell, a muscle cell or an endocrine cell.

20.40 (1) The neurotransmitter can be enzymatically inactivated. (2) The neurotransmitter may be returned to the presynaptic neuron and stored until it is needed again.

20.42 (1) An impulse arrives at the presynaptic neuron.
(2) Vesicles containing acetylcholine(ACh) move to the cell membrane, fuse with it, and release ACh.
(3) ACh crosses the synaptic cleft and binds to receptors on the postsynaptic neuron.
(4) The resulting change in the permeability of the postsynaptic neuron to ions initiates the nerve impulse in that neuron.
(5) After the message is delivered, acetylcholinesterase catalyzes the breakdown of acetylcholine.
(6) Choline is reabsorbed into the presynaptic neuron, where new ACh is synthesized by reaction with acetyl coenzyme A.

Chemical Messengers and Drugs

20.44 Drugs that are agonists interact with receptors to produce or prolong the normal response of the receptor. Antagonists block or inhibit the normal response of a receptor.

20.46 The three major monoamine neurotransmitters are serotonin, norepinephrine and dopamine.

20.48 Both cocaine and amphetamines increase dopamine levels in the brain. Cocaine blocks reuptake of dopamine, and amphetamines accelerate release of dopamine.

20.50 When it was discovered that the brain had receptors for neurotransmitters that came from plants, scientists reasoned that there must also be animal neurotransmitters that acted on the same receptors. It seems to be a coincidence that the brain receptors that respond to animal neurotransmitters also respond to plant neurotransmitters.

20.52 An ethnobotanist works in remote regions of the world to learn what indigenous people have discovered about the healing power of plants.

20.54 Studies of the exact size and shape of biomolecules give scientists information about receptor sites of molecules of interest. This information allows scientists to design drugs with properties suitable for the desired drug–receptor interaction with the target biomolecule.

Applications

20.56 Since DHEA is extracted from yams, it is considered a natural "dietary supplement", rather than a drug. Dietary supplements aren't regulated by anyone and do not have to pass drug screening.

20.58 Epibatidine acts as a painkiller by binding to an acetylcholine receptor in the central nervous system (like nicotine) rather than to an opioid receptor (like morphine).

General Questions and Problems

20.60 The *hormone receptor* recognizes the hormone and sets into motion the series of reactions that result in the response of the cell to hormonal stimulation.
The hormone-receptor complex interacts with the *G protein* and causes it to bind GTP. The G-protein mediates the reaction between the receptor and adenylate cyclase.
The G protein–GTP complex activates *adenylate cyclase*, which catalyzes the formation of the second messenger, cyclic AMP. Cyclic AMP initiates the reactions that the hormone is designed to stimulate.

20.62 Signal amplification is the process in which a small signal induces a response much larger in magnitude than the original signal. For hormones, this amplification begins with the activation of the G-protein; one hormone–receptor complex can activate many G-protein–GTP complexes. Each G-protein–GTP complex, in turn, can activate many molecules of adenylate cyclase, which can stimulate production of many molecules of cyclic AMP. The importance of signal amplification is that a small amount of hormone can cause a very large response.

20.64 With the exception of the circled groups, testosterone and progesterone are identical.

Testosterone   Progesterone

20.66 The craving for chocolate might be explained by the stimulation of dopamine receptors by anandamides, producing feelings of satisfaction similar to those produced by THC. The effect of chocolate consumption may be a milder version of marijuana's effects.

Self–Test for Chapter 20

Multiple Choice:

1. Which of the following compounds is an acetylcholine agonist?
   (a) Nicotine   (b) Succinylcholine   (c) Tubocurarine   (d) Atropine

2. Which of the following hormones regulates the balance of Na^+ and K^+ ions in cellular fluid?
   (a) Androsterone   (b) Progesterone   (c) Aldosterone   (d) Cortisone

3. Cocaine affects the brain because it:
   (a) accelerates the release of dopamine   (b) blocks reuptake of dopamine   (c) raises the level of endorphins   (d) all of the above

4. An effective antihistamine has all of the structural elements listed except:
   (a) an ethylamine skeleton   (b) a tertiary amine   (c) an ether oxygen   (d) two bulky –R groups.

5. Which of the following compounds is a neurotransmitter but not a hormone?
   (a) dopamine   (b) norepinephrine   (c) epinephrine   (d) acetylcholine

6. Which of the following compounds does not reside in the cell membrane?
   (a) cyclic AMP   (b) epinephrine receptor   (c) adenylate cyclase   (d) G protein

7. Hormones and neurotransmitters have all of the following in common except:
   (a) They both regulate reaction rates.   (b) They both can be amino acid derivatives.   (c) They both interact with receptors at target tissues.   (d) They both travel through the bloodstream.

8. Which of the following events doesn't occur in fight or flight?
   (a) Epinephrine crosses the cell membrane.   (b) Epinephrine stimulates production of cyclic AMP.   (c) Glucose is released from storage.   (d) Cyclic AMP is converted to AMP.

9. Control of the endocrine system occurs in the:
   (a) pancreas   (b) pituitary gland   (c) adrenal glands   (d) hypothalamus

10. Which of the following isn't a site for hormone receptors?
    (a) outer cell surface   (b) cytoplasm within the cell   (c) cell nucleus   (d) blood stream

Complete the following sentences:

1. _____ is a life-threatening allergic response.

2. In direct neural control, the hypothalamus controls the release of hormones by the _____ gland.

3. Neurotransmitter molecules are stored in _____.

4. _____ is the neurotransmitter responsible for the symptoms of allergic reactions.

5. Nerves that rely on acetylcholine as their neurotransmitter are referred to as _____ nerves.

6. The hormone _____ prepares the uterus to receive a fertilized egg.

7. An _____ is a neuropeptide that acts at opiate receptors.

8. A person who studies the healing powers of plants from remote regions is a _____.

9. One neuron is separated from another by a gap called a _____ _____.

10. Heroin, alcohol, and cocaine all produce an elevated level of the neurotransmitter _____.

11. The hormone _____ contains iodine atoms.

12. After an emergency, the enzyme _____ catalyzes hydrolysis of cyclic AMP to AMP.

Tell whether the following statements are true or false:

1. Only steroid hormones can cross the cell membrane to activate enzymes.

2. Cocaine accelerates the release of dopamine.

3 In direct release of hormones, hormones move through the bloodstream to the posterior pituitary gland, where they are stored until needed.

4. Some neurotransmitters can act directly; others use second messengers.

5. Acetylcholine is synthesized at postsynaptic neurons.

6. Choline is a quaternary ammonium ion.

7. Epinephrine reduces blood pressure and slows the heart rate.

8. An enlarged thyroid gland is a symptom of excess iodine in the diet.

9. Polypeptide hormones vary greatly in size.

10. Succinylcholine is a competitive antagonist for acetylcholine.

Match the entries on the left with their partners on the right.

1. Androgen   (a) Polypeptide hormone

2. Tricyclic antidepressant   (b) Progesterone

3. Acetylcholine agonist   (c) Cortisone

4. Natural estrogen   (d) ACTH

5. Second messenger   (e) Testosterone

6. Oxytocin   (f) Norethindrone

7. Regulatory hormone   (g) Cyclic AMP

8. MAO inhibitor antidepressant   (h) Amitriptyline (Elavil)

9. Synthetic estrogen   (i) Fluoxetine (Prozac)

10 Acetylcholine antagonist   (j) Phenelzine (Nardil)

11. Glucocorticoid   (k) Nicotine

12 SSRI inhibitor antidepressant   (l) Atropine

Chapter 21 – The Generation of Biochemical Energy

Chapter Outline

I. Energy and Cells (Sections 21.1–21.3).
   A. Energy requirements for living things (Section 21.1).
      1. Energy must be released from food gradually.
      2. Energy must be stored in a readily accessible form.
      3. The rate of release of energy from storage must be finely controlled.
      4. Just enough energy must be released as heat to maintain body temperature.
      5. Energy in a form other than heat must be available to drive reactions that aren't spontaneous at body temperature.
   B. Free energy and biochemical reactions (Section 21.2).
      1. In favorable chemical reactions, free energy is released.
         a. Favorable reactions occur when heat is released and/or disorder increases.
         b. These reactions are described as exergonic.
         c. In favorable reactions, the products are more stable than the reactants.
         d. Favorable reactions have a negative value for ΔG.
      2. Free energy is absorbed in unfavorable chemical reactions.
         a. Unfavorable reactions are described as endergonic.
         b. Energy must be supplied in order for endergonic reactions to proceed.
         c. In unfavorable reactions, the products are less stable than the reactants.
         d. Unfavorable reactions have a positive value for ΔG.
   C. The cell and energy (Section 21.3).
      1. Simple organisms have prokaryotic cells.
      2. More complicated organisms have eukaryotic cells.
         These cells have membrane-enclosed nuclei and organelles.
      3. Structure of eukaryotic cells.
         a. Everything between the cell membrane and the nuclear membrane is the cytoplasm.
         b. The fluid of the cytoplasm is the cytosol.
         c. The most important organelles are the mitochondria.
            i. Mitochondria consist of a smooth outer membrane and a folded inner membrane.
            ii. The space between the two membranes is the intermembrane space.
            iii. The space enclosed by the inner membrane is the mitochondrial matrix.
            iv. Most of the energy-producing reactions of the cell begin in the mitochondrial matrix.
II. Metabolism (Sections 21.4–21.7).
   A. Overview of metabolism (Section 21.4).
      1. A sequence of reactions in metabolism is known as a metabolic pathway.
         a. Pathways may be linear, cyclic or spiral.
         b. Pathways that break molecules apart are known as catabolic pathways.
         c. Pathways that build molecules are known as anabolic pathways.
      2. Catabolism consists of four phases.
         a. Digestion occurs in the mouth and small intestine.
         b. Small molecules are degraded in the cell to yield acetyl–SCoA.
         c. Acetyl groups are oxidized to yield CO_2, H_2O and energy.
         d. Some of the energy is transferred to ATP and reduced coenzymes.

B. Strategies of metabolism (Sections 21.5–21.7).
  1. ATP and energy transfer (Section 21.5).
    a. ATP contains two phosphoric anhydride bonds and a phosphate ester bond.
    b. Hydrolysis of one phosphate anhydride bond provides –7.3 kcal/mol of energy.
    c. Synthesis of ATP from ADP and phosphate requires +7.3 kcal/mol of energy.
    d. Synthesis of ATP occurs when there is energy to store, and hydrolysis of ATP occurs when energy is needed.
  2. Metabolic pathways and coupled reactions (Section 21.6).
    a. In any reaction, the amount of energy consumed or released is the same, no matter what the path.
    b. The overall energy change for a series of reactions can be found by adding up the free energy changes for the individual steps.
    c. A reaction that is energetically unfavored can take place if it is coupled with a reaction that is energetically favored.
      i. The phosphorylation of glucose can take place by coupling with the conversion of ATP to ADP.
      ii. ATP can be synthesized by coupling with the transfer of a phosphoryl group from phosphoenolpyruvate.
  3. Oxidized and reduced coenzymes (Section 21.7).
    a. Many biochemical reactions are redox reactions.
      i. Oxidation may be loss of electrons, loss of hydrogen or addition of oxygen.
      ii. Reduction may be gain of electrons, gain of hydrogen or removal of oxygen.
      iii. Reductions and oxidations always occur together.
    b. Common redox coenzymes are NAD^+, $NADP^+$ and FAD (written in the oxidized form).
      i. NAD^+ and $NADP^+$ are used to oxidize alcohols to carbonyl compounds.
      ii. FAD catalyzes the formation of a double bond.
    c. The energy stored in $FADH_2$, $NADH/H^+$ and $NADPH/H^+$ can be passed on to ATP.
III. Metabolic pathways (Sections 21.8–21.10).
  A. The citric acid cycle (Section 21.8).
    1. Oxidation of two-carbon acyl groups from acetyl-SCoA to CO_2 occurs in the citric acid cycle.
    2. The citric acid cycle is a closed loop of eight reactions in which the product of step 8 is a reactant in step 1.
    3. The cycle operates only if:
      a. Acetyl groups are available.
      b. NAD^+ and FAD are in their oxidized form.
      c. Oxygen is available.
    4. A summary of steps:
      a. Steps 1, 2 : Preparation.
        i. Acetyl–SCoA + oxalate —> citrate.
        ii. Citrate is isomerized to isocitrate.
      b. Steps 3, 4 : Oxidative decarboxylation.
        i. Isocitrate is oxidized and decarboxylated to form α–ketoglutarate, with reduction of NAD^+.
        ii. α–Ketoglutarate is decarboxylated to form succinyl–SCoA and reduced NAD^+.
      c. Step 5 : Substrate-level phosphorylation
        Succinyl–SCoA + GDP —> succinate + HSCoA + GTP.
      d. Step 6 : Oxidation of succinate
        Succinate + FAD —> fumarate + $FADH_2$.
      e. Steps 7, 8 : Regeneration of oxaloacetate.
        i. Fumarate + H_2O —> malate.
        ii. Malate + NAD^+ —> oxaloacetate + $NADH/H^+$.

5. Net result of citric acid cycle:
   a. Production of four reduced coenzyme molecules.
   b. Conversion of an acetyl group to two CO_2 molecules.
   c. Production of one ATP.
B. The electron transport chain and production of ATP (Section 21.9).
   1. The end product of the electron transport chain is water in the reaction :
      $$O_2 + 4\,e^- + 4\,H^+ \longrightarrow 2\,H_2O$$
   2. The reactions of the electron transport chain are coupled to oxidative phosphorylation.
   3. Enzymes for electron transport are embedded in the mitochondrial membrane.
   4. Features of the electron transport chain:
      a. Hydrogen and electrons from NADH and $FADH_2$ enter the respiratory chain from the mitochondrial matrix.
      b. Electrons pass from weaker to stronger electron acceptors.
      c. Some of the energy released is used to transport H^+ into the intermembrane space.
      d. The H^+ concentration gradient creates a potential energy difference that is crucial for ATP synthesis.
      e. H^+ ions can return to the complex only by passing through a channel that is part of the ATP synthase complex.
         The energy that they release drives the phosphorylation of ATP.
   5. Various cofactors, including iron–sulfur clusters and cytochromes, are involved in electron transport.
   6. Ultimately, electrons are passed on to oxygen, which combines with H^+ to form H_2O.
   7. The energy needed for ATP synthesis is provided by the passage of H^+ ions through the ATP synthase enzyme complex.
   8. The passage of electrons from one mol NADH produces from 2.5–3 mol ATP.
C. Superoxide and other oxygen byproducts (Section 21.10).
   1. Oxygen can be consumed in other redox reactions besides electron transport.
   2. The products of these reactions may be H_2O_2, the $\cdot OH$ radical or superoxide ion, O_2^-.
   3. People are protected from the harmful effects of these species by several enzymes, as well as by antioxidants.

Solutions to Chapter 21 Problems

21.1 Use two facts to solve this problem:

(1) A reaction with a negative ΔG is exergonic, and a reaction with a positive ΔG is endergonic.
(2) A reaction with a larger negative ΔG releases more energy than a reaction with a smaller negative ΔG.

Thus, reactions (a) and (c) are exergonic, and reaction (b) is endergonic. Reaction (a) releases the most energy, because its ΔG has a larger negative value than the ΔG's of the other reactions.

21.2 (a) Carbohydrates are digested in the mouth, stomach and small intestine to yield sugars, which are degraded in the cytosol to pyruvate. Pyruvate is converted to acetyl–SCoA, which enters the citric acid cycle and is oxidized to CO_2. The reduced coenzymes that are generated by oxidation of acetyl–SCoA enter the electron-transport chain and are used in the production of ATP by oxidative phosphorylation.
(b) The products of amino acid catabolism can enter the central metabolic pathway as pyruvate, acetyl–SCoA and as citric acid cycle intermediates.

21.3

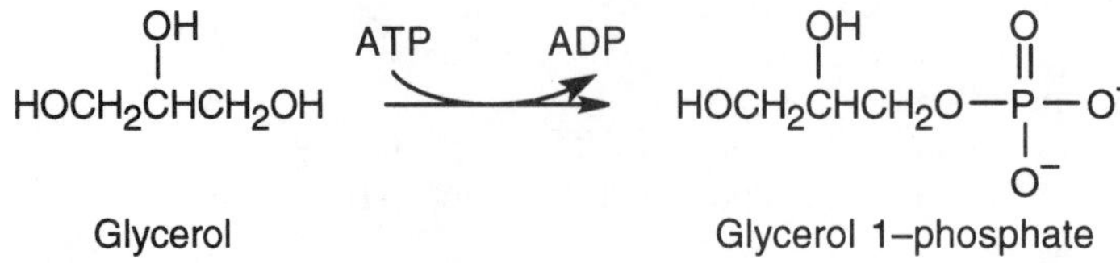

Glycerol   Glycerol 1–phosphate

21.4 If a metabolic pathway that breaks down a molecule is exergonic, the reverse of that pathway (synthesis) *must* be endergonic. The only way to synthesize the product is to couple the energetically unfavorable reactions with other reactions that are energetically favorable in a pathway that differs from the reverse of the breakdown pathway.

21.5

Acetyl phosphate + H_2O $\longrightarrow$ Acetate + $HOPO_3^{2-}$ $\Delta G = -10.3$ kcal/mol

$ADP + HOPO_3^{2-} + H^+$ $\longrightarrow$ $ATP + H_2O$ $\Delta G = +7.3$ kcal/mol

---

Acetyl phosphate + ADP $\longrightarrow$ Acetate + ATP $\Delta G = -3.0$ kcal/mol

The reaction is favorable because ΔG is negative.

21.6 The hydrogen atoms removed are circled.

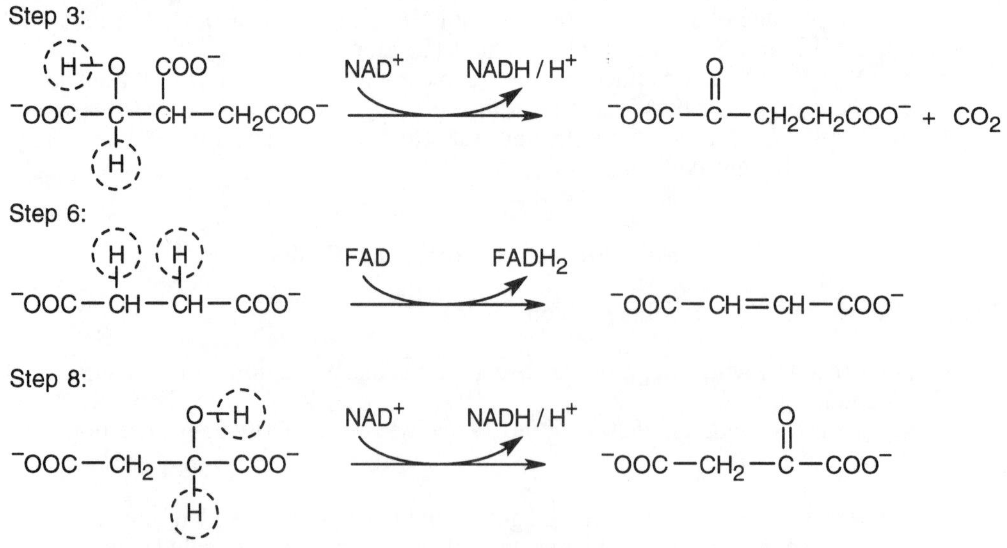

Step 3:

Step 6:

Step 8:

21.7 Citrate and isocitrate are the anions of tricarboxylic acids.

21.8 Reduced coenzymes are produced in steps 3, 4, 6, and 8.

21.9 In Step 6 of the citric acid cycle, succinate dehydrogenase catalyzes the removal of two hydrogens from succinate to yield fumarate. The hydrogens are transferred to the coenzyme FAD to produce the reduced coenzyme $FADH_2$.

21.10 α–Ketoglutarate and oxaloacetate are α–keto acids.

21.11 Isocitrate has two chiral carbon atoms.

21.12 The pH is higher in the mitochondrial matrix.

Understanding Key Concepts

21.13 (a) Exergonic reaction:

$$Succinyl\ phosphate + H_2O \longrightarrow Succinate + HOPO_3^{2-} + H^+$$

(b) Endergonic reaction:

$$ADP + HOPO_3^{2-} + H^+ \longrightarrow ATP + H_2O \qquad \Delta G = +7.3\ kcal/mol$$

(c) The total reaction is considered "substrate-level phosphorylation" because ATP is generated by a direct transfer of a phosphoryl group from a substrate without an accompanying oxidation.

21.14 (a) The digestion of starch to glucose occurs in Stage 1 of food metabolism.
(b) The synthesis of ATP takes place in Stage 4 of digestion.
(c) The reactions shown represent the citric acid cycle and occur in Stage 3 of food metabolism.
(d) Production of acetyl–SCoA from glucose is a result of Stage 2 of food metabolism.

21.15 When ATP "drives" a reaction, energy from ATP is used to enable another reaction to proceed. In this case, the reaction that forms fatty acid–SCoA from a fatty acid and coenzyme A is endergonic and is unfavorable in the absence of ATP. When a phosphoryl group from ATP is used to drive the reaction, the formation of fatty acid–SCoA can take place. Coupling is the metabolic strategy in which the energy from an energetically favorable reaction can be used to allow an energetically unfavorable reaction to take place.

21.16 In the steps of the citric acid cycle in which acetyl groups are oxidized to CO_2, NAD^+ is an acceptor of hydride ions, forming NADH. The hydrogen ions removed in an oxidation using NAD^+ are released to the mitochondrial matrix. NADH transfers electrons to the enzymes and coenzymes of the electron transport chain in the fourth stage of metabolism.

21.17

(a) The coenzyme NAD^+ is involved with reaction A.
(b) CO_2 is evolved and an H^+ is added in reaction B.
(c) Reaction A is catalyzed by an oxidoreductase, and reaction B occurs spontaneously.
(d) The product of step A is a β–keto acid because its keto group is two carbons away from the carboxylic acid group bonded to the middle carbon.

21.18

Step	Reaction	Reaction Type	Type of enzyme
1.	Oxaloacetate —> Citrate	Addition	Lyase
2.	Citrate —> Isocitrate	Isomerization	Isomerase
3.	Isocitrate —> α–Ketoglutarate	Oxidation, loss of CO_2	Oxidoreductase
4.	α-Ketoglutarate—>Succinyl-SCoA	Oxidation, loss of CO_2	Oxidoreductase; lyase
5.	Succinyl–SCoA —> Succinate	Hydrolysis, phosphorylation	Ligase
6.	Succinate —> Fumarate	Oxidation	Oxidoreductase
7.	Fumarate —> Malate	Addition of H_2O	Lyase
8.	Malate —> Oxaloacetate	Oxidation	Oxidoreductase

Free Energy and Biochemical Reactions

21.20 For a reaction to be favorable, it must release energy and thus have a negative ΔG.

21.22 Enzymes only increase the rate of reaction and have no effect on either the magnitude or the sign of ΔG.

21.24 Reactions (a) and (c) are exergonic; reaction (b) is endergonic. Reaction (a) proceeds furthest toward products at equilibrium because it has the largest negative value for ΔG.

Cells and their Structure

21.26 Prokaryotic cells are found in bacteria and algae. Eukaryotic cells are found in all other organisms.

21.28 The cytoplasm consists of everything between the cell membrane and the nuclear membrane; the cytosol is the medium that fills the interior of the cell and contains electrolytes, nutrients and many enzymes, in aqueous solution.

21.30 Mitochondria are called the body's "power plant" because 90% of the body's supply of ATP is synthesized there.

Metabolism

21.32 Metabolic processes that break down molecules are called *catabolism*. Metabolic processes that assemble larger molecules from smaller molecules are known as *anabolism*.

21.34 *First* ——————————————————————> *Last*
Digestion, citric acid cycle, electron transport, oxidative phosphorylation

Strategies of Metabolism

21.36 ATP is called a high-energy molecule because energy is released when ATP transfers a phosphoryl group to other molecules.

21.38 An ATP molecule transfers a phosphoryl group to another molecule in exergonic reactions.

21.40

1,3-Bisphosphoglycerate + H_2O $\longrightarrow$
3-Phosphoglycerate + HPO_4^{2-} $\Delta G = -11.8$ kcal/mol

$ADP + HPO_4^{2-}$ $\longrightarrow$ $ATP + H_2O$ $\Delta G = +7.3$ kcal/mol

---

1,3-Bisphosphoglycerate + ADP $\longrightarrow$
3-Phosphoglycerate + ATP $\Delta G = -4.5$ kcal/mol

The reaction is favorable because ΔG is negative.

21.42 The hydrolysis of fructose 6-phosphate ($\Delta G = -3.3$ kcal/mol) is not favorable for phosphorylating ADP ($\Delta G = +7.3$ kcal/mol) because the overall value of ΔG (+ 4.0 kcal/mol) is positive.

21.44 (a) FAD is reduced when a molecule is dehydrogenated.
(b) FAD is an oxidizing agent.
(c) FAD oxidizes $-CH_2CH_2-$ to $-CH=CH-$.
(d) Dehydrogenation converts FAD to $FADH_2$.
(e)

$$-CH_2CH_2- \quad \xrightarrow[\text{FADH}_2]{\text{FAD}} \quad -CH=CH-$$

The Citric Acid Cycle

21.46 The citric acid cycle is also known as the Krebs cycle or the tricarboxylic acid cycle.

21.48 The two acetyl–SCoA carbons are oxidized to CO_2 in the citric acid cycle.

21.50 Three molecules of $NADH/H^+$ and one molecule of $FADH_2$ are produced in each turn of the citric acid cycle.

21.52 Substrate-level phosphorylation occurs in step 5 of the citric acid cycle, in the conversion of succinyl–SCoA to succinate.

The Electron Transport Chain / Oxidative Phosphorylation

21.54 The two primary functions of the electron transport chain are the conversion of ADP to ATP and the oxidation of the coenzymes NADH and $FADH_2$.

21.56 The ultimate products of the electron transport chain are water and energy in the form of ATP.

21.58 The iron atoms of the cytochromes are oxidized and reduced in the electron transport chain. The oxygen atoms in the CoQ ring undergo oxidation and reduction.

21.60

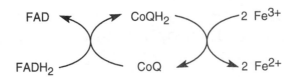

21.62 A pH differential is caused by the movement of H^+ ions across the inner mitochondrial membrane. There are more H^+ ions in the intermembrane space than in the mitochondrial matrix.

21.64 In oxidative phosphorylation, reduced coenzymes are oxidized, and ADP is phosphorylated.

Applications

21.66 Basal metabolic rate is the minimum amount of energy per unit time needed for breathing, maintaining body temperature, circulating blood and keeping all body organs functioning.

21.68 Daily activities such as walking use energy, and thus the body requires a larger caloric intake than that needed to maintain basal metabolism.

21.70 2,4-Dinitrophenol (2,4-DNP) has been used as an uncoupler of ATP synthesis. The uncoupling makes the body burn fat in an attempt to obtain ATP for metabolism. The use of 2,4-DNP was discontinued when it was found that the dose needed to slow ATP synthesis is very close to the dose that stops ATP synthesis, resulting in death.

21.72 The light reaction of photosynthesis occurs in the chloroplasts and is used to produce O_2, NADPH, and ATP. The NADPH and ATP are used in the dark reaction to produce carbohydrate molecules from water and carbon dioxide.

General Questions and Problems

21.74 The breakdown of molecules for energy must occur in several steps to avoid the production of large amounts of heat, to allow for storage of energy, and to control the rate of metabolism. Stepwise breakdown also allows energetically favorable steps to be coupled with other energetically unfavorable reactions.

21.76 Evidently, the fumarate isomer with a cis double bond cannot act as a substrate for the enzyme that is responsible for the next step in the citric acid cycle.

21.78 Electrons from the oxidation of reduced coenzymes pass through the electron-transport chain. Ultimately, the electrons are used to reduce O_2, which combines with H^+ ions to form H_2O. The reaction is catalyzed by cytochrome oxidase.

21.80 Enzymes at the site of injury (catalase, in particular) catalyze the decomposition of hydrogen peroxide to oxygen, which bubbles from the wound.

Self-Test for Chapter 21

Multiple choice:

1. Which of the following oxygen byproducts isn't produced in the human body?
   (a) O_2^- (b) O_3 (c) HO· (d) H_2O_2

2. The hydrolysis of which of the following substrates can be coupled with the reaction
   ADP + phosphate —> ATP to produce an energetically favorable reaction?
   (a) glucose 6-phosphate (b) glucose 1-phosphate (c) creatine phosphate
   (d) fructose 6-phosphate

3. Which of the following cofactors isn't held in a fixed position in electron transport?
   (a) Coenzyme Q (b) FMN (c) Iron–sulfur clusters (d) Cytochrome a

4. Which of the following reactions is an oxidation?
   (a) Fe^{3+} —> Fe^{2+} (b) CH_3COOH —> CH_3CHO
   (c) $CH_3CH_2CH_2COOH$ —> $CH_3CH{=}CHCOOH$(d) CH_3COOCH_3—> $CH_3COOH + CH_3OH$

5. All of the following statements about electron transport are true except:
   (a) A concentration gradient is established between the inner membrane and the mitochondrial
   matrix. (b) Electrons are passed from weaker electron acceptors to stronger electron
   acceptors. (c) A greater amount of energy is produced from oxidation of NADH than from
   oxidation of $FADH_2$. (d) Some of the enzyme cofactors in the electron transport chain are
   mobile.

6. All of the following reactions are oxidations except:
   (a) Isocitrate —> α-Ketoglutarate (b) α-Ketoglutarate —> Succinyl–SCoA
   (c) Succinate —> Fumarate (d) Fumarate —> Malate

7. Which of the following citric acid cycle enzymes is an isomerase?
   (a) Citrate synthetase (b) Aconitase (c) Succinyl–SCoA synthetase (d) Fumarase

8. Which coenzyme is not an oxidizing agent?
   (a) FAD (b) FMN (c) Acetyl–SCoA (d) NAD^+

9. All of the following reactions have positive ΔG except:
   (a) photosynthesis (b) hydrolysis of acetyl–SCoA (c) formation of ATP from ADP
   (d) formation of glucose 6-phosphate

10. Which of the following metabolic pathways doesn't occur in mitochondria?
    (a) oxidative phosphorylation (b) ATP synthesis (c) citric acid cycle (d) degradation of
    carbohydrates

Complete the following sentences:

1. _____ cells are found in higher organisms.

2. A → B → C is known as a _____ _____.

3. ATP is synthesized from _____ and _____.

4. A reaction that requires energy in order to take place is said to be energetically _____.

5. The citric acid cycle is also known as the _____ and as the _____ - _____ cycle.

6. α–Ketoglutaric acid reacts with acetyl–CoA to yield _____ and _____.

7. Reactions that use the coenzyme _____ remove two hydrogens from an alcohol to yield a ketone.

8. A complete citric acid cycle yields _____ molecules of ATP.

9. _____ is the material that fills the interior of a cell.

10. _____ is a fast-acting enzyme that catalyzes the decomposition of reactive oxygen species.

11. The reaction succinate —> fumarate is catalyzed by _____ _____ .

12. _____ _____ is the minimal amount of energy required to stay alive.

Tell whether the following statements are true or false:

1. ATP is a higher-energy molecule than ADP.

2. Both prokaryotic and eukaryotic cells are found in higher organisms.

3. Anabolism is the breakdown of high-energy molecules.

4. In a reaction that is energetically unfavorable, the energy of the products is less than the energy of the reactants.

5. The third and fourth stages of energy production take place in the mitochondria.

6. A reaction that is energetically unfavorable can use ATP as an energy source.

7. $FADH_2$ donates two electrons to cytochrome c in the respiratory chain.

8. FAD removes two hydrogens from a carbon chain to yield a double bond.

9. Release of heat and increase in order contribute to making a reaction favorable.

10. ATP is synthesized only in the respiratory chain.

11. In the synthesis of ATP from ADP, a phosphate ester bond is formed.

12. The reactions of the citric acid cycle may be exergonic or endergonic.

Match the entries on the left with their partners on the right:

1. Mitochondrion

2. Oxidative phosphorylation

3. Isocitrate

4. Anabolic reaction

5. Succinyl–SCoA → succinate

6. Citric acid cycle

7. Malate → oxaloacetate

8. Catabolic reaction

9. Respiratory chain

10. Cytochrome

11. Succinate → fumarate

12. Organelle

(a) Uses energy

(b) Yields one molecule of H_2O

(c) Releases energy

(d) Site of energy production in cell

(e) Reduces NAD^+ to $NADH/H^+$

(f) Tricarboxylic acid

(g) Contains an iron atom

(h) Subcellular structure

(i) Reduces FAD to $FADH_2$

(j) ATP synthesis

(k) Yields 2 molecules of CO_2

(l) Yields acetyl–SCoA plus ATP

Chapter 22 – Carbohydrates

Chapter Outline

I. General information about carbohydrates (Sections 22.1–22.3).
  A. Classification of carbohydrates (Section 22.1).
    1. By complexity.
      a. Monosaccharides don't yield smaller molecules when hydrolyzed.
      b. Disaccharides are composed of two monosaccharides.
      c. Polysaccharides are composed of a large number of monosaccharides.
    2. By carbonyl group.
      a. Aldoses contain an aldehyde carbonyl group.
      b. Ketoses contain a ketone carbonyl group.
    3. By number of carbons in a monosaccharide unit.
      Prefixes (tri-, tetra-, penta-) indicate the number of carbons in the monosaccharide.
  B. Handedness (Section 22.2–22.3).
    1. General characteristics of handed molecules (Section 22.2).
      a. Compounds having a carbon bonded to four different groups are chiral.
        i. A compound with a chiral carbon can exist in either a right-handed form (D) or a left-handed form (L).
        ii. These two forms are called enantiomers.
        iii. An "optically active" compound rotates the plane of plane-polarized light.
        iv. Enantiomers rotate the plane of plane-polarized light to the same extent but in opposite directions.
      b. Compounds having n chiral centers can have 2^n possible stereoisomers.
        i. Some of these isomers are enantiomers.
        ii. Stereoisomers that are not mirror images are diastereomers.
        iii. Some chiral compounds have fewer than the predicted number of stereoisomers because of symmetry.
    2. D and L sugars (Section 22.3).
      a. Stereoisomers can be drawn as Fischer projections.
        i. In these projections, the chiral carbon is drawn as the intersection of two perpendicular lines.
        ii. Bonds that point out of the page are shown as horizontal lines.
        iii. Bonds that point back into the page are vertical lines.
        iv. In sugars, the carbonyl group is at or near the top of a Fischer projection.
      b. Monosaccharides are divided into two families.
        i. In D sugars, the –OH group bonded to the chiral carbon farthest from the carbonyl group points to the right.
        ii. In L sugars, the –OH group bonded to the chiral carbon farthest from the carbonyl group points to the left.
        iii. Most of the carbohydrates that occur naturally are D stereoisomers.
      c. Fischer projections of molecules with more than one chiral carbon are drawn by stacking the chiral centers on top of each other.
      d. The enantiomer of a Fischer projection can be drawn by reversing the horizontal substituents on each chiral carbon.
II. Monosaccharides (Sections 22.4–22.6).
  A. Structure of monosaccharides (Section 22.4).
    1. Monosaccharides with five or more carbons can form cyclic internal hemiacetals.

    a. The hemiacetal carbon (C1) can have two stereoisomeric forms.
        i. In the α isomer, the –OH group points up.
        ii. In the β isomer, the –OH group points down.
    b. Stereoisomers that differ in configuration only at the hemiacetal carbon are called anomers and are diastereomers.
2. In solution, glucose exists as a mixture of open chain glucose (0.02%), the α anomer (36%) and the β anomer (64%).
    a. Any mixture of glucose anomers achieves the same percent of anomers in solution.
    b. This phenomenon is called mutarotation.
3. Fischer projections can be converted to cyclic Haworth projections.
    a. In a Haworth projection of the β anomer, the –CH$_2$OH group and the anomeric –OH group are on the same side of the ring.
    b. In a Haworth projection of the α anomer, the –CH$_2$OH group and the anomeric –OH group are on opposite sides of the ring.
    c. Groups that are on the left in a Fischer projection point up in a Haworth projection.
    d. Groups that are on the right in a Fischer projection point down in a Haworth projection.
    e. The –CH$_2$OH group at C6 points up in D sugars.
B. Important monosaccharides (Section 22.5).
1. Glucose is the most important monosaccharide in human metabolism.
2. Galactose.
    a. Galactose differs from glucose only in the configuration at C4.
    b. Galactose is a component of the disaccharide lactose.
    c. Galactosemia is an inherited disorder of galactose metabolism.
3. Fructose.
    a. Fructose is a component of the disaccharide sucrose.
    b. Fructose is a ketohexose.
4. Ribose and 2-deoxyribose.
    a. These monosaccharides are aldopentoses.
    b. In 2-deoxyribose, the –OH group at C2 is replaced by –H.
    c. Both of these sugars occur as components of nucleic acids.
C. Reactions of monosaccharides (Section 22.6).
1. Reaction with oxidizing agents.
    a. Aldoses can be oxidized to carboxylic acids.
    b. In basic solution, ketoses can also be oxidized to carboxylic acids.
        Ketoses and aldoses are in equilibrium with an intermediate enediol.
    c. Carbohydrates that react with oxidizing agents are called reducing sugars.
2. Reaction with alcohols.
    a. Hemiacetals react with alcohols to form acetals that are called glycosides.
    b. The bond between the anomeric carbon atom and the oxygen of the –OR group is a glycosidic bond.
3. Formation of a bond between two monosaccharides.
    a. Glycosidic bonds can form between two monosaccharides or between a monosaccharide and another molecule.
        i. These bonds may have either α or β orientation.
        ii. Glycosides are not reducing sugars.
    b. Bonds between monosaccharides in more complex carbohydrates are also glycosidic bonds.
        The bond is described by specifying the positions of the connected carbon atoms and by using α or β to indicate the orientation.
    c. Hydrolysis is the cleavage of a glycosidic bond.

III. Important disaccharides (Section 22.7).
    A. Maltose.
        1. Maltose consists of two glucose molecules joined by an α-1,4 glycosidic bond.
        2. Maltose occurs in prepared foods and occurs in the body as a product of starch digestion.
        3. Maltose is a reducing sugar.
    B. Lactose.
        1. Lactose consists of a β-D-glucose molecule joined to a β-D-galactose molecule by a β-1,4 glycosidic linkage.
        2. Lactose is a reducing sugar.
        3. Lactose occurs in milk.
        4. Lactose intolerance is a metabolic disorder in which lactose can't be digested.
    C. Sucrose.
        1. Sucrose consists of an α-D-glucose molecule joined to a β-D-fructose molecule by a glycosidic bond connecting the two anomeric carbons.
        2. Sucrose isn't a reducing sugar.
        3. Sucrose is the most common disaccharide.
IV. Important biomolecules derived from carbohydrates (Section 22.8).
    A. Chitin is a polymer of N-acetyl-D-glucosamine that occurs in the shells of shellfish and in insects.
    B. Cartilage and tendons consist of protein fibers and polysaccharides composed of β-D-glucuronic acid and N-acetyl-D-glucosamine or galactose derivatives.
    C. Hyaluronate and chondroitin 6-sulfate are present in joints, tendons and cartilage.
    D. Heparin is a polysaccharide that contains sulfate groups and that functions as an anticoagulant.
    E. Glycoproteins contain carbohydrates bonded to proteins and have important functions at cell surfaces.
V. Polysaccharides (Section 22.9).
    A. Polysaccharides consist of hundreds to thousands of monosaccharides connected by glycosidic bonds.
    B. Cellulose.
        1. Cellulose consists of thousands of β-D-glucose units connected by glycosidic bonds.
        2. Chains of cellulose fibers can form hydrogen bonds.
        3. Humans can't digest cellulose.
    C. Starch.
        1. Starch consists of glucose units joined by α-1,4 glycosidic bonds.
        2. There are two kinds of starch.
            a. Amylose consists of hundreds of glucose units joined by α-1,4 glycosidic bonds and is soluble in hot water.
            b. Amylopectin is much larger than amylose, also contains α-1,6 branches every 25 units, and is insoluble in water.
            c. Starch is digested in the small intestine by α amylase.
    D. Glycogen.
        1. Glycogen resembles amylopectin but is larger and has more branches.
        2. In humans and animals, glycogen is used for carbohydrate storage.

Solutions to Chapter 22 Problems

22.1

(a)

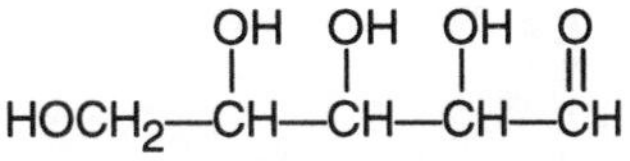

$$\underset{\text{An aldopentose}}{HOCH_2-\overset{\overset{\displaystyle OH}{|}}{CH}-\overset{\overset{\displaystyle OH}{|}}{CH}-\overset{\overset{\displaystyle OH}{|}}{CH}-\overset{\overset{\displaystyle O}{\|}}{CH}}$$

(b)

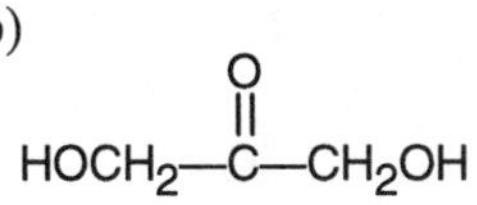

$$\underset{\text{A ketotriose}}{HOCH_2-\overset{\overset{\displaystyle O}{\|}}{C}-CH_2OH}$$

(c)

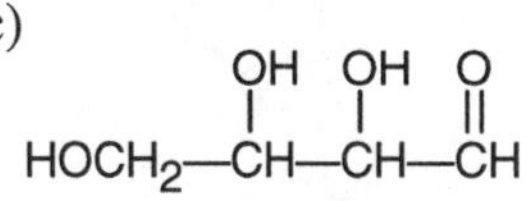

$$\underset{\text{An aldotetrose}}{HOCH_2-\overset{\overset{\displaystyle OH}{|}}{CH}-\overset{\overset{\displaystyle OH}{|}}{CH}-\overset{\overset{\displaystyle O}{\|}}{CH}}$$

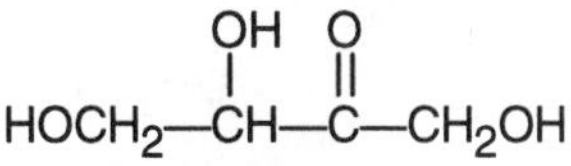

22.2

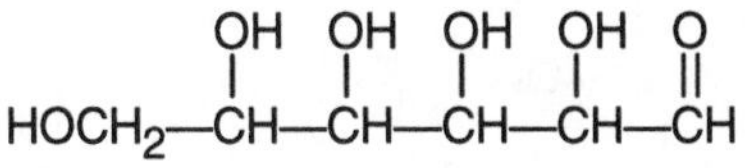

$$\underset{\text{An aldohexose}}{HOCH_2-\overset{\overset{\displaystyle OH}{|}}{CH}-\overset{\overset{\displaystyle OH}{|}}{CH}-\overset{\overset{\displaystyle OH}{|}}{CH}-\overset{\overset{\displaystyle OH}{|}}{CH}-\overset{\overset{\displaystyle O}{\|}}{CH}}$$

$$\underset{\text{A ketotetrose}}{HOCH_2-\overset{\overset{\displaystyle OH}{|}}{CH}-\overset{\overset{\displaystyle O}{\|}}{C}-CH_2OH}$$

22.3 An aldopentose (see illustration in Sec. 22.1) has three chiral carbon atoms. Using the fact that a molecule with n chiral carbons has 2^n stereoisomers, we calculate that an aldopentose has a maximum of $2^3 = 8$ stereoisomers.

22.4

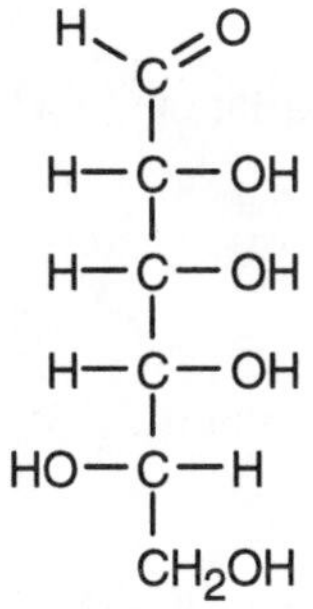

(a) 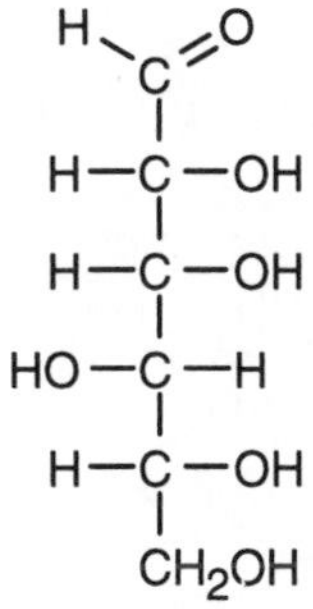   (b) 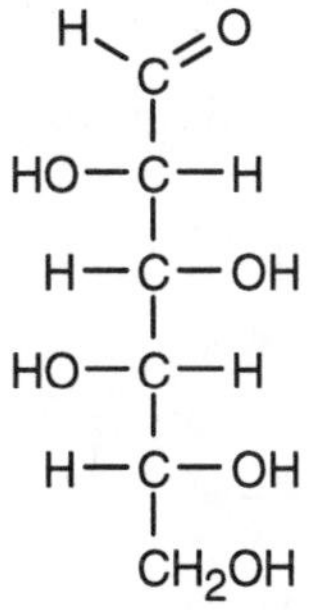   (c) 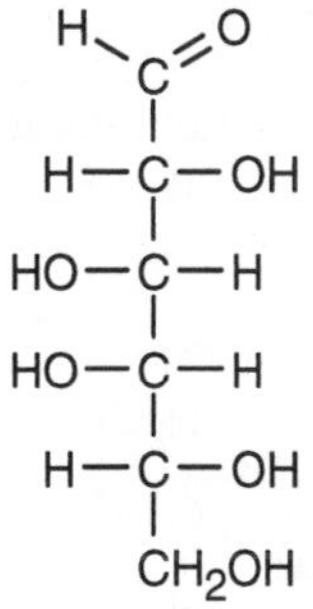   (d)

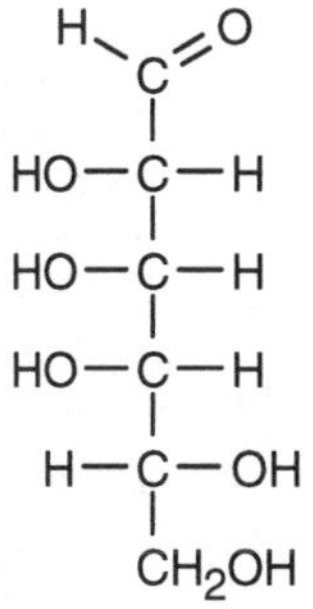

If the monosaccharide shown on the left were to look in the mirror, it would see monosaccharide (d), its enantiomer.

22.5

(a)

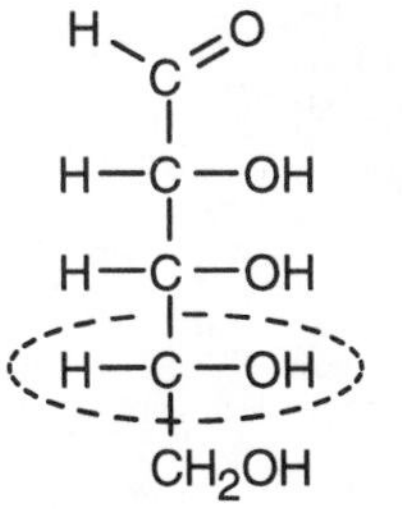

In this pentose, the hydroxyl group bonded to the carbon farthest away from the carbonyl carbon (circled) is on the right. Thus, this enantiomer is D–ribose.

(b)

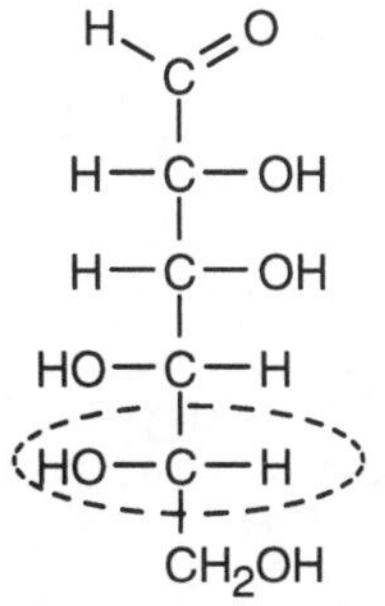

Since the –OH group of the circled carbon points to the left, the monocaccharide is L–mannose.

22.6

(a)

(b)

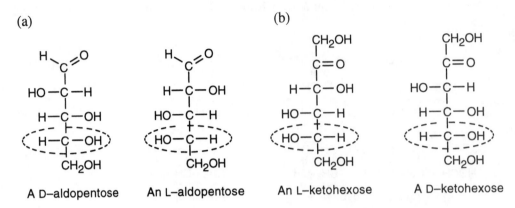

A D–aldopentose   An L–aldopentose   An L–ketohexose   A D–ketohexose

22.7   First, coil D-talose into a circular shape:

Next, rotate around the indicated single bond between C4 and C5 so that the –CH$_2$OH group (C6) points up.

Finally, form a hemiacetal bond between the aldehyde and the –OH group at C5.

β–anomer

α–anomer

22.8   Reverse the series of steps shown in Problem 22.7. First, break the hemiacetal bond.

Rotate around the single bond between C4 and C5 so that the hydroxyl group on C5 points down.

Uncoil D-mannose to arrive at the Fischer projection.

22.9

The drawing represents the β anomer because the –OH group bonded to the anomeric carbon is on the same side of the ring as carbon 6.

22.10 Chiral carbons are starred.

(a)

HOCH₂ ··· CH₂OH
OH
OH

α–D–Fructose

(b)

HOCH₂
OH

OH   OH

α–D–Ribose

(c)

HOCH₂   OH

OH

β–D–2–Deoxyribose

22.11

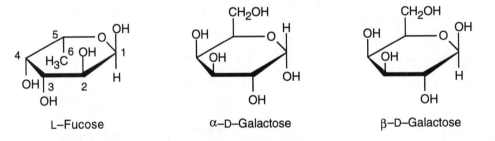

from ribose

cyclic AMP   ATP

22.12

CH₂OH   CH₂OH

5   OH   OH   H   OH   OH
4   6 OH   OH   OH
   H₃C   1   OH   H
OH 3   2   OH   OH
   OH   OH

L–Fucose   α–D–Galactose   β–D–Galactose

(a) L-Fucose is an α anomer because the anomeric hydroxyl group is on the opposite side of the hemiacetal ring from carbon 6.

(b) L-Fucose is missing a hydroxyl group on carbon 6.

(c) The –OH group at carbon 2 that is below the plane of the ring in D-galactose is above the plane of the ring in L-fucose. The –OH groups that are above the plane of the ring in D-galactose are below the plane of the ring in L-fucose.

(d) 6-Deoxy-L-galactose is a correct name for L-fucose.

22.13

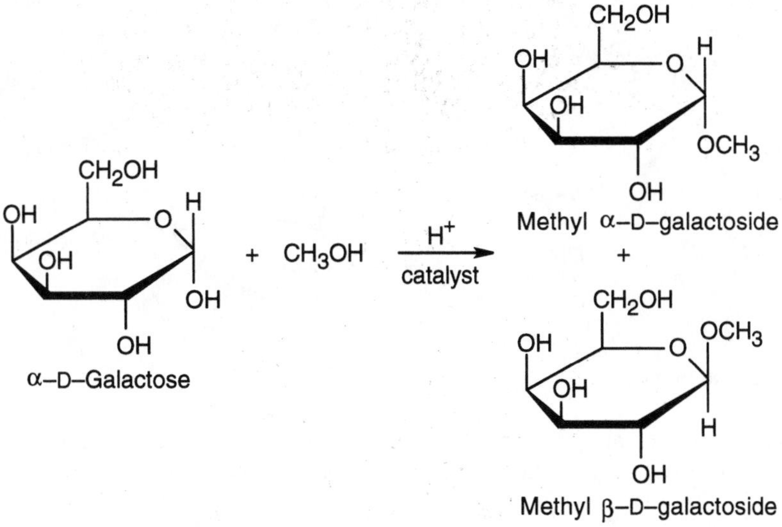

α–D–Galactose + CH₃OH →(H⁺ catalyst)→ Methyl α–D–galactoside + Methyl β–D–galactoside

Neither galactoside is a reducing sugar because the galactosides are no longer in equilibrium with an open-chain aldehyde.

22.14

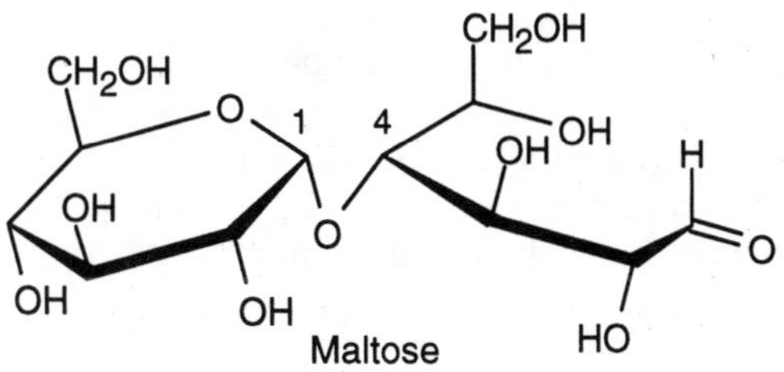

Maltose

22.15 Cellobiose is a reducing sugar because the hemiacetal linkage in the right-hand ring can exist as an open-chain aldehyde, which reacts with an oxidizing agent.

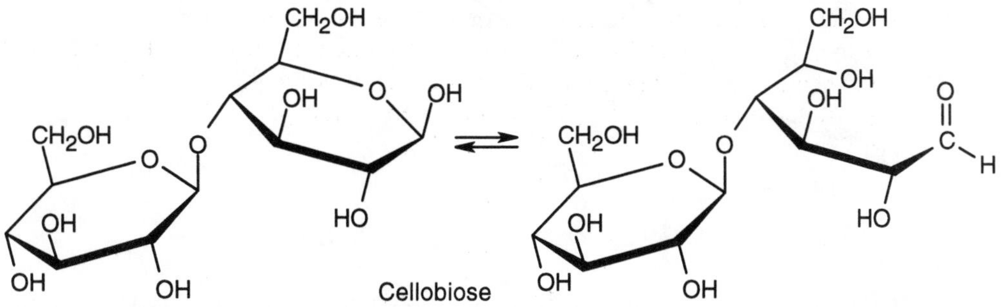

Cellobiose

22.16 Cellobiose has a β-1,4 glycosidic link.

22.17

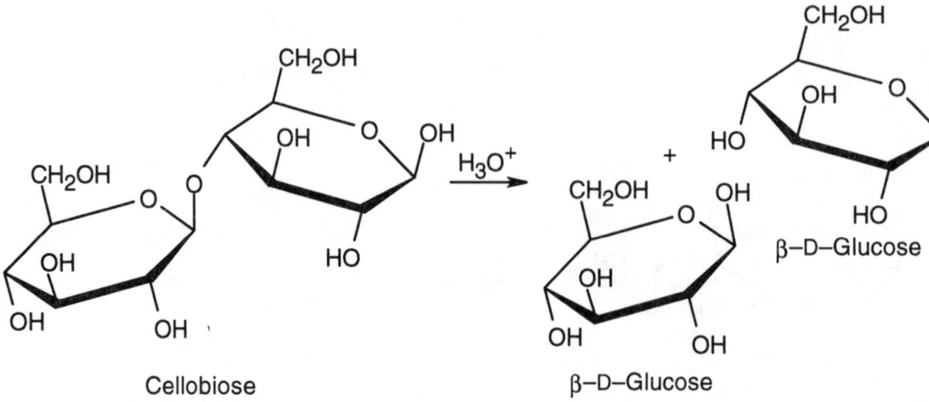

Cellobiose   β–D–Glucose   β–D–Glucose

22.18 Starch has so few hemiacetal units per molecule (only the one at the end of a very long chain) that a positive reducing-sugar reaction with Tollens' reagent or Benedict's reagent is undetectable.

Understanding Key Concepts

22.19

Starch   —Amylase→   Maltose   —Maltase→   Glucose
polysaccharide   disaccharide   monosaccharide

Starch is a large polysaccharide consisting of many glucose subunits connected by α-1,4 glycosidic bonds. α-Amylase hydrolyzes these bonds to yield maltose, a disaccharide, and maltase cleaves the α-1,4 glycosidic bond of maltose to give the monosaccharide glucose.

22.20 (a), (b)

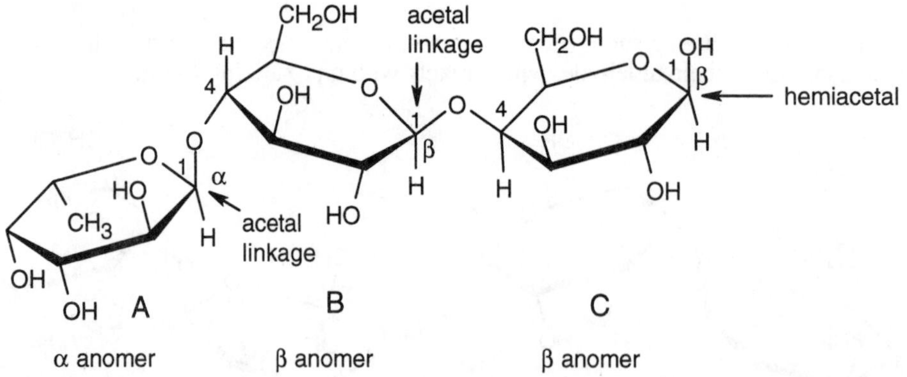

α anomer   β anomer   β anomer

(c) The linkage between monosaccharide A and monosaccharide B is an α-1,4 link that connects carbon 1 of A to carbon 4 of B.

(d) The linkage between monosaccharide B and monosaccharide C is an β-1,4 link that connects carbon 1 of B to carbon 4 of C.

(e) None of the three monosaccharides are identical, and none are enantiomers.

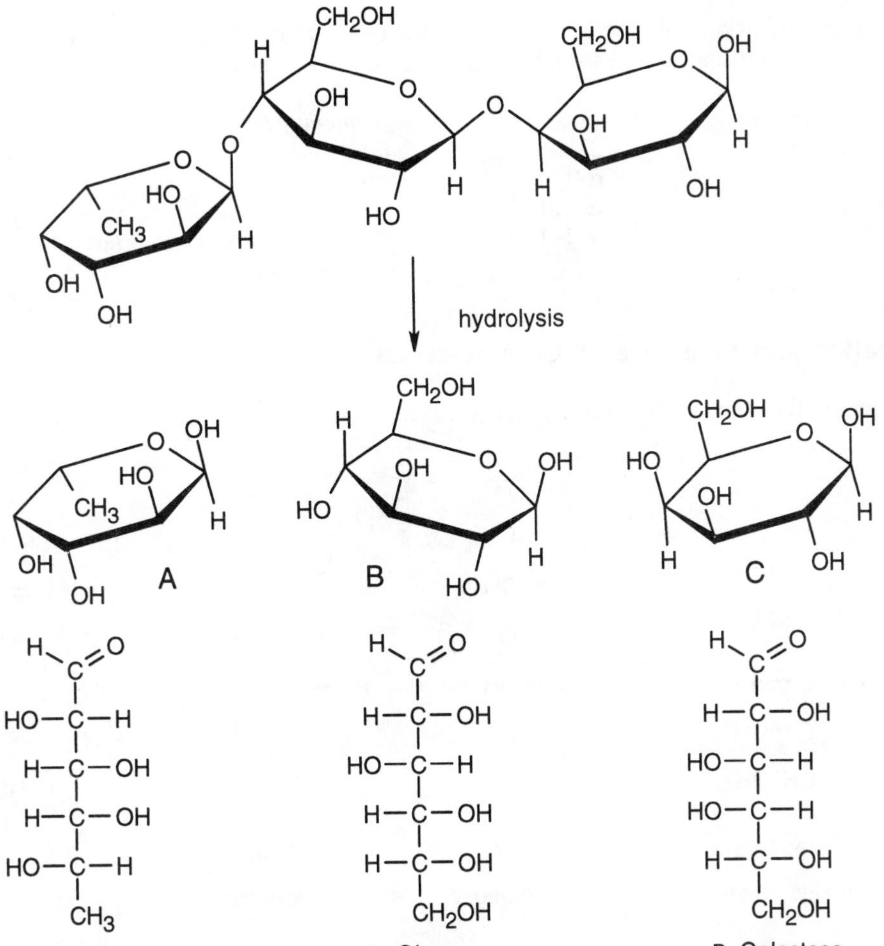

hydrolysis

A   B   C

L–Fucose   D–Glucose   D–Galactose

22.21 Monosaccharide C is oxidized by an oxidizing agent because it is the only one of the three monosaccharides that has a hemiacetal in equilibrium with an open-chain aldehyde. Isolation and identification of the resulting carboxylic acid also identifies the terminal hemiacetal monosaccharide.

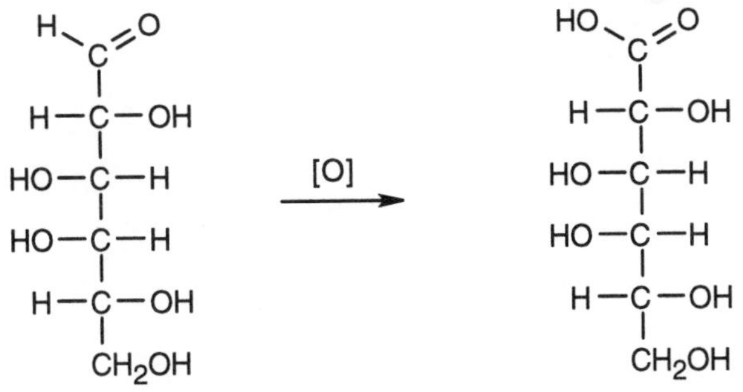

[O]

22.22 Monosaccharides B and C are the components of lactose, but B and C would have to be connected C–B, instead of B–C, in order for lactose to be part of the trisaccharide.

22.23 The trisaccharide is bound to a protein on the cell surface of cell X. Cell type Y binds to the trisaccharide because it has a cell surface receptor for the trisaccharide.

22.24

Polysaccharide	Linkage	Branching?
Cellulose	β-1,4	no
Amylose	α-1,4	no
Amylopectin	α-1,4	yes: α-1,6 branches occur ~ every 25 units
Glycogen	α-1,4	yes: even more α-1,6 branches than in amylopectin

Classification and Structure of Carbohydrates

22.26 The family-name ending for a sugar is *-ose*.

22.28

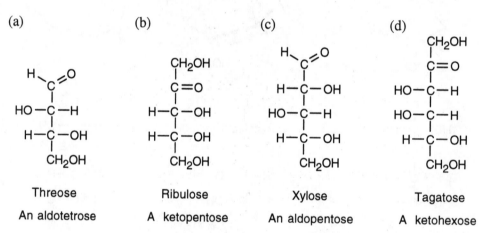

(a) Threose — An aldotetrose
(b) Ribulose — A ketopentose
(c) Xylose — An aldopentose
(d) Tagatose — A ketohexose

22.30

H—C=O
|
CH₂ ← oxygen missing here
|
H—C—OH
|
CH₂OH

A four-carbon deoxy sugar

22.32 *Dextrose* is another name for glucose.

Handedness in Carbohydrates

22.34 L-Glucose and D-glucose are mirror images (enantiomers).

22.36

The reduction product of D-erythrose has a symmetry plane and is achiral.

22.38 A polarimeter measures the degree of rotation of plane-polarized light by a solution of an optically active compound.

22.40 Equimolar solutions of enantiomers rotate light to the same degree but in opposite directions.

Reactions of Carbohydrates

22.42 Mutarotation occurs when either a pure anomer or a mixture of anomers is dissolved in water. In either case, if the rotation of plane-polarized light is measured, the degree of rotation changes until it reaches a constant value. At this point, an equilibrium mixture of both anomers is present in the solution.

22.44 In the β form of a carbohydrate hemiacetal, the –OH group attached to C1 (the hemiacetal carbon) is on the same side of the ring as the –CH$_2$OH group (carbon 6). In the α form, the –OH group at C1 and the –CH$_2$OH group are on opposite sides of the ring.

22.46

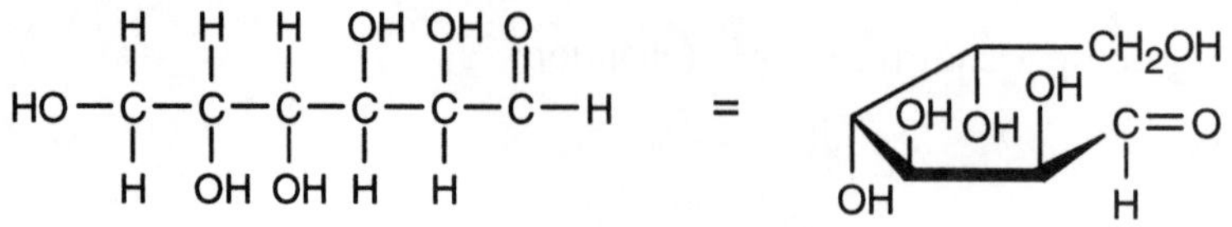

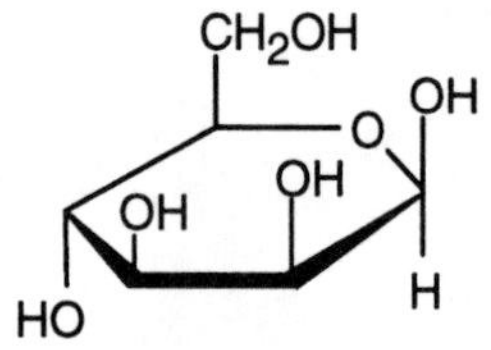

β–D–Mannose 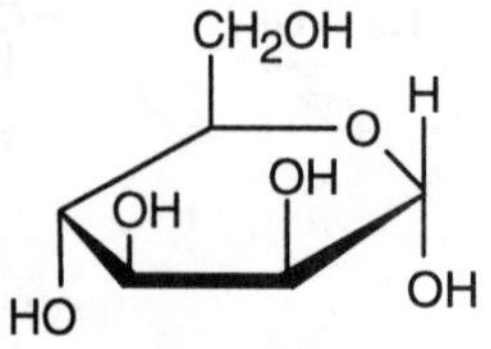   α–D–Mannose

22.48

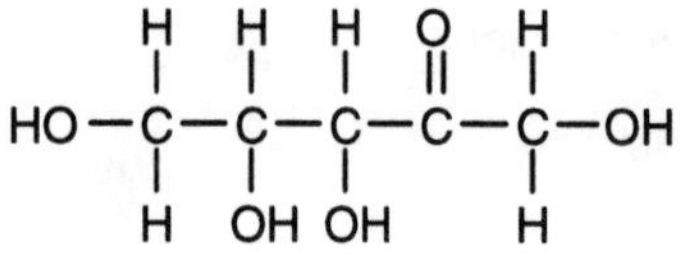

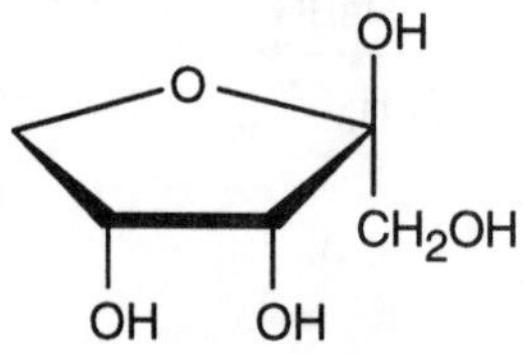

β–D–Ribulose

22.50

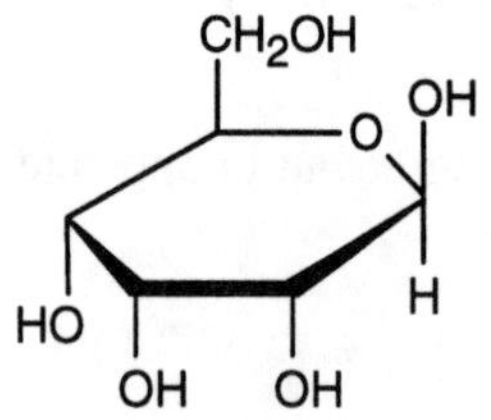

β–D–Allose

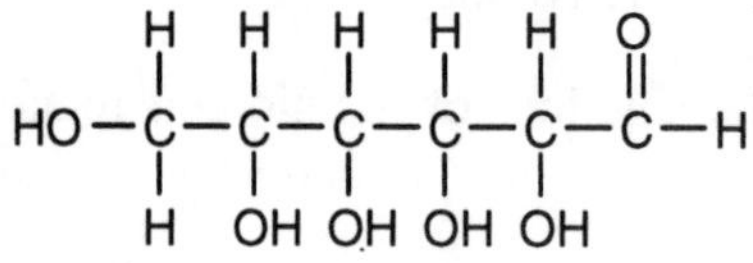

22.52

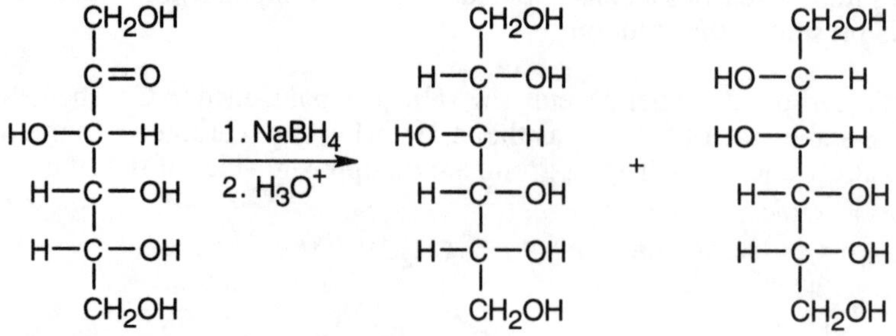

D–Fructose   Sorbitol

22.54

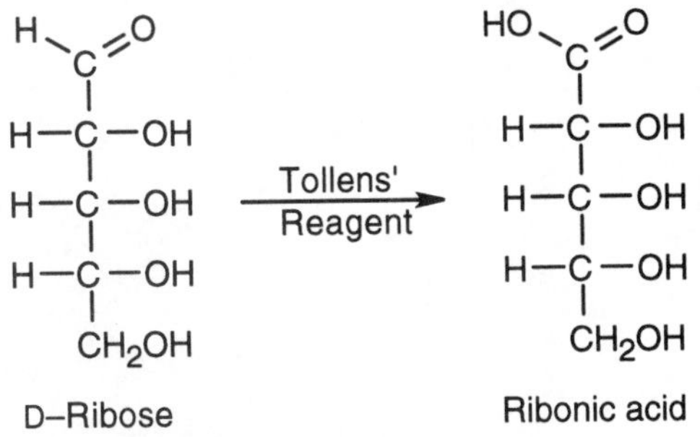

D–Ribose   Ribonic acid

22.56 A *glycoside* is the acetal product that results from reaction of the hemiacetal –OH group of a carbohydrate with an alcohol.

22.58

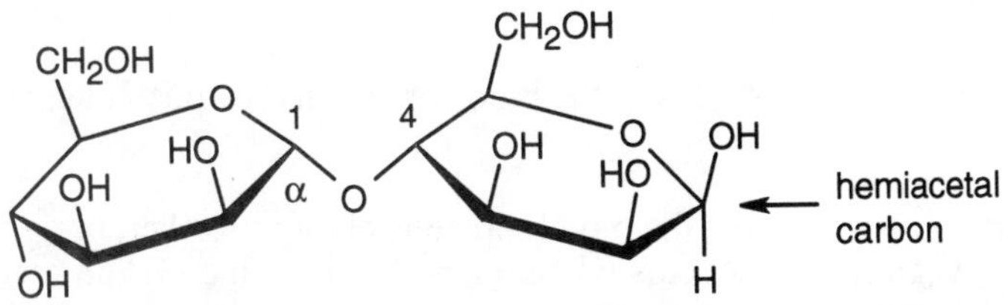

hemiacetal carbon

The product in this problem has a cyclic hemiacetal carbon and is in equilibrium with an open-chain aldehyde that is a reducing sugar. The glycosides in Problem 22.57 are acetals and are not in equilibrium with an aldehyde.

Disaccharides and Polysaccharides

22.60 Lactose and maltose have hemiacetal linkages that give positive Tollens' test results. Sucrose has no hemiacetal group and is thus unreactive toward Tollens' reagent.

22.62 Amylose and amylopectin are both components of starch and both consist of long polymers of α-D-glucose linked by α-1,4 glycosidic bonds. Amylopectin is much larger and has α-1,6 branches every 25 units or so along the chain.

22.64 Gentiobiose contains both an acetal grouping and a hemiacetal grouping. Gentiobiose is a reducing sugar because it has a hemiacetal group on the right-hand monosaccharide unit. A β-1,6 linkage connects the two monosaccharides.

22.66 Trehalose is a nonreducing sugar because it contains no hemiacetal linkages. The two D-glucose monosaccharides are connected by an α-1,1 acetal link.

22.68

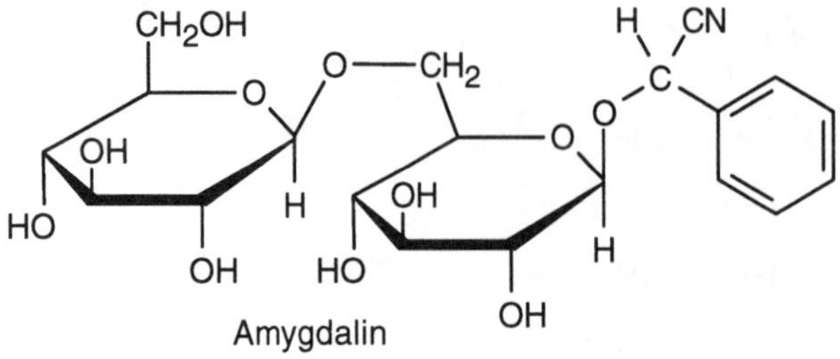

Amygdalin

Applications

22.70 Starch, a polysaccharide, is an example of a complex carbohydrate in the diet. Glucose and fructose are simple carbohydrates found in the diet. Soluble and insoluble fiber are complex carbohydrates that can't be hydrolyzed to simple carbohydrates and most of which pass undigested through the body.

22.72 Benedict's test detects all reducing sugars in the bloodstream and is thus not specific for glucose.

22.74 If incompatible blood types are mixed, the red blood cells clump together, or agglutinate, and death may result. Agglutination occurs when the body's immune system recognizes foreign cells and manufactures antibodies to them.

22.76 People with type O blood can receive blood only from other donors that have type O blood. People with type AB blood can give blood only to other people with type AB blood.

22.78 Pectin and vegetable gum are two kinds of soluble fiber, which can be found in fruits, barley, oats and beans.

General Questions and Problems

22.80

D-Ribose and D-xylose are diastereomers and differ in all properties listed.

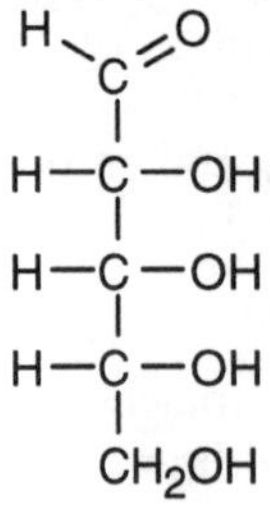

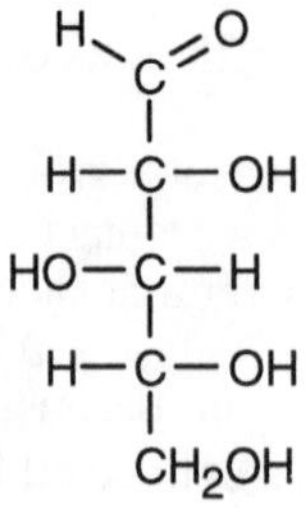

22.82

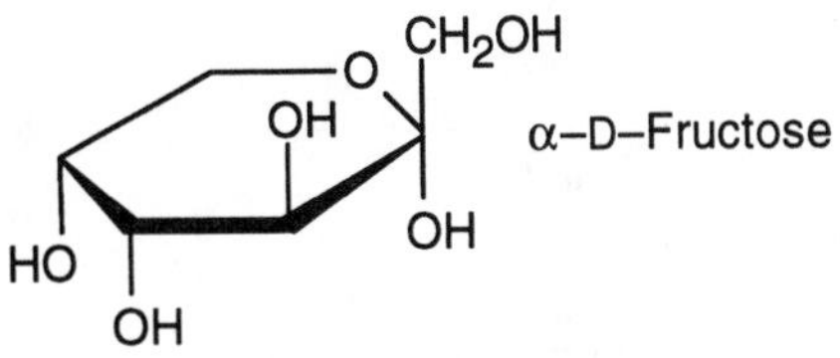

α–D–Fructose

22.84

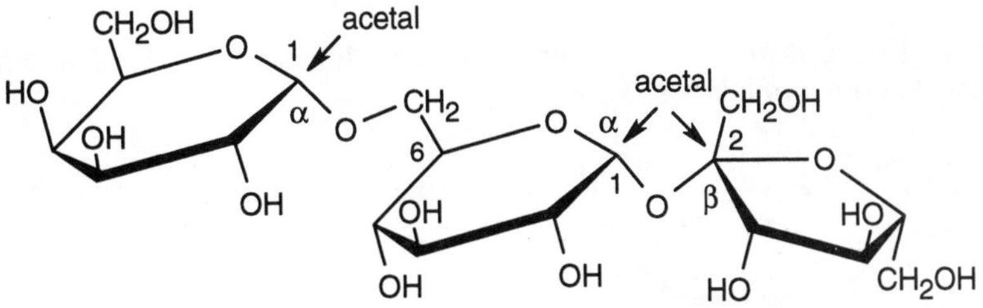

22.86 The sweet taste of a partially chewed cracker is due to the enzymatic breakdown of starch to glucose.

22.88 Symptoms of the disease galactosemia, which results when the body lacks an enzyme needed to digest galactose, include:
In infancy: vomiting, enlarged liver, failure to thrive.
Eventual: liver failure, mental retardation, cataracts.

22.90 Lactose intolerance is an inability to digest lactose. Symptoms include bloating, cramps and diarrhea.

22.92

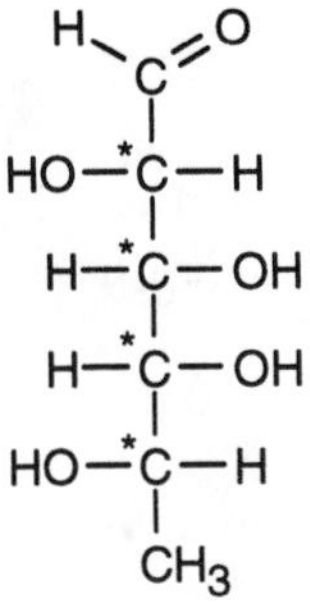

L–Fucose

L-fucose has four chiral carbons.

Self-Test for Chapter 22

Multiple choice:

1. One of these disaccharides is not a reducing sugar. Which one?
   (a) Sucrose   (b) Maltose   (c) Lactose   (d) Cellobiose

2. Which one of the following bonds doesn't occur in common polysaccharides?
   (a) α-1,4 bonds   (b) α-1,6 bonds   (c) β-1,4 bonds   (d) β-1,6 bonds

3. The compound shown is :
   (a) The α anomer of a ketopentose   (b) the α anomer of an aldohexose   (c) the β anomer of an aldopentose   (d) the β anomer of a ketohexose

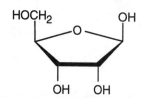

4. Oxidation of the aldotetroses pictured in Section 22.2 can be controlled to produce dicarboxylic acids known as tartaric acids. How many stereoisomeric tartaric acids are there?
   (a) 1   (b) 2   (c) 3   (d) 4

5. *N*-Acetyl-D-glucosamine is a component of all of the following, except:
   (a) chitin   (b) blood group determinants   (c) tendons   (d) heparin

6. Humans can't digest cellulose because:
   (a) Its molecules are too big.   (b) Humans don't produce enzymes to digest polysaccharides.
   (c) Humans can't digest branched polysaccharides.   (d) Human enzymes that digest carbohydrates can only hydrolyze α glycosidic bonds.

7. Which blood group is the "universal donor"?
   (a) A   (b) B   (c) AB   (d) O

8. Which of the following polysaccharides consists of only α-1,4 glycosidic bonds?
   (a) amylopectin   (b) cellulose   (c) amylose   (d) glycogen

9. Which of these errors of carbohydrate metabolism is not life-threatening?
   (a) galactosemia   (b) lactose intolerance   (c) diabetes mellitus   (d) blood-group incompatibility

10 How many stereoisomers does an open-chain 2-ketopentose have?
   (a) 2   (b) 4   (c) 6   (d) 8

Complete the following sentences:

1. An object that has handedness is said to be _____.

2. Starch molecules are digested by enzymes called _____.

3. The two mirror image forms of a chiral molecule are called _____.

4. A reaction between an aldehyde carbonyl group and an alcohol hydroxyl group in the same molecule yields a _____ _____.

5. *Levulose* is another name for _____.

6. _____ and _____ are two kinds of starch.

7. The reaction of a monosaccharide with an alcohol yields a _____.

8. _____ is used for food storage in animals.

9. D-Glucose can be classified as a _____.

10. 3-Pentanol is an _____ molecule.

11. A _____ is a stereoisomer that is not an enantiomer.

12. _____ have important functions at cell surfaces.

Tell whether the following statements are true or false:

1. All naturally-occurring carbohydrates are chiral.

2. Glucose is a reducing sugar.

3. In an L sugar, the –OH on the carbon nearest to the carbonyl group points to the left.

4. Humans can digest polysaccharides containing β-1,4 acetal links but not α-1,4 acetal links.

5. Achiral objects possess a plane of symmetry.

6. Crystalline glucose is a mixture of α anomer, β anomer, and open-chain forms.

7. Sucrose contains both acetal and hemiacetal groups.

8. Amylopectin and glycogen contain 1,4 and 1,6 acetal links.

9. An acetal is an ester.

10. Maltose is a disaccharide composed of glucose and galactose.

11. Two diastereomers rotate plane-polarized light in equal amounts but in opposite directions.

12. Not all compounds with n chiral carbons have 2^n stereoisomers.

Match the entries on the left with their partners on the right:

1. Maltose   (a) Aldohexose

2. Cellulose   (b) Glucose

3. Methyl glucoside   (c) Aldotriose

4. Ribose   (d) Glucose + fructose

5. Fructose   (e) Glucose + glucose

6. Glycogen   (f) Polysaccharide of α-D-glucose

7. Dextrose   (g) Glucose + galactose

8. Glucose   (h) Aldopentose

9. Sucrose   (i) Ketohexose

10. Lactose   (j) Acetal

11. Glyceraldehyde   (k) Animal starch

12. Amylose   (l) Polysaccharide of β-D-glucose

Chapter 23 – Carbohydrate Metabolism

Chapter Outline

I. Introduction to carbohydrate metabolism (Sections 23.1–23.2).
   A. Digestion of carbohydrates (Section 23.1).
      1. Digestion is the breakdown of food into small molecules.
      2. The products of digestion are absorbed from the intestinal tract.
      3. Digestion of carbohydrates.
         a. α–Amylase in the mouth breaks starch into smaller polysaccharides and maltose.
         b. α–Amylase in the small intestine further breaks down polysaccharides.
         c. Disaccharides are broken down to monosaccharides in the small intestine.
   B. Overview of glucose metabolism (Section 23.2).
      1. *Glycolysis* is the conversion of glucose to pyruvate; it occurs when energy is needed.
      2. *Glycogenesis* is the synthesis of glycogen from glucose; it occurs when excess glucose is present.
      3. The *pentose phosphate pathway* supplies other monosaccharides; it occurs when these are in short supply.
      4. *Glycogenolysis* is the breakdown of glycogen to glucose units; it occurs when the body needs glucose.
      5. Pyruvate has several fates:
         a. Under normal circumstances, pyruvate is converted to acetyl-SCoA.
         b. When oxygen is lacking, pyruvate is converted to lactate.
         c. When the body is starved for glucose, pyruvate is converted to glucose via *gluconeogenesis*.
II. Glycolysis and pyruvate metabolism (Sections 23.3–23.6).
   A. Glycolysis is the breakdown of glucose to two pyruvates (Section 23.3).
      Glycolysis occurs in the cytosol.
   B. Steps in glycolysis:
      1. Steps 1–3: Phosphorylation.
         a. Step 1: Glucose moves into the cell and is converted to glucose 6-phosphate, with the expenditure of one ATP.
         b. Step 2: Glucose 6-phosphate is isomerized to fructose 6-phosphate.
         c. Step 3: Fructose 6-phosphate is converted to fructose 1,6-bisphosphate, with the expenditure of one ATP.
      2. Steps 4,5: Cleavage and isomerization.
         a. Step 4: Fructose 1,6-bisphosphate is cleaved to glyceraldehyde 3-phosphate and dihydroxyacetone phosphate in a reverse aldol reaction.
         b. Step 5: Dihydroxyacetone phosphate is isomerized to glyceraldehyde 3-phosphate.
      3. Steps 6–10: Energy generation.
         a. Step 6: Glyceraldehyde 3-phosphate is phosphorylated and oxidized to 1,3-bisphosphoglycerate: $NAD^+ \longrightarrow NADH/H^+$.
         b. Step 7: 1,3-Bisphosphoglycerate transfers a phosphate to ADP to yield 3-phosphoglycerate.
         c. Step 8: 3-Phosphoglycerate is isomerized to 2-phosphoglycerate.
         d. Step 9: 2-Phosphoglycerate is dehydrated to phosphoenolpyruvate.
         e. Step 10: Phosphoenolpyruvate transfers a phosphate group to ADP to yield ATP and pyruvate.
   C. End results of glycolysis.
      1. Conversion of glucose to 2 pyruvates.
      2. Production of 2 ATPs.

3. Production of 2 NADH/H$^+$.

D. Entry of other sugars into glycolysis (Section 23.4).
1. Fructose is converted to fructose 6-phosphate and enters glycolysis.
2. Mannose is converted to fructose 6-phosphate and enters glycolysis.
3. Galactose is converted to glucose 6-phosphate and enters glycolysis.

E. Pyruvate metabolism (Section 25.5).
1. When oxygen is available, pyruvate is converted to acetyl-SCoA, with the conversion of NAD$^+$ to NADH/H$^+$ and the production of CO_2.
2. In yeast, pyruvate is converted to ethanol and CO_2.
3. Under anaerobic conditions, pyruvate is reduced to lactate, and NADH/H$^+$ is converted to NAD$^+$.

F. Energy output in complete catabolism of glucose (Section 23.6).
1. The total energy output from glucose metabolism is the combined result of:
    a. Glycolysis.
    b. Pyruvate —> acetyl-SCoA.
    c. Citric acid cycle of two acetyl-SCoA molecules (and passage of the resulting reduced coenzymes through the respiratory chain).
    d. Passage of two reduced coenzymes from glycolysis through the respiratory chain.
2. The number of ATPs produced depends on:
    a. The number of electrons that enter the respiratory chain from reduced coenzymes.
    b. The number of ATPs produced per reduced coenzyme.
    c. An estimated 30–38 ATPs are produced per mol glucose catabolized.

III. Regulation of glucose metabolism (Sections 23.7–23.9).
A. Regulation of glucose concentration in the blood (Section 23.7).
1. Hypoglycemia: low blood sugar.
    The hormone glucagon stimulates breakdown of glycogen to glucose to raise blood sugar.
2. Hyperglycemia: high blood sugar.
    The hormone insulin stimulates passage of glucose into cells to be used in energy production.

B. Fasting and starvation (Section 23.8).
1. First, glucose is released from glycogen.
2. Then, glucose is synthesized from proteins via gluconeogenesis.
3. Then, fats are metabolized to acetyl-SCoA, which enters the citric acid cycle.
4. As the citric acid cycle is overloaded, acetyl-SCoA is removed by formation of ketone bodies.
5. Ultimately, the body produces 50% of ATP from ketone bodies.
6. The body can endure this state for months.

C. *Diabetes mellitus* (Section 23.9).
1. There are two types of *diabetes mellitus*.
    a. In Type I (juvenile), the pancreas produces insufficient insulin.
        i. Juvenile diabetes is an autoimmune disease, in which insulin-producing cells are destroyed.
        ii. Juvenile diabetes is treated by supplying insulin.
    b. In Type II (adult-onset), insulin doesn't aid the passage of glucose across the cell membrane.
        i. Adult-onset diabetes results when cell receptors fail to recognize insulin.
        ii. Drugs that increase insulin levels are an effective treatment.
2. Complications of diabetes
    a. Cataracts may result from buildup of sorbitol in the eye.
    b. Ketoacidosis is caused by buildup of acidic ketones.
    c. Hypoglycemia may be due to an overdose of insulin or to failure to eat.

IV. Other pathways of carbohydrate metabolism (Sections 23.10–23.12).
   A. Glycogen metabolism (Section 23.10).
      1. Glycogenesis.
         a. Glycogenesis occurs when glucose levels are high.
         b. The pathway to glycogen synthesis:
            Glucose —> Glucose 6-phosphate —> Glucose 1-phosphate —>
            Glucose-UDP —> Glycogen
      2. Glycogenolysis.
         a. Glycogenolysis occurs when there is an immediate need for energy.
         b The pathway of glycogenolysis:
            Glycogen —> Glucose 1-phosphate —> Glucose 6-phosphate —> Glucose
   B. Gluconeogenesis (Section 23.11).
      1. Gluconeogenesis is the synthesis of glucose from any of several small molecules,
         including lactate, pyruvate, amino acids and glycerol.
      2. Gluconeogenesis occurs when the body is starved for glucose.
      3. Seven of the steps of gluconeogenesis are reversals of glycolysis steps.
         a. The other three steps are too endergonic, and alternate pathways must be used.
         b. Step 1 of gluconeogenesis:
            Pyruvate —> Oxaloacetate —> Phosphoenolpyruvate
         c. Oxaloacetate is an intermediate that allows amino acids to enter gluconeogenesis.
   C. Pentose phosphate pathway (Section 23.12).
      1. The pentose phosphate pathway produces carbohydrate intermediates for useful
         biomolecules, such as NADPH and ribose.
      2. The pentose phosphate pathway occurs near sites where lipid metabolism takes place.
      3. The pathway consists of two steps:
         a. The oxidative step: Glucose 6-phosphate + $NADP^+$ —> Ribulose 5-phosphate +
            CO_2 + 2 $NADPH/H^+$
         b. The nonoxidative step: Ribulose 5-phosphate —> Ribose 5-phosphate
         c. In addition, other 3-, 4-, 5- or 7-carbon monosaccharides can be produced.
         d. The ultimate products are glyceraldehyde 3-phosphate and fructose 6-phosphate.
      4. Uses of the pentose phosphate pathway.
         a. When NADPH demand is high, intermediates are recycled to glucose 6-phosphate
            for NADPH production.
         b. When ATP demand is high, intermediates are recycled to glycolysis.
         c. When nucleic acids need to be synthesized, ribose 5-phosphate is produced.

Solutions to Chapter 23 Problems

23.1 (a) Lactose + H_2O $\xrightarrow{\text{Lactase}}$ Glucose + Galactose

      (b) Sucrose + H_2O $\xrightarrow{\text{Sucrase}}$ Glucose + Fructose

23.2 (a) *Glycogenolysis* is the release of glucose units from glycogen.

      (b) *Gluconeogenesis* is the synthesis of glucose from pyruvate or other noncarbohydrates.

      (c) *Glycogenesis* is the synthesis of glycogen from glucose.

23.3 The following synthetic pathways have glucose 6-phosphate as their first reactant:
      Glycogenesis: synthesis of glycogen from glucose
      Pentose phosphate pathway: synthesis of five-carbon sugars from glucose
      Glycolysis: conversion of glucose to pyruvate

23.4 (1) In *Step 6*, 1,3-bisphosphoglycerate is synthesized. In *Step 7*, the energy is harvested in ATP as 3-phosphoglycerate is formed.

(2) In *Step 9*, phosphoenolpyruvate is synthesized. In *Step 10*, the energy is harvested in ATP as pyruvate is formed.

23.5 The following steps of glycolysis are isomerizations:

Step 2: Glucose 6-phosphate → Fructose 6-phosphate

Step 5: Dihydroxyacetone phosphate → Glyceraldehyde 3-phosphate

Step 8: 3-Phosphoglycerate → 2-Phosphoglycerate

23.6

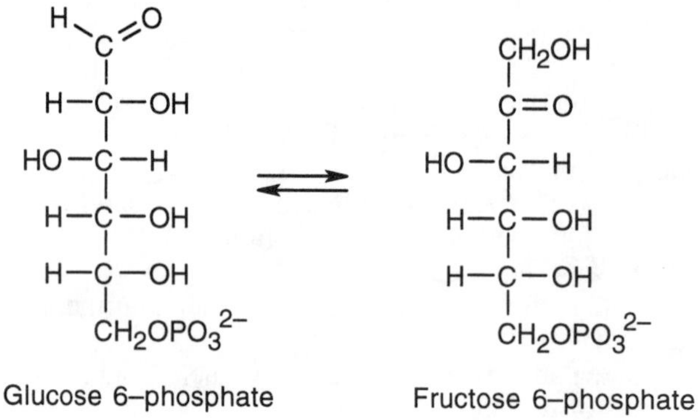

Glucose 6–phosphate   Fructose 6–phosphate

23.7

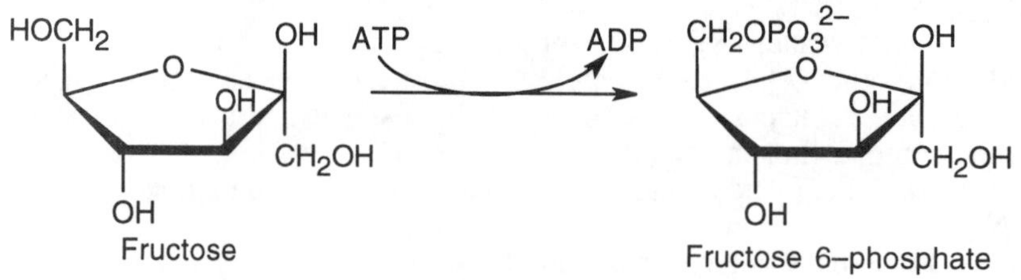

Fructose   Fructose 6–phosphate

Fructose 6-phosphate enters glycolysis at step 3.

23.8

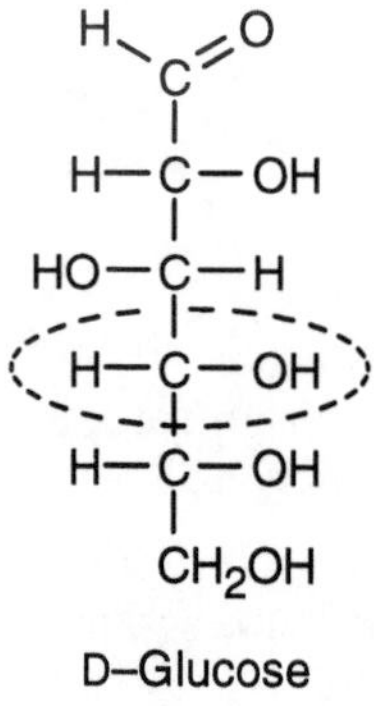

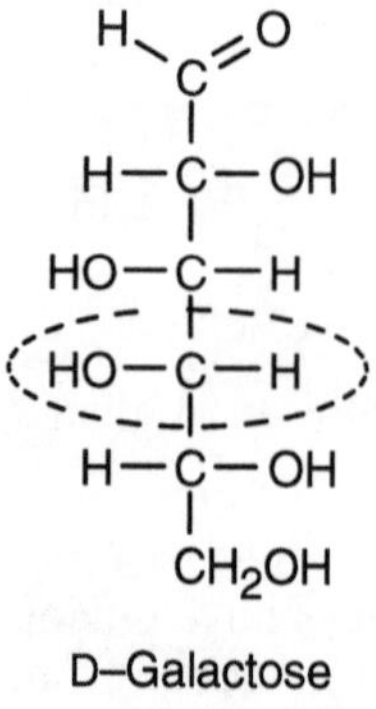

D–Glucose   D–Galactose

Glucose and galactose differ in configuration at carbon 4.

23.9 One molecule of CO_2 is formed when one molecule of pyruvate is converted to acetyl–SCoA. Two more molecules of CO_2 are formed in the citric acid cycle; one is formed in the conversion isocitrate —> α-ketoglutarate (Step 3), and the other is formed in the conversion α-ketoglutarate —> succinyl-SCoA (Step 4). Since each glucose provides two pyruvates (and thus two acetyl-SCoAs), a total of 6 CO_2 are formed.

23.10 When blood glucose concentration decreases, the level of the hormone glucagon increases. Glucagon stimulates the breakdown of liver glycogen and the release of glucose into the bloodstream to be used in gluconeogenesis. As glycogen is used up, triacylglycerols are hydrolyzed. The resulting glycerol can enter gluconeogenesis, and the fatty acids are available for fatty acid catabolism.

23.11

$$CH_2OH$$
$$H-C-OH$$
$$HO-C-H$$
$$H-C-OH$$
$$H-C-OH$$
$$CH_2OH$$

Sorbitol

Sorbitol can't form a cyclic hemiacetal because it doesn't have a carbonyl group.

23.12 $UTP + \text{Glucose 1-phosphate} \rightarrow \text{Glucose-UDP} + P_2O_7^{4-}$ $\Delta G = +1.1$ kcal/mol

$P_2O_7^{4-} + H_2O \rightarrow 2\ HOPO_3^{2-}$ $\Delta G = -8.0$ kcal/mol

———

$UTP + \text{Glucose 1-phosphate} + H_2O \rightarrow \text{Glucose-UDP} + 2\ HOPO_3^{2-}$ $\Delta G = -6.9$ kcal/mol

The common intermediate for these two reactions is $P_2O_7^{4-}$ (pyrophosphate). ΔG for the coupled reactions is –6.9 kcal/mol, indicating an exergonic overall reaction and a favorable free-energy change.

23.13

$$CH_2OH$$ $$CH_2OPO_3^{2-}$$ $$CH_2OPO_3^{2-}$$
$$H-C-OH$$ phosphorylation $$H-C-OH$$ oxidation $$C=O$$
$$CH_2OH$$ $\xrightarrow{}$ $$CH_2OH$$ $\xrightarrow{}$ $$CH_2OH$$

Glycerol   Glycerol 3–phosphate   Dihydroxyacetone phosphate

23.14 Each of the three glucose 6-phosphate molecules yields one CO_2 and one ribulose 5-phosphate molecule. Reactions of the three ribulose 5-phosphate molecules produce two fructose 6-phosphate molecules and one glyceraldehyde 3-phosphate molecule.

Understanding Key Concepts

23.15 Most of the enzymes involved with digestion are hydrolases, which catalyze the hydrolysis bonds in large molecules to produce smaller molecules.

23.16 (a) The *pentose phosphate pathway* operates when either ribose 5-phosphate or the reduced coenzyme NADPH are needed.
  (b) *Glycogenesis* occurs when the concentration of glucose in the blood is high and the body doesn't need glucose for energy production.
  (c) *Hydrolysis to free glucose* takes place when free glucose is needed in cells in other parts of the body. (Only free glucose can be transported in the blood.)
  (d) *Glycolysis* occurs when the body needs energy and the supply of glucose is adequate.

23.17 The energy investments made when glucose is converted to glucose 6-phosphate (Step 1) and when fructose 1-phosphate is converted to fructose 1,6-bisphosphate (Step 3) produce the phosphorylated intermediates needed in later stages of glycolysis. These intermediates take part in the reactions that ultimately repay the initial energy investment. A reverse aldol reaction at Step 4 generates the two three-carbon molecules whose transformations result in the formation of pyruvate.

23.18 (a) Pyruvate is directed to *gluconeogenesis* when the body needs glucose and both glucose and glycogen are in short supply. Gluconeogenesis takes place in the liver.
  (b) Pyruvate is *converted to lactate* in muscles and in red blood cells, under anaerobic conditions.
  (c) Pyruvate enters into the *citric acid cycle* when the body needs energy. To enter the cycle, pyruvate is first converted to acetyl-SCoA in mitochondria.
  (d) In yeast, pyruvate yields *ethanol and CO_2* in the absence of oxygen.

23.19

Step	Enzyme	Class
1	Hexokinase	transferase
2	Glucose 6-phosphate isomerase	isomerase
3	Phosphofructokinase	transferase
4	Aldolase	lyase
5	Triose phosphate isomerase	isomerase
6	Glyceraldehyde 3-phosphate dehydrogenase	oxidoreductase,transferase
7	Phosphoglycerate kinase	transferase
8	Phosphoglycerate mutase	isomerase
9	Enolase	lyase
10	Pyruvate kinase	transferase

Transferases are the most common class of enzymes in glycolysis because several reactions involve phosphate transfers to ADP and from ATP. Ligases are not represented among the enzymes of glycolysis because ligases are involved with the synthesis of larger molecules from smaller molecules, with the expenditure of ATP. Glycolysis is a pathway for the breakdown of larger molecules to smaller molecules, with the eventual generation of ATP.

23.20 (1) Insulin levels rise (d).
  (2) Glucose is taken up by cells (f)
  (3) Glycolysis occurs to replenish ATP supplies (a).
  (4) Glycogen synthesis occurs (glycogenesis) if there is excess glucose (g).
  (5) Blood levels pass through normal to below normal (hypoglycemic) (c).
  (6) Glucagon is secreted (b).
  (7) The liver releases glucose into the bloodstream (e).

23.21 In the absence of oxygen, the pyruvate product of catabolism of the glucose in wine is fermented by yeast enzymes to ethanol and CO_2, which increased the pressure in the bottle and popped the cork.

23.22 Compounds available for gluconeogenesis include pyruvate, lactate, many amino acids, glycerol and intermediates of the citric acid cycle, especially oxaloacetate. The conversion of fatty acids to glucose occurs in plants, where fatty acids stored in seeds can be used as a source of carbohydrate after germination . Unlike plants, animals don't need carbohydrates as structural materials and are able to obtain the carbohydrates they need from food.

Digestion and Metabolism

23.24 Maltose $+ H_2O \xrightarrow{\text{Maltase}}$ 2 Glucose

This process occurs in the mucous lining of the small intestine.

23.26 The major monosaccharide products of digestion are glucose, fructose and galactose.

23.28 Under aerobic conditions, pyruvate forms acetyl-SCoA.
Under anaerobic conditions, pyruvate forms lactate.
Under fermentation conditions, pyruvate forms ethanol and CO_2.

23.30 In *glycogenolysis*, the breakdown of glycogen produces glucose when it is needed.
In *glycogenesis*, glycogen is synthesized from glucose when glucose is in excess.

Glycolysis

23.32 The NADH generated in glycolysis can enter two pathways. (1) NADH can be reoxidized to NAD^+ in the conversion of pyruvate to lactate under anaerobic conditions. (2) Under aerobic conditions, NADH can enter the electron transport chain, where it is reoxidized to NAD^+ and ATP is produced.

23.34 Gluconeogenesis occurs in the cytosol of the liver.

23.36 (a) Glycolysis of 1 mol glucose produces 2 mol ATP as a result of substrate-level phosphorylation. (Actually, 4 mol ATP are produced by substrate-level phosphorylation, but 2 mol ATP are consumed in steps 1 and 3 of glycolysis.)
(b) Aerobic conversion of pyruvate to acetyl-SCoA doesn't produce ATP by substrate-level phosphorylation.
(c) One mol of acetyl-SCoA produces 1 mol ATP by substrate-level phosphorylation. Most of the ATP produced in the citric acid cycle results from passage of the reduced coenzymes NADH and $FADH_2$ through the electron-transport chain.

23.38

$$\underset{\text{Lactate}}{CH_3\overset{\overset{\displaystyle OH}{|}}{C}H-\overset{\overset{\displaystyle O}{||}}{C}-O^-} \xrightarrow[\underset{\text{dehydrogenase}}{\text{Lactate}}]{NAD^+ \quad NADH/H^+} \underset{\text{Pyruvate}}{CH_3\overset{\overset{\displaystyle O}{||}}{C}-\overset{\overset{\displaystyle O}{||}}{C}-O^-}$$

23.40 Catabolism of one mole of sucrose produces four moles of acetyl-SCoA.

Regulation of Glucose Metabolism / Metabolism in Diabetes Mellitus

23.42 Insulin is released when blood glucose levels are high and results in passage of glucose into cells, where it is metabolized. Glucagon is released when blood glucose levels are low and results in breakdown of glycogen in the liver to produce glucose.

23.44 Acetyl-SCoA is converted to ketone bodies to prevent buildup in the cells.

23.46 In diabetes, glucose in the eyes and extremities is converted to sorbitol, which can't be transported out of cells. This elevated sorbitol level changes the osmolarity of tissues and causes cataracts and gangrene.

23.48 *Juvenile diabetes* is caused by insufficient production of insulin in the pancreas. *Adult onset diabetes* is caused by the failure of cell membrane receptors to recognize insulin.

23.50 Unlike liver cells, muscle cells lack an enzyme that converts glucose 6-phosphate to glucose, which can pass into the bloodstream. Consequently the glucose 6-phosphate product of glycogenolysis in muscle cells enters directly into glycolysis.

23.52 The exact reverse of an energetically favorable reaction must be energetically unfavorable. Since glycogenolysis is energetically favorable, its exact reverse must be energetically unfavorable. Thus, glycogenesis must occur by an alternate pathway that is energetically favorable.

Glucose Anabolism

23.54 Lactate and pyruvate are two molecules that can serve as starting materials for glucose synthesis.

23.56 Several steps of the exact reverse of the energetically favorable conversion of glucose to pyruvate are energetically unfavorable.

23.58

If the body needs: then	*Fate of intermediates in pentose phosphate pathway:*
NADPH	Intermediates are recycled to glucose 6-phosphate for further production of NADPH.
ATP	Fructose 6-phosphate and glyceraldehyde 3-phosphate enter glycolysis.
Nucleic acid synthesis	Ribose 5-phosphate is the major product.

Applications

23.60 Plaque is composed of glycoproteins from saliva, bacteria, dextran and polysaccharide storage granules released by the bacteria.

23.62 The fasting level of glucose in a diabetic is 140 mg/dL or greater, as compared to an average level of 90 mg/dL for a nondiabetic.

23.64 Creatine phosphate quickly provides ATP in one step, whereas glucose metabolism takes many steps to provide ATP.

23.66 *First used* ————————————————————> *Last used*
ATP, creatine phosphate, glucose, glycogen, fatty acids from triacylglycerols

General Questions and Problems

23.68 Pyruvate can cross the mitochondrial membrane because it is the only molecule in glycolysis that is not a phosphate. (Phosphates can't cross the mitochondrial membrane.)

23.70 Fructose and glucose have the same net ATP production because fructose can be phosphorylated to form fructose 6-phosphate, which can enter glycolysis directly as a glycolysis intermediate.

23.72 (a) The net reaction is exergonic. The endergonic reaction galactose → glucose 1-phosphate is coupled with the energetically favorable consumption of ATP.
(b) The size of the energy yield depends on the energy requirements of the isomerization glucose 1-phosphate → glucose 6-phosphate, but the overall energy yield from glycolysis of galactose should be approximately the same as that from glycolysis of glucose.
(c) Besides galactokinase, an isomerase is involved in this process.
(d) The net production of energy from catabolism of lactose is very similar to that from catabolism of sucrose.

Self-Test for Chapter 23

Multiple choice:

1. The synthesis of glucose from small molecules is called:
(a) glycolysis (b) glucogenesis (c) gluconeogenesis (d) glycogenesis

2. Which one of the following substances can cross cell membranes?
(a) glucose 6-phosphate (b) ATP (c) glucose (d) acetyl-SCoA

3. The synthesis of glycogen occurs in the:
(a) liver and bloodstream (b) liver and muscles (c) liver and pancreas (d) muscles and pancreas

4. The exact reverse of which of the following steps of glycolysis also occurs in gluconeogenesis?
(a) glucose —> glucose 6-phosphate (b) phosphoenolpyruvate —> pyruvate
(c) fructose 6-phosphate —> fructose 1,6-bisphosphate
(d) 3-phosphoglycerate —> 2-phosphoglycerate

5. When the body needs to synthesize nucleic acids:
(a) The nonoxidative phase of the pentose phosphate path is bypassed. (b) The synthesis of NADPH is increased. (c) Glucose 6-phosphate enters glycolysis. (d) Three-, four-, or seven-carbon sugars are produced.

6. After several weeks of starvation, the body's principal energy source is:
(a) protein (b) fat (c) carbohydrate (d) all three

7. Type I *diabetes mellitus* is a disorder of:
   (a) insufficient insulin production   (b) faulty glucose metabolism   (c) autoimmune response
   (d) all three

8. Which of the following is not a route for pyruvate metabolism in the human body?
   (a) conversion to acetyl-SCoA   (b) reduction to lactate   (c) fermentation to alcohol
   (d) reformation of glucose

9. Glycogenesis resembles glycogenolysis in that:
   (a) both require the coenzyme UTP   (b) both occur when glucose is in good supply
   (c) both are stimulated by the hormone epinephrine   (d) both involve glucose 6-phosphate as
   an intermediate

10. Which of the following monosaccharides doesn't enter glycolysis?
    (a) ribose   (b) mannose   (c) galactose   (d) fructose

Complete the following sentences:

1. The _____ – _____ pathway is another name for glycolysis.

2. Step __ of glycolysis involves an oxidation and a phosphorylation.

3. _____ _____ _____catalyzes the formation of acetyl-SCoA from pyruvate.

4. _____ aids in the passage of blood glucose across cell membranes.

5. The first step of glycogenolysis is the formation of _____.

6. Steps ___ are known as the energy investment part of glycolysis..

7. The metabolic response to _____ resembles starvation.

8. _____ and _____ supply the energy for gluconeogenesis.

9. When pyruvate is converted to acetyl-SCoA, one molecule of _____ is lost.

10. The isomerization of glucose 6-phosphate to fructose 6-phosphate is catalyzed by _____.

11. The hormone _____ stimulates breakdown of glycogen.

12. _____ may be due to an overdose of insulin.

Tell whether the following statements are true or false:

1. The pentose phosphate pathway is important because it produces NADH.

2. Fructose, galactose, and mannose can all enter the glycolysis pathway.

3. Conversion of glucose 6-phosphate to fructose 6-phosphate requires ATP.

4. Glycogenesis is the exact reverse of glycogenolysis.

5. Hyperglycemia is a high level of blood glucose.

6. The reactions of glycolysis occur in the mitochondria.

7. 36 ATPs are produced for each glucose that passes through the glycolysis pathway.

8. Glucagon is the storage form of glucose.

9. All three transformations of pyruvate occur in the human body.

10. Cleavage of fructose 1,6-diphosphate yields two molecules of glyceraldehyde 3-phosphate.

11. Pyruvate is converted to lactate under anaerobic conditions.

12. Each conversion of glyceraldehyde 3-phosphate to pyruvate requires two ADPs.

Match the entries on the left with their partners on the right:

1. Glycolysis

2. Hyperglycemia

3. Enolase

4. Glycogenolysis

5. UDP-glucose

6. Ribose 5-phosphate

7. Gluconeogenesis

8. Ethanol

9. Hypoglycemia

10. Glycogenesis

11. Lactate

12. Aldolase

(a) Formed by fermentation of pyruvate

(b) Formed from pyruvate under anaerobic conditions

(c) Intermediate in glycogen synthesis

(d) Synthesis of glucose from pyruvate

(e) Catalyzes the cleavage of fructose 1,6-diphosphate

(f) Low blood sugar

(g) Synthesis of glycogen from glucose

(h) Product of pentose phosphate pathway

(i) Catalyzes loss of water from 2-phosphoglyceric acid

(j) Breakdown of glycogen to glucose

(k) High blood sugar

(l) Breakdown of glucose to pyruvate

Chapter Outline

I. Structure and classification of lipids (Section 24.1).
    A. Lipids are defined by solubility in nonpolar solvents.
    B. Classification of lipids.
        1. Triacylglycerols.
        2. Waxes.
        3. Glycerophospholipids.
        4. Sphingolipids.
        5. Steroids and eicosanoids.
II. Fatty acids and their esters (Sections 24.2–24.4).
    A. Fatty acids (Section 24.2).
        1. Fatty acids are long-chain carboxylic acids.
        2. Fatty acids are classified by the number of double bonds they have.
            a. Fatty acids with no double bonds are saturated.
            b. Fatty acids with one double bond are monounsaturated.
            c. Fatty acids with more than one double bond are polyunsaturated.
    B. Waxes are esters of long-chain alcohols with fatty acids.
    C. Fats and oils.
        1. Fats and oils are mixtures of esters of glycerol with three fatty acids and are known as triacylglycerols.
        2. Properties of fats and oils (Section 24.3).
            a. Hydrophobic.
            b. Uncharged.
            c. Melting point is determined by the length of the fatty acid side chains and the number of double bonds.
                i.   Solid fats have saturated fatty acid side chains.
                ii. Liquid fats have unsaturated fatty acid side chains.
        3. Reactions of triacylglycerols (Section 24.4).
            a. Hydrogenation.
                Control of hydrogenation determines the consistency of a fat.
            b. Hydrolysis.
                  i.   In the body, enzymes catalyze hydrolysis of triacylglycerols.
                ii. In the laboratory, strong aqueous base is used.
                iii. The resulting fatty acid salts are called soaps.
                iv. Soaps clean because the polar end dissolves in water and the nonpolar end dissolves in grease.
                v.   Soap molecules cluster together in water to form micelles; grease is trapped in the middle of a micelle.
III. Cell membrane lipids (Sections 24.5–24.6).
    A. Phospholipids (Section 24.5).
        1. Glycerophospholipids
            a. Glycerophospholipids are esters of glycerol with two fatty acids and a phosphate group that is bonded to one of a number of different compounds containing an –OH group.
            b. The phospholipid with choline as a phosphate ester is a lecithin.
                i.   Lecithins are components of cell membranes.
                ii. Lecithin is often used as an emulsifying agent.

2. Sphingolipids and other membrane lipids.
   a. Sphingolipids are derivatives of the amino alcohol sphingosine.
   b. Sphingolipids consist of:
      i. An amide bond between a fatty acid and sphingosine.
      ii. A phosphate ester also bonded to choline.
   c. Sphingomyelins are sphingolipids that are constituents of the coating around nerve fibers.
B. Glycolipids resemble sphingolipids, except that the phosphate group at C1 is replaced by a carbohydrate.
   1. Cerebrosides have a monosaccharide at C1.
      Cerebrosides are found in cell membranes.
   2. Gangliosides have a small polysaccharide at C1.
      Gangliosides are components of neurotransmitters and receptors.
C. Cholesterol (Section 24.6).
   1. Cholesterol has a tetracyclic steroid structure.
   2. Cholesterol serves as a starting material for steroid hormones.
   3. Cholesterol is a component of cell membranes that helps maintain the structure of the membrane.
IV. Cell membranes (Sections 24.7–24.8).
A. Structure of cell membranes (Section 24.7).
   1. Cell membranes are composed of two parallel layers of phospholipids, called a *lipid bilayer.*
   2. The nonpolar tails are clustered in the middle, and the polar heads point inward and outward.
   3. The fluid-mosaic model of a cell membrane explains the more complex structural details.
      a. Glycolipids and cholesterol are in the lipid part and provide membrane structure.
      b. Glycoproteins (20%) mediate the action of cell contents with the outer environment.
         i. Some proteins form channels to allow specific molecules to enter or leave.
         ii. Glycoproteins that extend through the bilayer are called integral proteins.
         iii. Glycoproteins that are partially embedded are peripheral proteins.
         iv. The carbohydrate portions act as receptors for enzymes and neurotransmitters.
      c. The membrane is fluid and doesn't rupture.
         Fluidity of the membrane increases with the amounts of saturated and unsaturated fatty acids in the lipid portion.
B. Transport across cell membranes (Section 24.8).
   1. Passive transport.
      a. Simple diffusion.
         i. Gases and small nonpolar molecules diffuse through the bilayer.
         ii. Small hydrophilic molecules pass through channels formed by integral proteins.
      b. Facilitated diffusion.
         Facilitated diffusion is passive transport, but proteins help solutes to pass across the membrane.
   2. Active transport.
      a. Ions and other substances that maintain concentration gradients inside and outside the cell move by active transport.
      b. Active transport requires an expenditure of energy and involves changing the shape of an integral protein.
V. Eicosanoids (Section 24.9).
A. General information.
   1. Eicosanoids are derivatives of 20-carbon fatty acids.
   2. Eicosanoids are synthesized from arachidonic acid.
   3. Eicosanoids are short-term messengers.

B. There are three classes of eicosanoids.
  1. Thromboxanes promote aggregation of blood platelets during clotting.
  2. Prostaglandins.
     a. Prostaglandins consist of a five-membered ring with two side chains.
     b. Biological effects include blood pressure lowering, stimulation of uterine contractions, and lowering the extent of gastric secretions.
  3. Leukotrienes mediate inflammatory and allergic responses.

Solutions to Chapter 24 Problems

24.1

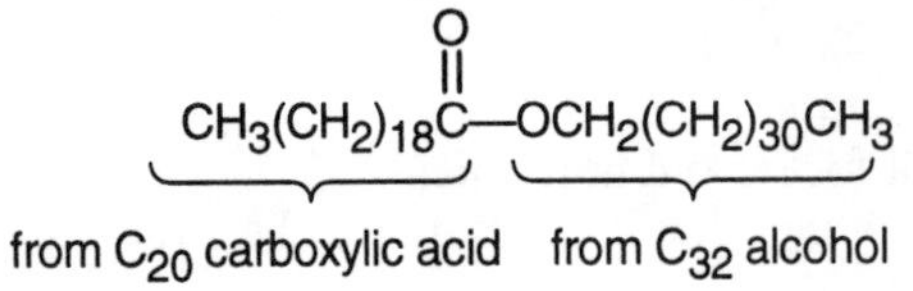

$$CH_3(CH_2)_{18}\overset{O}{\overset{\|}{C}}-OCH_2(CH_2)_{30}CH_3$$

from C_{20} carboxylic acid   from C_{32} alcohol

24.2

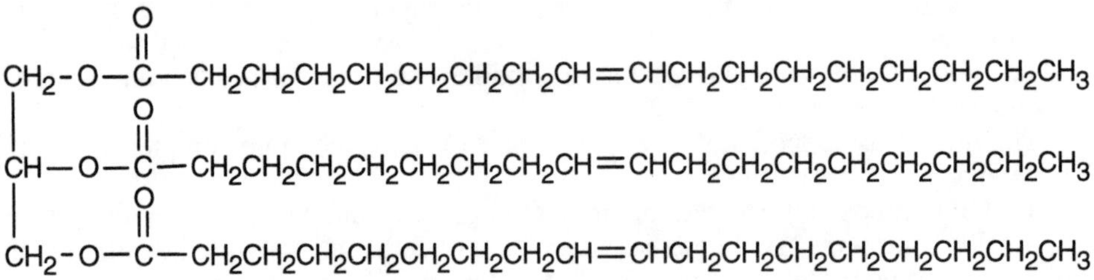

$$CH_2-O-\overset{O}{\overset{\|}{C}}-CH_2CH_2CH_2CH_2CH_2CH_2CH_2CH=CHCH_2CH_2CH_2CH_2CH_2CH_2CH_2CH_3$$

$$CH-O-\overset{O}{\overset{\|}{C}}-CH_2CH_2CH_2CH_2CH_2CH_2CH_2CH=CHCH_2CH_2CH_2CH_2CH_2CH_2CH_2CH_3$$

$$CH_2-O-\overset{O}{\overset{\|}{C}}-CH_2CH_2CH_2CH_2CH_2CH_2CH_2CH=CHCH_2CH_2CH_2CH_2CH_2CH_2CH_2CH_3$$

Glyceryl trioleate

24.3

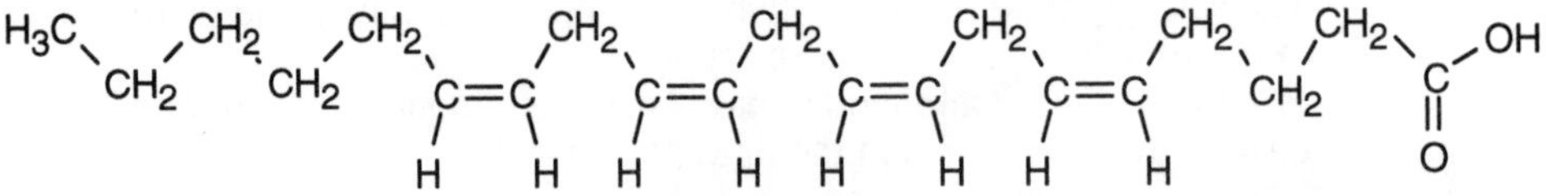

Arachidonic acid

24.4 Fatty acid (b) has a higher melting point because it is more saturated. Fatty acid (a) has more double bonds, which make it difficult for molecules of (a) to form crystals and which lower its melting point.

24.5 The starred carbon of the triacylglycerol pictured below is bonded to four different groups and is chiral. (Whenever two different fatty acids are bonded to carbon 1 and carbon 3 of glycerol, carbon 2 is chiral.)

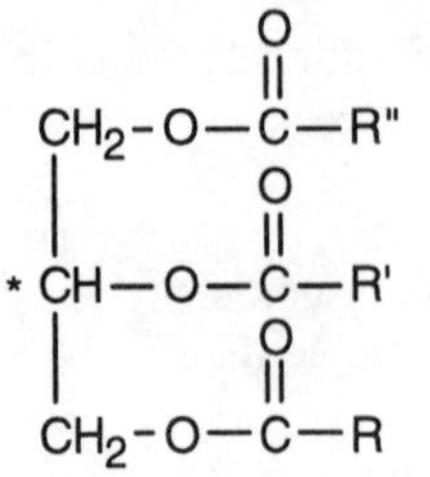

$$CH_2-O-\overset{O}{\overset{\|}{C}}-R''$$

$$*CH-O-\overset{O}{\overset{\|}{C}}-R'$$

$$CH_2-O-\overset{O}{\overset{\|}{C}}-R$$

24.6   Glyceryl trioleate (Problem 24.2)

$$\downarrow \begin{array}{l} 3\ H_2 \\ \text{catalyst} \end{array}$$

$$CH_2\text{-}O\text{-}\overset{\overset{\displaystyle O}{\|}}{C}\text{-}CH_2CH_2CH_2CH_2CH_2CH_2CH_2CH_2CH_2CH_2CH_2CH_2CH_2CH_2CH_2CH_2CH_3$$

$$CH\text{-}O\text{-}\overset{\overset{\displaystyle O}{\|}}{C}\text{-}CH_2CH_2CH_2CH_2CH_2CH_2CH_2CH_2CH_2CH_2CH_2CH_2CH_2CH_2CH_2CH_2CH_3$$

$$CH_2\text{-}O\text{-}\overset{\overset{\displaystyle O}{\|}}{C}\text{-}CH_2CH_2CH_2CH_2CH_2CH_2CH_2CH_2CH_2CH_2CH_2CH_2CH_2CH_2CH_2CH_2CH_3$$

Glyceryl tristearate

The acyl groups of the above triacylglycerol are derived from stearic acid.

24.7

$$\left[CH_3(CH_2)_7CH{=}CH(CH_2)_7\text{-}\overset{\overset{\displaystyle O}{\|}}{C}\text{-}O^- \right]_2 Ca^{2+} \qquad \text{Calcium oleate}$$

24.8

$$CH_2\text{-}O\text{-}\overset{\overset{\displaystyle O}{\|}}{C}\text{-}(CH_2)_{16}CH_3$$
$$CH\text{-}O\text{-}\overset{\overset{\displaystyle O}{\|}}{C}\text{-}(CH_2)_{16}CH_3$$
$$CH_2\text{-}O\text{-}\overset{\overset{\displaystyle O}{\|}}{C}\text{-}(CH_2)_7CH{=}CH(CH_2)_7CH_3$$

or

$$CH_2\text{-}O\text{-}\overset{\overset{\displaystyle O}{\|}}{C}\text{-}(CH_2)_{16}CH_3$$
$$CH\text{-}O\text{-}\overset{\overset{\displaystyle O}{\|}}{C}\text{-}(CH_2)_7CH{=}CH(CH_2)_7CH_3$$
$$CH_2\text{-}O\text{-}\overset{\overset{\displaystyle O}{\|}}{C}\text{-}(CH_2)_{16}CH_3$$

$$\downarrow \ NaOH,\ H_2O$$

$$\begin{array}{l} CH_2OH \\ CHOH \\ CH_2OH \end{array} + \ 2\ CH_3(CH_2)_{16}\text{-}\overset{\overset{\displaystyle O}{\|}}{C}\text{-}O^-Na^+ + \ CH_3(CH_2)_7CH{=}CH(CH_2)_7\text{-}\overset{\overset{\displaystyle O}{\|}}{C}\text{-}O^-Na^+$$

24.9

(a)

$$CH_2\text{-}O\text{-}\overset{\overset{\displaystyle O}{\|}}{C}\text{-}R$$
$$CH\text{-}O\text{-}\overset{\overset{\displaystyle O}{\|}}{C}\text{-}R'$$
$$CH_2\text{-}O\text{-}\overset{\overset{\displaystyle O}{\|}}{P}\text{-}O\text{-}CH_2CH_2\overset{+}{N}(CH_3)_3$$
$$O^-$$

$$\xrightarrow{\ NaOH,\ H_2O\ }$$

$$\begin{array}{l} CH_2OH \\ CHOH \\ CH_2OH \\ \text{Glycerol} \end{array} + \begin{array}{l} R\text{-}\overset{\overset{\displaystyle O}{\|}}{C}\text{-}O^-Na^+ \quad \longleftarrow \text{Fatty acid salt} \\ R'\text{-}\overset{\overset{\displaystyle O}{\|}}{C}\text{-}O^-Na^+ \\ HO\text{-}CH_2CH_2\overset{+}{N}(CH_3)_3 \\ \text{Choline} \end{array} + \begin{array}{l} \overset{\overset{\displaystyle O}{\|}}{^-O\text{-}P\text{-}O^-} \\ O^- \\ \text{Phosphate} \end{array}$$

R' is an unsaturated hydrocarbon group, and R is a saturated hydrocarbon group.

(b)

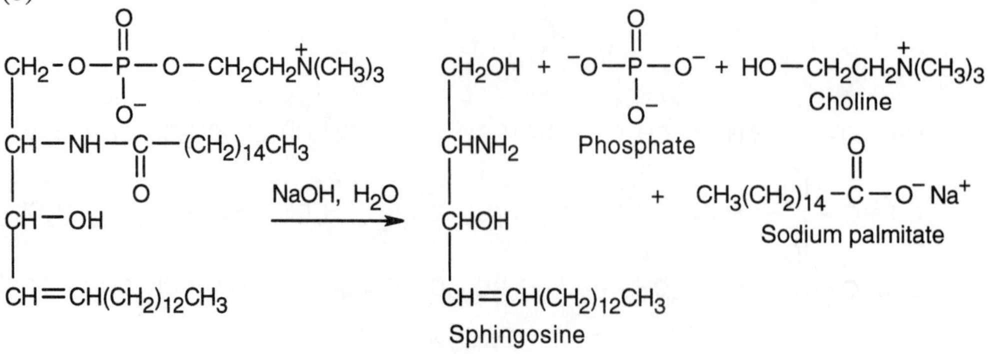

$$CH_2-O-\overset{\overset{\displaystyle O}{\|}}{\underset{\underset{\displaystyle O^-}{|}}{P}}-O-CH_2CH_2\overset{+}{N}(CH_3)_3$$

$$\underset{\underset{\displaystyle O}{\|}}{CH-NH-C}-(CH_2)_{14}CH_3$$

$$CH-OH$$

$$CH=CH(CH_2)_{12}CH_3$$

$\xrightarrow{\text{NaOH, H}_2\text{O}}$

$$CH_2OH \ + \ ^-O-\overset{\overset{\displaystyle O}{\|}}{\underset{\underset{\displaystyle O^-}{|}}{P}}-O^- \ + \ HO-CH_2CH_2\overset{+}{N}(CH_3)_3$$

Choline

$$CHNH_2 \quad \text{Phosphate}$$

$$CHOH$$

$$+ \quad CH_3(CH_2)_{14}-\overset{\overset{\displaystyle O}{\|}}{C}-O^- Na^+$$

Sodium palmitate

$$CH=CH(CH_2)_{12}CH_3$$

Sphingosine

24.10

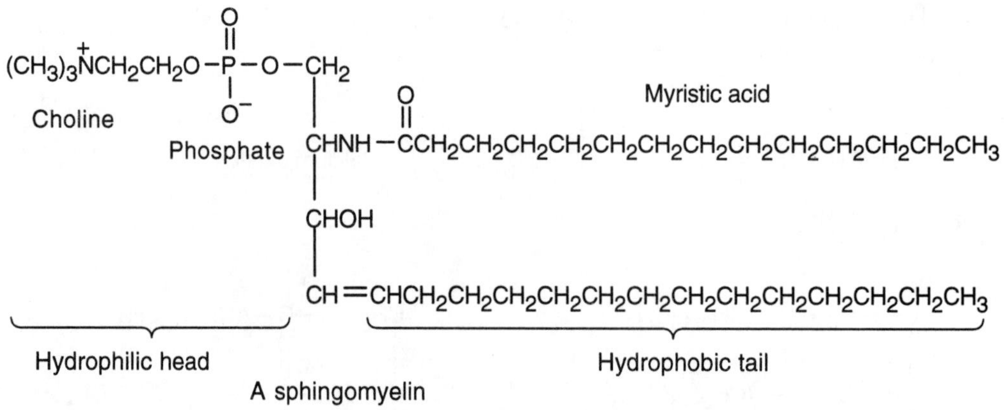

$$(CH_3)_3\overset{+}{N}CH_2CH_2O-\overset{\overset{\displaystyle O}{\|}}{\underset{\underset{\displaystyle O^-}{|}}{P}}-O-CH_2$$

Choline

Phosphate

$$CHNH-\overset{\overset{\displaystyle O}{\|}}{C}CH_2CH_2CH_2CH_2CH_2CH_2CH_2CH_2CH_2CH_2CH_2CH_2CH_3 \qquad \text{Myristic acid}$$

$$CHOH$$

$$CH=CHCH_2CH_2CH_2CH_2CH_2CH_2CH_2CH_2CH_2CH_2CH_2CH_3$$

Hydrophilic head   Hydrophobic tail

A sphingomyelin

24.11

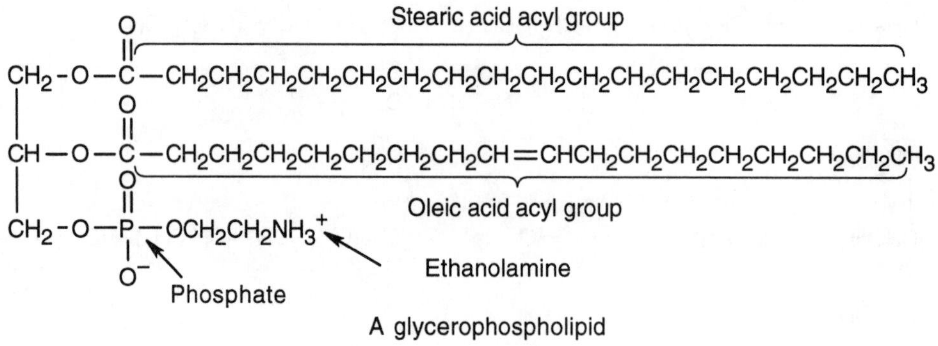

Stearic acid acyl group

$$CH_2-O-\overset{\overset{\displaystyle O}{\|}}{C}-CH_2CH_2CH_2CH_2CH_2CH_2CH_2CH_2CH_2CH_2CH_2CH_2CH_2CH_2CH_2CH_2CH_3$$

$$CH-O-\overset{\overset{\displaystyle O}{\|}}{C}-CH_2CH_2CH_2CH_2CH_2CH_2CH_2CH=CHCH_2CH_2CH_2CH_2CH_2CH_2CH_2CH_3$$

Oleic acid acyl group

$$CH_2-O-\overset{\overset{\displaystyle O}{\|}}{\underset{\underset{\displaystyle O^-}{|}}{P}}-OCH_2CH_2NH_3^+$$

Phosphate   Ethanolamine

A glycerophospholipid

24.12

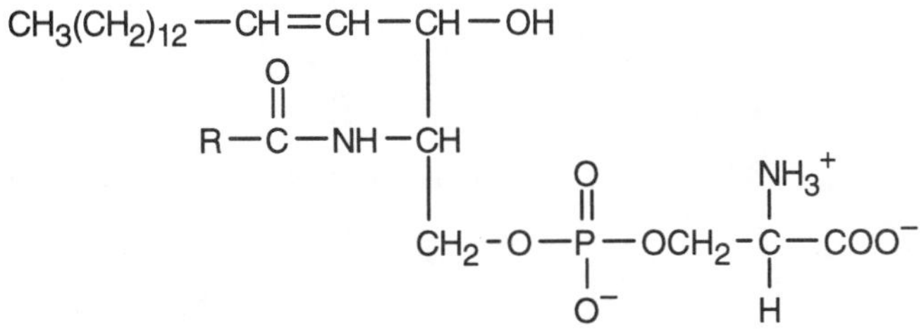

The illustrated structure is a phospholipid (a) because it contains a phosphate group. It is a sphingolipid (c) because it has a sphingosine backbone. It is a lipid (e) because it is soluble in nonpolar solvents. It contains a phosphate ester group (f).

24.13 You would predict that NO would cross a lipid bilayer by simple diffusion because it is small and relatively nonpolar.

24.14 Glucose 6-phosphate has a charged phosphate group and can't pass through the hydrophobic lipid bilayer.

Understanding Key Concepts

24.15 The triacylglycerol that has the highest melting point has the greatest percent of saturated fatty acids. Of the four fatty acids listed, palmitic acid and stearic acid are saturated, and oleic acid and linoleic acid are unsaturated. Thus, if you add the percentages in the table, you arrive at a new table.

Triacylglycerol	*Percent saturated fatty acids*	*Percent unsaturated fatty acids*
Triacylglycerol A	49.2%	47.5%
Triacylglycerol B	28.9%	70.8%
Triacylglycerol C	19.5%	76.8%

This table shows that Triacylglycerol A has the highest melting point. Triacylglycerols B and C are probably liquids at room temperature because their fatty acid composition more closely resembles that of the oils in Table 24.2 than that of the animal fats.

24.16 Three of the fatty acids in the table shown in the previous problem are C_{18} fatty acids (stearic acid, oleic acid, and linoleic acid). When the triacylglycerols are hydrogenated, the unsaturated fatty acids are converted to stearic acid. The composition of the triacylglycerols after hydrogenation can be found by adding the percentages of C_{18} fatty acids.

Triacylglycerol	*Percent C_{16} fatty acids*	*Percent C_{18} fatty acids*
Triacylglycerol A	21.4%	75.3%
Triacylglycerol B	12.2%	87.5%
Triacylglycerol C	11.2%	85.1%

After hydrogenation, triacylglycerol B would be composed of 12.2% palmitic acid and 87.5% stearic acid. The hydrogenation product of triacylglycerol B closely resembles the hydrogenation product of triacylglycerol C because they have similar percentages of C_{16} fatty acids and C_{18} fatty acids.

24.17

$$CH_2OC(CH_2)_{16}CH_3 \quad \xrightarrow[H_2O]{NaOH,} \quad CH_2OH \quad Na^+ \; {}^-OC(CH_2)_{16}CH_3$$

The fatty acid salts that are most likely to be found in soap made from lard are sodium palmitate, sodium stearate, and sodium oleate. Other fatty acid salts may also be present.

24.18

The membrane lipid is a glycerophospholipid that is a phosphatidylserine.

24.19 Because the membrane is fluid, rather than rigid, it is able to flow together after an injury, instead of shattering.

24.20 As in enzyme action, the interactions between the carrier protein and the substance to be transported in facilitated diffusion (transport across a membrane from regions of high concentration to regions of low concentration, using carrier proteins) are noncovalent. This interaction is similar to an enzyme–substrate interaction. Unlike an enzyme-mediated reaction, there is no energy input in facilitated diffusion. Active transport involves movement of substrates from regions of low concentration to regions of high concentration. Carrier proteins are also needed to move substrates against a concentration gradient, and energy must be supplied. The energy needed for active transport is provided by coupling transport to the conversion of ATP to ADP.

Waxes, Fats and Oils

24.22 There are many different structural kinds of lipids because many different types of naturally occurring molecules dissolve in nonpolar solvents.

24.24 *Saturated fatty acids* are long-chain carboxylic acids that contain no carbon–carbon double bonds. *Monounsaturated fatty acids* contain one carbon–carbon double bond. *Polyunsaturated fatty acids* contain two or more carbon–carbon double bonds.

24.26 Linoleic acid and linolenic acid are two essential fatty acids. Vegetable oils and nuts are good sources of these acids.

24.28 Saturated fatty acids are straight and can easily order themselves in a crystal. A double bond in a fatty acid produces a kink, which makes it more difficult for molecules to be arranged in a crystal, and thus a double bond lowers the melting point of the fatty acid. A cis fatty acid is lower melting than a trans fatty acid because a cis double bond produces a larger kink in a fatty acid hydrocarbon chain than a trans double bond produces.

24.30 Fats are composed of triacylglycerols containing both saturated and unsaturated fatty acids, are solids at room temperature, and are usually obtained from animal sources. Oils are made up of triacylglycerols containing mainly unsaturated fatty acids, are liquids at room temperature, and are obtained from plant sources.

24.32

$$CH_2-O-\overset{\overset{\displaystyle O}{\|}}{C}-CH_2CH_2CH_2CH_2CH_2CH_2CH_2CH_2CH_2CH_2CH_2CH_2CH_2CH_2CH_2CH_2CH_3 \quad \longleftarrow \text{Stearic acid}$$

$$CH-O-\overset{\overset{\displaystyle O}{\|}}{C}-CH_2CH_2CH_2CH_2CH_2CH_2CH_2CH_2CH_2CH_2CH_2CH_2CH_2CH_2CH_2CH_2CH_3 \quad \longleftarrow \text{Stearic acid}$$

$$CH_2-O-\overset{\overset{\displaystyle O}{\|}}{C}-CH_2CH_2CH_2CH_2CH_2CH_2CH_2CH_2CH_2CH_2CH_2CH_2CH_2CH_2CH_3 \quad \longleftarrow \text{Palmitic acid}$$

$$CH_2-O-\overset{\overset{\displaystyle O}{\|}}{C}-CH_2CH_2CH_2CH_2CH_2CH_2CH_2CH_2CH_2CH_2CH_2CH_2CH_2CH_2CH_2CH_2CH_3 \quad \longleftarrow \text{Stearic acid}$$

$$CH-O-\overset{\overset{\displaystyle O}{\|}}{C}-CH_2CH_2CH_2CH_2CH_2CH_2CH_2CH_2CH_2CH_2CH_2CH_2CH_2CH_2CH_3 \quad \longleftarrow \text{Palmitic acid}$$

$$CH_2-O-\overset{\overset{\displaystyle O}{\|}}{C}-CH_2CH_2CH_2CH_2CH_2CH_2CH_2CH_2CH_2CH_2CH_2CH_2CH_2CH_2CH_2CH_2CH_3 \quad \longleftarrow \text{Stearic acid}$$

In one isomer, palmitic acid forms an ester with the central hydroxyl group of glycerol; in the other, palmitic acid forms an ester with a terminal hydroxyl group. (The first isomer is chiral.)

24.34 A wax serves as a protective coating for fruits, berries, leaves, animal fur, and feathers.

24.36 Spermaceti is a wax.

Chemical Reactions of Lipids

24.38 If some, but not all, of the double bonds in corn oil were hydrogenated, the resulting product would be a semisolid fat that could be used as margarine.

24.40

$$CH_2-O-\overset{O}{\underset{||}{C}}-(CH_2)_{16}CH_3$$
$$CH-O-\overset{O}{\underset{||}{C}}-(CH_2)_7CH=CH(CH_2)_7CH_3 \qquad \xrightarrow{H_2,\ Pd\ catalyst}$$
$$CH_2-O-\overset{O}{\underset{||}{C}}-(CH_2)_7CH=CHCH_2CH=CHCH_2CH=CHCH_2CH_3$$

$$CH_2-O-\overset{O}{\underset{||}{C}}-(CH_2)_{16}CH_3$$
$$CH-O-\overset{O}{\underset{||}{C}}-(CH_2)_{16}CH_3 \qquad \text{Glyceryl tristearate}$$
$$CH_2-O-\overset{O}{\underset{||}{C}}-(CH_2)_{16}CH_3$$

Glyceryl tristearate is higher melting than the original lipid because it has fewer double bonds and can solidify easier.

Phospholipids, Glycolipids, and Cell Membranes

24.42 Glycerophospholipids have an ionic part (the *head*) and a nonpolar part (the *tail*). The ionic head protrudes outward toward the aqueous environment of the cell or inward toward the cell contents, and the nonpolar tails cluster together to form the membrane. Triacylglycerols don't have an ionic head and thus can't function as membrane components.

24.44 Sphingomyelins and glycolipids are two different kinds of sphingosine-based lipids.

24.46 In a soap micelle, the polar hydrophilic heads are on the exterior, and the hydrophobic tails cluster in the center. In a membrane bilayer, hydrophilic heads are on both the exterior and interior surfaces of the membrane, and the region between the two surfaces is occupied by hydrophobic tails.

24.48 If cell membranes were freely permeable, the concentrations of all substances would be the same on both sides of the cell membrane, and it would be impossible for cells to maintain concentration gradients.

24.50

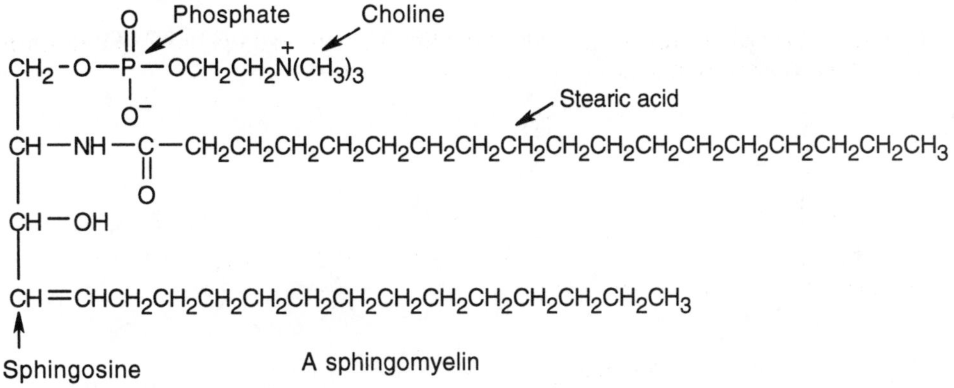
Phosphate
Choline
Stearic acid
Sphingosine
A sphingomyelin

24.52 Aqueous NaOH cleaves all ester bonds, including phosphate esters.

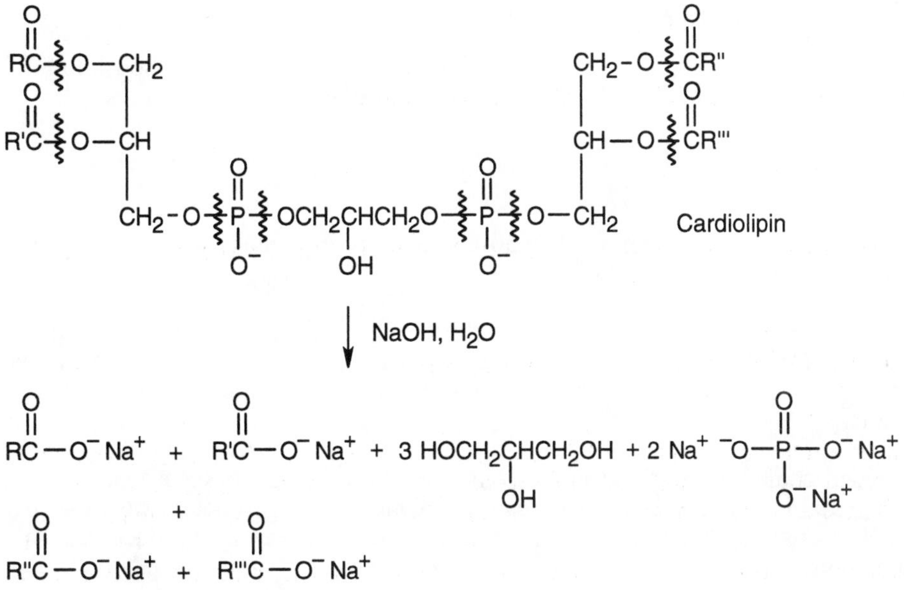
Cardiolipin
NaOH, H2O

24.54 In both simple diffusion and facilitated diffusion, substances cross cell membranes from areas of high concentration to areas of low concentration. In facilitated diffusion, substances are helped by proteins in crossing cell membranes.

Eicosanoids

24.56 A prostaglandin that stimulates uterine contractions is an example of an eicosanoid serving as a local hormone.

24.58

Thromboxane A$_2$ Arachidonic acid

Thromboxane A$_2$ is an eicosanoid. Arachidonic acid is the precursor of thromboxane A$_2$, just as it is the precursor of all other eicosanoids.

24.60 By transferring its acetyl group, aspirin inhibits the enzyme that is responsible for the first step in the conversion of arachidonic acid to prostaglandins.

Applications

24.62 According to the FDA, no more than 30% of daily caloric intake should come from fats and oils.

24.64 Detergents and soaps both have hydrocarbon "tails" and polar "heads," and both form micelles, in which the hydrocarbon "tails" surround greasy dirt and aggregate in the center of a cluster. The polar "heads" protrude into the aqueous medium and make the cluster soluble.

24.66 Branched-chain hydrocarbons are no longer used for detergents because they aren't biodegradable. Bacteria in sewage treatment plants can't digest detergents made from branched-chain hydrocarbons, and the undecomposed detergents produce suds in waterways.

24.68 Peanut oil and olive oil are the best sources of monounsaturated fatty acids.

24.70 An effective semiochemical must be volatile and structurally unique, so that it is species-specific.

General Questions and Problems

24.72 A lecithin (b), a sphingomyelin (d), a cerebroside (e) and glyceryl trioleate (f) are saponifiable lipids.

24.74

$$CH_2-O-\overset{\overset{\displaystyle O}{\|}}{C}-(CH_2)_7CH=CHCH_2CH=CHCH_2CH=CHCH_2CH_3$$

$$CH-O-\overset{\overset{\displaystyle O}{\|}}{C}-(CH_2)_7CH=CHCH_2CH=CHCH_2CH=CHCH_2CH_3$$

$$CH_2-O-\overset{\overset{\displaystyle O}{\|}}{C}-(CH_2)_{12}CH_3$$

or

$$CH_2-O-\overset{\overset{\displaystyle O}{\|}}{C}-(CH_2)_7CH=CHCH_2CH=CHCH_2CH=CHCH_2CH_3$$

$$CH-O-\overset{\overset{\displaystyle O}{\|}}{C}-(CH_2)_{12}CH_3$$

$$CH_2-O-\overset{\overset{\displaystyle O}{\|}}{C}-(CH_2)_7CH=CHCH_2CH=CHCH_2CH=CHCH_2CH_3$$

24.76 Cholesterol isn't saponifiable because it contains no ester linkages.

24.78 Sphingomyelins, cerebrosides, and gangliosides are abundant in brain tissue.

24.80 Prostaglandins can lower blood pressure, assist in blood clotting, stimulate uterine contractions, lower gastric secretions, and cause some of the pain and swelling associated with inflammation.

24.82

$$CH_2-O-\overset{\overset{\displaystyle O}{\|}}{C}-R$$
$$CH-O-\overset{\overset{\displaystyle O}{\|}}{C}-R' \ + \ 3\ NaOH \ \xrightarrow{H_2O}$$
$$CH_2-O-\overset{\overset{\displaystyle O}{\|}}{C}-R''$$

$$CH_2OH \qquad Na^+ \ {}^-O-\overset{\overset{\displaystyle O}{\|}}{C}-R$$
$$CHOH \ + \ Na^+ \ {}^-O-\overset{\overset{\displaystyle O}{\|}}{C}-R'$$
$$CH_2OH \qquad Na^+ \ {}^-O-\overset{\overset{\displaystyle O}{\|}}{C}-R''$$

Molar mass of fat = 1500 g

Molar mass of NaOH = 40 g

$$5.0 \text{ g oil } \times \ \frac{1 \text{ mol}}{1500 \text{ g}} \ = 3.3 \times 10^{-3} \text{ mol oil}$$

Since 3 mol of NaOH are needed to saponify 1 mol of oil, 9.9×10^{-3} mol of NaOH is needed to saponify 3.3×10^{-3} mol of oil.

$$9.9 \times 10^{-3} \text{ mol NaOH } \times \ \frac{40 \text{ g}}{1 \text{ mol}} \ = 0.39 \text{ g NaOH, or approximately 0.4 g NaOH}$$

Self-Test for Chapter 24

Multiple choice:

1. Small polar molecules pass through the lipid bilayer by:
    (a) simple diffusion through the lipid bilayer   (b) facilitated transfer   (c) active transport
    (d) simple diffusion through channels

2. Cholesterol is :
    (a) a male sex hormone   (b) a saponifiable lipid   (c) a component of cell membranes
    (d) common to plants and animals

3. Which of the following is not an effect of prostaglandins?
    (a) stimulation of allergic response   (b) lowering of blood pressure   (c) reduction of gastric
    secretions   (d) stimulation of uterine contractions

4. Active transport requires all of the following except:
    (a) the solutes to be nonpolar organic molecules   (b) the expenditure of ATP   (c) the need for
    cells to maintain a concentration gradient between the inside and the outside   (d) the assistance
    of integral proteins

5. Which of the following contain a glycosidic bond?
    (a) triacylglycerols   (b) sphingomyelins   (c) lecithins   (d) cerebrosides

6. The basic hydrolysis of which of the following triacylglycerols produces only polyunsaturated
    fatty acids?
    (a) glyceryl trioleate   (b) glyceryl tristearate   (c) glyceryl linoleate dioleate   (d) glyceryl
    trilinolenate

7. How many different triacylglycerols (including enantiomers!) can be formed from glycerol,
    two stearic acids and one oleic acid?
    (a) 1   (b) 2   (c) 3   (d) 4

8. Which of the following molecules aren't components of glycolipids?
    (a) sphingosine   (b) phosphate groups   (c) fatty acids   (d) sugars

9. A cell membrane is composed of all of the following except:
    (a) triacylglycerols   (b) phosphoglycerides   (c) sphingomyelins   (d) glycolipids

10. Waxes:
    (a) are triacylglycerols   (b) can be hydrolyzed by base   (c) contain no more than thirty carbons
    (d) are only produced by plants

Complete the following sentences:

1. A glycolipid contains an _____ link between sphingosine and a sugar.

2. _____ is a mixture of long-chain fatty acid salts.

3. The carboxylate end of a fatty acid is _____ and the organic chain end is _____.

4. _____ and _____ are two components of cell membranes.

5. The common model of a cell membrane is called the _____ _____ model.

6. Steroid structures are based on a _____ ring system.

7. Prostaglandins are synthesized in the body from a fatty acid called _____ acid.

8. Clusters of soap molecules in water are called _____.

9. _____ are phospholipids that are abundant in brain tissue.

10. Phospholipids aggregate in a closed, sheetlike membrane called a _____ _____.

11. _____ are a group of compounds derived from 20-carbon unsaturated fatty acids.

12. _____ proteins are involved with active transport across cell membranes.

Tell whether the following statements are true or false:

1. Lipids are defined by their physical properties, not by their structure.

2. Saturated fats are lower melting than unsaturated fats.

3. Sphingolipids contain a carboxylic acid ester group.

4. Cholesterol is synthesized by the human body.

5. Sphingosine is a component of both phospholipids and glycolipids.

6. When soap molecules are dissolved in water, they form a lipid bilayer.

7. Cholesterol is a hormone.

8. The main difference between fats and oil is in their melting points.

9. Cerebrosides are a major constituent of the coating around nerve fibers.

10. Waxes and fats are both carboxylic acid esters.

11. Leukotrienes are synthesized in the cells where they act.

12. Facilitated diffusion requires an energy investment.

Match the entries on the left with their partners on the right:

1. Decyl stearate

2. Prostaglandin

3. Choline

4. Stearic acid

5. Integral protein

6. Glyceryl trilaurate

7. Cerebroside

8. Oleic acid

9. Lecithin

10. Linoleic acid

11. Sphingomyelin

12. Peripheral protein

(a) Extends completely through the cell membrane

(b) Monounsaturated fatty acid

(c) Partially embedded in the cell membrane

(d) Phosphoglyceride

(e) Amino alcohol

(f) Saturated fatty acid

(g) Polyunsaturated fatty acid

(h) C_{20} acid with a five-membered ring

(i) Sphingolipid

(j) Fat

(k) Glycolipid

(l) Wax

Chapter 25 – Lipid Metabolism

Chapter Outline

I. Triacylglycerols (Sections 25.1–25.4).
  A. Digestion of triacylglycerols (Section 25.1).
    1. Triacylglycerols (TAGs) pass through the mouth unchanged.
    2. In the stomach, TAGs are broken down into small droplets.
    3. As TAGs pass into the intestines, lipases and bile are produced.
      a. Bile acids solubilize lipid droplets.
      b. Lipases hydrolyze lipids to mono- and diacylglycerols, fatty acids, and glycerol.
    4. Products of TAG digestion are absorbed through the intestinal wall.
      a. Smaller molecules are transported to the liver.
      b. Free fatty acids and acylglycerols are reconverted to triacylglycerols and packaged into lipoproteins (chylomicrons).
  B. Lipoproteins for lipid transport (Section 25.2).
    1. Triacylglycerols and fatty acids enter metabolism from 3 sources:
      a. Diet.
      b. Storage in adipose tissue.
      c. Synthesis in the liver.
    2. These lipids must be made soluble by association with lipoproteins.
    3. A lipoprotein is a globule of TAGs and fatty acids surrounded by a layer of phospholipids.
    4. Four kinds of lipoproteins are important.
      a. Chylomicrons carry lipids in the diet through the lymphatic system into the blood.
      b. VLDLs carry TAGs from the liver to tissues for storage or energy production.
      c. LDLs carry cholesterol from the liver to tissues.
      d. HDLs carry cholesterol from cells to the liver, where it is converted to bile acids.
  C. Metabolism of triacylglycerols (Section 25.3–25.4).
    1. Overview (Section 25.3).
      a. TAGs are hydrolyzed.
        i. TAGs in the diet are hydrolyzed by lipoprotein lipase in capillary walls in adipose tissue.
        ii. TAGs in adipocytes are hydrolyzed within the cells, and the fatty acids travel into the bloodstream with albumins.
      b. Glycerol is carried to the liver or kidneys.
        Glycerol is converted to dihydroxyacetone phosphate, which enters glycolysis or gluconeogenesis.
      c. Fatty acids have two fates.
        i. When energy is in good supply, fatty acids are converted to TAGs for storage.
        ii. When energy is needed, fatty acids are metabolized to acetyl-SCoA.
      d. Acetyl-SCoA is used for:
        i. Generation of energy via the citric acid cycle and oxidative phosphorylation.
        ii. Biosynthesis of fatty acids.
        iii. Production of ketone bodies.
    2. Storage and mobilization of TAGs (Section 25.4).
      a. When blood glucose are high, TAGs are synthesized for storage.
        i. The glycerol 3-phosphate needed is made from dihydroxyacetone phosphate, which comes from glycolysis.
        ii. The fatty acyl-SCoAs needed come from digestion or biosynthesis.

iii. Two fatty acyl-SCoAs are added to glycerol 3-phosphate.

iv. After removal of phosphate from glycerol 3-phosphate, the third fatty acyl-SCoA is added.

   b. When blood glucose levels are low, fatty acids and glycerol are released from adipocytes and enter the bloodstream.

II. Fatty acid oxidation (Sections 25.5–25.7).

  A. Steps in fatty acid oxidation (Section 25.5).

    1. Activation.

      a. Fatty acids react with HSCoA to form fatty acyl-SCoAs.

      b. At the same time, ATP is converted to AMP + 2 $HOPO_3^{2-}$.

    2. Transport.

    Fatty acyl-SCoAs are transported across the mitochondrial membrane via a shuttle mechanism involving carnitine.

    3. Oxidation (β Oxidation).

      a.

$$RCH_2CH_2\overset{\overset{\textstyle O}{\|}}{C}-SCoA \xrightarrow{\ FAD \quad FADH_2\ } RCH=CH\overset{\overset{\textstyle O}{\|}}{C}-SCoA$$

      b.

$$RCH=CH\overset{\overset{\textstyle O}{\|}}{C}-SCoA + H_2O \longrightarrow RCH\overset{\overset{\textstyle OH}{|}}{}CH_2\overset{\overset{\textstyle O}{\|}}{C}-SCoA$$

      c.

$$R\overset{\overset{\textstyle OH}{|}}{C}HCH_2\overset{\overset{\textstyle O}{\|}}{C}-SCoA \xrightarrow{\ NAD^+ \quad NADH/H^+\ } R\overset{\overset{\textstyle O}{\|}}{C}CH_2\overset{\overset{\textstyle O}{\|}}{C}-SCoA$$

      d.

$$R\overset{\overset{\textstyle O}{\|}}{C}CH_2\overset{\overset{\textstyle O}{\|}}{C}-SCoA \xrightarrow{\ HSCoA\ } R\overset{\overset{\textstyle O}{\|}}{C}-SCoA + CH_3\overset{\overset{\textstyle O}{\|}}{C}-SCoA$$

      e. An n-carbon fatty acid produces $n/2$ acetyl-SCoAs.

  B. Energy from fatty acid oxidation (Section 25.6).

    1. The number of molecules of ATP produced from a fatty acid that yields n acetyl-SCoA molecules is $17n-7$.

    2. Fats produce more than twice the amount of energy per unit weight than carbohydrates do.

  C. Production of ketone bodies (ketogenesis) (Section 25.7).

    1. Ketone bodies are formed when the body produces excess acetyl-SCoA.

    2. Synthesis of ketone bodies.

      a. 2 acetyl-SCoA —> acetoacetyl-SCoA + HSCoA

      b. acetoacetyl-SCoA + acetyl-SCoA —> 3-hydroxy-3-methylglutaryl-SCoA + HSCoA

      c. 3-hydroxy-3-methylglutaryl-SCoA —> acetyl-SCoA + acetoacetate

      d. acetoacetate + NADH/H$^+$ —> 3-hydroxybutyrate + NAD$^+$

      e. acetoacetate —> acetone + CO_2

    3. Catabolism of ketone bodies during starvation produces much of the energy that the body needs.

    4. When ketone bodies are formed faster than the body can utilize them, ketoacidosis occurs.

      In ketoacidosis, blood pH drops, ketone bodies are excreted in the urine, and coma and death may result.

III. Fatty acid biosynthesis (lipogenesis) (Section 25.8).

  A. Lipogenesis occurs when amino acids and carbohydrates are in good supply.

B. Lipogenesis resembles fatty acid oxidation but isn't its exact reverse.
   Lipogenesis occurs in the cytosol, and intermediates are carried by ACP.
C. Mechanism of lipogenesis.
   1. Condensation.
      a. acetyl-SCoA + HCO$_3^-$ —> H$_2$O + malonyl-SCoA
      b. malonyl-SCoA + HSACP —> malonyl-SACP + HSCoA
      c. acetyl-SCoA + HSACP —> acetyl-SACP + HSCoA
      d. acetyl-SACP + malonyl-SACP —> acetoacetyl-SACP + SACP
   2. Reduction, using NADPH/H$^+$
   3. Dehydration
   4. Reduction, using the coenzyme NADPH/H$^+$
   5. Addition of acetyl-SACP units, followed by steps 2–5, occurs until the chain is the correct length.

Solutions to Chapter 25 Problems

25.1

(a)

CH$_3$CH$_2$–CH$_2$CH$_2$–CH$_2$CH$_2$–CH$_2$CH$_2$–CH$_2$CH$_2$–CH$_2$CH$_2$–CH$_2$CH$_2$–CH$_2$COH

⟶ 8 CH$_3$C—SCoA

Seven β oxidations are needed.

(b)

CH$_3$CH$_2$–CH$_2$CH$_2$–CH$_2$CH$_2$–CH$_2$CH$_2$–CH$_2$CH$_2$–CH$_2$CH$_2$–CH$_2$CH$_2$–CH$_2$CH$_2$–CH$_2$CH$_2$–CH$_2$COH

⟶ 10 CH$_3$C—SCoA

Nine β oxidations are needed.

25.2 In the citric acid cycle, steps 6 (dehydrogenation of succinate to produce fumarate),7 (hydration of fumarate to produce malate),and 8 (oxidation of malate to produce oxaloacetate) are similar to the first three reactions of the β oxidation of a fatty acid.

25.3 The formation of 3-hydroxybutyrate from acetoacetate is a reduction (iii).

25.4 Two acetyl-SCoA molecules condense to form acetoacetyl-SCoA. A third acetyl-SCoA adds to them to form 3-hydroxy-3-methylglutaryl-SCoA, which is hydrolyzed to form acetoacetate, the first ketone body. Acetoacetate can either be reduced to form hydroxybutyrate, the second ketone body, or it can be decarboxylated to form acetone, the third ketone body.

Understanding Key Concepts

25.5 1. Lipids separate from other biomolecules and form lipid droplets (d).
2. Bile acids, phosphatidylcholine and cholesterol emulsify the dietary lipids into micelles (c).
3. Pancreatic lipase binds the polar coat of the micelles and catalyzes hydrolysis of TAGs (b).
4. TAGs are hydrolyzed into monoacylglycerols, fatty acids and glycerol (h).
5. Water-soluble fatty acids and glycerol pass through the villi into the bloodstream to the liver (a).
6. Water-insoluble larger fatty acids and acylglycerols enter intestinal mucosal cells (g).
7. Long-chain fatty acids are re-esterified to acylglycerols and glycerol to form TAGs for packaging into chylomicrons (f).
8. TAG-loaded chylomicrons enter the lymph system and slowly make their way to the thoracic duct and into the blood stream (e).

25.6 (a) HDL has the highest ratio of protein to lipid.
(b) Chylomicrons have the lowest density because they have the highest percentage of lipids, and lipids are less dense than protein.
(c) VLDL carries TAGs from the liver to peripheral tissue, where they are used either for storage or for energy generation.
(d) Chylomicrons carry TAGs from the diet.
(e) LDL carries cholesterol from the liver to peripheral tissue.
(f) HDL removes cholesterol from circulation and transports it to the liver, where it is converted to bile acids and excreted.
(g) LDL contains "bad" cholesterol, which is deposited in tissues and contributes to atherosclerosis.

25.7 1. Fatty acid activation to fatty acyl-SCoA (c).
2. Fatty acyl-carnitine formation from fatty acyl-SCoA (b).
3. Transport of fatty acyl-carnitine into mitochondria (g).
4. Exchange of fatty acyl group from carnitine to acetyl-SCoA (h).
5. FAD-linked dehydrogenation (e).
6. Addition of water across a double bond (f).
7. NAD$^+$-linked dehydrogenation (a).
8. Cleavage to acetyl-SCoA and fatty acyl-SCoA (d).
9. Citric acid cycle oxidation of acetyl-SCoA (i).

25.8

A	B	C

high blood glucose / high glucagon / low insulin / fatty acid and TAG synthesis

low blood glucose \ high insulin / low glucagon \ TAG hydrolysis and fatty acid oxidation

25.9 In fatty acid oxidation, as in glucose catabolism, there is an initial energy investment. Conversion of a fatty acid to a fatty acid-SCoA is coupled with the conversion of ATP to AMP and pyrophosphate, which is subsequently hydrolyzed to two hydrogen phosphate ions. This energy investment is equivalent to the two ATPs spent in the early stages of glucose catabolism.

25.10 When oxaloacetate in liver is used for gluconeogenesis, less oxaloacetate is available for the citric acid cycle, and less acetyl-SCoA is able to enter the cycle. Instead, there is a buildup of acetyl-SCoA in the bloodstream. Heart and muscle use the excess acetyl-SCoA for synthesis of ketone bodies. Buildup of ketone bodies leads to ketoacidosis, in which blood pH is lowered and the odor of acetone is noticeable in urine and on the breath. Ketoacidosis can lead to dehydration, labored breathing, and death.

25.11 The "carbon calories" that enter fatty acid biosynthesis are in the form of acetyl-SCoA, which can originate from catabolism of fats, carbohydrates or proteins. The "reducing calories" come from NADPH, which is produced in the pentose phosphate pathway by the conversion of glucose 6-phosphate to ribulose 5-phosphate. Since practically all food is catabolized to acetyl-SCoA, it doesn't matter where the excess calories come from.

Digestion and Catabolism of Lipids

25.12 Lipids make you feel full because they slow the rate of movement of food through the stomach.

25.14 Bile emulsifies lipid droplets so that they can be attacked by enzymes.

25.16 Acylglycerols and fatty acids are rejoined and combined into *chylomicrons*, which are lipoproteins used to transport lipids from the diet into the bloodstream.

25.18 Fatty acids from adipose tissue are carried in the bloodstream by albumins.

25.20 For each molecule of glycerol, 5.5 molecules of ATP are released in forming pyruvate. One ATP results from the conversion of glycerol to glyceraldehyde-3-phosphate, and 4.5 more arise from the conversion of glyceraldehyde-3-phosphate to pyruvate (2 substrate-level phosphorylations, which produce 2 ATP, and production of one NADH, which enters the electron transport chain to produce 2.5 more ATP).

25.22 An adipocyte is a cell, almost entirely filled with fat globules, in which TAGs are stored and mobilized.

25.24 Fatty acid oxidation occurs primarily in heart, liver and muscle cells.

25.26 A fatty acid is converted to its fatty acyl-SCoA in order to activate it for catabolism.

25.28 Stepwise oxidation of fatty acids is known as β oxidation because the carbon β to the –SCoA group (2 carbons away from the –SCoA group) is oxidized in the process.

25.30 Each cycle of β oxidation produces 4 molecules of ATP (2.5 from the formation of the reduced coenzyme NADH and 1.5 from the formation of the reduced coenzyme $FADH_2$), plus one molecule of acetyl-SCoA, which enters into the citric acid cycle to yield 10 more molecules of ATP, for a total of 14.

25.32

(a)

$$CH_3CH_2CH_2CH_2CH_2\overset{\overset{\displaystyle O}{\|}}{C}SCoA \xrightarrow[\substack{Acyl-SCoA \\ dehydrogenase}]{FAD \quad FADH_2} CH_3CH_2CH_2CH=CH\overset{\overset{\displaystyle O}{\|}}{C}SCoA$$

(b)

$$CH_3CH_2CH_2CH=CH\overset{\overset{\displaystyle O}{\|}}{C}SCoA + H_2O \xrightarrow[\substack{hydratase}]{Enoyl-SCoA} CH_3CH_2CH_2\overset{\overset{\displaystyle OH}{|}}{C}HCH_2\overset{\overset{\displaystyle O}{\|}}{C}SCoA$$

(c)

$$CH_3CH_2CH_2\overset{\overset{\displaystyle OH}{|}}{C}HCH_2\overset{\overset{\displaystyle O}{\|}}{C}SCoA \xrightarrow[\substack{\beta-Hydroxyacyl-SCoA \\ dehydrogenase}]{NAD^+ \quad NADH/H^+} CH_3CH_2CH_2\overset{\overset{\displaystyle O}{\|}}{C}CH_2\overset{\overset{\displaystyle O}{\|}}{C}SCoA$$

(d)

$$CH_3CH_2CH_2\overset{\overset{\displaystyle O}{\|}}{C}CH_2\overset{\overset{\displaystyle O}{\|}}{C}SCoA \xrightarrow[\substack{Acetyl-SCoA \\ transferase}]{HSCoA} CH_3CH_2CH_2\overset{\overset{\displaystyle O}{\|}}{C}SCoA + CH_3\overset{\overset{\displaystyle O}{\|}}{C}SCoA$$

25.34 The number of moles of acetyl-SCoA produced from one mole of fatty acid is half the number of carbons in the acid. The number of cycles of β oxidation is one less than the number of moles of acetyl-SCoA produced.

Acid	Acetyl-SCoA Produced	Number of cycles
(a) $CH_3(CH_2)_6COOH$	4	3
(b) $CH_3(CH_2)_{12}COOH$	7	6

Fatty Acid Anabolism

25.36 The anabolic pathway for synthesizing fatty acids is called *lipogenesis*.

25.38 Acetyl-SCoA is the starting material for fatty-acid synthesis.

25.40 Palmitic acid has 16 carbons and is synthesized from 8 acetyl-SCoA units through 7 rounds of the lipogenesis spiral.

Applications

25.42 Malabsorption is an inability to absorb lipids into the bloodstream, and it is detected by large amounts of fat in the feces.

25.44 A normal blood cholesterol range is 150–200 mg/dL.

25.46 LDL carries cholesterol from the liver to tissues; HDL carries cholesterol from tissues to the liver, where it is converted to bile and excreted.

25.48 Olestra is a polyester formed between the hydroxyl groups of sucrose and fatty acyl groups from cottonseed and soybean oil. Although its components come from nature, the human body doesn't have enzymes to digest Olestra and it passes through the digestive system undigested.

25.50 Important functions of the liver include:

(a) Synthesis of glycogen, glucose, triacylglycerols, fatty acids, cholesterol, bile acids, plasma proteins, and blood clotting factors.
(b) Catabolism of glucose, fatty acids, and amino acids.
(c) Storage of glycogen, lipids, amino acids, iron, and fat-soluble vitamins.
(d) Inactivation of toxic substances.

General Questions and Problems

25.52 An excess of carbohydrates produces an excess of acetyl-SCoA. If more acetyl-SCoA is produced than is needed in the respiratory chain, it is used to synthesize fatty acids, which are used to produce the triglycerides that are deposited in adipose tissue. Once carbohydrates have been catabolized to acetyl-SCoA, it is not possible to resynthesize carbohydrates, because animals don't have enzymes to synthesize carbohydrates from acetyl-SCoA.

25.54 Acetone, acetoacetate and 3-hydroxybutyrate are ketone bodies, which are produced when blood sugar is low and the body metabolizes fats. If more acetyl-SCoA is produced than can enter the citric acid cycle, it is converted to ketone bodies, in the process known as ketogenesis, to be used as an alternate energy source. Ketone bodies are so named because they either contain the ketone functional group or are directly derived from ketones.

25.56

Glyceryl trimyristate

Glycerol is converted to glyceraldehyde 3-phosphate, which enters glycolysis, is converted to pyruvate and yields one acetyl-SCoA. Each myristate produces 7 acetyl-SCoA molecules; three myristates yield 21 acetyl-SCoA molecules. A total of 22 acetyl-SCoA molecules are thus formed.

25.58 An *exogenous lipid* originates in the diet. An *endogenous lipid* is formed in a metabolic process.

Self-Test for Chapter 25

Multiple choice:

1. ATP is ultimately produced in all of the following steps of fatty acid catabolism except:
(a) fatty acid activation   (b) introduction of a double bond into a fatty acid   (c) oxidation of an alcohol to a ketone   (d) entry of acetyl-SCoA into the citric acid cycle

2. An excess of ketone bodies in the blood is known as:
(a) ketosis   (b) ketonuria   (c) ketoacidosis   (d) ketonemia

3. The reactants for TAG synthesis are:
(a) glycerol and fatty acids   (b) glycerol 3-phosphate and fatty acids   (c) glyceraldehyde 3-phosphate and fatty acyl-SCoAs   (d) glycerol and fatty acyl-SCoAs

4. Production of ketone bodies occurs in:
(a) the liver   (b) adipose tissue   (c) muscle   (d) all of the above

5. Which of the following statements about lipogenesis is false?
(a) Synthesis occurs two carbons at a time.   (b) Formation of acyl-SACP intermediates requires ATP.   (c) The coenzyme NADPH is needed   (d) Lipogenesis occurs when acetyl-SCoA is in abundance.

6. Chylomicrons transport all of the following except:
(a) acylglycerols   (b) small-chain fatty acids   (c) phospholipids   (d) cholesterol

7. Fatty acids from storage in adipose tissue are transported :
(a) by chylomicrons   (b) by VLDLs   (c) by serum albumin   (d) free in the bloodstream

8. Acetyl-SCoA is the starting material for synthesis of all of the following except:
(a) steroids   (b) fatty acids   (c) ketone bodies   (d) glycerol

9. β Oxidation of $CH_3(CH_2)_8COOH$ produces a maximum of how many ATPs?
(a) 78   (b) 72   (c) 64   (d) 60

10. When glucose is in good supply, the body:
(a) synthesizes ketone bodies from acetyl-SCoA   (b) hydrolyzes TAGs from adipocytes
(c) breaks down fatty acids via β-oxidation   (d) synthesizes TAGs for storage

Complete the following sentences:

1. One _____ and one _____ are needed for each β oxidation cycle.

2. Bile acids solubilize lipids by forming _____.

3. Triacylglycerols are stored in _____.

4. TAG synthesis begins with the conversion of glycerol to _____ _____.

5. An alternate name for β oxidation is the___ - ____ _____.

6. The first step in β oxidation involves introduction of a _____ _____.

7. _____ is the presence of ketone bodies in the urine.

8. _____ is a coenzyme for fatty-acid biosynthesis.

9. _____ is a ketone body containing a hydroxyl group.

10. Chylomicrons are transported in the _____ _____ and in the bloodstream.

11. TAGs that are released from storage are said to be _____.

12. All fatty acids are synthesized from _____.

Tell whether the following statements are true or false:

1. Bile acids are steroids.

2. TAGs are hydrolyzed by pancreatic lipases to glycerol and fatty acids.

3. Activation of fatty acids for fatty-acid oxidation requires two phosphates to be cleaved.

4. A chylomicron is a type of lipoprotein.

5. Chylomicrons carry fatty acid-SCoA across the mitochondrial membrane.

6. A fatty acid with n carbons requires $n/2 - 1$ cycles of β-oxidation for complete breakdown.

7. TAGs are synthesized from glycerol and fatty acyl-SCoAs.

8. HDL transports cholesterol to tissues, where it can accumulate.

9. A fatty acid with a molecular weight similar to that of glucose yields more ATPs per molecule than glucose.

10. Fatty acid synthesis occurs in mitochondria.

11. The terminal $-CH_3$ group of a fatty acid comes from malonyl-SCoA.

12. Most naturally-occurring fatty acids have an even number of carbon atoms.

Match the entry on the left with its partner on the right:

1. Chylomicron   (a) Lipoprotein rich in cholesterol

2. Lipogenesis   (b) Protein that carries fatty acids in the bloodstream

3. LDL   (c) Solubilizes fats

4. Carnitine   (d) Hydrolyzes TAGs in adipose tissue

5. Malonyl-SCoA   (e) Lipoprotein that aids in lipid transport of fats in the diet

6. Fatty-acid spiral   (f) Lipoprotein rich in protein

7. Chyme   (g) Starting material in lipogenesis

8. Lipoprotein lipase   (h) Ketone body

9. HDL   (i) Fatty acid biosynthesis

10. Albumin   (j) Breakdown of fatty acids into acetyl-SCoA

11. Bile   (k) Mixture of partially digested food

12. Acetoacetate   (l) Carrier of fatty-acyl-SCoA molecules

Chapter Outline

I. Nucleic acids (Sections 26.1–26.4).
    A. Introduction (Section 26.1).
        1. When a cell isn't dividing, its nucleus consists of chromatin, a tangle of fibers composed of protein and DNA.
        2. Just before dividing, the DNA is duplicated.
        3. During division, chromatin organizes itself into chromosomes, each of which is a huge DNA molecule.
        4. The chromosomes are made up of genes, individual segments of DNA that contain instructions for synthesizing a single protein.
        5. The human body has 23 pairs of chromosomes, containing 100,000 genes.
    B. Composition of nucleic acids (Section 26.2).
        1. Nucleic acids are polymers of nucleotides.
            DNA and RNA are the two types of nucleic acids.
        2. Nucleotides consist of:
            a. A heterocyclic base.
                i. The bases for DNA are the purines adenine and guanine, and the pyrimidines cytosine and thymine.
                ii. For RNA, uracil replaces thymine.
            b. A pentose.
                i. For DNA, the pentose is D-ribose.
                ii. For RNA, the pentose is D-2-deoxyribose.
                ii. The pentose is connected to the base by a β-N-glycosidic bond to the anomeric carbon.
            c. A phosphate group.
                The phosphate group is attached at C5 of the pentose.
        3. The combination of sugar + base is known as a nucleoside.
            a. Nucleosides are named by replacing the -*ine* of the base name by -*osine* for purines and -*idine* for pyrimidines.
            b. If the pentose is 2-deoxyribose, the prefix "deoxy" is added to the name.
            c. To indicate position, numbers without primes are used for bases and numbers with primes are used for the pentose.
            d. Nucleosides have important biochemical functions other than as components of nucleic acids.
        4. Nucleotides.
            a. Nucleotides are named by adding "5'-monophosphate" to the nucleoside name.
            b. Nucleotides can form di- and triphosphates.
                ATP plays an important role in biochemical energetics.
    C. The structure of nucleic acid chains (Section 26.3).
        1. Nucleotides are joined by phosphate ester bonds between the 5' phosphate and the 3' –OH group of the sugar of the next nucleotide.
        2. Vast numbers of nucleotides can be connected by these bonds to form immense polynucleotides.
        3. The structure and function of nucleic acids depends on the sequence of nucleotides.
        4. The sequence is described by starting at the 5' end and identifying the bases by one-letter abbreviations.

D. Base-pairing in DNA (Section 26.4).
   1. In DNA, two polynucleotide strands coil around each other in a double helix.
       a. The sugar–phosphate backbone is on the outside.
       b. The bases are inside.
   2. The two strands run in opposite directions.
   3. The two strands are held together by H-bonding between bases.
       a. A and T form two hydrogen bonds to each other.
       b. C and G form three hydrogen bonds to each other.
   4. The two strands are complementary.
       a. A and T always occur in DNA in the same percentage.
       b. C and G always occur in DNA in the same percentage.
   5. The strands of the double helix coil so as to create two grooves—a major groove and a minor groove—that can accommodate various hydrogen-bonding molecules.
   6. Aromatic rings can fit between base pairs and distort the double helix.
II. The function of nucleic acids (Sections 26.5–26.11).
   A. The central dogma of molecular genetics (Section 26.5).
       1. The function of DNA is to store genetic information.
       2. The function of RNA is to read and decode DNA and use the information to synthesize proteins.
       3. Nucleic acids take part in three major processes.
           a. Replication is the process in which DNA makes a copy of itself.
           b. Transcription is the process in which RNA reads the genetic message.
           c. Translation is the process in which the genetic message is used to make proteins.
   B. Replication of DNA (Section 26.6).
       1. Mechanism of replication.
           a. The double helix partially unwinds.
           b. Bases line up and hydrogen-bond with their complements.
           c. DNA polymerase catalyzes bond formation between the 5' phosphate group on the arriving nucleotide and the 3' –OH of the old strand.
       2. Two identical new copies of the double helix are formed.
       3. Because strand growth occurs in one direction (5' —> 3'), only one strand of DNA is synthesized continuously.
           a. The other strand is synthesized in segments, beginning at the replication fork.
           b. DNA ligase attaches the segments of the other strand.
       4. The copying of DNA requires several hours, involves many replication forks, and proceeds virtually without error.
   C. RNA (Section 26.7).
       1. Structure of RNA.
           a. RNA resembles DNA but has the following differences;
               i.   The pentose is ribose.
               ii. Uracil replaces thymine.
           b. RNA chains are shorter than DNA chains.
           c. RNA chains may be single-stranded or double-stranded.
       2. Types of RNA.
           a. Ribosomal RNA has a molecular weight of 5×10^6 amu and occurs in ribosomes, which are the site of protein synthesis.
           b. Messenger RNA reads DNA and carries the message to the ribosomes.
           c. Transfer RNA delivers amino acids to the growing protein chain.
   D. Transcription (Section 26.8).
       1. mRNA is synthesized by transcription of DNA.
           a. RNA polymerase recognizes a control segment of DNA that precedes the nucleotides to be transcribed.
           b. A small section of DNA unwinds.
           c. Complementary bases are attached.

    d. Transcription stops when RNA polymerase recognizes a "stop" nucleotide sequence.

    e. All RNAs are synthesized in the same way, although we will focus on mRNA in this description.

2. Only one DNA strand is transcribed — the template strand.

    a. The other strand is the information strand.

    b. mRNA is a copy of the information strand (with U replacing T).

3. Not all genes are continuous strands of DNA.

    a. The coding sections of DNA (exons) are interrupted by noncoding sections (introns).

    b. In the final mRNA, the intron sections are cut out.

4. Each mRNA controls the synthesis of one protein.

5. Regulation of genes can occur by use of negative feedback, repressors and inducers.

E. Translation (Sections 26.9–26.10).

1. The genetic code (Section 26.9).

    a. A sequence of three mRNA bases codes for a specific amino acid.

    b. The codes are written in the 5' —> 3' direction.

    c. Each amino acid is represented by one or more codes.

2. Transfer RNA (Section 26.10).

    a. The message carried by mRNA is decoded by tRNA.

    b. Each amino acid is transported by its own tRNA to the ribosome.

    c. Amino acids are bonded to the tRNAs by an ester bond between the –COOH group of an amino acid and C3' of ribose at the end of the tRNA.

    d. Each tRNA has an anticodon that corresponds to a codon sequence on mRNA.

3. Protein synthesis.

    a. Initiation.

        i. The first AUG codon on the 5' end of mRNA is a "start" codon (which also codes for methionine).

        ii. When the Met tRNA comes together with the mRNA codon and occupies one of the two binding sites in the ribosome, elongation can start.

        iii. If Met isn't the first amino acid in the protein, it is removed after protein synthesis.

    b. Elongation.

        i. A tRNA with an anticodon complementary to the second mRNA codon occupies the second binding site.

        ii. An enzyme in the ribosome catalyzes peptide bond formation and breaks the bond between the first amino acid and its tRNA.

        iii. This tRNA leaves the ribosome.

        iv. The ribosome shifts one position along the mRNA chain (translocation).

        v. The second site is free to accept the next tRNA.

        vi. A single mRNA can be read by many ribosomes.

    c. Termination.

        i. A "stop" codon signals the end of translation.

        ii. An enzyme called releasing factor frees the polypeptide chain from the last tRNA, and the mRNA is released from the ribosome.

F. Gene mutation and hereditary disease (Section 26.11).

1. An error in mRNA transcription is not serious.

2. An error in DNA replication is a mutation and is passed on each time DNA replicates.

    a. Substances that cause mutations are mutagens.

    b. Each time mRNA is transcribed, the resulting protein will have an error.

    c. The consequences of a mutation range from insignificant to lethal.

3. If the error occurs in a somatic cell, cancer may result.

4. If the error occurs in a germ cell, a genetic defect may be passed on to the offspring.

III. Recombinant DNA (Section 26.12–26.13).
   A. Recombinant DNA technology is used to cut a specific gene out of one organism and insert it into the DNA of another organism (Section 26.12).
      1. The second organism is usually a bacterium.
      2. Bacterial DNA is contained in plasmids, which are easy to isolate.
   B. Technique of recombinant DNA.
      1. The plasmid is cleaved by a restriction endonuclease.
         a. There are more than 200 restriction endonucleases.
         b. Cleavage occurs at a specific site in a base sequence.
         c. Each DNA strand is left with a few unpaired bases, called "sticky ends".
      2. The gene to be inserted is also cleaved by the same endonucleases and thus has complementary sticky ends.
      3. The gene and the plasmid are mixed in the presence of a DNA ligase enzyme and the gene is inserted into the plasmid.
      4. The plasmid can be reinserted into a bacterial cell, and the bacteria, which multiply rapidly, manufacture the protein.
   C. Uses of recombinant DNA technology (Section 26.13).
      1. Medicine.
         a. Recombinant anticancer drugs, such as interferon and interleukin, have been approved.
         b. Diagnostic tests for hereditary diseases are being developed.
         c. Recombinant proteins can be used to treat diseases.
         d. Gene therapy.
      2. Agriculture.
         Transgenic plants and animals have been bred; their DNA contains single genes that code for desirable traits.

Solutions to Chapter 26 Problems

26.1

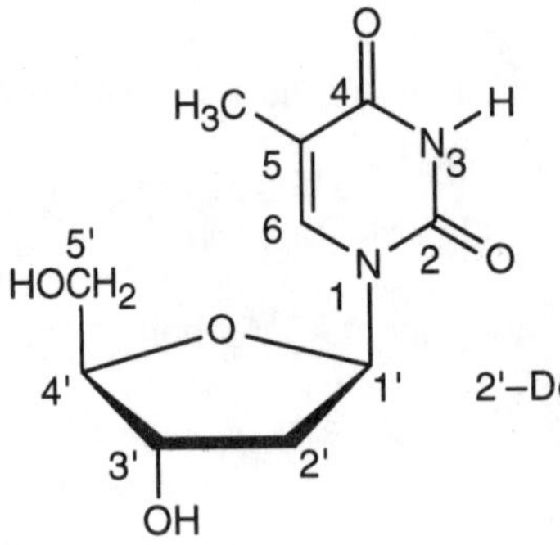

2'-Deoxythymidine

26.2

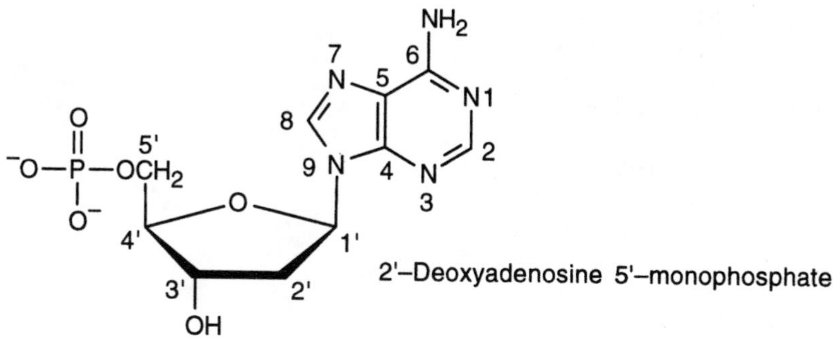

2'–Deoxyadenosine 5'–monophosphate

26.3

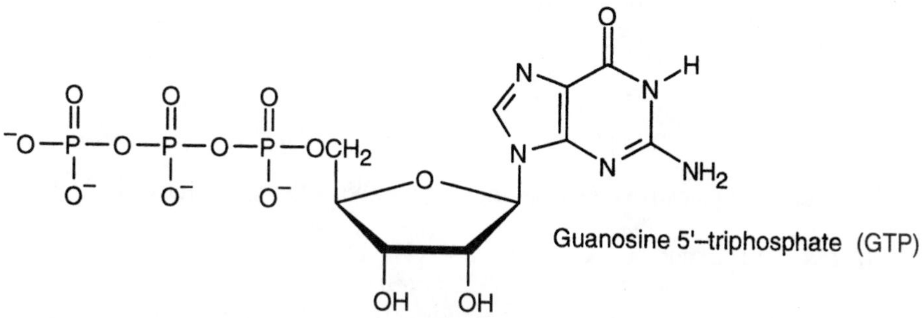

Guanosine 5'–triphosphate (GTP)

26.4 dTMP – 2'-Deoxythymidine 5'-monophosphate
CMP – Cytidine 5'-monophosphate
UDP – Uridine 5'-diphosphate
AMP – Adenosine 5'-monophosphate
ATP – Adenosine 5'-triphosphate

26.5

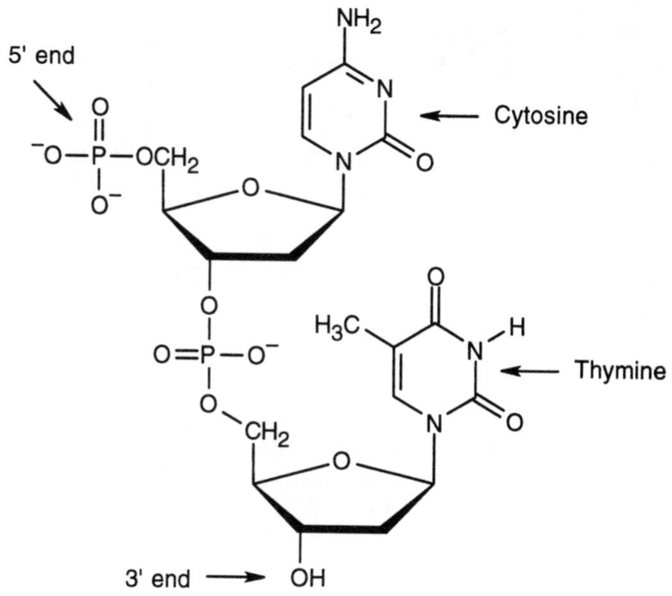

5' end

Cytosine

Thymine

3' end → OH

26.6   (a) Original strand: G-C-C-T-A-G-T

                      ⋮ ⋮ ⋮ ⋮ ⋮ ⋮ ⋮

       Complement: C-G-G-A-T-C-A

     (b) Original strand: A-A-T-G-G-C-T-C-A

                      ⋮ ⋮ ⋮ ⋮ ⋮ ⋮ ⋮ ⋮ ⋮

       Complement: T-T-A-C-C-G-A-G-T

26.7

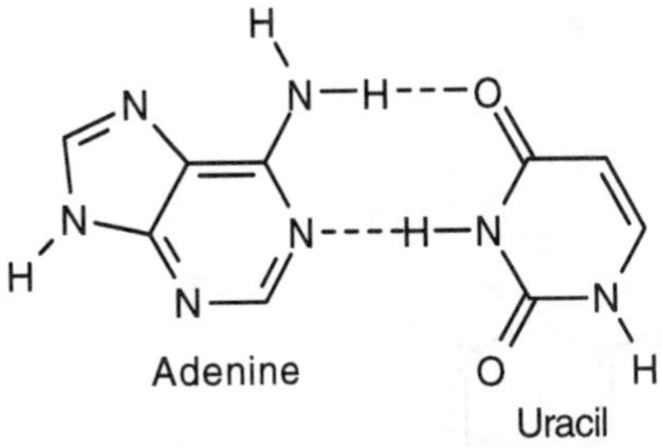

Adenine   Uracil

26.8   The phosphate groups cause the DNA molecule to be negatively charged.

26.9   (a) DNA template strand: -G-A-T–T–A-C-C-G-T–A-

                                ⋮ ⋮ ⋮ ⋮ ⋮ ⋮ ⋮ ⋮ ⋮ ⋮

         mRNA complement: -C-U-A-A-U-G-G-C-A-U-

     (b) DNA template strand: -T-A–T-G-G-C-T-A-G-G-C-A-

                                ⋮ ⋮   ⋮ ⋮ ⋮ ⋮ ⋮ ⋮ ⋮ ⋮ ⋮ ⋮

         mRNA complement   -A-U-A-C-C-G-A-U-C-C-G-U-

26.10 *Amino Acid*   *Possible Codons*

(a) Ala	G-C-U,	G-C-C,	G-C-A,	G-C-G	
(b) Phe	U-U-U,	U-U-C			
(c) Leu	U-U-A,	U-U-G,	C-U-U,	C-U-C,	C-U-A, C-U-G
(d) Val	G-U-U,	G-U-C,	G-U-A,	G-U-G	
(e) Tyr	U-A-U,	U-A-C			

26.11 The sequence guanine, uracil, cytosine (G-U-C) codes for the amino acid valine.

26.12   *Codon*   *Amino Acid*

Codon	Amino Acid
(a) A-U-U	Ile
(b) G-C-G	Ala
(c) C-G-A	Arg
(d) A-A-C	Asn

26.13 - 26.15

mRNA sequence:	CUU—AUG—GCU—UGG—CCC—UAA
Amino-acid sequence:	Leu——Met——Ala——Trp——Pro——Stop
tRNA anticodons:	GAA UAC CGA ACC GGG AUU
DNA template sequence:	GAA—TAC——CGA—ACC——GGG—ATT

26.16 The sequence T-G-G on the informational strand of DNA codes for U-G-G on mRNA, and T-G-A codes for U-G-A, which is a stop codon. Instead of adding an amino acid to the peptide chain, chain growth would stop.

26.17 (a)

	Original strand	*Mutated strand*
DNA	A-T-C	A-T-G
mRNA	U-A-G	U-A-C
Amino acid	Stop	Tyr

(b)

	Original strand	*Mutated strand*
DNA	C-C-T	C-G-T
mRNA	G-G-A	G-C-A
Amino acid	Gly	Ala

In the first mutation, a protein would add tyrosine instead of stopping. In the second mutation, a protein would add an alanine instead of a glycine.

Understanding Key Concepts

26.18

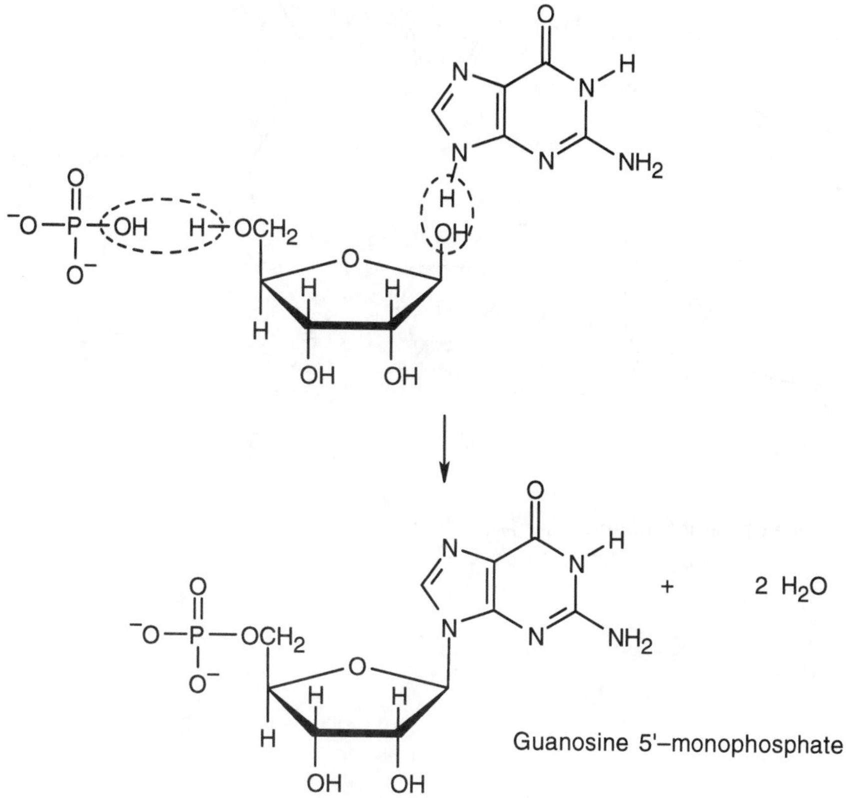

Guanosine 5'–monophosphate

26.19

The sequence of the left chain: –A–G–T–C–.
The sequence of the right chain: –G–A–C–T–.

26.20

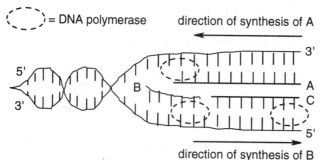

Segments B and C are joined by the action of a DNA ligase.

26.21

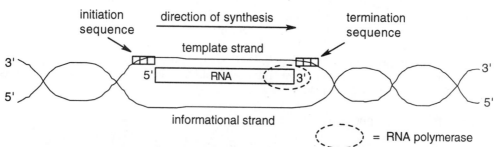

The nucleotides adenosine 5'-monophosphate, cytidine 5'-monophosphate, guanosine 5'-monophosphate and uridine 5'-monophosphate are used to synthesize messenger RNA.

26.22 Each amino acid has more than one mRNA codon.
Codons for Tyr: UAU, UAC.
Codons for Gly: GGU, GGC, GGA, GGC.
Codons for Phe: UUU, UUC.
Using the first codon listed:

(a) 5' | U | A | U | G | GU | G | G | U | U | U | U | 3' mRNA

(b) 3' | A | T | A | C | C | A | C | C | A | A | A | A | 5' DNA template strand

(c) 5' | T | A | T | G | G | T | G | G | T | T | T | T | 3' DNA informational strand

The upper strand of DNA is the template for the synthesis of mRNA, and its sequence of bases is the complement of the sequence of bases that make up the enkephalin gene. The lower strand is the informational strand.

(d) To find the number of DNA sequences, multiply the numbers of different codons for each amino acid.
2 x 4 x 4 x 2 = 64 possible DNA sequences code for the first four amino acids in enkephalins.

Structure and Function of Nucleic Acids

26.24 Ribose is the sugar in RNA, and deoxyribose is the sugar in DNA. Ribose has an –OH group at carbon 2, and deoxyribose has no –OH group at carbon 2.

26.26 The purine bases (two fused heterocyclic rings) are adenine and guanine. The pyrimidine bases (one heterocyclic ring) are cytosine, thymine (in DNA) and uracil (in RNA).

26.28 DNA is also found in the mitochondria of cells.

26.30 DNA is the largest nucleic acid, mRNA is intermediate, and tRNA is the smallest of the three nucleic acid.

26.32 *Similarities:* Replication, transcription and translation are all polymerizations in which a nucleic acid is used as a template for the synthesis of another biopolymer. In all of these processes, hydrogen bonding is used to bring the subunits into the correct position for bond formation and to determine the order of assembly.
Differences: In replication, DNA makes a copy of itself. In transcription, DNA is used as a template for the synthesis of mRNA. In translation, mRNA is used as a template for the synthesis of proteins. Replication and transcription take place in the nucleus of cells, and translation takes place in ribosomes.

26.34 Chromatin is composed of protein and DNA.

26.36 There are approximately 100,000 genes in the human genome.

26.38 Bases that are complementary form hydrogen bonds with each other and thus always occur in pairs. For example, adenine is always hydrogen-bonded to thymine or uracil, and guanine is always hydrogen-bonded to cytosine.

26.40 If a sample of DNA is 28% T, the percent of A is also 28%, since A and T are complementary. The sample contains 22% G and 22% C, because G and C are also complementary.

26.42 Polynucleotides are written from 5' to 3'.

26.44

Water is removed in the formation of the sugar–base linkage.

26.46

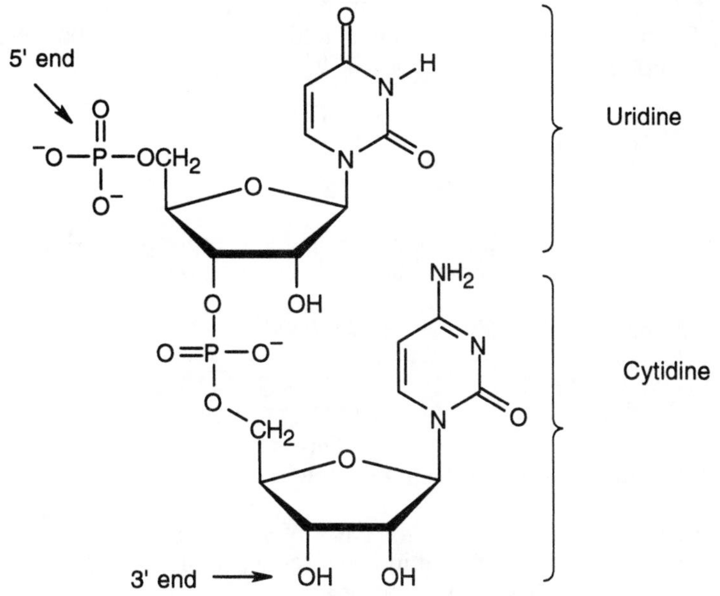

Nucleic Acids and Heredity

26.48 Transcribed RNA is complementary to the template strand of DNA.

26.50 To say that DNA replication is semiconservative means that each of the two new copies of DNA has a strand of DNA that was the original template and one strand that is newly synthesized.

26.52 An anticodon is a sequence of three nucleotides that is complementary to a sequence on a codon. The anticodon occurs on tRNA and matches the codon sequence on mRNA when it brings the correct amino acid into position for protein synthesis.

26.54 The tRNAs for each amino acid differ in their anticodon sequences.

26.56

Amino Acid	Codons			
(a) Pro	C-C-U,	C-C-C,	C-C-A,	C-C-G
(b) Lys	A-A-A,	A-A-G		
(c) Met	A-U-G			

26.58

Codon (5' —> 3')	· tRNA Anticodon (3' —> 5')
(a) A-C-U	U-G-A
(b) G-G-A	C-C-U
(c) C-U-U	G-A-A

26.60, 26.62

The DNA sequence of the template strand is complementary to the DNA sequence of the informational strand. The mRNA sequence is identical to the DNA sequence on the informational strand, except that U in mRNA replaces T in DNA.

Informational strand: (5' —> 3')	T-A-C-C-G-A
Template strand: (3' —> 5')	A-T-G-G-C-T
Dipeptide:	Tyr——Arg

26.64 A mutation is an error in base sequence that occurs during DNA replication. Mutations can occur spontaneously, or they can be caused by chemicals or radiation.

26.66

	Normal	*Mutated*
DNA:	A-T-T-G-G-C-C-T-A	A-C-T-G-G-C-C-T-A
mRNA:	A-U-U-G-G-C-C-U-A	A-C-U-G-G-C-C-U-A
Amino acids:	Ile—Gly—Leu	Thr—Gly—Leu

The mutation would substitute a Thr for an Ile in the protein.

26.68 A hereditary disease is caused by a mutation in the DNA of a germ cell and is passed from parent to offspring. The mutation affects the amino-acid sequence of an important protein and causes a change in the biological activity of the protein.

26.70 Metenkephalin:

mRNA (5' —> 3'):

Tyr—	Gly—	Gly——	Phe—	Met	Stop
UAU–	GGU–	GGU–	UUU–	AUG–	UAA
UAC	GGC	GGC	UUC		UAG
	GGG	GGG			UGA
	GGA	GGA			

26.72 The DNA of bacterial cells occurs in plasmids, each of which carries only a few genes. The plasmids are easy to isolate, and several copies of each are present in a bacterial cell.

Applications

26.74 A polymerase chain reaction is used to produce a large number of copies of a specific DNA chain.

26.76 Viruses consist of a strand of nucleic acid wrapped in a protein coat. Unlike higher organisms, viruses can't replicate or manufacture protein independent of a host cell.

26.78 A vaccine is used to stimulate an organism to produce antibodies against a killed or weakened version of the original virus. It will be difficult to design a vaccine against AIDS because the AIDS virus is constantly mutating.

26.80 If you knew your own genetic map, you could learn what diseases might sooner or later be a problem for you, and you might be able to take precautions to postpone their onset. It might be unsettling to know what illness could cause your death, and you might worry about keeping the information confidential.

26.82 In DNA fingerprinting, it is possible to compare DNA from different tissues because all tissues from the same individual contain identical DNA.

General Questions and Problems

26.84 A genetic map might be used to locate a defective gene, all or part of which can be excised with a restriction endonuclease. Using DNA ligase, a DNA strand might be inserted to produce a gene capable of coding for the nondefective protein.

26.86 To code for prepoinsulin, 81 x 3 = 243 bases are needed to code for the protein's 81 amino acids. In addition, a three-base "start" codon and a three-base "stop" codon are needed, for a total of 249 bases .

26.88 If a protein doesn't have methionine as its first amino acid, the methionine is removed after protein synthesis is complete.

Self-Test for Chapter 26

Multiple choice:

1. The name for a nucleoside formed from cytidine and 2'-deoxyribose is:
    (a) deoxycytidine 5'-monophosphate   (b) 2'-deoxycytidine   (c) 2'-deoxycytosine
    (d) 2'-deoxycytosine 5'-monophosphate

2. Adenine and thymine are complementary because:
    (a) they are both purines   (b) they are both pyrimidines   (c) they both occur in DNA
    (d) they form two hydrogen bonds to each other

3. If the base sequence CAC-TTA-GGT appears on the informational strand of DNA, which sequence occurs in mRNA?
    (a) CAC-TTA-GGT   (b) CAC-UUA-GGU   (c) GTG-AAT-CCA   (d) GUG-AAU-CCA

4. Which statement about the RNA base sequence CGG-AAA-GUU is true?
    (a) It codes for a basic tripeptide.   (b) It contains a "stop" codon.   (c) Changing the third codon from GUU to GUC changes the amino acids in the tripeptide.   (d) The 5' end is on the right, and the 3' end is on the left.

5. A hereditary disease caused by a defect in hemoglobin is:
    (a) cystic fibrosis   (b) sickle-cell anemia   (c) Tay-Sachs disease   (d) albinism

6. The process by which the genetic message contained in DNA is read is called:
    (a) replication   (b) transcription   (c) translation   (d) translocation

7. Which of the following is not a characteristic of plasmids?
    (a) They are easy to isolate.   (b) They replicate in the same way as human DNA does.
    (c) They are circular.   (d) Each cell has one plasmid.

8. An enzyme involved in translation is:
    (a) DNA polymerase   (b) restriction endonuclease   (c) RNA polymerase   (d) releasing factor

9. Which of the following statements about DNA replication is untrue?
    (a) Replication is semiconservative.   (b) Each DNA strand has many replication forks.
    (c) DNA ligase catalyzes bond formation between each arriving nucleotide.
    (d) Replication proceeds in the 5'—>3' direction.

10. Which heterocyclic base contains only carbon, hydrogen and nitrogen?
    (a) adenine   (b) guanine   (c) cytosine   (d) thymine

Complete the following sentences:

1. _____ is the process by which an identical copy of DNA is made.

2. The two strands of DNA have base sequences that are _____.

3. When a cell is not actively dividing, its nucleus is occupied by _____.

4. Mutations may be caused by exposure to _____ _____ or to chemicals called _____.

5. An _____ is a segment of a gene that does not code for protein synthesis.

6. tRNA binds to an amino acid by an _____ linkage.

7. A _____ consists of a heterocyclic amine base bonded to an aldopentose.

8. An enzyme called a _____ _____ frees the polypeptide chain from the last tRNA during protein synthesis.

9. An enzyme called a _____ _____ cleaves a DNA molecule at a particular base sequence.

10. The sugar _____ has an -H instead of an -OH at its 2' position.

11. The _____ - _____ model describes DNA as two polynucleotide strands coiled about each other in a double helix.

12. The enzyme _____ _____ catalyzes the bonding of nucleotides to form new strands of DNA.

Tell whether the following statements are true or false:

1. There are a total of 64 codons for the 20 amino acids.

2. The amount of adenine in an organism's DNA is equal to the amount of guanine.

3. In transcription, mRNA is a copy of the informational strand of DNA.

4. An amino acid codon occurs on tRNA.

5. A mutation in RNA causes little damage.

6. Synthetase enzymes catalyze the formation of ester bonds between amino acids and their tRNAs.

7. The individual units of RNA and DNA are called nucleotides.

8. The two strands of the DNA double helix run in the same direction.

9. Transcription is the process by which the genetic message is decoded and used to make proteins.

10. Most human DNA contains genetic instructions.

11. Each amino acid is specified by more than one codon.

12. The correct name for the RNA nucleotide containing G is guanidine 5'-monophosphate.

Match the entries on the left with their partners on the right:

1.	5' end	(a) 3 billion base pairs
2.	A-C-G	(b) Cysteine codon
3.	U-G-C	(c) Forms three hydrogen bonds
4.	Adenine	(d) Coded for by six codons
5.	human genome	(e) May cause cancer
6.	3' end	(f) "stop" codon
7.	Leu	(g) Purine
8.	Cytosine	(h) Occurs only in RNA
9.	Somatic-cell mutation	(i) –OH group
10.	Uracil	(j) Cysteine anticodon
11.	U-G-A	(k) May cause hereditary disease
12.	Germ-cell mutation	(l) Phosphate group

Chapter 27 – Protein and Amino Acid Metabolism

Chapter Outline

I. Introduction to protein and amino acid metabolism (Sections 27.1–27.2).
   A. Protein digestion (Section 27.1).
      1. Proteins are denatured in the stomach.
      2. In the stomach, the enzyme pepsin hydrolyzes proteins to polypeptides.
      3. In the intestine, other enzymes hydrolyze the polypeptides to amino acids.
      4. Amino acids cross the cell membrane of the intestine and are absorbed directly into the bloodstream.
         Active transport is required for amino acids to cross the intestinal lining.
   B. Overview of amino acid metabolism (Section 27.2).
      1. The amino acid pool is the collection of all free amino acids in the body.
         The amino acid pool is the source of amino acids for protein synthesis and of nitrogen for the synthesis of nitrogen-containing biomolecules.
      2. Amino acid catabolism occurs in two steps:
         a. Removal of nitrogen, which can be:
            i. Used for synthesis of nitrogen-containing biomolecules.
            ii. Excreted as urea.
         b. Entry of the remaining carbon atoms into metabolic pathways.
            i. Citric acid cycle.
            ii. Gluconeogenesis.
            iii. Ketogenesis
            iv. Lipogenesis.

II. Amino acid catabolism (Section 27.3–27.5).
   A. Removal of the amino group (Section 27.3).
      1. Transamination.
         a. In transamination, the amino group of an amino acid and the keto group of an α-keto acid change places.
         b. Transaminase enzymes are usually specific for α-ketoglutarate as the amino group acceptor.
         c. Transamination reactions are equilibria that regulate amino acid concentration.
      2. Deamination.
         a. If the glutamate from transamination is in excess, the $-NH_3^+$ group can be removed and excreted and α-ketoglutarate regenerated.
         b. This reaction is known as oxidative deamination.
         c. Either NAD^+ or $NADP^+$ is required.
         d. The reverse reaction reductive amination, occurs in biosynthesis.
   B. The urea cycle (Section 27.4).
      1. Because ammonia is toxic, the human body converts it to urea in order to excrete it.
      2. The reactions of the urea cycle take place in the liver.
      3. Ammonia is first converted to carbamoyl phosphate.
         $NH_4^+ + HCO_3^- + 2\ ATP \longrightarrow$ carbamoyl phosphate $+ 2\ ADP + HOPO_3^{2-} + H_2O$.
      4. Steps of the cycle:
         a. Step 1: Carbamoyl phosphate + ornithine $\longrightarrow$ citrulline $+ HOPO_3^{2-}$.
         b. Step 2: Citrulline + aspartate + ATP $\longrightarrow$ argininosuccinate $+ AMP + P_2O_7^{4-}$.
         c. Step 3: Argininosuccinate $\longrightarrow$ fumarate + arginine.
         d. Step 4: Arginine $+ H_2O \longrightarrow$ urea + ornithine.

5. Results of the cycle:
   a. Urea is eliminated.
      The urea carbon comes from bicarbonate, the nitrogen comes from aspartate, and the other nitrogen comes from ammonia.
   b. Four phosphate bonds are broken.
   c. Fumarate, a citric acid cycle intermediate, is produced.
      Fumarate is converted to oxaloacetate, which undergoes transamination to yield aspartate, which reenters the cycle. (Fumarate can also enter gluconeogenesis.)
C. Fate of the carbon atoms (Section 27.5).
   1. All amino acid carbon skeletons are either citric acid cycle intermediates or fatty acid metabolism intermediates.
   2. Glucogenic amino acids.
      a. Amino acids that are converted to pyruvate or enter the citric acid cycle as α-ketoglutarate, succinyl-SCoA, fumarate, or oxaloacetate are glucogenic.
      b. These amino acids can be converted to glucose.
   3. Ketogenic amino acids.
      a. Amino acids that are converted to acetyl-SCoA or acetoacetyl-SCoA are known as ketogenic amino acids.
      b. These amino acids can enter either ketogenesis to form ketone bodies or fatty acid biosynthesis.
   4. Some amino acids are both glucogenic and ketogenic.
III. Biosynthesis of nonessential amino acids (Section 27.6).
   A. The human body can synthesize 11 of the 20 common amino acids.
   B. All 11 amino acids derive their amino group from glutamate.
   C. Pyruvate, oxaloacetate, α-ketoglutarate and 3-phosphoglycerate are the precursors of all nonessential amino acids.
   D. Tyrosine is formed from phenylalanine.
      An inability of the body to perform this conversion is the metabolic error in phenylketonuria.

Solutions to Chapter 27 Problems

27.1

$$\underset{\text{Leucine}}{\overset{\overset{\displaystyle CH_3}{|}\ \ \overset{\displaystyle NH_3^+}{|}}{CH_3CHCH_2CHCOO^-}} \quad + \quad \underset{\alpha\text{–Ketoglutarate}}{^-OOCCH_2CH_2\overset{\overset{\displaystyle O}{||}}{C}COO^-}$$

$$\underset{\alpha\text{–Keto–4–methylpentanoate}}{\overset{\overset{\displaystyle CH_3}{|}\ \ \overset{\displaystyle O}{||}}{CH_3CHCH_2CCOO^-}} \quad + \quad \underset{\text{Glutamate}}{^-OOCCH_2CH_2\overset{\overset{\displaystyle NH_3^+}{|}}{C}HCOO^-}$$

27.2

27.3   The conversion of glutamate to α-ketoglutarate can be identified as an oxidation by noting the reduction of the coenzymes NAD⁺ or NADP⁺.

27.4

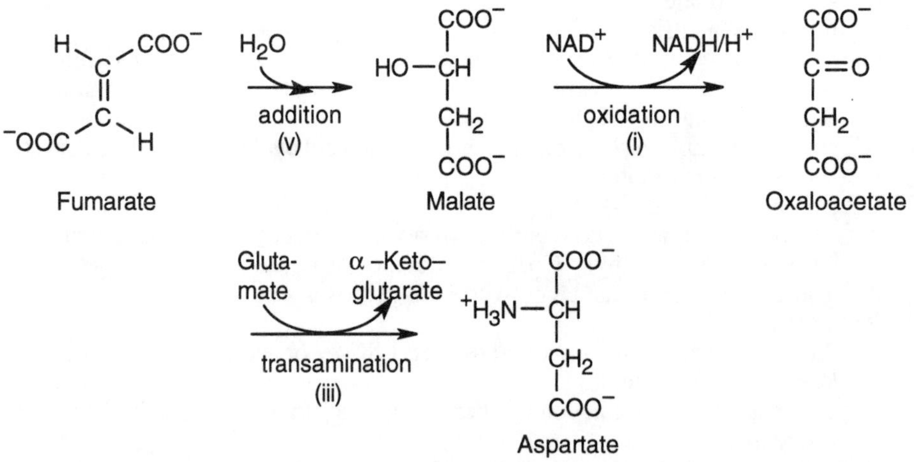

Fumarate   Malate   Oxaloacetate

Aspartate

(Actually, most of the fumarate is converted to glucose by the gluconeogenesis pathway.)

27.5

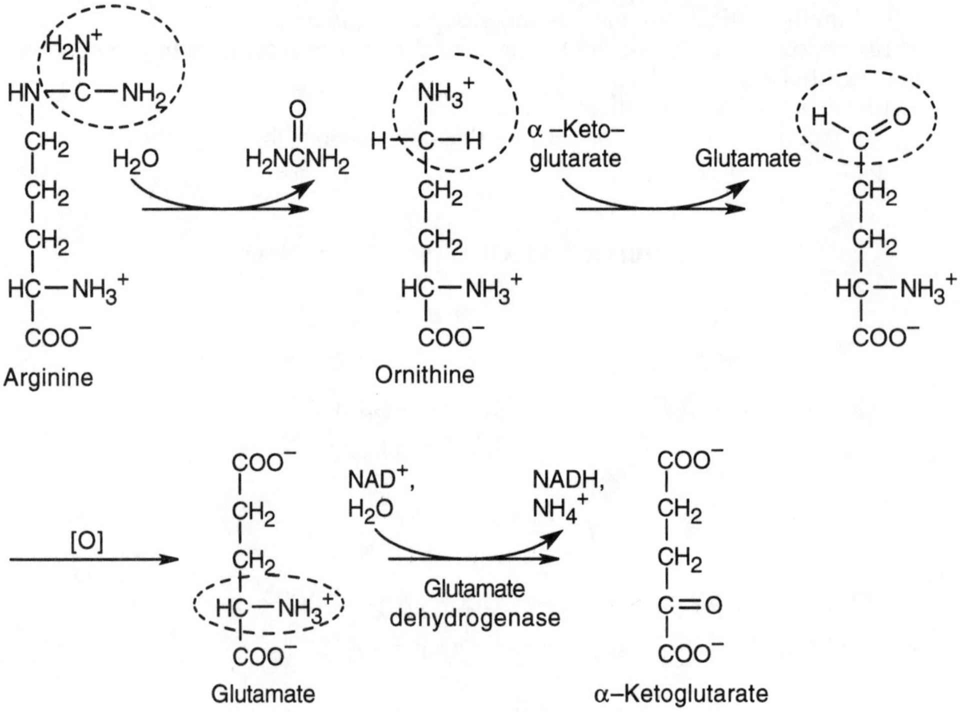

Arginine   Ornithine

Glutamate   α–Ketoglutarate

NADP⁺ can also be used as an enzyme cofactor.

27.6

$$\underset{\text{3–Phosphoglycerate}}{^-\text{OOCCHCH}_2\text{OPO}_3{}^{2-}} \quad \overset{\text{oxidation}}{\underset{\text{(c)}}{\longrightarrow}} \quad \underset{\text{3–Phosphohydroxypyruvate}}{^-\text{OOCCCH}_2\text{OPO}_3{}^{2-}} \quad \overset{\text{transamination}}{\underset{\text{(a)}}{\longrightarrow}}$$

with OH above the first structure and O (double bond) above the second.

$$\underset{\text{3–Phosphoserine}}{^-\text{OOCCHCH}_2\text{OPO}_3{}^{2-}} \quad \overset{\text{hydrolysis}}{\underset{\text{(b)}}{\longrightarrow}} \quad \underset{\text{Serine}}{^-\text{OOCCHCH}_2\text{OH}} \ + \ \text{HOPO}_3{}^{2-}$$

with $\text{NH}_3{}^+$ above both serine structures.

Understanding Key Concepts

27.7

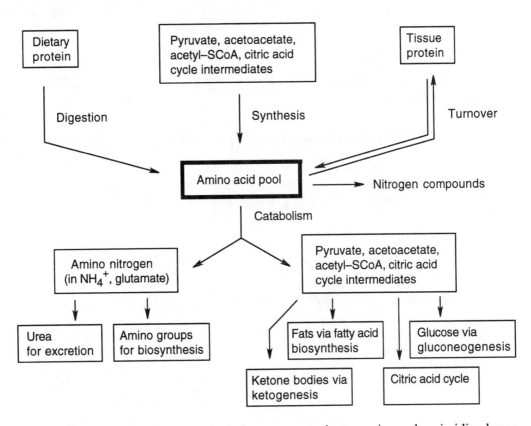

Non-amino acid nitrogen products include neurotransmitters, purine and pyrimidine bases, bile acids, heme, thyroid hormone, nicotinamide, melanin, amino sugars and creatine phosphate.

27.8   Catabolism of an amino acid begins with a transamination reaction that removes the amino acid nitrogen.

$$\underset{\substack{\text{NH}_3^+ \\ | \\ \text{RCHCOO}^- \\ \alpha\text{–amino acid}}}{} + \underset{\substack{\text{O} \\ || \\ ^-\text{OOCCH}_2\text{CH}_2\text{CCOO}^- \\ \alpha\text{–Ketoglutarate}}}{} \underset{\alpha\text{–Aminotransferase}}{\rightleftharpoons} \underset{\substack{\text{O} \\ || \\ \text{RCCOO}^- \\ \alpha\text{–keto acid}}}{} + \underset{\substack{\text{NH}_3^+ \\ | \\ ^-\text{OOCCH}_2\text{CH}_2\text{CHCOO}^- \\ \text{Glutamate}}}{}$$

The carbon atoms:
The resulting α-keto acid, which contains the carbons from the original amino acid, undergoes reactions that convert it to a common metabolic intermediate. This intermediate may be a citric acid cycle intermediate, pyruvate, acetyl-SCoA, or acetoacetyl-SCoA.

The nitrogen atoms:
Glutamate, which contains the amino group from the original amino acid, undergoes an oxidative deamination reaction that converts the amino group to ammonium ion and that regenerates α-ketoglutarate. Either NAD^+ or $NADP^+$ can be used as the enzyme cofactor.

$$\underset{\substack{\text{NH}_3^+ \\ | \\ ^-\text{OOCCH}_2\text{CH}_2\text{CHCOO}^- \\ \text{Glutamate}}}{} + \text{H}_2\text{O} \xrightarrow[\substack{\text{Glutamate} \\ \text{dehydrogenase}}]{\text{NAD}^+ \quad \text{NADH/H}^+} \underset{\substack{\text{O} \\ || \\ ^-\text{OOCCH}_2\text{CH}_2\text{CCOO}^- \\ \alpha\text{–Ketoglutarate}}}{} + \text{NH}_4^+$$

Ammonium ion enters the urea cycle, where it is transformed to urea and is excreted.

$$\text{NH}_4^+ + \text{HCO}_3^- + \underset{\substack{\text{NH}_3^+ \\ | \\ ^-\text{OOCCH}_2\text{–CHCOO}^- \\ \text{Aspartate}}}{}$$

$$\downarrow \underset{}{\overset{\displaystyle 3\ \text{ATP}}{\underset{\displaystyle 2\ \text{ADP} + \text{AMP} + \text{HOPO}_3^{2-} + \text{P}_2\text{O}_7^{4-}}{}}}$$

$$\underset{\substack{\text{O} \\ || \\ \text{H}_2\text{N–C–NH}_2 \\ \text{Urea}}}{} + \underset{\substack{ ^-\text{OOCCH=CHCOO}^- \\ \text{Fumarate}}}{}$$

27.9

$$\text{NH}_4^+ + \underset{\substack{\text{O} \\ || \\ ^-\text{OOCCH}_2\text{CH}_2\text{CCOO}^- \\ \alpha\text{–Ketoglutarate}}}{} \xrightarrow[\substack{\text{Glutamate} \\ \text{dehydrogenase}}]{\text{NADH/H}^+ \quad \text{NAD}^+} \underset{\substack{\text{NH}_3^+ \\ | \\ ^-\text{OOCCH}_2\text{CH}_2\text{CHCOO}^- \\ \text{Glutamate}}}{} + \text{H}_2\text{O}$$

$NADPH/H^+$ can also be used as an enzyme cofactor.

$$\underset{\text{Glutamate}}{{}^-OOCCH_2CH_2\overset{\overset{\displaystyle NH_3^+}{|}}{C}HCOO^-} + \underset{\text{Pyruvate}}{CH_3\overset{\overset{\displaystyle O}{\|}}{C}COO^-} \underset{\underset{\text{aminotransferase}}{\text{Alanine}}}{\rightleftharpoons} \underset{\alpha\text{-Ketoglutarate}}{{}^-OOCCH_2CH_2\overset{\overset{\displaystyle O}{\|}}{C}COO^-} + \underset{\text{Alanine}}{CH_3\overset{\overset{\displaystyle NH_3^+}{|}}{C}HCOO^-}$$

The enzymes for both reactions can catalyze reaction in both directions. The product is the amino acid alanine.

27.10 It is important for ornithine transcarbamylase to have a high activity in order to remove NH_4^+ from the body quickly. It is also important that arginase activity be high in order to release urea for excretion by the kidneys and to provide the ornithine needed to react with carbamoyl phosphate.

27.11 All amino acids are "essential" in the sense that all of them are necessary for protein synthesis. The body, however, can synthesize only about half of them from non-amino acid precursors. The other amino acids must be provided by food, and thus it is "essential" that they be part of the diet.

Amino Acid Pool

27.12 The digestion of proteins begins in the stomach.

27.14 Pyruvate and 3-phosphoglycerate are glycolytic precursors of amino acids.

Amino Acid Catabolism

27.16 In a transamination reaction, a keto group of an α-keto acid and an amino group of an α-amino acid change places.

27.18

27.20 In an oxidative deamination reaction, an $-NH_3^+$ group of an amino acid (usually glutamate) is replaced by a carbonyl oxygen, and ammonium ion is eliminated.

27.22

| Amino Acid | α–Keto acid |

(a)

Phenylalanine

(b)

Tryptophan

27.24 A glucogenic amino acid is an amino acid that is catabolized to pyruvate or to citric acid cycle intermediates and thus can enter gluconeogenesis.

The Urea Cycle

27.26 Ammonia is toxic and must be eliminated as nontoxic urea, which is water-soluble.

27.28 The *urea carbon* comes from carbamoyl phosphate, which is synthesized from bicarbonate produced from CO_2 in the citric acid cycle.

Amino Acid Anabolism

27.30 Nonessential amino acids can be synthesized in 1–3 steps by most organisms. Plants and microorganisms synthesize essential amino acids in many more steps.

27.32 Amino acids are synthesized from non-nitrogen metabolites by transamination reactions with glutamate, which is itself synthesized from α-ketoglutarate and ammonium ion by reductive amination, the reverse of oxidative deamination.

27.34 Phenylketonuria (PKU) is caused by a genetic inability to convert phenylalanine to tyrosine, leading to the accumulation of phenylalanine and its metabolites in the body. PKU causes mental retardation if not detected early in life. Treatment consists of a diet restricted in phenylalanine.

Applications

27.36 Ketosis is the major hazard of a high-protein, low carbohydrate diet. Ketosis occurs when the body produces a large amount of acetyl-SCoA that can't enter the citric acid cycle because of a shortage of citric acid cycle intermediates (due to the low level of carbohydrates in the diet). Instead, acetyl-SCoA undergoes ketogenesis, which results in the production of ketone bodies and the lowering of blood pH.

27.38

Allopurinol   Hypoxanthine   Xanthine   Uric acid

Allopurinol is identical to hypoxanthine in all but one respect: the nitrogen at position 7 of the hypoxanthine ring is at position 8 of the allopurinol ring. Just as hypoxanthine can be oxidized to xanthine, allopurinol can be oxidized to a compound similar to xanthine (alloxanthine). The product of allopurinol oxidation, however, is an inhibitor of the enzyme that converts xanthine to uric acid. Instead of producing uric acid, purine catabolism ends with the formation of the more soluble hypoxanthine and xanthine, which can be easily excreted.

Oxidation of xanthine to uric acid occurs at position 8 of the purine ring system. In allopurinol, this site is occupied by nitrogen.

27.40 The body responds to a xenobiotic compound in two ways. (1) Xenobiotic compounds are hydroxylated to make them less hydrophobic and more water-soluble. (2) Enzyme-catalyzed reactions of xenobiotics with polar molecules yield compounds that are easier to excrete.

General Questions and Problems

27.42 Three molecules of ATP are consumed in producing each molecule of urea, making the process energy-intensive.

27.44 Amino acids can enter the citric acid cycle as α-ketoglutarate, succinyl-SCoA, fumarate and oxaloacetate. α-Ketoglutarate enters the cycle at step 4, succinyl-SCoA enters at step 5, fumarate enters at step 7 , and oxaloacetate enters at step 1.

27.46 Carbons from amino acids can be catabolized to acetyl-SCoA, which can be used in fatty acid biosynthesis. The fatty acids can form triacylglycerols, which are transported to adipose tissue. There, the TAGs can be hydrolyzed to fatty acids.

27.48 Storage: Unlike fats and carbohydrates, amino acids aren't stored in the body. Instead, when excess amino acids accumulate, amino acid nitrogen is excreted and the resulting compounds are converted to either fats or carbohydrates.

Energy: Fats and carbohydrates that are not stored are catabolized. Surplus amino acids must be converted to either fats or carbohydrates in order to be an energy source.

Self-Test for Chapter 27

Multiple choice:

1. Which of the following amino acids is strictly ketogenic?
    (a) proline   (b) threonine   (c) leucine   (d) isoleucine

2. The product of transamination of valine is:
    (a) α-keto-3-methylbutanoic acid   (b) α-ketobutanoic acid   (c) α-keto-4-methylpentanoic acid
    (d) α-ketopentanoic acid

3. The amino acid proline is probably synthesized by cyclization of:
    (a) arginine   (b) glutamate   (c) leucine   (d) threonine

4. The urea cycle takes place in the:
    (a) muscles   (b) kidneys   (c) bloodstream   (d) liver

5. Which of the following proteases is necessary for the activation of other proteases?
    (a) pepsin   (b) chymotrypsin   (c) carboxypeptidase   (d) trypsin

6. How many grams of protein tissue are broken down in an adult body per day?
    (a) none   (b) 50 g   (c) 300 g   (d) 1000 g

7. Ornithine is:
    (a) a urea cycle intermediate   (b) an amino acid   (c) an acceptor of a carbamoyl group
    (d) all three

8. Which of the following nitrogen-containing compounds is used to treat gout?
    (a) hypoxanthine   (b) xanthine   (c) allopurinol   (d) uric acid

9. Which of the following isn't a precursor in nonessential amino acid biosynthesis?
    (a) fumarate   (b) pyruvate   (c) α-ketoglutarate   (d) 3-phosphoglycerate

10. Glucogenic amino acids enter gluconeogenesis via:
    (a) acetyl-SCoA   (b) oxaloacetate   (c) α-ketoglutarate   (d) fumarate

Complete the following sentences:

1. In the transamination reaction of alanine and α-ketoglutarate, _____ and _____ are formed.

2. A _____ is a chemical compound foreign to the body

3. Ketogenic amino acids are catabolized to _____ _____ or _____ _____.

4. The first step in the urea cycle is the formation of _____ _____ from ammonia, CO_2, and ATP.

5. A _____ is an enzyme that carries out peptide hydrolysis.

6. The amino acid serine enters the citric acid cycle as _____.

7. _____ is the key reaction in amino acid anabolism.

8. The essential amino acid _____ is part of the urea cycle.

9. PKU is a metabolic error in converting _____ to _____.

10. The pain of gout is caused by an inflammatory response to _____ _____ in tissues.

11. Liver damage is associated with a high level of the enzyme _____.

12. The carbon in urea comes from _____.

Tell whether the following statements are true or false:

1. 3-Phosphoglycerate is a precursor in the synthesis of nonessential amino acids.

2. Protein digestion starts in the mouth.

3. All ketogenic amino acids except lysine and isoleucine are also glucogenic amino acids.

4. Essential amino acids can neither be synthesized nor catabolized in the human body.

5. Some organisms can excrete nitrogen as ammonia without undergoing any harm.

6. Amino acid catabolism occurs in the intestinal lining.

7. Some intermediates in the urea cycle also occur in the citric acid cycle.

8. The urea cycle is an endergonic process.

9. Both nitrogens of urea come from ammonium ion.

10. Proline is a nonessential amino acid.

11. Each amino acid is associated with its own transaminase enzyme.

12. Oxidative deamination is the reverse of reductive amination.

Match the entries on the left with their partners on the right:

1. Oxidative deamination

2. Ornithine

3. α-Ketoglutarate

4. Serine

5. Trypsin

6. Reductive amination

7. Leucine

8. Phenylketonuria

9. Pepsin

10. Uric acid

11. Transamination

12. Threonine

(a) Hydrolyzes proteins in the small intestine

(b) Process for synthesizing glutamate from α-ketoglutarate and NH_4^+

(c) Ketogenic amino acid

(d) End product of purine catabolism

(e) Process that transfers an amino group from an amino acid to α-ketoglutarate

(f) Nonessential amino acid

(g) Intermediate in the urea cycle

(h) Process that regenerates α-ketoglutarate from glutamate

(i) Glucogenic amino acid

(j) Intermediate in both the citric acid cycle and in amino acid metabolism

(k) Hydrolyzes proteins in the stomach

(l) Metabolic disease

Chapter 28 – Body Fluids

Chapter Outline

I. Water (Sections 28.1–28.2).
   A. Body water and its solutes (Section 28.1).
      1. Types of body fluids.
         a. Intracellular fluid is within cells.
         b. Extracellular fluid.
            i. Blood plasma
            ii. Interstitial fluid, which fills the spaces between cells.
      2. Components of body fluids.
         a. Electrolytes (inorganic ions).
         b. Gases — O_2 and CO_2.
         c. Small organic molecules.
         d. Ionized biomolecules.
         e. All body fluids have the same osmolarity, even if they differ in composition.
      3. Movement of body fluids.
         a. Blood travels through peripheral tissues in capillaries.
            i. At the arterial end, blood pressure is higher and pushes solutes into interstitial fluid.
            ii. At the venous end, blood pressure is lower, and solutes reenter blood plasma.
            iii. Blood plasma and interstitial fluid have similar composition.
         b. Lymph capillaries collect excess interstitial fluid and other molecules too large to pass through capillary walls; this combination is called lymph.
            i. Lymph can't return to surrounding tissue.
            ii. Lymph enters the blood stream at the thoracic duct.
         c. Solutes in interstitial and intracellular fluid are exchanged by crossing cell membranes.
            Often, active transport is needed to maintain concentration differences.
   B. Maintenance of fluid balance (Section 28.2).
      1. Fluid balance is controlled by hormones.
      2. Receptors in the hypothalamus monitor concentration of blood solutes.
      3. If the concentration of solutes is too high, secretion of antidiuretic hormone increases.
         a. In SIADH, too much hormone keeps kidneys from excreting enough water.
         b. In *diabetes insipidus*, excessive amounts of dilute urine are excreted.
II. Blood (Sections 28.3–28.6).
   A. Components of blood (Section 28.3).
      1. Whole blood contains:
         a. Plasma.
         b. Blood cells.
      2. Blood serum is the fluid portion that remains after blood has clotted.
   B. Functions of blood.
      1. Transport.
      2. Regulation: redistribution of heat and solutes, and buffering of tissues.
      3. Defense.
         a. Immune response.
         b. Clotting.
   C. Immune response (Section 28.4).
      1. A foreign invader (antigen) is a substance that the body does not recognize as part of itself.

2. The body responds to antigens in three ways.
   a. Inflammatory responses (nonspecific).
      i. Inflammation produces swelling, warmth and pain.
      ii. The chemical messenger histamine is released at the site of injury.
      iii. Histamine dilates capillaries and increases blood flow to the injured area, allowing clotting factors and white blood cells to pass.
      iv. Bacteria are destroyed by phagocytes (white blood cells), which can also initiate specific immune response.
      v. Inflammation disappears when infectious agents have been removed.
   b. Cell-mediated immune response (specific).
      i. The cell-mediated immune response is under the control of T lymphocytes.
      ii. The cell-mediated immune response guards against abnormal cells due to bacteria, viruses or cancer.
      iii. When a T cell recognizes an invader, it produces killer T cells (that destroy the invader), helper T cells (that enhance defenses), and memory T-cells (that remain on guard).
   c. Antibody-mediated immune response (specific).
      i. The antibody-mediated immune response is under the control of B lymphocytes (with the assistance of T lymphocytes).
      ii. A B cell is activated when it binds to an antigen and encounters a helper T cell.
      iii. The B cells divide to produce plasma cells, which form non-cell-bound antibodies called immunoglobulins.
      iv. The antibodies find their antigens and inactivate them by one of several methods.
      v. Memory cells produce more antibodies if the same antigen reappears.
      vi. The body contains thousands of different immunoglobulins, and many have been identified.
D. Blood clotting (Section 28.5).
   1. A blood clot consists of blood cells trapped in a mesh of the protein fibrin. The process of clot formation requires many steps.
   2. The body's mechanism for halting blood loss is called hemostasis.
      a. The first event is constriction of blood vessels and formation of a plug of platelets.
      b. Then, blood clotting occurs by either of two pathways.
         i. In the intrinsic pathway, blood makes contact with the negatively charged surface of collagen.
         ii. In the extrinsic pathway, damaged tissue releases a glycoprotein called tissue factor.
      c. In either pathway, several zymogen clotting factors are released.
      d. After several steps, the enzyme thrombin catalyzes the formation of insoluble fibrin, which forms the clot.
   3. After the injury has healed, the clot is broken down by hydrolysis of its peptide bonds.
E. Red blood cells and blood gases (28.6).
   1. The purpose of red blood cells (erythrocytes) is to transport blood gases.
   2. Hemoglobin is responsible for transporting O_2 and CO_2. Hemoglobin consists of four protein chains and four heme molecules.
   3. Oxygen transport.
      a. Oxygen is transported via bonding with Fe^{2+} through an unshared electron pair.
      b. The percent of heme molecules that carry oxygen is the percent saturation.
      c. The binding curve is s-shaped.
         i. The uptake of the first molecule of oxygen is more difficult than the uptake of the remaining molecules.
         ii. The release of the first O_2 is more difficult than the release of the other three.

4. CO_2 transport.
   a. CO_2 can be transported in three ways.
      i. Dissolved (about 7%).
      ii. Bonded to Hb.
      iii. As HCO_3^- in solution.
   b. Carbonic anhydrase in erythrocytes catalyzes the formation of HCO_3^- from CO_2.
   c. The HCO_3^- can be transported in blood to the lungs, where it is exhaled as CO_2.
   d. Electrolyte balance in erythrocytes is maintained by entry of one Cl^- for every HCO_3^- removed.
   e. Excess acidity is controlled by binding of H^+ to hemoglobin, with release of O_2.
5. The effects of changes in the oxygen saturation curve with changing pCO_2 and $[H^+]$ are illustrated in Figure 28.12.
6. Acidosis and alkalosis result from disruption of the body's mechanism for maintaining pH and by imbalances in CO_2 metabolism.

III. Urine (Sections 28.7–28.8)
   A. The kidney and urine formation (Section 28.7).
      1. The kidney is composed of nephrons.
      2. Blood enters the nephrons at the glomerulus, where filtration occurs. Plasma and smaller solutes are filtered into the surrounding fluid.
      3. Reabsorption recaptures water and smaller solutes.
      4. In secretion, some solutes are excreted in higher concentration than occurs in the filtrate.
      5. Some substances move by passive diffusion; others move by active transport.
      6. Hormones influence urine composition.
   B. Urine composition and function (Section 28.8).
      1. Composition of urine.
         a. The components of urine are mainly electrolytes and nitrogen-containing wastes.
         b. The concentration of these substances varies with water intake, temperature, exercise and state of health.
      2. Acid–base balance.
         a. Of the 50–100 mEq of H^+ produced in metabolism, very little appears in the urine.
         b. H^+ is produced from CO_2 in the reaction:
            $$CO_2 + H_2O \longrightarrow H^+ + HCO_3^-$$
         c. The resulting H^+ combines with either NH_3 or HPO_4^{2-} and is excreted.
         d. H^+ also combines with HCO_3^- in urine filtrate to produce CO_2, which enters the bloodstream.
      3. Fluid and Na^+ balance.
         a. The amount of H_2O reabsorbed depends on:
            i. The osmolarity of the fluid passing through the kidney.
            ii. Antidiuretic hormone-controlled membrane permeability.
            iii. The amount of Na^+ reabsorbed.
         b. Reabsorption of Na^+ is under the control of aldosterone.

Solutions to Chapter 28 Problems

Understanding Key Concepts

28.1 (a) The body fluid found inside cells is called intracellular fluid.
(b) The body fluid found outside cells is called extracellular fluid.
(c) Blood plasma and interstitial fluid are the major body fluids found outside of cells.
(d) K^+, Mg^{2+} and HPO_4^{2-} are the major electrolytes found inside cells.
(e) The major electrolytes found outside cells are Na^+ and Cl^-.

28.2

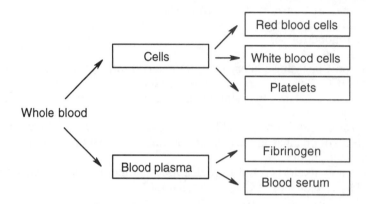

28.3 (a) Blood carries CO_2 (dissolved and as HCO_3^-) from the tissues to the lungs.
(b) Blood carries O_2 from lungs to tissues.
(c) Blood transports nutrients from the digestive system to the tissues.
(d) Blood carries waste products from the tissues to the site of excretion.
(e) Blood transports hormones from endocrine glands to their site of binding.
(f) Blood transports defensive agents such as white blood cells (to destroy foreign material) and platelets (to prevent blood loss).

28.4 Symptoms of inflammation include swelling, redness, warmth and pain. Histamine causes these symptoms by dilating capillaries, causing an increased blood flow that reddens and warms the skin. Pain and swelling occur when blood-clotting factors and defensive proteins enter the intercellular space.

Histamine is produced by the enzymatic decarboxylation of histidine.

28.5 Cell-mediated immune response, which is under the control of T cells, arises when abnormal cells, bacteria or viruses enter cells. The invading cells are killed by T cells that destroy the invader.
Antibody-mediated immune response, which is under the control of B cells, assisted by T cells, occurs when antigenic substances enter cells. When an antigen is recognized, B cells divide to produce plasma cells, which form antibodies to the antigen. These antibodies form an antibody-antigen complex that inactivates the antigen.

Body Fluids

28.6 The three principal body fluids are intracellular fluid, extracellular fluid and interstitial fluid.

28.8 To be soluble in bodily fluids, a substance must be an ion, a gas, a small molecule, or a molecule with many polar or ionic groups on its surface.

28.10 Blood pressure in arterial capillaries is higher than interstitial fluid pressure, and blood pressure in venous capillaries is lower than interstitial fluid pressure.

28.12 The lymphatic system collects excess interstitial fluid, cellular debris, proteins, and lipid droplets and ultimately returns them to the bloodstream.

28.14 Antidiuretic hormone is also known as vasopressin.

28.16 Blood plasma is the fluid portion of blood that contains water-soluble solutes.

28.18 The three main types of blood cells are erythrocytes (red blood cells), platelets, and white blood cells.

28.20 The prefix "hypo-" refers to a below-normal condition or a below-normal concentration of a solute in body fluids.

28.22 An antigen is a foreign substance that the body identifies as an invader. Three types of bodily responses to antigens are inflammation, antibody-mediated immune response, and cell-mediated immune response.

28.24 Specific immune responses, like enzyme–substrate interactions, involve a noncovalent interaction between an antigen and a defender specific to that antigen.

28.26 The antibody-directed immune response involves B lymphocytes, a type of white blood cell. These B lymphocytes identify antigens and divide into plasma cells that produce antibodies specific to the antigen present.

28.28 When a T cell recognizes an antigen on the surface of an invader, three kinds of T cells are produced. *Killer* T cells destroy the invader, *helper* T cells enhance defenses against the invader, and *memory* T cells can produce new killer T cells if the invader reappears.

28.30 A blood clot is a mass of blood cells trapped in a fibrin mesh.

28.32 Blood clotting can be triggered by either the intrinsic pathway, which occurs when blood is exposed to negatively charged surfaces, or by the extrinsic pathway, which occurs when a substance called tissue factor is released by injured cells.

28.34 Each hemoglobin tetramer can bind 4 O_2 molecules.

28.36 Oxyhemoglobin is bright red, whereas deoxyhemoglobin is dark red-purple.

28.38 Because of oxygen's allosteric interaction with hemoglobin, uptake of the first oxygen facilitates the uptake of the remaining oxygens. In the reverse direction, release of the first oxygen facilitates the release of the other three oxygens.

28.40 CO_2 can be transported as a dissolved gas, as bicarbonate ion, or bonded to hemoglobin.

28.42 (a) Increasing the temperature causes hemoglobin to release more O_2 to tissues.
(b)(c) Production of CO_2 brings about an increase of $[H^+]$, which causes the release of O_2.

28.44 Ketoacidosis due to diabetes is classified as metabolic acidosis because it is caused by increased production of acid as a result of metabolic dysfunction.

28.46 In addition to filtration, kidneys also recapture water and essential solutes (reabsorption) and excrete excess solutes (secretion).

Applications

28.48 Emollients are fats such as lanolin, vegetable oils or petroleum jelly.

28.50 Endothelial cells in brain capillaries form tight junctions so that no substances can pass between them.

28.52 Substances that are soluble in membrane lipids can cross the blood–brain barrier. Ethanol crosses this barrier because it's soluble in membrane lipids.

28.54 *Advantages:*

Modified hemoglobin:	Because antigens are left behind when hemoglobin is extracted, blood typing is unnecessary.
	Modified hemoglobin has a long shelf-life.
Perfluorocarbons:	Perfluorocarbons are relatively inexpensive.
	Perfluorocarbons are chemically inert.

Disadvantages:

Modified hemoglobin:	The cost of extracting modified hemoglobin is higher than the cost of manufacturing perfluorocarbons.
	Modified hemoglobin has a short lifetime in the body.
	Modified hemoglobin might be altered in the body by biochemical reactions.
Perfluorocarbons:	Perfluorocarbons might be (but probably aren't) toxic.
	The amount of oxygen delivered by perfluorocarbons is hard to regulate.

28.56 Cells rupture as they freeze because the large ice crystals formed rip apart cellular and organelle membranes.

28.58 In order to maintain metabolism, frozen tissues must be able to produce limited amounts of ATP, with no blood supply and no oxygen supply. The metabolites must be nontoxic, and enzymes that accelerate tissue decay must be inhibited more than ATP-producing enzymes.

28.60 A change in enzyme level in body fluids may indicate organ damage. An automatic analyzer can reproducibly measure the rate of an enzyme-catalyzed reaction to detect the presence of elevated or reduced levels of enzymes.

General Questions and Problems

28.62 Ethanol is soluble in blood because it is a small, polar molecule.

28.64 When the concentration of sodium in the blood is high, the secretion of antidiuretic hormone (ADH) increases. ADH causes the water content of the urine to decrease, and causes the amount of water retained by the body to increase, causing swelling.

28.66 Active transport is necessary when a cell needs a substance that has a higher concentration inside the cell than outside, or when a cell needs to secrete a substance that has a higher concentration outside the cell than inside.

28.68 *Homeostasis* is the maintenance of a constant internal environment in the body. *Hemostasis* is the body's mechanism for preventing blood loss and could be considered a part of homeostasis.

Self-Test for Chapter 28

Multiple choice:

1. Which oxygen is taken up by heme with the most difficulty?
   (a) the first oxygen   (b) the second oxygen   (c) the last oxygen   (d) all bind with equal ease

2. Cardiac arrest may result in:
   (a) metabolic alkalosis   (b) metabolic acidosis   (c) respiratory alkalosis   (d) respiratory acidosis

3. Cell-mediated immune response guards against all of the following except:
   (a) cancer cells   (b) transplanted organs   (c) allergens   (d) bacteria

4. Potassium ion is most abundant in:
   (a) interstitial fluid   (b) intracellular fluid   (c) plasma   (d) extracellular fluid

5. All of the following are involved in blood clotting except:
   (a) tissue factor   (b) zymogens   (c) thrombin   (d) memory cells

6. Which of the following disorders is not an autoimmune disease?
   (a) hemophilia   (b) arthritis   (c) lupus erythematosus   (d) diabetes mellitus

7. The amount of water reabsorbed in kidney tubules depends on:
   (a) the amount of sodium reabsorbed   (b) control of membrane permeability by antidiuretic hormone   (c) aldosterone   (d) all three

8. Blood is at its lowest percent saturation with oxygen in:
   (a) peripheral tissue   (b) muscles   (c) veins   (d) arteries

9. All of the following decrease the oxygen affinity of hemoglobin except:
   (a) increased $[H^+]$ (b) increased $[O_2]$ (c) increased $[CO_2]$ (d) increased temperature

10. B cells divide to produce all of the following except:
    (a) memory cells   (b) antibodies   (c) phagocytes   (d) plasma cells

Complete the following sentences:

1. The percentage of heme molecules that carry oxygen is dependent on the _____ _____ of O_2.

2. Antigens can be small molecules known as _____.

3. In the process of blood clotting, _____ are activated to give active clotting factors.

4. Inorganic ions are the major contributors to the _____ of body fluids.

5. Histamine is synthesized from _____.

6. _____ ion and vitamin ____ assist in blood clotting.

7. In _____ _____, substances move from regions of low concentration to regions of high concentration.

8. The three functions of blood are _____, _____, and _____.

9. Bacteria at the site of inflammation are attacked by _____.

10. Arthritis and allergies are known as _____ diseases.

11. _____ is caused by the absence of one or more clotting factors.

12. Fibrin molecules are bound into fibers by cross-links between the side chains of the amino acids _____ and _____.

Tell whether the following sentences are true or false:

1. The walls of lymph capillaries are constricted so that lymph can't return to surrounding tissues.

2. Homeostasis is the body's mechanism for halting blood loss.

3. O_2, H^+, and CO_2 all bond to heme.

4. Secreted H^+ is eliminated in the urine as NH_4^+ or $H_2PO_4^-$.

5. When the partial pressure of CO_2 increases, the percent saturation of hemoglobin decreases.

6. Allergies and asthma are caused by an underproduction of immunoglobulin E.

7. Blood plasma is the fluid remaining after blood has completely clotted.

8. Blood clotting begins with the release of tissue factor from injured tissue.

9. Reabsorption is the movement of solutes and water out of the kidney.

10. The metabolism of food contributes to one's water intake.

11. Lymphocytes surround and destroy bacteria.

12. Caffeine causes increased output of urine.

Match the item on the left with its partner on the right:

1. B cells

(a) Foreign substance

2. Active transport

(b) Enzyme that catalyzes the formation of histamine

3. Fibrin

(c) Movement of solute against a concentration gradient

4. Carbonic anhydrase

(d) White blood cells involved in antibody-directed immune response

5. Erythrocytes

(e) Controls reabsorption of Na^+

6. T cells

(f) Blood protein responsible for clotting

7. Antigen

(g) Enzyme that catalyzes reaction between H_2O and CO_2

8. Histidine decarboxylase

(h) Movement of water in response to a concentration difference

9. Osmosis

(i) White blood cells involved in cell-directed immune response

10. Antidiuretic hormone

(j) Red blood cells

11. Antibody

(k) Protein molecule that identifies a foreign substance

12. Aldosterone

(l) Causes a decrease in the water content of urine

Answers to Self Tests

Chapter One

Multiple choice: 1. b 2. d 3. b 4. d 5. a 6. a 7. c 8. b
Sentence completion: 1. kinetic 2. physical 3. Bi 4. condenses 5. mass and volume
6. liquid 7. pure substance 8. potential *or* chemical 9. malleable 10. carbon, hydrogen,
oxygen and nitrogen
True/false: 1. T 2. T 3. T 4. F (physical methods) 5. F (seven atoms) 6. T 7. F (Ag)
8. T 9. F (a gas) 10. T

Chapter Two

Number questions: 1. (a) micrometer (b) deciliter (c) megagram (d) liter (e) nanogram
2. (a) kL (b) pg (c) cm (d) hL 3. (a) 5 (b) 2 (c) 1 (d) exact (e) 3,4,5 or 6
4. (a) 7.03×10^{-5} g; 3 sig. fig. (b) $1.371\,00 \times 10^5$ m; 4,5,or 6 sig. fig. (c) 1.1×10^{-2} L; 2 sig.
fig. (d) $1.837\,100\,8 \times 10^7$ mm; 8 sig. fig. 5. (a) 8.07×10^2 L (b) 4.77×10^6 people
(c) 1.27×10^{-3} g (d) 1.04×10^4 μm 6. (a) 0.564 lb (b) 0.417 m (c) 7.6 L (d) 85.4 in.
(e) 95°F (f) 25°C (g) 5.92 fl oz (h) 6.17×10^{-3} oz 7. 31 cal 8. 217 g
Multiple choice: 1. b 2. d 3. b 4. a 5. c 6. d 7. b 8. c 9. c 10. a
Sentence completion : 1. kilogram, meter, cubic meter, Kelvin 2. number, unit 3. specific
heat 4. nano- 5. 3 6. 1 lb/454 g 7. calorie, joule 8. factor-label 9. Specific gravity
10. Celsius, Kelvin
True/false: 1. F (specific gravity is unitless) 2. T 3. F (three sig. fig.) 4. F (0.9464 L/1 qt.)
5. T 6. F 7. F 8. T 9. F 10. T
Matching: 1. e 2. j 3. g 4. i 5. h 6. l 7. f 8. k 9. c 10. a 11. d 12. b

Chapter Three

Multiple choice: 1. c 2. b 3. a 4. c 5. d 6. d 7. a 8. b 9. d 10. d 11. a 12. b
Sentence completion: 1. *p* 2. dalton 3. protons, neutrons 4. atomic number 5. shells
6. group 7. 13 8. subatomic particles 9. isotopes 10. 18 11. quantized
True/false: 1. T 2. F (5.486×10^{-4} amu) 3. F 4. T 5. F (atomic number indicates only
protons) 6. F (They're less reactive.) 7. F (in the same group) 8. T 9. T 10. F (Subshells can
contain 2,6,10 ·· electrons.) 11. T 12. F
Matching: 1. h 2. e 3. k 4. a 5. j 6. l 7. c 8. b 9. i 10. d 11. g 12. f

Chapter Four

Multiple choice: 1. d 2. a 3. d 4. c 5. a 6. b 7. b 8. d 9. b 10. d
Sentence completion: 1. Ionization energy 2. potassium phosphate 3. 2 4. polyatomic
5. simplest 6. 8 7. base 8. Hypokalemia 9. crystalline 10. 4A or 5A
True/false: 1. F (It forms only Zn^{2+}.) 2. T 3. F (energy needed to form an ion) 4. T 5. F
(ions formed may be H^+, $H_2PO_4^-$, and HPO_4^{2-}.) 6. F (Solutions of ions conduct electricity.) 7. T
8. T 9. T 10. F (group 8A) 11. T 12. F
Matching: 1. e 2. l 3. k 4. a 5. h 6. j 7. i 8. b 9. f 10 g 11. d 12. c

Chapter Five

Multiple choice: 1. c   2. d   3. b   4. c   5. a   6. a   7. d   8. b   9. d   10. a
Sentence completion: 1. electronegative   2. biomolecule   3. covalent   4. C≡C, C≡N
5. diatomic   6. planar trigonal   7. *d*   8. triple   9. Binary   10. organic   11. Homeostasis
True/false: 1. T   2. T   3. F   4. F (valence electrons) 5. F (It's planar.) 6. F (covalent
compounds) 7. T   8. F   9. F (Some bent molecules have bond angles that are approx. 109.5°.)
10. T   11. T
Matching: 1. h(or c)   2. j   3. f   4. a   5. k   6. i   7. e   8. c   9. b   10. g   11. d   12. l

Chapter Six

Multiple choice: 1. a   2. a   3. c   4. b   5. d   6. c   7. c   8. b   9. a   10. d
Sentence completion: 1. coefficients   2. precipitate   3. spectator   4. aqueous   5. molar mass
6. percent yield   7. reactants   8. +3   9. reducing   10. neutralization
True/false: 1. F (It has the same number of atoms.) 2. T   3. T   4. F   5. T   6. F (Molar mass
is the conversion factor.) 7. F   8. F (The mole ratio is 1/2.) 9. T   10. T
Matching: 1. h   2. f   3. k   4. a   5. i   6. c   7. j   8. b   9. g   10. l   11. d   12. e

Chapter Seven

Multiple choice: 1. c   2. b   3. d   4. d   5. b   6. a   7. c   8. a   9. d   10. d
Sentence completion: 1. 1   2. Conservation of Energy   3. catalyst   4. reversible   5.
endothermic   6. equilibrium-constant expression   7. temperature, pressure, catalyst
8. metabolism   9. Reaction rate   10. collide
True/false: 1. F (produced) 2. F (At equilibrium, the ratio of concentrations is constant.) 3. T
4. T   5. F (The size of E_{act} and ΔH are unrelated.) 6. F (not always true for biochemical
reactions) 7. T   8. F (Catalysts lower the height of the energy barrier.) 9. F (At equilibrium, the
rate of the forward reaction equals the rate of the reverse reaction.) 10. T
Matching: 1. c   2. j   3. l   4. i   5. a   6. k   7. b   8. f   9. d   10. e   11. g   12. h

Chapter Eight

Multiple choice: 1. b   2. c   3. d   4. a   5. d   6. c   7. a   8. b   9. c   10. d
Sentence completion: 1. pressure, volume   2. definite, indefinite   3. Dalton's   4. standard
temperature and pressure   5. Avogadro's   6. equilibrium   7. atmosphere, Pascal, mm Hg,
pounds per square inch   8. heat of fusion   9. number of atoms, volume   10. temperature
11. change of state   12. volatile
True/false: 1. T   2. F (Only ideal gases have similar physical behavior.) 3. T   4. F (Doubling
pressure halves the volume.) 5. T   6. F (only true in crystals) 7. F (273 K) 8. T   9. F (higher)
10. F (Vapor pressure doesn't depend on quantity of liquid.) 11. T
Matching: 1. g   2. e   3. k   4. f   5. h   6. a   7. j   8. l   9. b   10. d   11. c   12. i

Chapter Nine

Multiple choice: 1. b 2. d 3. a 4. b 5. c 6. d 7. c 8. c 9. a 10. b
Sentence completion: 1. miscible 2. equivalent 3. volumetric flask 4. solubility, partial pressure 5. isotonic 6. hygroscopic 7. M_1 x V_1 = M_2 x V_2. 8. colloid 9. solvent, small solute molecules 10. saturated 11. glucose 12. lower
True/false: 1. F (solvent) 2. T 3. F (A quantity of the second liquid is added to make 100 mL of solution.) 4. F 5. T 6. F (Weight/weight percent is rarely used.) 7. T 8. F (Effect of temperature is unpredictable.) 9. T (It also differs with respect to particle size.) 10. F (hemolysis) 11. F (raise) 12. T
Matching: 1. h 2. f 3. d 4. j 5. a 6. k 7. b 8. i 9. g 10. l 11. e 12. c

Chapter Ten

Multiple choice: 1. b 2. a 3. c 4. d 5. c 6. c 7. b 8. a 9. b 10. d
Sentence completion: 1. equivalent 2. red 3. diprotic 4. strong 5. Dissociation 6. OH^- ions 7. Neutralization 8. pH 9. 30.0 mL 10. conjugate 11. carbonate / bicarbonate 12. amphoteric
True/false: 1. F (60 mL of 0.1 M NaOH) 2. T 3. F (H_2SO_4 is a strong acid.) 4. F 5. F 6. T 7. T 8. F (According to this definition, an acid donates H^+.) 9. F (Ammonia yields ammonium ion, plus the anion of the acid.) 10. T 11. F 12. T
Matching: 1. d 2. e 3. g 4. l 5. a 6. b 7. i 8. j 9. c 10. f 11. k 12. h

Chapter Eleven

Multiple choice: 1. c 2. d 3. c 4. a 5. c 6. d 7. a 8. d 9. b 10. c
Sentence completion: 1. transmutation 2. Gamma radiation 3. tracer 4. background 5. nucleons 6. ^{14}C 7. curie 8. nuclear fission 9. film badges 10. body imaging 11. nuclear fusion 12. critical mass
True/false: 1. F (3/4 will have decayed after 24 days.) 2. T 3. T 4. F (Becquerel) 5. T 6. F 7. F (Atomic number increases by 1.) 8. F (Hazards are due to emissions of radiation.) 9. F (The rem is more common.) 10. T 11. F (Most are synthetic.) 12. F
Matching: 1. f 2. i 3. l 4. k 5. c 6. j 7. d 8. h 9. b 10. a 11. e 12. g

Chapter Twelve

Multiple choice: 1. a 2. c 3. d 4. c 5. b 6. d 7. c 8. a 9. c 10. a
Sentence completion: 1. paraffins 2. triple 3. oxygen 4. distillation 5. condensed structure 6. quaternary 7. lower 8. ring 9. IUPAC 10. isomers 11. Combustion 12. higher
True/false: 1. F (They have different molecular formulas.) 2. T 3. F (It's puckered.) 4. F (3–Methylhexane) 5. T 6. T 7. F (It's polar covalent.) 8. T 9. T 10. F (Reactivity depends on the nature of the functional groups.) 11. T 12. F
Matching: 1. i 2. j 3. f 4. l 5. h 6. c 7. a 8. k 9. e 10. b 11. g 12. d

Chapter Thirteen

Multiple choice: 1. d 2. b 3. a 4. c 5. a 6. c 7. c 8. c 9. d 10. d
Sentence completion: 1. 2-heptyne 2. hydrogenation 3. *para* 4. more, fewer 5. hydration
6. catalyst 7. carbocation 8. unsaturated 9. Toluene 10. substitution 11. Polycyclic aromatic
compounds 12. thermal cracking
True/false: 1. F 2. T 3. T 4. F (2-bromobutane) 5. F (Halogenation is the reaction of X_2
with an alkene, where X is a halogen.) 6. T 7. F 8. F (Hydration requires a strong acid as a
catalyst.) 9. T 10. F 11. F 12. T
Matching: 1. e 2. k 3. i 4. j 5. b 6. l 7. d 8. c 9. a 10. f 11. g 12. h

Chapter Fourteen

Multiple choice: 1. c 2. b 3. b 4. a 5. d 6. d 7. a 8. b 9. c 10. d
Sentence completion: 1. wood alcohol 2. glycols 3. phenols 4. alkene 5. thiols
6. $KMnO_4$ or $K_2Cr_2O_7$ 7. lower 8. BHT 9. greater 10. free radical 11. peroxide 12. CFC
Matching: 1. j 2. g 3. f 4. h 5. l 6. b 7. e 8. a 9. k 10. d 11. i 12. c
True/false: 1. T 2. F (A ketone is formed from the oxidation of a secondary alcohol.) 3. T
4. F (carbolic acid) 5. T 6. T 7. F (Ethyl chloride is an anesthetic.) 8. F (two hydrogen atoms)
9. T 10. T 11. F 12. T

Chapter Fifteen

Multiple choice: 1. c 2. a 3. d 4. c 5. c 6. a 7. b 8. d 9. a 10. b
Sentence completion: 1. *amino-* 2. quaternary 3. DNA 4. Toxicology 5. heterocycle 6.
Alkaloids 7. hydrogen bonding 8. ammonium 9. free radical 10. nonaromatic amines
True/false: 1. T 2. T 3. F (They're lower-boiling.) 4. T 5. F 6. T 7. F (It's synthetic.) 8.
T 9. F (NO lowers blood pressure.) 10. F (*N*-Methylbutylamine)
Matching: 1. d 2. l 3. h 4. i 5. a 6. j 7. b 8. k 9. f 10. g 11. e 12. c

Chapter Sixteen

Multiple choice: 1. c 2. b 3. a˙ 4. d 5. c 6. b 7. b 8. a 9. d 10. b
Sentence completion: 1. carbonyl 2. silver 3. Hydrolysis 4. positive, negative 5. Acetone
6. carbon-carbon 7. more 8. reduction 9. disinfectant or preservative 10. hemiacetal
11. Benedict's 12. Acetone
True/False: 1. F (a hemiacetal link) 2. T 3. F (Ketones don't undergo Tollens' reaction.) 4. F
($NaBH_4$ is used for reduction.) 5. F 6. F (Both aldehydes and ketones form acetals.) 7. T 8. T
9. F (3–Hydroxybutanal is the product.) 10. T 11. T 12. T
Matching: 1. e 2. i 3. d (or l) 4. a 5. h 6. j 7. k 8. b 9. l 10. f 11. g 12. c

Chapter Seventeen

Multiple choice: 1. d 2. c 3. a 4. d 5. b 6. d 7. b 8. a 9. d 10. b
Sentence completion: 1. carbonyl group substitution 2. polyamide 3. carboxylate salt
4. esterification 5. attracts 6. -oic acid 7. propyl propanoate 8. esters 9. Phosphorylation
10. fats 11. hydrolysis or saponification 12. propanedioic acid
True/false: 1. T 2. F (basic hydrolysis) 3. F (Amides are nonbasic.) 4. T 5. F (The products
are acetate ion and ethanol.) 6. F (*N,N*–dimethylformamide) 7. F 8. T 9. T 10. F
(Esterification is acid-catalyzed.) 11. F (It's an acid anhydride.) 12. T
Matching: 1. j 2. f 3. k 4. b 5. i 6. d 7. a 8. e 9. 1 10. h 11. c 12. g

Chapter Eighteen

Multiple choice: 1. a 2. d 3. c 4. b 5. b 6. a 7. d 8. b 9. c 10. d
Sentence completion : 1. 5.0-6.3 2. enantiomers 3. zwitterions 4. backbone 5. loop
6. glycoprotein 7. Tertiary 8. β–sheet 9. polar 10. sulfur 11. polypeptide 12. Hydrophobic
True/false: 1. F (Glycine is achiral.) 2. T 3. F (Denaturation disrupts all structural elements
except primary structure.) 4. F (They're different.) 5. T 6. F 7. T 8. T 9. T 10. F (Fibrous
proteins are insoluble.) 11. T 12. T
Matching: 1. e 2. g 3. j 4. a 5. b 6. k 7. c 8. 1 9. f 10. h 11. d 12. i

Chapter Nineteen

Multiple choice: 1. c 2. a 3. c 4. d 5. b 6. b 7. d 8. c 9. b 10. d
Sentence completion: 1. isomerase 2. Isoenzymes 3. K 4. induced-fit 5. noncompetitive
6. denature 7. turnover number 8. phosphoryl 9. proximity 10. 10^9 11. allosteric 12.
zymogen
True/false: 1. T 2. F 3. F 4. F (a dehydrase) 5. F (Enzyme-substrate interactions are
noncovalent.) 6. F (Minerals, not vitamins, are inorganic ions.) 7. T 8. F (Retinol, retinal,
retinoic acid are all active forms of vitamin A.) 9. T 10. T 11. F (Reaction rate increases.) 12. T
Matching: 1. c 2. h 3. i 4. g 5. k 6. j 7. b 8. a 9. d 10. f 11. e 12. 1

Chapter Twenty

Multiple choice: 1. a 2. c 3. b 4. c 5. d 6. a 7. d 8. a 9. d 10. d
Sentence Completion: 1. Anaphylaxis 2. adrenal 3. vesicles 4. Histamine 5. cholinergic
6. progesterone 7. enkephalin 8. ethnobotanist 9. synaptic cleft 10. dopamine 11. thyroxine
12. phosphodiesterase
True/false: 1. F (Thyroxine can cross the cell membrane.) 2. F (It blocks reuptake.) 3. T 4.
T 5. F (presynaptic neurons) 6. T 7. F (It increases blood pressure and heart rate.) 8. F (It's a
symptom of iodine deficiency.) 9. T 10. T
Matching: 1. e 2. h 3. k 4. b 5. g 6. a 7. d 8. j 9. f 10. 1 11. c 12. i

Chapter Twenty-one

Multiple choice: 1. b 2. c 3. a 4. c 5. a 6. d 7. b 8. c 9. b 10. d
Sentence completion: 1. Eukaryotic 2. metabolic pathway or linear sequence 3. ADP and phosphate 4. unfavorable 5. Krebs cycle, tricarboxylic acid cycle 6. succinyl–SCoA, CO_2 7. NAD^+ 8. one (plus 4 reduced coenzymes) 9. Cytoplasm 10. Catalase 11. succinate dehydrogenase 12. Basal metabolism
True/false: 1. T 2. F (Only eukaryotic cells are found in higher organisms.) 3. F (Anabolism is the synthesis of complicated molecules from simpler molecules.) 4. F 5. T 6. T 7. F ($FADH_2$ donates electrons to coenzyme Q.) 8. T 9. F (decrease in order) 10. F (ATP can be formed by substrate-level phosphorylation.) 11. F (a phosphate anhydride) 12. T
Matching: 1. d 2. j 3. f 4. a 5. l 6. k 7. e 8. c 9. b 10. g 11. i 12. h

Chapter Twenty-two

Multiple choice: 1. a 2. d 3. c 4. c 5. d 6. d 7. d 8. c 9. b 10. b
Sentence completion: 1. chiral 2. amylases 3. enantiomers 4. cyclic hemiacetal 5. fructose 6. amylose, amylopectin 7. glycoside 8. Glycogen 9. aldohexose 10. achiral 11. diastereomer 12. Glycoproteins
True/false: 1. T 2. T 3. F (The hydroxyl group on the chiral carbon farthest from the carbonyl group is on the left.) 4. F (α, not β) 5. T 6. F (Crystalline glucose is the α-anomer.) 7. F (Sucrose contains only an acetal bond.) 8. T 9. F (An acetal resembles an ether.) 10. F (Maltose is composed of two glucose molecules.) 11. F (The relationship between the rotations of diastereomers is not predictable.) 12. T
Matching: 1. e 2. l 3. j 4. h 5. i 6. k 7. b 8. a 9. d 10. g 11. c 12. f

Chapter Twenty-three

Multiple choice: 1. c 2. c 3. b 4. d 5. a 6. b 7. d 8. c 9. d 10. a
Sentence completion: 1. Embden-Meyerhof 2. 6 3. Pyruvate dehydrogenase complex 4. Insulin 5. glucose 1–phosphate 6. 1-5 7. diabetes mellitus 8. GTP, ATP 9. CO_2 10. glucose 6-phosphate isomerase 11. glucagon 12. Hypoglycemia
True/false: 1. F (It produces NADPH.) 2. T 3. F 4. F 5. T 6. F (Glycolysis occurs in the cytosol.) 7. F (The yield of ATP was formerly considered to be 38 ATP/ 1 mol glucose. The new estimate is 30-32 ATP/ 1 mol glucose.) 8. F (glycogen) 9. F (Fermentation occurs only in yeasts.) 10. T (but one results from isomerization of dihydroxyacetone phosphate) 11. T 12. F (It produces two ATPs.)
Matching: 1. l 2. k 3. i 4. j 5. c 6. h 7. d 8. a 9. f 10. g 11. b 12. e

Chapter Twenty-four

Multiple choice: 1. d 2. c 3. a 4. a 5. d 6. d 7. c 8. b 9. a 10. b
Sentence completion: 1. glycoside 2. Soap 3. hydrophilic, hydrophobic 4. Glycolipids, cholesterol, glycoproteins 5. fluid-mosaic 6. tetracyclic 7. arachidonic 8. micelles 9. Sphingomyelins 10. lipid bilayer 11. Eicosanoids 12. Integral
True/false: 1. T 2. F 3. F (They contain an amide group.) 4. T 5. T 6. F (They form a micelle.) 7. F (Cholesterol is a steroid component of cell membranes.) 8. F (The major difference is in the quantity of unsaturated fatty acids they contain.) 9. F (Cerebrosides are components of nerve cell membranes in the brain.) 10. T 11. T 12. F (In facilitated diffusion, solutes are transported across cell membranes by proteins, but no energy investment is required.)
Matching: 1. l 2. h 3. e 4. f 5. a 6. j 7. k 8. b 9. d 10. g 11. i 12. c

Chapter Twenty-five

Multiple choice: 1. a 2. d 3. c 4. a 5. b 6. b 7. c 8. d 9. c 10. d
Sentence completion: 1. NAD^+, FAD 2. micelles 3. adipocytes 4. dihydroxyacetone phosphate 5. fatty-acid spiral 6. double bond 7. Ketonuria 8. NADPH 9. 3–Hydroxybutyrate 10. lymphatic system 11. mobilized 12. acetyl–SCoA
True/false: 1. T 2. F (The products are mainly mono- and diacylglycerols.) 3. T 4. T 5. F (Carnitine transports the fatty-acyl–SCoAs.) 6. T 7. F (Dihydroxyacetone phosphate, not glycerol) 8. F (LDL transports cholesterol.) 9. T 10. F (It occurs in the cytosol.) 11. F (It comes from acetyl–SCoA.) 12. T.
Matching: 1. e 2. i 3. a 4. l 5. g 6. j 7. k 8. d 9. f 10. b 11. c 12. h

Chapter Twenty-six

Multiple choice: 1. c 2. d 3. b 4. a 5. b 6. b 7. d 8. d 9. c 10. a
Sentence completion: 1. Replication 2. complementary 3. chromatin 4. ionizing radiation, mutagens 5. intron 6. ester 7. nucleoside 8. releasing factor 9. restriction endonuclease 10. deoxyribose 11. Watson-Crick 12. DNA polymerase
True/false: 1. F (61 codons code for the 20 amino acids; the other three are "stop" codons.) 2. F (The amount of adenine equals the amount of thymine.) 3. T 4. F (An anticodon occurs on tRNA.) 5. T 6. T 7. T 8. F (They run in opposite directions.) 9. F (translation) 10. F (Most DNA consists of introns.) 11. F (Two have only one codon.) 12. F (guanosine 5'-monophosphate)
Matching; 1. l 2. j 3. b 4. g 5. a 6. i 7. d 8. c 9. e 10. h 11. f 12. k

Chapter Twenty-seven

Multiple choice: 1. c 2. a 3. b 4. d 5. a 6. c 7. d 8. c 9. a 10. b
Sentence completion: 1. pyruvate, glutamate 2. xenobiotic 3. acetyl–SCoA, acetoacetyl–SCoA 4. carbamoyl phosphate 5. protease 6. pyruvate 7. Transamination 8. arginine 9. phenylalanine, tyrosine 10. urate crystals 11. ALT 12. bicarbonate
True/false: 1. T 2. F (It starts in the stomach.) 3. F (lysine and leucine) 4. F (The human body can catabolize essential amino acids.) 5. T 6. F (Catabolism occurs in the liver and in the cytosol.) 7. T 8. T 9. F (One is from aspartate; the other is from ammonium ion.) 10. T 11. F (Some transaminases have several amino acid donors.) 12. T
Matching: 1. h 2. g 3. j 4. f 5. a 6. b 7. c 8. l 9. k 10. d 11. e 12. i

Chapter Twenty-eight

Multiple choice: 1. a 2. d 3. c 4. b 5. d 6. a 7. d 8. b 9. b 10. c
Sentence completion: 1. partial pressure 2. haptens 3. zymogens 4. osmolarity 5. histidine 6. calcium, K 7. active transport 8. transport, regulation, defense 9. phagocytes 10. autoimmune 11. Hemophilia 12. lysine, glutamine
True/false: 1. F (constructed) 2. F (hemostasis) 3. F (CO_2 bonds to hemoglobin) 4. T 5. T 6. F (overproduction) 7. F (blood serum) 8. T 9. F (tubule) 10. T 11. F (phagocytes) 12. T
Matching: 1. d 2. c 3. f 4. g 5. j 6. i 7. a 8. b 9. h 10. l 11. k 12. e